GCSE MATHEMATICS

Robert Powell
Head of Mathematics
Burton Borough School, Shropshire
and
Mark Patmore
Principal Moderator
Lecturer in Mathematics Education

Letts Educational
Aldine House
Aldine Place
London W12 8AW

Tel: 0181 740 2266
Fax: 0181 743 8451
E-mail: mail@lettsed.co.uk

First published 1993
Reprinted 1994 (twice), 1995 (twice), 1996
New edition 1997

British Library Cataloguing-in-Publication Data
A CIP record for this book is available from the British Library.

ISBN 1 85758 586 0

Acknowledgements
We are grateful to the following Examining Groups for permission to use the specimen questions included in this book:
Northern Examinations and Assessment Board (NEAB),
Midland Examining Group (MEG), Southern Examining Group (SEG),
Edexcel Foundation: London Examinations (formerly ULEAC),
Welsh Joint Education Committee (WJEC), Northern Ireland Council for the Curriculum Examinations and Assessment (NICCEA), Scottish Qualifications Authority (formerly SEB). The answers provided are the authors' alone, and the Examining Groups can accept no responsibility for them.

R G Powell and M Patmore

Printed and bound in Great Britain by Ashford Colour Press

Letts Educational is the trading name of BPP (Letts Educational) Ltd.

Contents

Starting points

Section 1 Number

Section 2 Algebra

Section 3 Shape, space and measure

Section 4 Data handling

Section 5 Examination practice

Mathematics in the National Curriculum

The National Curriculum deals with the period of compulsory education from age 5 to 16 in four Key Stages. At the end of each Key Stage (i.e. at ages 7, 11, 14 and 16), attainments in specified subjects are tested. At the end of Key Stage 4 (KS4), assessment is made through the GCSE.

Attainment Targets

The knowledge, understanding and skills which you are expected to have acquired at the end of each Key Stage are defined in broad areas of study known as Attainment Targets (ATs). In Mathematics there are four ATs:

AT1 Using and Applying Mathematics
AT2 Number and Algebra
AT3 Shape, Space and Measures
AT4 Data Handling

The weighting of these areas is described later.

A Programme of Study common to every pupil in the country is provided within the National Curriculum and, although teaching methods may differ from school to school, each school has an obligation to ensure that the Programme of Study appropriate to each pupil's needs is provided. The Programme of Study forms the basis of this book.

In Northern Ireland the National Curriculum is virtually identical to that in England and Wales. Scotland has its own National Curriculum and most of the topics covered by this book will be taught in Scottish schools and examined at Standard Grade.

GCSE/Key Stage 4

At Key Stage 4 the GCSE is the means of assessing attainment in the National Curriculum. Attainment is recorded by grades – the grades available at GCSE are:

A*, A, B, C, D, E, F, G

with A* representing the highest achievement possible.

For all the Mathematics GCSE examinations there are 3 'tiers' of entry – Foundation, Intermediate and Higher. There are different grades available for each tier as shown below:

Foundation G, F, E, D
Intermediate E, D, C, B
Higher C, B, A, A*

How to use this book

This book contains all the Mathematics you will need while you work through Key Stage 4 and towards GCSE at intermediate and higher level assessment in England, Wales and Northern Ireland, as well as most of the topics needed for Standard Grade in Scotland. It provides topic-by-topic coverage of the Programme of Study on which the Mathematics syllabuses are based. Throughout the book there are worked examples and questions to help you to practise what you have learned.

This book is divided into four main sections which reflect the four Attainment Targets of Using and Applying Mathematics, Number and Algebra, Shape, Space and Measures, and Handling Data.

Using and Applying Mathematics

Attainment Target 1 – Using and Applying Mathematics – will be assessed either through coursework, through tasks or by performance on a written paper. Details of which method is used with each syllabus are given later. Section 1 offers guidance on the various methods.

Sections 2 to 4

Your final examinations will assess your ability in each of these areas: Number and Algebra, Shape, Space and Measures, and Handling Data. Sections 2 to 4 cover each of these in turn.

Before you begin to revise for your written papers you should know from your teacher which tier of GCSE examination you are likely to be entered for. This is important so that you can revise the work appropriate to the grades available at that tier.

In this book, each area is presented firstly with work appropriate to the Intermediate tier and then the additional work necessary to obtain a grade at the Higher tier. Throughout, the concepts are explained followed by questions to enable you to practise these skills and ensure that you understand each idea. Check that you have the correct answers before you continue.

It is almost impossible to revise mathematics successfully without working through questions, either from this book or from your school text book. The first questions in each section are specific to one idea but by the end you will find that the questions contain a mixture of ideas.

If you have difficulty with an idea, go back through the notes and, if you are still having problems, ask your teacher to explain the idea to you again. Most importantly, don't ignore problem areas because later work may depend on your understanding of this idea.

If you are entered for the Intermediate tier then you will need to work through those sections only but if you are entered for the Higher tier you will need to cover all the 'Intermediate' work as well. In this case there are two different ways in which you could continue once you have completed one of the sections:

1. You could continue to work at the same topic and with similar concepts but at higher levels. The advantage of this method is that you are developing ideas which are fresh in your mind. The disadvantage is that if you do not allow yourself sufficient time to revise you may run out of time to revise the later sections thoroughly.
2. You could continue to work through all the intermediate sections through the book. This has advantages as it will ensure that you cover the whole examination syllabus equally and that you allow yourself time between studying the same concept at higher levels to digest the ideas you have worked on. The disadvantage is that you will have to move around the book. If you do this, make sure you keep a record of the work you have revised.

Whichever way you choose to work, the book contains Examiner's Tips and Notes which will help you when you come to revise.

You will require a scientific calculator for your final examination and for your revision, but remember to show your working.

Examination questions

The section containing examination questions will familiarise you with the different types of question you will face in the exam. By the time you come to revise, you will already have successfully completed many questions that could have been set on GCSE or SCE papers. The questions in this section assess concepts from the higher levels of study, so don't be worried if you find them difficult – they are!

Remember to omit Chapters 4, 7, 11 and 14 if you are studying Mathematics at Intermediate level; Higher level candidates should work through all chapters.

Revision and exams

Hints for revision

Past exam questions play an important part in revising for examinations. However, it is important not to start practising these questions too early. Nothing can be more disheartening than trying to do a question that you do not understand because you have not mastered the concepts. Therefore, it is important to have studied a topic thoroughly by working through the appropriate section in this book before attempting any examination question on it.

It is unlikely that any question you try will appear in exactly the same form on the papers you are going to take. However, the number of totally original questions that can be set on any part of the syllabus is limited and so similar ideas occur over and over again. It will certainly help you if the style of question you are trying to answer in an exam is familiar and you are used to the type of language used. Your confidence will be boosted and confidence is important for exam success.

Practising exam questions will also indicate gaps in your knowledge and understanding and provide you with the opportunity to turn back in this book and work through the appropriate section again and/or seek help from your teacher. Past papers will probably be provided by your school. You can also purchase books of practice papers or past papers direct from the examination boards. Their addresses are given under the relevant examination board on pages 7–15.

Revision technique is important. At school, your time is planned, organised and supervised by your teachers. Your homework and coursework have to be done because there are deadlines for completing it. Revising is different: it has to be planned by you, and only you can decide when you have done enough. Remember that it is better to revise than to resit. Remember also that you will have to revise for all subjects. Split your revision time into sessions and allocate enough study time for each subject. Be honest with yourself about what you can achieve in each session, and remember to take breaks from studying so that you don't become over-tired or frustrated.

By allowing yourself a long period of revision, you will improve your chances of achieving a good grade. It is not a good idea to try to cram all your revision into a short period. The best way to revise mathematics is to practise it. Get into the habit of doing some mathematics every day, even if you have exams in other subjects before you take your maths exams.

Most young people are able to **work** with background music (a fact that older people find difficult to accept), but when you do **revise** try to do it in surroundings that you are comfortable in. For many, this means finding a quiet room where they won't be disturbed by people, pets, television or music. Whatever room you use, study at a desk or table where you have everything that you will need. Choose a question and attempt it. If you get stuck, refer back to the section which covers the relevant topic, then attempt the question again.

Hints on taking exams

Don't try to revise much the night before the exam. It is more important to keep a clear head and get an early night. Make sure you have got together all of the equipment you will need, e.g. pens, pencils, calculator, spare batteries, etc.

In the exam, you should check that you have been given the correct paper, that you know how many questions you have to answer on that paper and how long you have to do it. Try to spread your time equally between the questions; if you do this it will avoid the desire to rush the paper or to spend too much time on some questions and not finish the paper.

Some papers show the marks available for each question and these will generally be given at the side of each question. These are a good indicator of how much work is expected, and therefore of what proportion of your time you should spend on each part of the question. Make sure you read each question carefully.

It is very important that you write out all of your working clearly on the paper, including writing down answers shown on your calculator before you do any 'rounding'. Marks are given for the following: using an appropriate method to answer a question; for facts found as you work through a question; and for the final answer. Remember, if all that is written down is an answer and if that answer is wrong, you gain no marks.

Once you think you have finished the paper, if you have any time left, check the work you have done. The best way to do this is to work through the questions again.

- The easiest way to lose marks is to fail to read the questions properly.
- Always make sure that the answers to your calculations are accompanied by the correct units.
- From 1998, examination questions will have less structure to lead you through the question.
- From 1998, where you have two papers to complete, both will be equally difficult.
- Questions will no longer be restricted to one area of the National Curriculum but may involve several different skills.

Syllabus tables and paper analysis

All the GCSE examinations that you will take are approved by SCAA (in England) or by ACAC (in Wales). The syllabuses of each board have the same content. There are three tiers of entry for each syllabus and the grades available from each tier are the same for each board. The main difference between the syllabuses is in the assessment of 'Using and Applying Mathematics' which will be assessed either through coursework or through performance on timed tasks. Before you begin to use this study guide you must find out from your teacher which examination syllabus you are following and at what tier.

This is a list of the syllabuses approved for England and Wales for examination in 1998.

Title	Syllabus code	Examining Group
Mathematics (Syllabus A)	1385	EDEXCEL (London)
Mathematics (Syllabus B)	1386	EDEXCEL (London)
Mathematics (Syllabus A)	1131	NEAB
Mathematics (Syllabus B)	1132	NEAB
Mathematics (Syllabus A)	1662	MEG
Mathematics (Syllabus B)	1664	MEG
Mathematics (Syllabus C) SMP Graduated Assessment	1666	MEG
Mathematics (Syllabus A)	2500	SEG
Mathematics (Modular)	2520	SEG
Mathematics (Syllabus A)	01840 (1–3)	WJEC
Mathematics (Syllabus B)	01840 (4–6)	WJEC

The next pages give you a guide to what you can expect in each of these examinations. For more details you should ask your teacher for a syllabus or write directly to the appropriate examination group. Remember, you need only read the syllabus details for the course up to the level you are doing.

Study checklist for GCSE Mathematics

The following table lists all of the topics that you will need to revise for your maths course whichever syllabus you are studying. It also has spaces for you to fill in work dates and notes, and a tick column for you to indicate when you have finished a topic. This should help you see what you still have to do.

Intermediate and higher tiers

Topic	Chapter reference	Target finish date	Notes	✓
Place value and the number system	1			
Using numbers	2			
Solving numerical problems	3			
Understanding relationships	5			
Equations and formulae	6			
Properties of shape	8			
Position, movement and transformation	9			
Measure	10			
Processing and interpreting	12			
Probability	13			

Higher tier only

Topic	Chapter reference	Target finish date	Notes	✓
Further number	4			
Further algebra	7			
Further shape, space and measure	11			
Further data handling	14			

Specific details of each syllabus are given below.

EDEXCEL (formerly ULEAC)

London Examinations – EDEXCEL Foundation
Stewart House, 32 Russell Square, London WCIB 5DN
Tel: 0171 331 4000

Syllabuses 1385 and 1386

The written papers for both syllabuses are identical and in both you will complete two parallel examination papers, each worth 40% of your final marks. The content of the papers will assess Number and Algebra (40%), Shape, Space and Measures (20%), Data Handling (20%). The remaining 20% will be given either for coursework marked by your teacher (syllabus 1385), or for externally assessed terminal tasks, assessing the same skills and using the same criteria (syllabus 1386).

Tier	Grades available	Paper	Time given	%
Foundation	G–D	Paper 1	$1\frac{1}{2}$ hrs	40
		Paper 2	$1\frac{1}{2}$ hrs	40
Intermediate	E–B	Paper 3	2 hrs	40
		Paper 4	2 hrs	40
Higher	C–A*	Paper 5	2 hrs	40
		Paper 6	2 hrs	40

In syllabus 1385, coursework is marked by your teacher and moderated by the examination board. You must complete at least two pieces of coursework.

If you are following syllabus 1386 the time given for the terminal tasks is 2 hours for Foundation and Intermediate candidates and $2\frac{1}{2}$ hours for Higher candidates. You will have the opportunity on the terminal paper to attempt two tasks. These terminal task papers are set on a third examination session shortly after the two written papers have been taken.

NEAB

Northern Examinations and Assessment Board
12 Harter Street, Manchester M1 6HL
Tel: 0161 953 1180

Syllabuses 1131 (Syllabus A) and 1132 (Syllabus B)

In both these syllabuses you will complete two parallel examination papers. The assessment of your ability to understand and use mathematics is assessed in syllabus A by coursework completed throughout your GCSE course, assessed by your teacher and moderated by the board, and in syllabus B through externally set and assessed terminal tasks taken as Paper 3, on a date after Papers 1 and 2 have been sat. At the Intermediate and Higher tiers about 50% of the questions will be based on new mathematical ideas introduced at that level.

Tier	Grades available	Paper	Time given	%
Foundation	G–D	Paper 1F	$1\frac{1}{2}$ hrs	40
		Paper 2F	$1\frac{1}{2}$ hrs	40
Intermediate	E–B	Paper 1I	2 hrs	40
		Paper 2I	2 hrs	40
Higher	C–A*	Paper lH	2 hrs	40
		Paper 2H	2 hrs	40

For syllabus A you will be required to provide a portfolio of evidence based on coursework tasks set by the examination board or by your school. Over the two years of your course *you must complete a minimum of two pieces of coursework.* For syllabus B the third paper in each tier will have two questions. These will include investigation of real life situations where explanations and reasoning will be expected in addition to the selection of appropriate techniques. You should spend an equal amount of time on each question. The mark scheme is the same as in syllabus A. The time given for Paper 3 is $1\frac{1}{2}$ hours for Foundation tier, and 2 hours for the Intermediate and Higher tiers.

MEG

Midland Examining Group
1 Hills Road, Cambridge CB1 2EU
Tel: 01223 553311

Syllabus 1662 (Syllabus A)

MEG Syllabus A has two terminal papers each worth 40% of your final marks. Each paper will assess Number and Algebra (40%), Shape, Space and Measure (20%) and Data Handling (20%). At Intermediate and Higher tiers about 50% of the questions will be based on mathematical ideas introduced at that tier.

Tier	Grades available	Paper	Time given	%
Foundation	G–D	Paper 1	$1\frac{1}{2}$ hrs	40
		Paper 2	$1\frac{1}{2}$ hrs	40
Intermediate	E–B	Paper 3	2 hrs	40
		Paper 4	2 hrs	40
Higher	C–A★	Paper 5	2 hrs	40
		Paper 6	2 hrs	40

The remaining 20% will be given for the MEG marked tasks. You will be required to submit two tasks carried out between September and April of the school year that you will sit your final examination. These tasks are provided by the examination board and will be appropriate to your tier of entry. Each task should take a maximum of three hours to complete.

Syllabus 1664 (Syllabus B)

This syllabus contains two terminal papers which together are worth 75% of your final marks and an orally given non-calculator paper worth 5%. Marks on each paper are given for Number and Algebra (37% + 3% from the oral), Shape, Space and Measure (18% + 2% from the oral) and Data Handling (20%). At Intermediate and Higher tiers when the two question papers are considered together about half the marks will address the top two grades in each tier.

Tier	Grades available	Paper	Time given	%
Foundation	G, F	Paper 1	$1\frac{3}{4}$ hrs	$37\frac{1}{2}$
	F, E, D	Paper 2	$1\frac{3}{4}$ hrs	$37\frac{1}{2}$
		Oral	20 mins	5
Intermediate	E, D, C	Paper 3	$1\frac{3}{4}$ hrs	$37\frac{1}{2}$
		Paper 4	2 hrs	$37\frac{1}{2}$
		Oral	20 mins	5
Higher	C, B, A	Paper 5	2 hrs	$37\frac{1}{2}$
	B, A, A★	Paper 6	2 hrs	$37\frac{1}{2}$
		Oral	20 mins	5

The remaining 20% will be given for coursework which will be marked by your teacher and moderated by the examination board.

You will be required to submit two tasks which must be chosen from two of the following three types:

1. A pure investigation.
2. Statistical or other experimental work.
3. A design task involving mathematical concepts.

Each task should take between one and two and a half weeks of class and homework time to complete.

Syllabus 1666 Graduated Assessment (Syllabus C)

If you are following this syllabus your final marks will be given for three aspects of your work:

Module tests	30%
Coursework	20%
A terminal examination paper	50%

Module tests are completed in stages in March of year 10, November and April/May of year 11. Each test is one hour long. You will have the results for the first two stage tests before you sit your terminal examination.

Remember

- only one module test can be taken at each 'sitting'.
- module tests cannot be retaken
- you have to take a minimum of two and a maximum of three module tests.
- only module tests taken at the same tier of entry as the terminal paper will be used to obtain your final score.

If you are using this book to revise for stage tests ask your teacher for a list of the contents of each stage test.

Level	Module tests stage	Grades available
Foundation	1	G
	2	G, (F)
	3	(G), F
	4	G, F, E
	5	F, E, (D)
	6	(F), E, D
Intermediate	1	F, E, D
	2	E, D, C
	3	D, C, B
Higher	1	E, D, C
	2	D, C, B
	3	C, B, A
	4	B, A, A*

The coursework, which is worth 20%, will be marked by your teacher and moderated by the examination board.

You will be required to submit two tasks which must be chosen from two of the following three types:

1. A pure investigation.
2. Statistical or other experimental work.
3. A design task involving mathematical concepts.

Each task should take between one and two and a half weeks of class and homework time to complete.

The terminal examinations will be $1\frac{3}{4}$ hours at Foundation tier and 2 hours at the Intermediate and Higher tiers. At the Foundation tier the terminal paper will be in two sections – Part 1 lasting $\frac{3}{4}$ hour where calculators are not to be used and Part 2 lasting 1 hour.

SEG

Southern Examining Group
Stag Hill House, Guildford, GU2 5XJ
Tel: 01483 506506

Mathematics Syllabuses 2500T and 2500X

In these SEG syllabuses you will sit two papers which will both contain questions across the full range of grades available at that level. You will also sit an aural test of approximately 20 minutes which carries 5% of your final marks. Calculators are not allowed in this test.

In syllabus 2500T your coursework is set and marked by your teacher and moderated by the board. In syllabus 2500X your coursework is set and marked by the board. You *must* complete a minimum of two pieces of coursework.

Tier	Grades available	Paper	Time given	%
Foundation	G–D	Paper 11	$1\frac{1}{2}$ hrs	$37\frac{1}{2}$
		Paper 12	$1\frac{1}{2}$ hrs	$37\frac{1}{2}$
		Aural test	20 mins	5
Intermediate	E–B	Paper 13	2 hrs	$37\frac{1}{2}$
		Paper 14	2 hrs	$37\frac{1}{2}$
		Aural test	20 mins	5
Higher	C–A*	Paper 15	2 hrs	$37\frac{1}{2}$
		Paper 16	2 hrs	$37\frac{1}{2}$
		Aural test	20 mins	5

Approximately 25% of the marks on the Intermediate papers will be allocated to questions common to the Foundation tier and approximately 25% to questions common to the Higher tier.

Modular Mathematics Syllabuses 2520T and 2520X

These syllabuses are normally only available to post-16 students. The content of each syllabus is identical and you will study this content of the syllabus in modules and sit the module tests when appropriate.

Modules can be taken as follows:

	Modules
Winter	1, 2, 3
Spring	1, 2
Summer	1, 2, 3

Marks are given for each module and for coursework and these relate to the final grade you will achieve.

Mark range	360–400	320–359	280–319	240–279	200–239	160–199	120–159	80–119	0–79
Grade	A*	A	B	C	D	E	F	G	U

The modules are assessed as follows:

	Foundation (Grades D–G)	Intermediate (Grades B–E)	Higher (Grades A*–C)
Money Management and Number module ($18\frac{3}{4}$%)	2520 MF 1 hr	2520 MI 1 hr	2520 MH 1 hr
Statistics and Probability Module ($18\frac{3}{4}$%)	2520 SF 1 hr	2520 SI 1 hr	2520 SH 1 hr
Terminal Module ($37\frac{1}{2}$%)	Paper 11	Paper 11	Paper 11
Algebra, Shape, Space and Measure	$1\frac{3}{4}$ hrs	$1\frac{3}{4}$ hrs	$1\frac{3}{4}$ hrs
Aural test	20 mins	20 mins	20 mins

The coursework in these syllabuses consists of two tasks. The first is common to both.
Task 1: This is set and marked by the board (10%).
Task 2: Syllabus 2520T This is set and marked by your teacher (10%).
or
Syllabus 2520X This is set and marked by the board (10%).
If you wish to use this book to revise for your module tests ask your teacher for a list of the contents of each module or obtain a syllabus of your own from SEG.

WJEC

Welsh Joint Education Commitee
245 Western Avenue, Cardiff CF5 2YX
Tel: 01222 265000

Syllabuses A and B

The written papers for both syllabuses are identical and in both you will complete two parallel examination papers, each worth 40% of your final marks. The content of the papers will assess Number and Algebra (40%), Shape, Space and Measures (20%) and Data Handling (20%). The remaining 20% will, for syllabus A, be given for coursework marked by your teacher and moderated by the examination board, or, for syllabus B, be given for externally assessed terminal tasks taken as a third paper on a date after the two written examination papers.

Tier	Grades available	Paper	Time given	%
Foundation	G–D	Paper 1	$1\frac{1}{2}$ hrs	40
		Paper 2	$1\frac{1}{2}$ hrs	40
Intermediate	E–B	Paper 3	2 hrs	40
		Paper 4	2 hrs	40
Higher	C–A*	Paper 5	2 hrs	40
		Paper 6	2 hrs	40

For syllabus B the time for the terminal tasks is:
$1\frac{1}{2}$ hours for the Foundation tier
2 hours for the Intermediate tier
$2\frac{1}{4}$ hours hours for the Higher tier.

IGCSE

International General Certificate of Secondary Education
University of Cambridge Local Examinations Syndicate
1 Hills Road, Cambridge, CB1 2EU
Tel: 01223 553311

This syllabus is based on the National Curriculum for England and Wales but does contain some additional content. It is designed to meet the needs of students on an international basis.

There are two options: without coursework (syllabus 0580) and with coursework (syllabus 0581). There are two tiers of entry in each option – students may follow either the Core curriculum only or they may follow the Extended curriculum which involves both the Core and Supplement. Students aiming for grades A to C will follow the Extended curriculum.

Without coursework (0580)

Tier	Grades available	Papers	%	Time
Core	C–G	1	35%	1 hr
		3	65%	2 hrs
Extended	A–E	2	35%	$1\frac{1}{2}$ hrs
		4	65%	$2\frac{1}{2}$ hrs

With coursework (0581)

Tier	Grades available	Papers	%	Time
Core	C–G	1	30	1 hr
		3	50	2 hrs
Extended	A–E	2	30	$1\frac{1}{2}$ hrs
		4	50	$2\frac{1}{2}$ hrs

Coursework is worth 20% of the final marks. It is recommended that all candidates submit one project and one investigation. Each piece of coursework could be expected to take between 10 and 20 hours.

SQA

Scottish Qualifications Authority (formerly SEB)
Ironmills Road, Dalkeith, Midlothian EH22 1LE
Tel: 0131 663 6601

The National Curriculum for England and Wales does not apply in Scotland. However, the mathematics within the Standard Grade Examination in Scotland is similar to that taught to England and Wales.

In Scotland all candidates are assessed by a system common to all levels, and grades are given on a seven-point scale, one being the highest. The final certificate also records your level of attainment in each of the following units.

(i) Knowledge and Understanding
This element covers facts, skills and concepts needed to solve mathematical problems. It includes appropriate notation and use of symbols. You can think of this section as the tool kit from which you can use ideas in the other elements of your work.

(ii) Reasoning and Application
This element assesses your understanding and ability to make decisions about your work. You are encouraged to show initiative and present the best possible solutions.

(iii) Investigation
This reflects the use of important mathematical activities like the collection of data and the exploration of patterns, making conjectures and generalising a solution or mathematical model of the results.

External assessment is at two of three levels where you sit papers at either Foundation and General levels or at General and Credit levels. In some cases you may be advised by your teacher to sit only one paper.

Paper	Grades assessed	Element assessed	Time
Foundation	6, 5	Knowledge and Understanding Reasoning and Application	70 mins
General	4, 3	Knowledge and Understanding Reasoning and Application	90 mins
Credit	2, 1	Knowledge and Understanding Reasoning and Application	135 mins

Papers consist of a mixture of short and extended-response questions set in context. To achieve a grade you must gain approximately 55% as your final mark. Your grade in the Investigation element will be derived from a set of three dissimilar investigations representing your best work.

Note: There are a number of mathematical topics within this book which you will not need for Scottish Standard Grade Mathematics.

Not needed: Sampling, probability, tree diagrams, cumulative frequency histograms, standard deviation, polar coordinates.
Pupils at all levels should understand bar charts, pictograms, pie charts, tabulated results, straight-line graphs, mean of ungrouped data.

Partially needed: Vectors are not included in S-Grade but are required if you decide to do Revised Highers.
You should understand the term 'congruent' but the proofs are not required.

You are advised to get a syllabus from your teacher before you start using this book for revision.

CCEA

Northern Ireland Council for the Curriculum Examinations and Assessment
Clarendon Dock, 29 Clarendon Road, Belfast BTI 3BG
Tel: 01232 261200

The National Curriculum in Northern Ireland is virtually identical to that used in England and Wales.

CCEA Syllabuses A and B

These syllabuses contain two terminal papers which together are worth 70% of your final marks and an aural worth 10%. The written papers for both syllabuses are identical and in both you will complete two parallel examination papers. The remaining 20% will be given for coursework marked by your teacher (syllabus A), or for an externally assessed task, marked using the same criteria (syllabus B). The content of the written papers and the aural will assess Number and Algebra (40%), Shape, Space and Measures (20%), Data Handling (20%).

Tier	Grades available	Paper	Time given	%
Foundation	G–D	Paper 1	$1\frac{1}{2}$ hrs	35
		Paper 2	$1\frac{1}{2}$ hrs	35
		Aural	30 mins	10
Intermediate	E–B	Paper 3	2 hrs	35
		Paper 4	2 hrs	35
		Aural	30 mins	10
Higher	C–A*	Paper 5	$2\frac{1}{2}$ hrs	35
		Paper 6	$2\frac{1}{2}$ hrs	35
		Aural	30 mins	10

In syllabus A the coursework is marked by your teacher and moderated by the examination board. You must complete at least two pieces of coursework, one of a practical nature and one of an investigational nature – each piece normally taking about 3–4 hours to complete, under teacher supervision.

If you are following syllabus B the time given for your terminal task is 1 hour for foundation candidates, $1\frac{1}{2}$ hours for intermediate candidates and 2 hours for higher candidates. These terminal task papers are set on a third examination session and under examination conditions.

Coursework or terminal tasks

Attainment Target 1 (Using and Applying Mathematics) of the National Curriculum is different from the other attainment targets. This is because it develops the processes used to solve problems mathematically. These processes, concerned with mathematical thinking, are divided into three main areas or strands:

1. Making and monitoring decisions to solve problems
2. Communicating mathematically
3. Developing skills of mathematical reasoning

As you will see from the comparisons of the different syllabuses, on pages 7 to 15, there are three different methods used to assess your performance in this component at GCSE. The methods, which are discussed later, are:

- coursework
- tasks set during Y11
- tasks set on terminal papers

All three methods share the same assessment criteria. These General Criteria are given on the following pages.

You will, for most syllabuses, be expected to submit two pieces of coursework or attempt two tasks. Marks are awarded in each strand for each piece of work that you. The final mark for this component is calculated by adding together the highest mark obtained in each strand. For example the final mark sheet for two pieces of work could look like this:

	Making and monitoring decisions	Communicating mathematically	Developing the skills of mathematical reasoning	Total
Investigation	6	4	5	
Practical	4	5	4	
Highest mark	6	5	5	**16**

giving a final mark of 16 (out of 24).

General criteria for assessing using and applying mathematics in England and Wales

Mark	Making and monitoring decisions	Communicating mathematically	Developing the skills of mathematical reasoning
	Description	Description	Description
1	Candidates try different approaches and find ways of overcoming difficulties that arise when they are solving problems. They are beginning to organise their work and check results.	Candidates discuss their mathematical work and are beginning to explain their thinking. They use and interpret mathematical symbols and diagrams.	Candidates show that they understand a general statement by finding particular examples that match it.
2	Candidates are developing their own strategies for solving problems and are using these strategies both in working within mathematics and in applying mathematics to practical contexts.	Candidates present information and results in a clear and organised way, explaining the reasons for their presentation.	Candidates search for a pattern by trying out ideas of their own.
3	In order to carry through tasks and solve mathematical problems, candidates identify and obtain necessary information; they check their results, considering whether these are sensible.	Candidates show understanding of situations by describing them mathematically using symbols, words and diagrams.	Candidates make general statements of their own, based on evidence they have produced, and give an explanation of their reasoning.
4	Candidates carry through substantial tasks and solve quite complex problems by breaking them down into smaller, more manageable tasks.	Candidates interpret, discuss and synthesise information presented in a variety of mathematical forms. Their writing explains and informs their use of diagrams.	Candidates are beginning to give a mathematical justification for their generalisations; they test them by checking particular cases.
5	Starting from problems or contexts that have been presented to them, candidates introduce questions of their own, which generate fuller solutions.	Candidates examine critically and justify their choice of mathematical presentation, considering alternative approaches and explaining improvements they have made.	Candidates justify their generalisations or solutions, showing some insight into the mathematical structure of the situation being investigated. They appreciate the difference between mathematical explanation and experimental evidence.
6	Candidates develop and follow altemative approaches. They reflect on their own lines of enquiry when exploring mathematical tasks; in doing so they introduce and use a range of mathematical techniques.	Candidates convey mathematical meaning through consistent use of symbols.	Candidates examine generalisations or solutions reached in an activity, commenting constructively on the reasoning and logic employed, and make further progress in the activity as a result.
7	Candidates analyse alternative approaches to problems involving a number of features or variables. They give detailed reasons for following or rejecting particular lines of enquiry.	Candidates use mathematical language and symbols accurately in presenting a convincing reasoned argument.	Candidates' reports include mathematical justifications, explaining their solutions to problems involving a number of features or variables.
8	Candidates consider and evaluate a number of approaches to a substantial task. They explore extensively a context or area of mathematics with which they are unfamiliar. They apply independently a range of appropriate mathematical techniques.	Candidates use mathematical language and symbols efficiently in presenting a concise reasoned argument.	Candidates provide a mathematically rigorous justification or proof of their solution to a complex problem, considering the conditions under which it remains valid.

Some general comments

1. **Coursework**
   - You will usually be expected to undertake two tasks – see the appropriate syllabus for details. Your teacher will explain the choice of tasks that you will have.
   - Make sure you know how long you have to complete each task and how much work is to be undertaken at school under supervision.
   - Make sure you include a plan explaining what you intend to do.
   - Try to explain your working, reasoning and findings and make sure that your work is mathematical and that the answers are sensible.
2. **Terminal tasks**
   MEG Syllabus A (1662) is the only syllabus which offers this model of assessment for the Using and Applying Matematics component. The model, in a sense, 'fits in between' coursework tasks and tasks on terminal papers. Tasks will be provided by the board, one in the Autumn term and one in the Spring term of the final year at school. Each task will have to be completed in a maximum time of 3 hours and, apart from some preliminary data collection that may be required for some tasks, this time will all be spent under supervision, i.e. at school. The titles of the tasks that will be set will be similar to those set in both other models but the tasks themselves may have more structure, perhaps in the form of introductory questions, than those set for coursework, but less structure than the tasks set on the terminal papers.
3. **Tasks on terminal papers**
   The tasks set on terminal papers will have to be completed within a given time and some details of the requirements are given in the syllabus information on pages 7 to 15. An example of a terminal task is given below together with an abridged marking guide, showing the sort of work expected for 4, 6 and 8 marks, derived from the General Criteria.

Note: This guide must not be taken as having the approval of any examination board. It will, however, be representative of the criteria used for such a task.

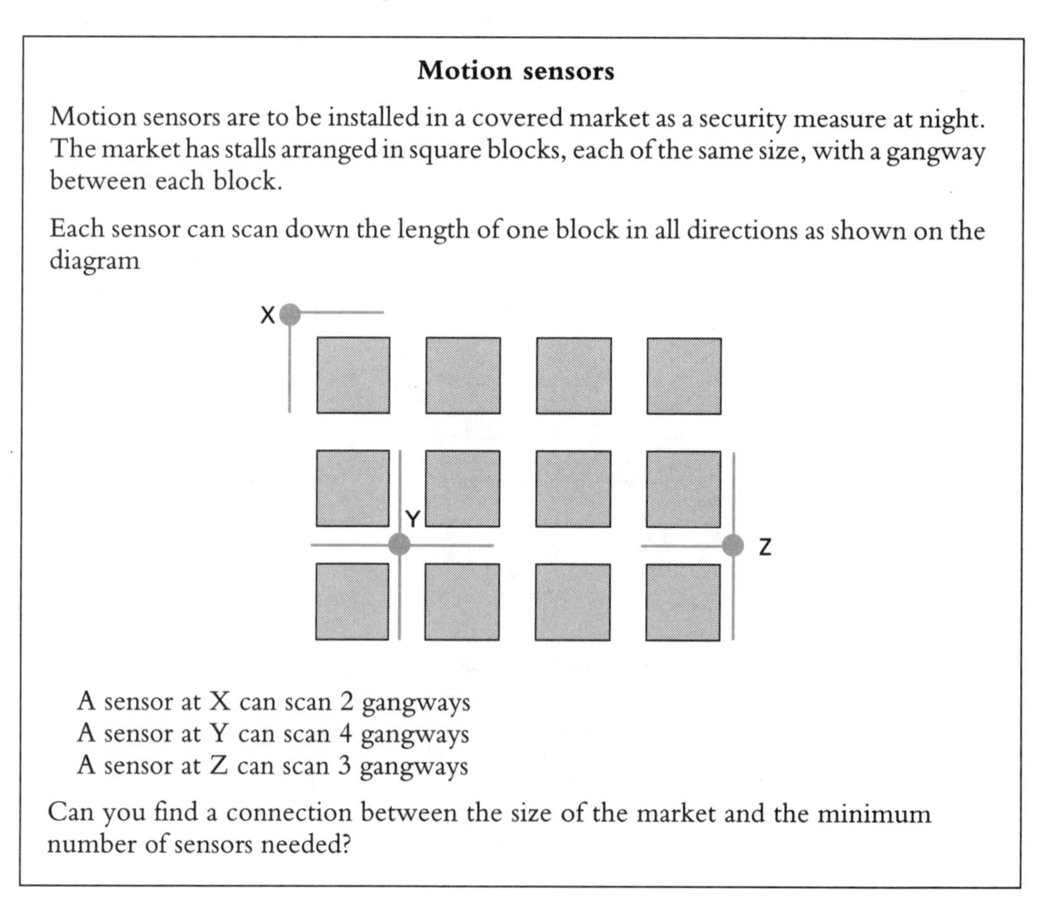

Motion sensors

Motion sensors are to be installed in a covered market as a security measure at night. The market has stalls arranged in square blocks, each of the same size, with a gangway between each block.

Each sensor can scan down the length of one block in all directions as shown on the diagram

A sensor at X can scan 2 gangways
A sensor at Y can scan 4 gangways
A sensor at Z can scan 3 gangways

Can you find a connection between the size of the market and the minimum number of sensors needed?

Marking guidance:

Mark	Making and monitoring decisions	Communicating mathematically	Developing the skills of mathematical reasoning
4	Use the results and patterns you have discovered to try to give some rule/relationship. Look at different arrangements with a fixed number of rows of stall.	Draw diagrams showing different positions for sensors. Show results for minimum number of sensors in a table.	Make one or more general statements based on table of results obtained. Test the general statement on a grid not already used.
6	Look for patterns in the results when, say, the number of rows and columns are both even.	Write up the work logically and in full. Use symbols consistently.	Make a general statement for the patterns explored with, for example, even numbers of rows and columns.
8	Consider and evaluate several different approaches to the task.	Use mathematical language and symbols efficiently in presenting a concise reasoned argument.	Provide a mathematically rigorous justification of the solution considering the conditions under which it is valid.

Chapter 1
Place value and the number system

1.1 Understanding place value

Rounding

Calculations often produce answers which would be more sensible if they were rounded up or down to an appropriate degree of accuracy.

E.g. $46\text{ m} \div 13 = 3\cdot\dot{5}38461\dot{5}38$

You may be asked to round an answer by expressing the answer to a number of significant figures (s.f.).

Significant figures

Significant figures considers all the digits of a number.

E.g. $3\cdot\dot{5}38461\dot{5}38$ to 2 s.f. is 3·5 m.
to 1 s.f. is 4 m.
to 3 s.f. is 3·54 m.

Note: If the next digit is 5 or more the last digit of the number is rounded up.
A 0 in the middle of a number is counted as significant, e.g. 2·034 to 3 s.f. is 2·03.

Decimal places

In some questions you will be asked to give your answer to a number of decimal places (d.p.).

E.g. $3\cdot\dot{5}38461\dot{5}38$ to 2 d.p. is 3·54 m.
to 1 d.p. is 3·5 m.
to 3 d.p. is 3·538 m.

xaminer's tip

Always make sure you give the units of measurement with your answers.

Decimal places includes only digits after the decimal point.

Note: 5·403 to 2 d.p. should be written 5·40.
Whole numbers, positive and negative, are called integers.

Ordering decimals and fractions

When you have to put a list of decimals in order it is easier if they are all expressed to the same number of places.

E.g. Write the following numbers in order, largest first:

0·2 0·21 0·021 0·201 0·1002 0·0201

Since adding zeros after the last digit on the right hand side of the decimal point has no effect on the number you can add extra zeros at the end to make the numbers the same length.

0·2000 0·2100 0·0210 0·2010 0,1002 0·0201

You should now find it much easier to put them in order:

0·2100 0·2010 0·2000 0·1002 0·0210 0·0201

Putting them back into their original form:

0·21 0·201 0·2 0·1002 0·021 0·0201

1 Put the following numbers in order, smallest first:

0·1 0·106 0·16 0·016 0·1006

Note: Put zeros after each number to make them the same length.

To order fractions convert them into decimal form by dividing the top value (numerator) by the bottom value (denominator). They can then be ordered in the same way as the decimals.

E.g. Write the following fractions in order, largest first: $\frac{3}{8}$ $\frac{4}{5}$ $\frac{5}{6}$ $\frac{1}{2}$ $\frac{4}{7}$

$\frac{3}{8} = 0{\cdot}375$, $\frac{4}{5} = 0{\cdot}8$, $\frac{5}{6} = 0{\cdot}833$, $\frac{1}{2} = 0{\cdot}5$, $\frac{4}{7} = 0{\cdot}571$ (to 3 d.p.)

Largest to smallest = $\frac{5}{6}$ $\frac{4}{5}$ $\frac{4}{7}$ $\frac{1}{2}$ $\frac{3}{8}$

2 Place the following fractions in order, largest first:

(a) $\frac{2}{3}$ $\frac{4}{5}$ $\frac{5}{7}$ $\frac{7}{10}$ $\frac{5}{8}$ (b) $\frac{2}{5}$ $\frac{3}{7}$ $\frac{1}{4}$ $\frac{4}{11}$ $\frac{3}{8}$

1.2 Ratios

Ratio is a comparison between similar quantities. It can be expressed as a ratio *m* to *n* or *m* : *n* or as a fraction m/n. *m* and *n* can be multiplied or divided by the same number without changing their ratio.

E.g. Two people receive money. *m* receives £250 and *n* receives £150. What is the ratio of *m* : *n* expressed in its lowest form?
The ratio *m* : *n* is 250 : 150.
Each of these numbers can be divided by 50 giving:
The lowest ratio of *m* : *n* is 5 : 3.

Note: Ratios should usually be expressed as whole numbers e.g. 1 : 1·5 will normally be written as 2 : 3.

1 Reduce the following ratios to their lowest form:

(a) 12 : 8 (b) 15 : 20 (c) 60 : 40 (d) 54 : 36

Using ratio

If you know the ratio between numbers and you know one of the numbers, then you can calculate the other number.

E.g. Two lengths are in the ratio 3 : 5. If the first length is 120 m what is the second length?
Multiplying both sides of the ratio by 40 gives 120 : 200.
This is equivalent to the ratio 3 : 5.

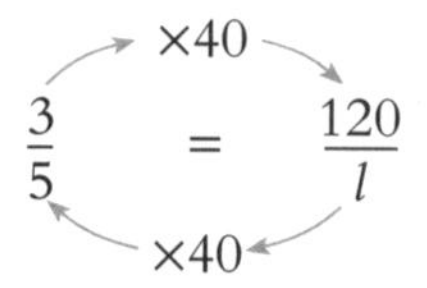

So if the ratio of the length is 3 : 5 then the ratio of the lengths is 120 : 200.
So the second length is 200 m.

2 The length and width of a room are in the ratio 4 : 3.
(a) What is the width of the room if the length is 3·2 m?
(b) What is the length of the room if the width is 3·6 m?

Remember: Find an equivalent ratio which includes the number given in the question.

1.3 Negative numbers

Adding and subtracting

When you are adding or subtracting negative numbers try to imagine moving on a number line.

+ : $^{+}6$, $^{+}5$, $^{+}4$, $^{+}3$, $^{+}2$, $^{+}1$, 0, $^{-}1$, $^{-}2$, $^{-}3$, $^{-}4$, $^{-}5$, $^{-}6$, $^{-}7$: –

E.g. $^{-}3 - 2$ means start at -3 and then go down 2 places giving $^{-}5$

$^{-}3 - 2 = {}^{-}5$

When both digits have a + or – sign then the following method can be used.
Call the operations add (+) and take away (–) and the signs positive ($^{+}$) and negative ($^{-}$)

E.g. In $^{-}5 - {}^{-}3$ the symbols between the $^{-}5$ and the 3 now read 'take away the negative' which makes the 3 into +3.

1 Complete the following

(a) $^{-}5 - {}^{-}8 =$ (b) $^{+}5 - {}^{-}3 =$ (c) $^{-}6 + {}^{+}7 =$ (d) $^{-}13 + {}^{-}3 =$

(e) $^{+}8 - {}^{+}12 =$ (f) $^{-}16 - {}^{+}8 =$ (g) $^{-}43 - {}^{-}54 =$ (h) $^{-}25 - {}^{-}12 =$

Note: If operation and sign are the same they become positive.

$+^{+}$ works like $+$
$-^{-}$ works like $+$

If operation and sign are different the result will be negative

$+^-$ works like $-$
$-^+$ works like $-$

Multiplying and dividing

When multiplying and dividing the following rules apply:

$$(+) \times (+) = (+) \qquad (+) \div (+) = (+)$$
$$(-) \times (-) = (+) \qquad (-) \div (-) = (+)$$
$$(-) \times (+) = (-) \qquad (-) \div (+) = (-)$$
$$(+) \times (-) = (-) \qquad (+) \div (-) = (-)$$

E.g. $^-5 \times {}^-3 = {}^+15$
$^+5 \times {}^-3 = {}^-15$
$^-5 \times {}^+3 = {}^-15$

Note: The positive sign on the answer may be omitted.

xaminer's tip

Use the change of sign key on your calculator to give you negative numbers.

2 Complete the following

(a) $^-5 \times {}^-8 =$	(b) $^+5 \times {}^-6 =$	(c) $^-6 \times {}^+7 =$	(d) $^-9 \times {}^-3 =$
(e) $^+8 \times {}^+9 =$	(f) $^-6 \times {}^+8 =$	(g) $^-4 \times {}^-7 =$	(h) $^-5 \times {}^-12 =$
(i) $^+16 \div {}^+2 =$	(j) $^-24 \div {}^+3 =$	(k) $^+42 \div {}^-6 =$	(l) $^-36 \div {}^-4 =$

1.4 Standard index form

Standard index form (SI form) or scientific notation is used to enable us to write very large or very small numbers more easily. Instead of having to write in all the zeros in numbers like 2 000 000 (two million) or 0·000002 (two millionths), we can express them as powers of 10.

E.g. 2 000 000 (two million) $= 2 \times 10 \times 10 \times 10 \times 10 \times 10 \times 10$
Hence 2 000 000 can be written as 2×10^6.

Note: 10^2 is one hundred
10^3 is one thousand
10^6 is one million

To change a number to standard form, put a decimal point after the first digit and then count how many places the decimal point has moved. This gives you the power of 10.

E.g. Change 3 567 000 to standard index form.

3·567 000·

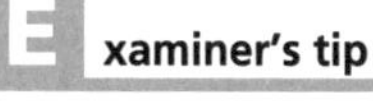

xaminer's tip

In standard form only one digit must be used before the decimal point.

The point appears to have moved 6 places so multiply by 10^6.
3 567 000 = $3{\cdot}567 \times 10^6$

Note: A common mistake made in exams is to put the point after the digits, e.g. $3567{\cdot}0 \times 10^3$.

The number is written as $a \times 10^n$ where $1 \leq a < 10$ (a is between 1 and 10) and n is a whole number.

E.g. 35 000 is $3{\cdot}5 \times 10^4$
26 is $2{\cdot}6 \times 10^1$

1 Write the following numbers in standard index form:
(a) The radius of Mercury is 2 420 000 m.
(b) The radius of Venus is 6 085 000 m.
(c) The radius of Jupiter is 71 400 000 m.

2 Write the following numbers in ordinary form:
(a) The radius of Pluto is 3×10^6 m.
(b) The distance of the earth from the sun is $1{\cdot}496 \times 10^{11}$ m.

Numbers less than 1 can also be written in standard index form.

E.g. Write 0·000002 in standard form.

0·000002 is 2 millionths or $\frac{2}{1\,000\,000}$

which can be written as $\frac{2}{10^6}$ or $2 \times \frac{1}{10^6}$

The general rule is that $\frac{1}{10^n}$ is written as 10^{-n}

so $0{\cdot}000002 = 2 \times 10^{-6}$

Note: 10^{-1} is one 10th
10^{-2} is one 100th
10^{-3} is one 1000th
10^{-6} is one 1 000 000th

To change a number less than 1 to standard form, put a decimal point after the first digit and then count how many places the decimal point has moved to the right. The power of 10 is that number preceded by a negative sign.

3 Write each of the following numbers in standard index form:

(a) 0·003 (b) 0·052 (c) 0·00000861 (d) 0·00703

4 Write each of the following numbers in ordinary notation:

(a) 5×10^{-5} (b) 8×10^{-1} (c) $9{\cdot}3 \times 10^{-4}$ (d) $6{\cdot}32 \times 10^{-2}$

Look for the key marked EXP or E or EE
This is called the exponent key.

xaminer's tip

5·38 04 is not an acceptable answer – you must write 5.38×10^4.

To enter $5{\cdot}38 \times 10^4$ press

5 · 3 8 EXP 4

Display: 5.38 04 or 5.38 E 04 or 5.38 04

Calculations in standard index form

Note: You would normally complete standard form questions using a calculator.

If you're working without a calculator start by grouping the numbers and the powers of 10. Do the calculation and then put the answer in standard form.

E.g. (a) Multiply 4×10^3 by 6×10^5

$$(4 \times 10^3) \times (6 \times 10^5) = (4 \times 6) \times (10^3 \times 10^5)$$
$$= 24 \times (10 \times 10 \times 10) \times (10 \times 10 \times 10 \times 10 \times 10)$$
$$= 24 \times 10^8$$

which is $2{\cdot}4 \times 10^9$ in standard form

(b) Divide 8×10^5 by 2×10^3

$$(8 \times 10^5) \div (2 \times 10^3) = (8 \div 2) \times (10^5 \div 10^3)$$
$$= 4 \times \frac{10 \times 10 \times \cancel{10} \times \cancel{10} \times \cancel{10}}{\cancel{10} \times \cancel{10} \times \cancel{10}}$$
$$= 4 \times 10^2$$

(c) Multiply 2×10^3 by 3×10^{-5}

$$(2 \times 10^3) \times (3 \times 10^{-5}) = (2 \times 3) \times \frac{\cancel{10} \times \cancel{10} \times \cancel{10}}{\cancel{10} \times \cancel{10} \times \cancel{10} \times 10 \times 10}$$
$$= \frac{6}{10^2}$$
$$= 6 \times 10^{-2}$$

When you answer the following questions, give your answers in standard index form. (You may use a calculator.)

5 (a) $(7 \times 10^4) \times (5 \times 10^7)$ (b) $(8 \times 10^6) \div (2 \times 10^2)$

(c) $(4{\cdot}3 \times 10^5) \times (7{\cdot}8 \times 10^9)$ (d) $(2{\cdot}7 \times 10^{20}) \div (9{\cdot}5 \times 10^{14})$

6 A light year is approximately $9{\cdot}46 \times 10^{15}$ m. Calculate in metres the distance to the star Rigel in Orion's belt which is $5{\cdot}4 \times 10^2$ light years from the earth.

7 The volume of the earth is approximately $1{\cdot}4 \times 10^{27}$ m^3.
The mass of the earth is approximately 2×10^{30} kg.
Calculate the density of the earth in kg/m^3 $\left(\text{density} = \dfrac{\text{mass}}{\text{volume}}\right)$.

8 Calculate $(4{\cdot}8 \times 10^3) \div (1{\cdot}6 \times 10^{-2})$.

9 The common cold virus is 5×10^{-7} m long.
(a) How long would a chain of 12 000 viruses be?
(b) How many viruses would fit into 1 mm?

Addition and subtraction

To add or subtract numbers with the same power of 10 you add or subtract the digits then multiply by the power of 10 and convert your answer to standard form.

E.g. $(5 \times 10^3) + (6 \times 10^3) = (5 + 6) \times 10^3$
$= 11 \times 10^3$
$= 1{\cdot}1 \times 10^4$

If you have to add or subtract numbers with different powers of 10 without a calculator it is often easiest if you convert them back to normal notation first.

E.g. (a) $(2 \times 10^3) + (3 \times 10^5) = 2000 + 300\,000 = 302\,000$

which is $3{\cdot}02 \times 10^5$ in standard form.

(b) $(2 \times 10^6) - (3 \times 10^5) = 2\,000\,000 - 300\,000 = 1\,700\,000$ which is $1{\cdot}7 \times 10^6$

Chapter 2
Using numbers

2.1 Working with powers and roots

Squares and square roots

Squaring and taking the square root are inverse (opposite) operations so if you square n and then take the square root you get

$$\sqrt{n^2} = n \quad (n \geq 0)$$

Note: $\sqrt{}$ means taking the positive square root.

If you have to square and square root the order in which you carry out these operations is not critical.

$$\left(\sqrt{n}\right)^2 = \sqrt{n} \times \sqrt{n} = n$$

Note: If n is negative then you can't take the square root.

Try using your calculator to find the square of the square root or the square root of the square for different values of n. (You won't always get back the original number because of rounding by the calculator.)

Cubes and cube roots

If you cube n and then take the cube root you get

$$\sqrt[3]{n^3} = \sqrt[3]{n \times n \times n}$$

The cube root is the number you have to multiply by itself 3 times to get n^3 so

$$\sqrt[3]{n^3} = n$$

If you cube the cubed root you get

$$(\sqrt[3]{n})^3 = \sqrt[3]{n} \times \sqrt[3]{n} \times \sqrt[3]{n}$$

By definition, $\sqrt[3]{n}$ is the number you multiply by itself 3 times to get n so

$$(\sqrt[3]{n})^3 = n$$

So cubing and taking the cube root are inverse operations. Each one undoes the effect of the other.

Higher powers

All powers follow the same pattern.

If n is an odd number, raising to the power n and taking the nth root are inverse operations.

$$\sqrt[n]{x^n} = x$$

If n is even then

$$\pm\sqrt[n]{x^n} = x$$

1 Simplify the following expressions:

(a) $\left(\sqrt{xy}\right)^2$ (b) $\sqrt[5]{a^5}$ (c) $\sqrt[7]{(3y)^7}$ (d) $\sqrt[3]{8a^3}$ (e) $\sqrt[3]{b^6}$ (f) $\sqrt{a^4b^2}$

2 Write x as a power or root of y in each of the following cases:

(a) $y = x^6$ (b) $y = \sqrt[5]{x}$ (c) $y = \sqrt[3]{x^2}$

Hint: If $y = x^2$ then $x = \sqrt{y}$

Negative indices

When the index or power of a number is negative it is one divided by the positive version of the power

$x^{-n} = \dfrac{1}{x^n}$ where n represents any number

E.g. Simplify 2^{-3}

$$2^{-3} = \frac{1}{2^3} = \frac{1}{8}$$

3 Simplify the following:

(a) 3^{-1} (b) 4^{-2} (c) 2^{-5}

2.2 Fractions

Note: If you have a fraction calculator any calculation involving fractions can be done on that using the key marked

To carry out these operations without a calculator you do the following.

Adding and subtracting

To add and subtract fractions they should first be changed to give a common denominator (bottom value).

E.g. $\frac{2}{3} + \frac{4}{5}$

The smallest number divisible by both 3 *and* 5 is $3 \times 5 = 15$
so the lowest common denominator is 15.
3 goes into 15 five times so you multiply the top and bottom of $\frac{2}{3}$ by 5:

$$\frac{2}{3} = \frac{10}{15}$$

5 goes into 15 three times so you multiply the top and bottom of $\frac{4}{5}$ by 3:

$$\frac{4}{5} = \frac{12}{15}$$

So $\frac{2}{3} + \frac{4}{5} = \frac{10}{15} + \frac{12}{15} = \frac{22}{15} = \frac{15+7}{15} = 1\frac{7}{15}$

The same method is used when you are subtracting.

E.g. $\frac{5}{6} - \frac{1}{4}$

The lowest common denominator is 12.
6 goes into 12 twice so

$$\frac{5}{6} = \frac{10}{12}$$

4 goes into 12 three times so $\frac{1}{4} = \frac{3}{12}$

So $\frac{5}{6} - \frac{1}{4} = \frac{10}{12} - \frac{3}{12} = \frac{7}{12}$

1 Complete the following calculations:

(a) $\frac{3}{4} + \frac{1}{3} = \frac{\ }{12} + \frac{\ }{12} = 1\frac{\ }{12}$

(b) $\frac{2}{5} - \frac{1}{4} =$

(c) $\frac{5}{8} + \frac{1}{4} =$

(d) $\frac{3}{4} - \frac{1}{2} =$

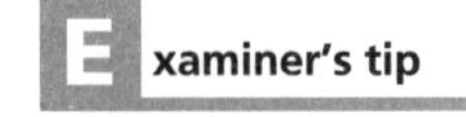
xaminer's tip

Always simplify the answer you get to its lowest form.

Mixed numbers

If the calculation involves mixed numbers, if possible add or subtract the whole numbers first.

E.g. $2\frac{2}{3} + 4\frac{1}{6}$ is $2 + 4 + \frac{2}{3} + \frac{1}{6}$ which can be written $6 + \frac{2}{3} + \frac{1}{6} = 6\frac{5}{6}$

2 Solve the following:

(a) $3\frac{1}{4} + 5\frac{1}{2}$ (b) $6\frac{5}{8} - 4\frac{1}{4}$ Note: (–) (c) $5\frac{3}{10} - 1\frac{2}{5}$ Note: $5\frac{3}{10} = \frac{53}{10}$

Multiplying and dividing

To multiply fractions first express them as top heavy or improper fractions.

E.g. $3\frac{1}{4} \times 5\frac{1}{2}$ becomes $\frac{13}{4} \times \frac{11}{2}$ then multiply the top values together and the bottom values together

$\frac{13}{4} \times \frac{11}{2} = \frac{143}{8} = 17\frac{7}{8}$

To divide fractions first express them as top heavy or improper fractions.

E.g. $2\frac{1}{4} \div 1\frac{1}{2}$ becomes $\frac{9}{4} \div \frac{3}{2}$ then invert the second fraction to give you its reciprocal and then multiply the top values together and the bottom values together

$\frac{9}{4} \div \frac{3}{2} = \frac{9}{4} \times \frac{2}{3} = \frac{18}{12} = 1\frac{1}{2}$

3 Complete the following:

(a) $\frac{3}{4} \times \frac{1}{2}$ (b) $2\frac{1}{5} \times 3\frac{1}{2}$ (c) $\frac{3}{4} \div \frac{1}{2}$ (d) $4\frac{1}{2} \div 2\frac{1}{5}$

One number as a fraction of another

In some questions you may be asked to express one value as a fraction of another.

E.g. 15 out of 25 pupils passed a test. What fraction of the pupils is this?

Write the first value over the second and cancel down $\frac{15}{25} = \frac{3}{5}$

E xaminer's tip

The answer will be in the form a ⌟ b ⌟ c. You must change this back to the form a b/c

4 In each of the following express the first number as a fraction of the second:

(a) 12 as a fraction of 20 (b) 12 as a fraction of 18 (c) 96 as a fraction of 144

Note: If your calculator will do fractions it will cancel down fractions to their lowest form.

2.3 Calculating with ratios

It is very important that when you are writing two numbers as a ratio they must first be expressed in the same units.

E.g. Express 15p to £3 in its lowest form.
This becomes 15p : 300p and dividing both sides by 15 gives 1 : 20.

xaminer's tip

A common mistake made in exams is to compare values with different sized units. Always work with the same types of units.

1 Express the following ratios in their lowest form:
(a) 450 g : 1·35 kg (1 kg = 1000 g)
(b) 3 feet : 4 inches (there are 12 inches in a foot)

Note: Make sure your units are the same.

Sharing out a quantity in a given ratio

E.g. Mr Sharp and Mrs West share an inheritance of £64 000 in the ratio 5 : 3. How much will each get?
You add the numbers in the ratio to get the total number of shares or parts.
5 + 3 = 8 so there are 8 parts in all.

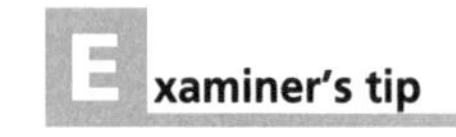
xaminer's tip

You can check the answer by adding the two results. They should add up to the total value.

Method 1 Work out how much each part is worth.
64 000 ÷ 8 = 8000
Mr Sharp receives 5 of the 8 parts or 5 shares at £8000 each.
5 × 8000 = 40 000
So Mr Sharp's share of the inheritance is £40 000.

Method 2 Mrs West receives 3 of the 8 parts or $\frac{3}{8}$
$\frac{3}{8}$ × 64 000 = 24 000
So Mrs West's share of the inheritance is £24 000.

2 You can make concrete by mixing gravel, sand and cement in the ratio 3 : 2 : 1 by volume.
(a) How much gravel will be needed to make 12 cubic metres of concrete?
(b) How much cement is needed to make 30 cubic metres of concrete?
(c) If you have 2 cubic metres of sand how much concrete can you make?

Remember: As the units are the same they can be ignored in the calculation but must be put in the answer.

Increasing or decreasing by a given ratio

E.g. A cook book gives the following recipe for apple pie. This quantity is enough for 4 people. How much of each ingredient would you need to make an apple pie for 6 people?

500 g cooking apples
Granulated sugar to taste
200 g plain flour
2·5 ml salt
50 g lard
50 g margarine
Cold water to mix

The ratio of the amount required to the amount in the recipe is 6 : 4 which can be simplified to 3 : 2.

To calculate the amount of each ingredient needed you could divide by 2 (because the amount in the recipe represents 2 parts) and then multiply by 3.

The quantity of apples you would now need is

$$(500\text{ g} \div 2) \times 3 = 250\text{ g} \times 3 = 750\text{ g}$$

An alternative is to convert the ratio to a fraction or a decimal and then use it to increase each of the values in the recipe.

To convert the ratio, divide the size you want by the size you have:

$$\frac{6}{4} = \frac{3}{2} = 1{\cdot}5$$

This gives you the multiplier you can then use to increase each of the values in the recipe.

If you multiply the 500 g of apples by 1·5 you get 500 g × 1·5 = 750 g.

The two methods have the same result.

3 The recipe below for beef, tomato and mushroom stew makes enough for 4 people. Calculate the ingredients necessary to feed 10 people, using whichever method you find easier.

800 g stewing steak
30 g plain flour
Salt and pepper to taste
1 medium sized onion
3 medium sized leeks
100 g button mushrooms
50 g lard
400 g tinned tomatoes

4 Using the recipe in the example above, calculate the amount of apples and flour required to make apple pie for 3 people.

Examiner's tip

To get the multiplier, divide the size you want by the size you have.

You can use this method for any list of quantities. For example, if you want to enlarge a design the measurements of the design are like the ingredients in a recipe.

2.4 Percentage change

Increasing or decreasing by a given percentage

E.g. Calculate an 8% increase on the price of a television costing £450.

Method 1 First, calculate 8% of £450.
$8\% = \frac{8}{100} = 0{\cdot}08$ so 8% of £450 is 0·08 × 450 = £36
This gives a total new cost of £450 + £36 = £486.

Method 2 An 8% increase can also be calculated by adding the 8% to the original 100% of the cost.
100% + 8% = 108% which can be written as $\frac{108}{100}$ or 1·08.
So an 8% increase is 1·08 × £450 = £486.

1 Calculate the values of the following after the % increases:
(a) £250 after an increase of 12%
(b) a 16% increase on 80 m
(c) a 25% increase on an attendance of 6500
(d) a 9% increase on sales of £2400
(e) the cost of a £1500 computer after VAT at 17·5% is added

There are two similar methods which can be used to calculate % decreases.

E.g. In a sale prices have been reduced by 15%. Calculate the sale price of a coat that originally cost £80.

Method 1 Calculate 15% of £80 and take this away from £80.
$15\% = \frac{15}{100} = 0{\cdot}15$ so 15% of £80 is $0{\cdot}15 \times 80 = £12$

This gives a sale price for the coat of £80 – £12 = £68.

Method 2 Take the 15% from the original 100% leaving 85%.
$85\% = \frac{85}{100} = 0{\cdot}85$ giving $0{\cdot}85 \times £80 = £68$

2 Calculate the values of the following after the % decreases:
(a) £150 after a decrease of 8%
(b) a decrease of 12% on £250
(c) the price of an £11 500 car after a discount of 15%
(d) a 6% drop in an attendance of 850

Note: % change is given by change ÷ original value.

Calculating increases and decreases as a fraction or percentage

You may be given the original value and the new value and asked to calculate the change (increase or decrease) as a fraction or percentage.

E.g. The cost of a computer game goes up from £40 to £45.
The increase in cost is £45 – £40 = £5.
The original cost is £40.
Dividing the increase by the original cost gives $\frac{5}{40} = \frac{1}{8}$
So the change in price is an increase of $\frac{1}{8}$.
Converting to a percentage:
$\frac{1}{8} = 0{\cdot}125$, $0{\cdot}125 \times 100 = 12{\cdot}5\%$
So the percentage increase in the price is 12·5%.

Percentage decreases are calculated in the same way.

Note: The original value often appears in the question after the word 'from'.

Examiner's tip

Always divide the change by the original value **not** the value after the change has taken place.

3 (a) Calculate the percentage increase if a concert ticket goes up from £25 to £27.
(b) Calculate the percentage change if the cost of a CD increases from £10 to £10·40.
(c) Calculate the percentage decrease if a camera is reduced from £160 to £148·80.

Using percentage to find the original value

If you are told that a value has been increased by a percentage and then given the final value you cannot simply take that percentage off to find the original value. The following process must be applied.

E.g. 55% of the cars using a street were speeding. If 22 cars were speeding calculate how many cars went down the street.

$0{\cdot}55$ of cars = 22 hence $0{\cdot}55 \times C = 22$ therefore $C = \dfrac{22}{0{\cdot}55}$ giving $C = 40$

4 Find the original value in each of the following:
(a) There are pictures on 65% of the pages in a book. If there are 52 pages with pictures, how many pages are there in the book?
(b) A computer and monitor are bought. The computer costs £1139 which is 67% of the total. What was the cost of the computer and monitor?

Chapter 3
Solving numerical problems

3.1 Compound interest

In simple interest when £1000 is invested at 5% for a number of years, the sum invested remains at £1000.

If the interest is compound then the interest each year is added to the sum invested each year. To solve this type of problem you should use a multiplication factor.

5% of a £1000 can be calculated by multiplying by 1·05.
Over two years this multiplier will be applied twice giving $1{\cdot}05^2$.
After *n* years the original amount will have been multiplied by $1{\cdot}05^n$.

E.g. A population is increasing by 2% per year. If the population is 5000 now what will it be in 5 years' time?

$5000 \times 1{\cdot}02^5 = 5520{\cdot}404016$
$= 5520$

Note: This is a population and so it should be given to the nearest whole number.

1 (a) What is the value of £2000 invested at 7% for 10 years?
(b) The population of a country is increasing at a rate of 4% per year. If the population is 20 000 000 this year what will it be in 10 year's time?
(c) The value of a house increases by 6% a year. If the house is valued at £90 000 today what will it be worth in 25 years' time?

Decreasing

A similar method can be used to calculate decrease. This time the multiplier will be less than 1.

E.g. The value of a car decreases by 16% per year. If the car cost £12 000 how much will it be worth in 3 years' time?
The multiplier this time is given by $1 - 0{\cdot}16 = 0{\cdot}84$.
The value of the car is given by $12000 \times 0{\cdot}84^3 = 7112{\cdot}448$.

Note: This is money and so it should be given to 2 decimal places.

The value of the car is £7112·45.

Examiner's tip

The amount is multiplied by the multiplier which is made up of 1+/- the percentage expressed as a decimal. The years become the power this value is raised to.

2 (a) Radioactive material decays at 4% per year. If there is 10 kg of the material at the moment how much will there be in 10 years' time?
(b) The amount of forests in a country are decreasing by 2% a year. If there are 300 000 square miles of forests today how many will there be in 15 years' time?

Using compound interest tables

In examinations you may be given compound interest tables and asked to use them to solve this type of problem.

E.g. Use the given compound interest table to calculate the interest on £2500 invested for 7 years at 3%.

Rate of growth p.a.	Number of years									
	1	2	3	4	5	6	7	8	9	10
6%	1·060	1·124	1·191	1·262	1·338	1·419	1·504	1·594	1·689	1·791
7%	1·07	1·145	1·225	1·311	1·403	1·501	1·606	1·718	1·838	1·967
8%	1·08	1·166	1·260	1·360	1·469	1·587	1·714	1·851	1·999	2·159
9%	1·090	1·188	1·295	1·412	1·539	1·677	1·828	1·993	2·172	2·367
10%	1·100	1·210	1·331	1·464	1·611	1·772	1·949	2·144	2·358	2·594
11%	1·110	1·232	1·368	1·518	1·685	1·870	2·076	2·305	2·558	2·839

From the table, 6% for 7 years gives 1·504. You multiply this by the £2500 invested to give £3760.

3 Use the compound interest tables to calculate the following:
(a) £6000 invested at 10% for 7 years
(b) £900 invested at 8% for 10 years
(c) £7500 invested at 9% for 4 years

3.2 Compound measures

Speed is an example of a compound measure. It is a combination of two other measures: distance and time. Speed can be measured in miles per hour (mph), metres per second (m/s) or any other combination of a unit of distance divided by a unit of time. Units of compound measures often include the word 'per', which tells you to divide.

The formula for speed is

$$\text{average speed} = \frac{\text{distance travelled}}{\text{time taken}}$$

E.g. Calculate the average speed (s) of a car travelling 80 miles (d) in 2 hours (t).

$$s = \frac{d}{t} = \frac{80}{2} = 40$$

The units are miles ÷ hours
therefore s = 40 miles per hour (mph)

The formula for finding speed can be rearranged to enable you to calculate distance travelled or time taken.

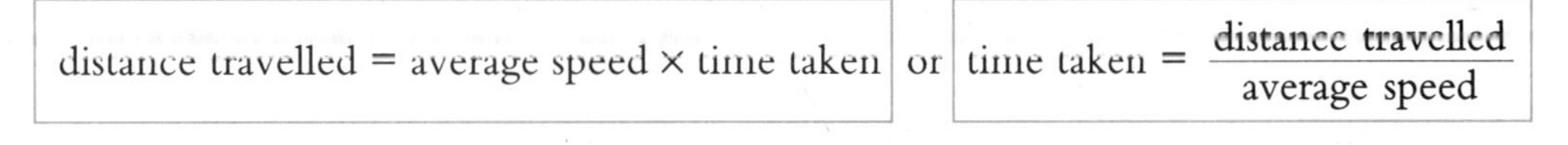

$$\text{distance travelled} = \text{average speed} \times \text{time taken} \quad \text{or} \quad \text{time taken} = \frac{\text{distance travelled}}{\text{average speed}}$$

1 (a) David's car travels 120 miles in 3 hours. Calculate his average speed.
(b) Amajit jogs at a steady 6 miles per hour for half an hour. How far does she travel?
(c) How long will it take a launch cruising at a speed of 8 km/h to travel 40 km?

Another example of a compound measure is **density**.

$$\text{density} = \frac{\text{mass}}{\text{volume}}$$

Density may be measured in kilograms per litre or g/cm^3 or any other combination of a unit of weight divided by a unit of volume.

This formula can also be rearranged:

$$\text{mass} = \text{density} \times \text{volume} \quad \text{or} \quad \text{volume} = \frac{\text{mass}}{\text{density}}$$

2 (a) Gold has a density of 19·3 g/cm^3. Calculate the mass of a bar of gold with a volume of 20 cm^3.
(b) The density of aluminium is 2·7 g/cm^3. What is the volume of a block of aluminium with a mass of 810 grams?
(c) Calculate the density of a 3 cm^3 block of copper with a mass of 26·7 g.

An everyday example of a compound measure is **value for money**. We use this to compare the value of products which come in different sized packs.

E.g. Which of these two boxes of washing powder is better value?

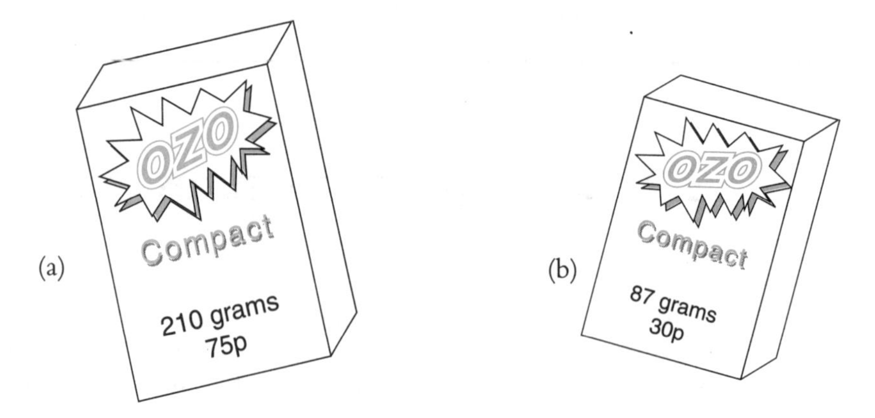

To find out which is better value you divide the quantity by the cost to get the number of grams per penny in each box.

(a) $\frac{210\text{g}}{75\text{p}} = 2{\cdot}8$ g/p (b) $\frac{87\text{g}}{30\text{p}} = 2{\cdot}9$ g/p

So pack (b) gives you more for your money.

3 Which of the following are better value?

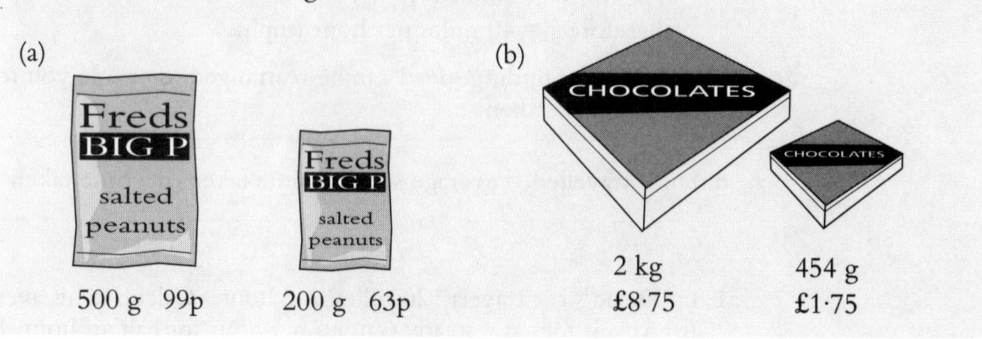

Examiner's tip

Using compound measure, e.g. (speed in miles per hour), the calculation is the first quantity ÷ by the second. The most common mistake is dividing upside down.

3.3 Choosing an appropriate degree of accuracy

xaminer's tip

It is usual practice to give answers to one more decimal place in the answer than was used in the question.

When you are calculating the answers to questions involving measurements you will be expected to work to a reasonable degree of accuracy.

If you use Pythagoras' theorem to find the diagonal length of a gate 3·25m wide and 1·25m high, the result given on a calculator is 3·4820971m with the digit 1 being $\frac{1}{10\,000}$ of a millimetre

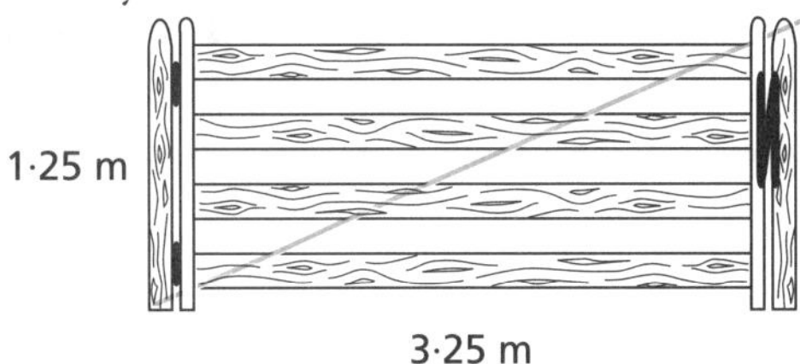

The accuracy that can be achieved in a calculation depends on the instruments you measure with.

xaminer's tip

State the degree of accuracy in your answer.

1 Describe an appropriate instrument for measuring each of the following. Say what degree of accuracy you would expect in each case.
(a) An angle in a maths lesson.
(b) The time for the 100 metre sprint in the Olympics.
(c) The distance between London and Manchester on a map.
(d) The distance between London and Manchester in a car.
(e) The speed of a car.
(f) A patient's temperature.
(g) Your weight.
(h) The ingredients for a recipe.

2 Give your answers to the following questions to the appropriate degree of accuracy.
(a) A book has 150 pages and is 11 mm thick. How thick is chapter 1, which has 29 pages?
(b) The total weight of 11 people in a lift is 801·7 kg. What is their average weight?

3 Pens were 15p each last week. This week they have gone up to 16p each.
Calculate the percentage increase.
Give your answer to an appropriate degree of accuracy.

4 A gas bill shows that 931 units of gas were used.
The cost of the gas is £0·17 per unit .
The total bill will include a standing charge of £10·29.
VAT at 8% is then added on to the bill.
The total bill in £ is given by 1.08 ((931 x 0·17) + 10·29) =
Calculate the total bill giving your answer to an appropriate degree of accuracy.

5 Last year a school minibus drove 7864 miles .
The minibus does an average of 27 miles per gallon. Diesel costs 58p per litre.
(a) If one gallon is equal to 4·55 litres, calculate the cost of the petrol used. Give your answer to an appropriate degree of accuracy.
(b) Show how you can use an approximation to check the magnitude of your answer.

E xaminer's tip

1 Marks may be deducted if you do not give the units with your answer.
2 Always make sure the units you give in your answer are sensible.

Units

If a question involves the use of different types of units it is advisable to convert them to the same type of unit.
The answer space on the paper may help you by indicating which units are expected. If it does not, work in one type of unit and give your answer and the units you have used.

Chapter 4
Further number

4.1 Proportion

Direct proportion

If A and B are in **direct proportion**, then as one grows bigger the other also grows bigger by the same proportion e.g. if B doubles then A also doubles.
We write

$$A \propto B \quad \text{or} \quad A = KB \text{ (where } K \text{ is a constant multiplier)}$$

E.g. Imagine you buy some bulbs.

Number of bulbs	0	1	2	3	4	5
Cost (pence)	0	20	40	60	80	100

(×4 from 1 to 4 bulbs; ×4 from 20 to 80 pence)

For every extra bulb you buy the cost goes up by the same amount (20p). So the cost of the bulbs will be proportional to the number you buy.
Number of bulbs $\propto$ cost

If $A \propto B$ then there are three things which are true.

1. **The multiplier rule**
   If A is multiplied by a value then B must be multiplied by the same value.
2. **The constant ratio rule**
   The ratio of $A : B$ is the same for every pair of values A and B.
3. The **graph** of A against B is a straight line through (0, 0) and the gradient of the graph is the same as the ratio of $A : B$.

E.g. The cost of heating a greenhouse is directly proportional to the time that the heater is on.
If the cost in pence, $c = 17{\cdot}6$ when the time in hours, $t = 8$ calculate
(a) the cost of heating the greenhouse for 15 hours.
(b) the time if the cost is 41·8p.

You can set out this information like this:

t	8	15	b
c	17·6	a	41·8

You can use either the multiplier rule or the constant ratio rule for both parts of the question. Here is one example of each.

The multiplier rule

t	8	15
c	17·6	a

The constant ratio rule

t	8	b
c	17·6	41.8

The multiplier from 8 to 15 is $\frac{15}{8} = 1{\cdot}875$

Multiplying 17·6 by 1·875 gives $a = 33$

So the answer to part (a) is 33p.

The ratio $t : c = 8 : 17{\cdot}6 = b : 41{\cdot}8$

So $\frac{b}{41{\cdot}8} = \frac{8}{17{\cdot}6}$

$b = \frac{41{\cdot}8 \times 8}{17{\cdot}6}$

$b = 19$

So the answer to part (b) is 19 hours.

1 In an electroplating process the mass (m) of the metal deposited on a surface is proportional to the time (t) that the process is applied for.
If $m = 27{\cdot}5$ when $t = 5{\cdot}5$ calculate to 1 d.p. the values of
(a) m when $t = 9$.
(b) t when $m = 43$.

2 On holiday you change £150 into 26 100 Pesetas. If the exchange rate remains the same, find out the number of Pesetas you would get for
(a) £250.
(b) £60.
(c) What is the cost in £ of a gift which costs 10 092 Pesetas?

Inverse proportion

If A is **inversely proportional** to B, then if B gets bigger A gets smaller by the same factor e.g. if B increases by a factor of 2 (B doubles) then A decreases by a factor of 2 (A is halved). We write

$$A \propto \frac{1}{B} \quad \text{or} \quad A = \frac{k}{B}$$

When the variables are inversely proportional, as one is multiplied by a number the second is divided by the same number.

E.g. Imagine a group of people want to hire a minibus. The hire charge is £60 a day. If only 1 person uses the minibus it will cost them £60, for 2 people the cost will be £30 each and for 3 people the cost will be £20 each.
We can complete a table and graph showing number of people and cost.

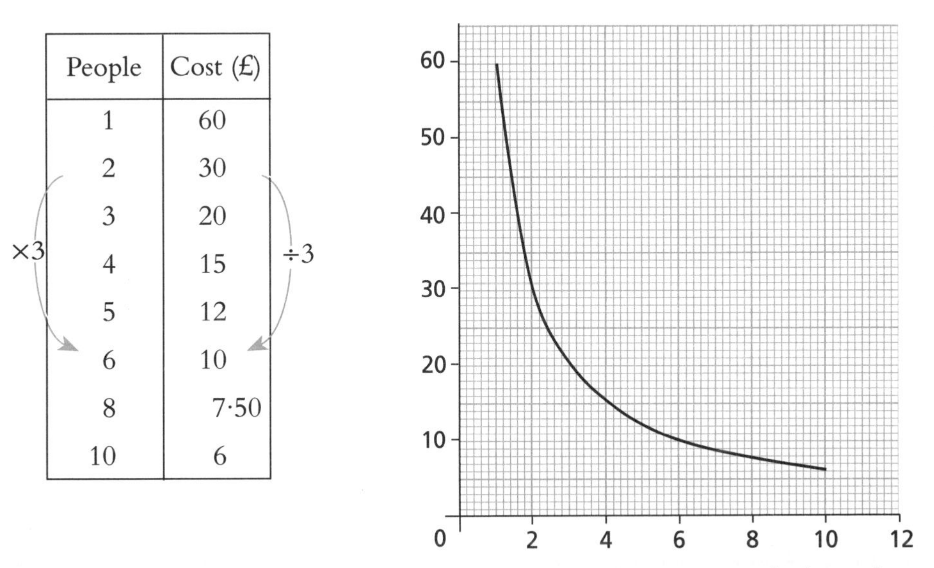

People	Cost (£)
1	60
2	30
3	20
4	15
5	12
6	10
8	7·50
10	6

Look carefully at the shape of the graph. It is typical of an inversely proportional relationship.

E.g. Boyle's law states that the volume of a gas at a constant temperature is inversely proportional to its pressure.
V represents the volume in litres and P the pressure in millibars.
$V = 45$ when $P = 600$
Calculate V when $P = 1050$.

The multiplier from 600 to 1050 is $\frac{1050}{600} = 1{\cdot}75$

$$\begin{array}{lll} & \times 1{\cdot}75 \rightarrow & \\ P & 600 & 1050 \\ V & 45 & x \\ & \div 1{\cdot}75 \rightarrow & \end{array}$$

The multiplier for pressure becomes the divisor for volume.
Volume at 1050 millibars is 45 ÷ 1·75 = 25·7 litres (to 1 d.p.)

3 The length of a string and the frequency of the note it produces are inversely proportional. A string of length 65 cm is tuned to D which has a frequency of 147 Hz (Hertz).
Calculate the lengths of the strings which would produce the following frequencies:
(a) 110 Hz (A)
(b) 196 Hz (G)
Note: Use the memory or brackets facility on your calculator.

Examiner's tip

In direct proportion both values increase or both decrease.

Inverse square law

This law occurs naturally in physics and other areas of science. It states that one quantity varies inversely as the square of another.
We write

$$A \propto \frac{1}{B^2} \quad \text{or} \quad A = \frac{k}{B^2}$$

If B increases, then A decreases by the **square** of the same factor e.g. if B doubles then A is divided by 4.

Newton's law of gravity follows this rule. The force of attraction between two objects weighing m_1 and m_2 in kg separated by a distance s in metres is given by

$F = \frac{Gm_1m_2}{s^2}$ (where G is the gravitational constant $6{\cdot}670 \times 10^{-11}$ Nm²/kg²)

So $F \propto \frac{1}{s^2}$

E.g. The effect of a light source on a point varies inversely as the square of the distance between them. Readings are taken of the illumination 1 m away from the source and 3 m away from the source. By how much does the light intensity change?
Let I be the illumination and d the distance from the source.

$$I \propto \frac{1}{d^2}$$

When d increases × 3, I decreases by a factor of $3^2 = 9$.
So the illumination of a surface 3 m away from the light source will be $\frac{1}{9}$ of the illumination 1 m away.

4 Using Newton's law the force of attraction between two objects is found to be 40 N.
(a) Calculate the new force if the distance between the objects is doubled.
(b) Calculate the new force if the distance between the objects is decreased to $\frac{1}{5}$ of the original distance.

4.2 Rational and irrational numbers

Rational numbers

Most of the numbers we use in everyday life are rational numbers.

A **rational** number is any number that can be expressed as a vulgar fraction, i.e. written in the form $\frac{a}{b}$, where a and b are whole numbers.

All integers (positive and negative whole numbers) are rational because they can be written as $\frac{a}{1}$.

All vulgar fractions are rational because they are already in the form $\frac{a}{b}$.

All terminating decimals (decimals which stop after a number of places) are rational because they can be written in the form $\frac{a}{10^n}$.

E.g. 0·375 stops after 3 decimal places so it can be written as $\frac{375}{1000}$.

All recurring decimals (decimals which repeat after a number of places) are rational. (Remember dots are used to indicate the first and last number in any repeating pattern.)

E.g. $0{\cdot}\dot{5}\dot{4} = 0{\cdot}545454\ldots$ repeats after two decimal places.

Multiplying by 100 gives 54·54545...

$$
\begin{array}{ll}
54{\cdot}5454545\ldots & \text{this is } 100 \times \text{the value} \\
-\ 0{\cdot}5454545\ldots & \text{this is } 1 \times \text{the value} \\
\hline
54{\cdot}0000000\ldots & \text{this is } 99 \times \text{the value}
\end{array}
$$

so $0{\cdot}\dot{5}\dot{4} \times 99 = 54$

$0{\cdot}\dot{5}\dot{4} = \frac{54}{99} = \frac{6}{11}$

Note: All rational numbers can be expressed as decimals.

This can be done for any recurring decimal but you are not required to learn it. All vulgar fractions will terminate or recur before the number of terms equal to the denominator.

1 Investigate using your calculator which vulgar fractions less than 1 recur when written as decimals.

Some of your answers will have had obvious repeats. Others may have appeared not to repeat at all. Some have a recurring pattern which is too long to show up on your calculator.

E.g. $\frac{9}{19} = 0{\cdot}\dot{4}7368421052631578\dot{9}$

This decimal repeats after 18 digits!

If your calculator does not have sufficient display to show you the solution, you can use pen and paper methods or write a simple programme to carry out the process for you.

2 Without using your calculator, write the following fractions as decimals:

(a) $\frac{1}{7}$ (b) $\frac{2}{13}$ (c) $\frac{4}{21}$

Irrational numbers

An **irrational** number is one which is **not** rational. An irrational number cannot be expressed as $\frac{a}{b}$ with a and b both whole numbers. If you expressed an irrational number as a decimal it would go on for ever (to infinity) without repeating.

There are many more irrational numbers than rational numbers but you will mainly use rational numbers. However, there are two irrational numbers you will use often. These are π (pi) and $\sqrt{2}$ (the square root of 2).

If you look at each of these values on your calculator you will see that they do not repeat.

3 (a) Which of the following can be expressed as recurring decimals?

$\frac{2}{7}$ π $\frac{1}{19}$ $\sqrt{8}$ $\frac{5}{43}$

(b) Which of the following are rational numbers?

π^{-2} $\pi^{\frac{1}{2}}$ $4^{\frac{1}{2}}$ 2^{-2} $2^{\frac{1}{2}}$

(c) Give two irrational numbers which multiply together to give a rational number.

(d) Which of these numbers are irrational?

$3 + \sqrt{5}$ $3\sqrt{5}$ $(\sqrt{5})^2$

Note: An irrational number × or ÷ by an irrational number may become rational.

4.3 Upper and lower bounds

You have seen that a measurement to the nearest unit really refers to an interval of one unit centred on that measurement. Now you need to be able to find the possible values of a number expressed to any degree of accuracy, not just to the nearest unit.

If you think of the range of possible values, the bottom end of the range is called the **lower bound** (lower limit), and the top end of the range is called the **upper bound** (upper limit). When you are asked to give the upper and lower bounds of a number you need to know whether the quantity you are dealing with is discrete or continuous. Money is an example of a **discrete** quantity because you have to count it in whole numbers of pence. You either have one value or the next.

E.g. A work surface is 3 m long to the nearest cm. What are the limits of its actual lengths?

$$2{\cdot}995\text{m} \leq 3\text{m} < 3{\cdot}005$$

Measurement is continuous so although there is an exact starting point for the interval which rounds to 3m there is no fixed upper limit. The upper limit approaches 3·005 m but can never get there. Hence a < symbol is used at the upper limit.

By convention we round 5 up so the lower limit is included.

1 Give the upper and lower bounds for the following amounts:

(a) £12 (to the nearest £) (b) £60 (to the nearest £10)

(c) £750 (to the nearest £50) (d) £8·90 (to the nearest 10p)

2 Give the upper and lower bounds for the following measurements:

(a) 638 kg (to the nearest kg) (b) 1700 g (to the nearest 100 g)

(c) 10 m (to the nearest m) (d) 495 cm (to the nearest 5 cm)

If the degree of accuracy is not given in a question it may be implied by the way the number is written.

If a measurement is given as 4·6 m the possible range of values is $4{\cdot}55 \leq 4{\cdot}6 < 4{\cdot}65$.

If the measurement is given as 4·60 m then the range becomes $4{\cdot}595 \leq 4{\cdot}60 < 4{\cdot}605$.

Note: 4·6 is accurate to 1d.p. and 4·60 is accurate to 2 d.p.

3 Give the upper and lower bounds for the following:
(a) A room is 3·7 m long.
(b) A newspaper report indicates that the attendance at a football match was 11 000.

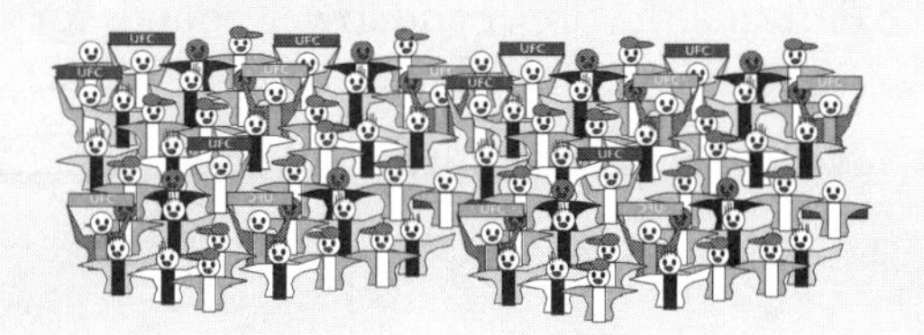

(c) An object is weighed on two different sets of scales, one of which is more accurate than the other. The scales show the following amounts:
(i) 2·61 kg (ii) 2·610 kg

Addition

E.g. Find the upper bound for the perimeter of a rectangular building plot which has sides of 40 m and 18 m measured to the nearest metre.

The upper bounds of the plot's measurements are 40·5 m and 18·5 m. The upper bound of the perimeter is therefore

$$2(l + w) = 2(40{\cdot}5 + 18{\cdot}5) = 118 \text{ m}$$

4 Calculate the lower bound length for the perimeter of the building plot.

5 Calculate the upper and lower bounds for the perimeters of the following rectangles:

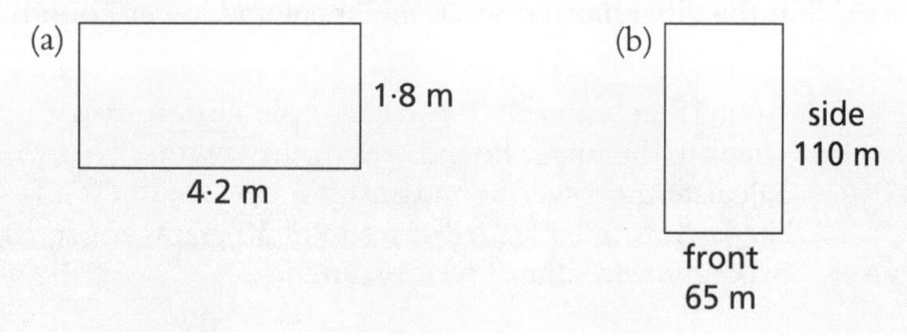

Subtraction

There are two types of subtraction problem involving upper and lower bounds. In the first type, you have to subtract numbers which are both approximations.

E.g. The plot of land represented by the rectangle in question 5(b) above is to be fenced all round apart from a distance of about 50 m, where there is already a wall. Calculate the maximum and minimum lengths of fence needed.

Length of fencing = perimeter – length of wall
The minimum length of fencing is required when the perimeter is at its minimum value and the wall is at its maximum value.
So minimum fencing = 348 – 50·5 = 297·5 m
Similarly, maximum fencing = upper bound perimeter – minimum wall
Maximum fencing = 352 – 49·5 = 302·5 m

6 If a space is to be left in the fencing for gates measuring 2·3 m, calculate the new upper and lower bounds for the amount of fencing needed.

7 If $a = b - 2c$ find the upper and lower bounds for a when $b = 4{\cdot}8$ (to 1 d.p.) and $c = 1{\cdot}7$ (to 1 d.p.).

The second type of subtraction question involves subtracting from a fixed total.

E.g. On the day of the St Joseph's school photograph about 30 of the 927 pupils were absent. Find the upper and lower bounds for the number of pupils in the photograph.

First find the upper and lower bounds for the number of pupils who were away:

$$25 \leq 30 \leq 34$$

Now subtract these from the total:

$$927 - 25 = 902$$
$$927 - 34 = 893$$

Note: Subtracting the minimum number of absent pupils gives the maximum number in the photograph and vice versa.

8 (a) Of the 927 pupils at St Joseph's about 500 are boys. Calculate the maximum number of girls.
(b) To the nearest 50, 750 pupils are under 16. Calculate the minimum number of pupils who are 16 or over.

Multiplication

Multiplying approximations together means the errors are also multiplied.

E.g. A square has sides of 3 m. Find the possible values for its area.

$2{\cdot}5 \text{ m} \leq \text{side length} < 3{\cdot}5 \text{ m}$
$2{\cdot}5^2 \text{ m}^2 \leq \text{area} < 3{\cdot}5^2 \text{ m}^2$
$6{\cdot}25 \text{ m}^2 \leq \text{area} < 12{\cdot}25 \text{ m}^2$

So there is 1 m between the upper and lower bounds for the sides of the square but the difference between the upper and lower bounds for the area is 6 m^2.

9 A lawn is 15 m long and 8 m wide to the nearest metre.
(a) Calculate the upper bound area of the lawn.
(b) Calculate the lower bound area.
(c) The lawn is to be seeded at a rate of 30 grams per square metre. Calculate the maximum amount of seed required.

Division

E.g. The ceiling of the room shown is to be painted. The instructions on the paint state that 1 litre of paint will cover 13 m^2. Calculate the upper and lower bounds of the amount of paint needed.

First you need to know the upper and lower bounds for the area of the ceiling.
Upper bound $= 5{\cdot}25 \times 6{\cdot}65$
$= 34{\cdot}9125 \text{ m}^2$
Lower bound $= 5{\cdot}15 \times 6{\cdot}55$
$= 33{\cdot}7325 \text{ m}^2$

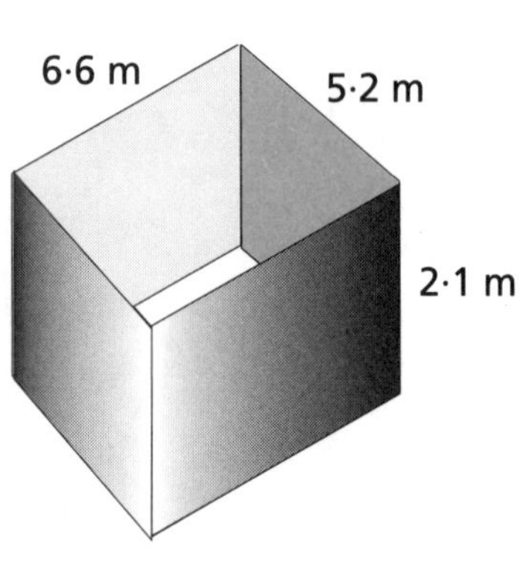

The upper and lower bounds for the area covered by 1 litre of paint are 13·5 m^2 and 12·5 m^2. To calculate the amount of paint needed you must divide the area of the ceiling by the amount that 1 litre will cover. To calculate the *maximum* amount needed you assume the worst: maximum ceiling area and minimum paint coverage.

$$\frac{\text{maximum area of ceiling}}{\text{minimum coverage}} = \frac{34{\cdot}9125}{12{\cdot}5}$$

$$= 2{\cdot}793 \text{ litres}$$

10 (a) Which measurements would you need to use to find the minimum amount of paint needed?
(b) Assuming the room has no doors or windows, calculate the minimum number of 1 litre tins needed to paint the walls.
(c) Again ignoring any doors or windows, what is the maximum number of 1 litre tins needed to paint the walls?

4.4 Using index notation for powers and roots

Powers

You already know that $2 \times 2 \times 2 \times 2 \times 2 \times 2$ can be written as 2^6. We say *2 to the power 6*. This way of writing a number which is repeatedly multiplied by itself is called **index notation** or index form.

In the expression

2^6 — this is the index (6); this is the base (2)

the **index** tells us how many times the number (called the base) has been multiplied by itself.

1 Write the following in index form:

(a) $5 \times 5 \times 5 \times 5$ (b) $3 \times 3 \times 3 \times 3 \times 3 \times 3 \times 3$

(c) $\frac{1}{2} \times \frac{1}{2} \times \frac{1}{2}$ (d) 6

(e) $\frac{1}{7 \times 7 \times 7 \times 7}$ (f) $0{\cdot}21 \times 0{\cdot}21$

Look for the key marked x^y or y^x

E.g. Calculate the value of 2^{16}

2 x^y 1 6 = 65536

2 Use your calculator to work out the value of the following:

(a) $3{\cdot}5^5$ (b) 4·15 to the power 4 (c) $\left(\frac{1}{2}\right)^6$

3 The number of germs on a slide doubles every minute. If you begin with just one germ calculate the number of germs after 24 minutes.

Negative powers

Look at this list of numbers. Can you say what is happening from one number in the sequence to the next?

$2^4 = 16$
$2^3 = 8$
$2^2 = 4$
$2^1 = 2$

You can extend the sequence to find values for 2^0, 2^{-1}, 2^{-2}, 2^{-3} etc.

If you continue to apply the same rule (divide by 2) you get these results.

$2^0 = 1$
$2^{-1} = \frac{1}{2}$
$2^{-2} = \frac{1}{4}$
$2^{-3} = \frac{1}{8}$

If you compare positive and negative powers (indices) you should notice that a relationship exists between them.

Positive index — $2^3 = 8$ — Number

Negative index — $2^{-3} = \frac{1}{2^3} = \frac{1}{8}$ ← Inverse or reciprocal of number

4 Write each of the following as a fraction:
(a) 3^{-2} (b) 4^{-2} (c) 2^{-5} (d) 5^{-2}

You can use the x^y key on your calculator for negative powers too.

E.g. Calculate the value of 3^{-4}

5 Calculate the values of each of the numbers in the following sequences:

(a) $3^3, 3^2, 3^1, 3^0, 3^{-1}, 3^{-2}, 3^{-3}$

(b) $5^3, 5^2, 5^1, 5^0, 5^{-1}, 5^{-2}, 5^{-3}$

(c) $4^3, 4^2, 4^1, 4^0, 4^{-1}, 4^{-2}, 4^{-3}$

Examiner's tip

Any number to the power 0 is 1.

6 You should already have noticed something about 2^0, 3^0, 4^0 and 5^0.
Use your calculator to work out the value of the following:
(a) 23^0 (b) 15^0 (c) 1000^0 (d) $\left(\frac{1}{2}\right)^0$ (e) $0{\cdot}23^0$

Calculating with index numbers

E.g. Calculate the value of $2^3 + 3^2$
$2^3 + 3^2 = (2 \times 2 \times 2) + (3 \times 3) = 8 + 9 = 17$

7 Calculate the value of the following:
(a) $3^3 - 2^2$ (b) $2^3 \times 3$ (c) $4^3 \times 2^{-2}$ (d) $16^9 \div 4^{17}$ (e) $2{\cdot}5^{-3} - 5^{-2}$

Roots

You know that $4^0 = 1$ and $4^1 = 4$

But what is $4^{\frac{1}{2}}$?

Using the rules of indices $4^{\frac{1}{2}} \times 4^{\frac{1}{2}} = 4^1 = 4$

This means $4^{\frac{1}{2}}$ must be 2 which is $\sqrt{4}$

So $a^{\frac{1}{2}}$ must be the square root of a.

$$a^{\frac{1}{2}} = \sqrt{a}$$

Note: This fact is often useful in exams.

In the same way that the index $\frac{1}{2}$ represents the square root, other roots can also be represented by fractions.

$$a^{\frac{1}{3}} = \sqrt[3]{a}$$

$$a^{\frac{1}{4}} = \sqrt[4]{a} \text{ etc.}$$

The nth root is represented by the index $\frac{1}{n}$.

8 Write the following in index form:

(a) $\sqrt{9}$ (b) $\sqrt[3]{64}$ (c) the 5th root of 10 (d) $\sqrt[16]{487{\cdot}49}$

To calculate a root on your calculator you can use the inverse of the key used to calculate powers.

Above the x^y key you should see $x^{\frac{1}{y}}$ (the yth root of x).

E.g. Calculate the value of $2{\cdot}48832^{\frac{1}{5}}$ (the 5th root of 2·48832)

2 · 4 8 8 3 2 INV x^y 5 = 1.2

9 Use your calculator to work out the value of the following:

(a) $\sqrt[3]{4913}$ (b) $6{\cdot}25^{\frac{1}{2}}$ (c) $1\,679\,616^{\frac{1}{4}}$ (d) $32^{\frac{1}{5}}$

Simplifying roots (surds)

Expressions involving roots can also be factorised numerically to simplify them.

E.g. Simplify $\sqrt{8} + \sqrt{2}$

$\sqrt{8} = \sqrt{(4 \times 2)}$ which is the same as $\sqrt{4} \times \sqrt{2}$ but $\sqrt{4} = 2$ hence $\sqrt{8} = 2\sqrt{2}$

Hence $\sqrt{8} + \sqrt{2} = 2\sqrt{2} + \sqrt{2} = 3\sqrt{2}$.

10 Simplify the following:

(a) $\sqrt{20} + \sqrt{5}$ (b) $\sqrt{24} - \sqrt{12}$ (c) $\sqrt{18} \times \sqrt{27}$ (d) $\sqrt{28} \div \sqrt{12}$

Chapter 5
Understanding relationships

5.1 Rules for generating sequences

A sequence is a list of numbers arranged according to a rule.

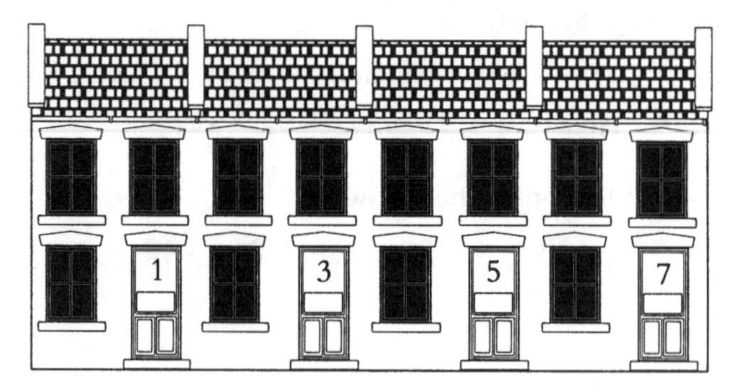

The rule here is + 2 starting at 1.

1 Write the first five numbers in the sequences generated by these rules:

(a) Rule + 3 starting at 1
(b) − 2 starting at 20
(c) × 5 starting at 1
(d) − 2 starting at 1

Sequences can also be generated by a combination of rules.

2 Write down the first five numbers generated by the following rules:

(a) × 3 + 2 starting at 1
(b) × 2 − 2 starting at 1
(c) − 2 × 3 starting at 10

Describing sequences

Some sequences are easier to describe in words.

E.g. Describe the sequence 2, 5, 10, 17, 26, …

"In this sequence you start with 2 then add on 3 and then 5 and then 7 and so on."

or "Starting with 2 you add on 3 and then each time you add on 2 more than you added on the last time."

or "Start with 2 and add on consecutive odd numbers beginning with 3."

3 Explain in words how these sequences are generated:
(a) 1, 3, 6, 10, 15, 21, …
(b) The Fibonacci sequence 1, 1, 2, 3, 5, 8, …

Using the difference method to find the rule

Looking at a sequence of numbers you should be able to find the rule which generated the sequence. First look at the **difference** between the numbers in the sequence.

E.g. Look at this sequence:

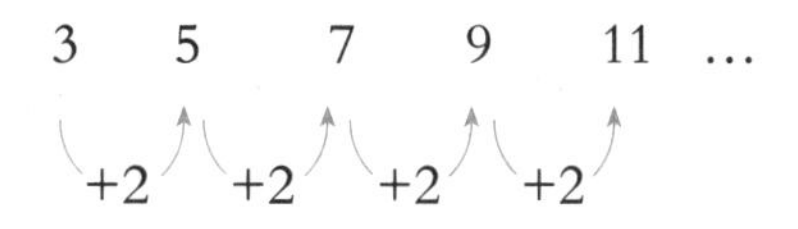

The gap here is always 2 so the rule is + 2 starting with 3.

Sometimes you will need to use the difference method twice to find the rule.

E.g. Look at this sequence:

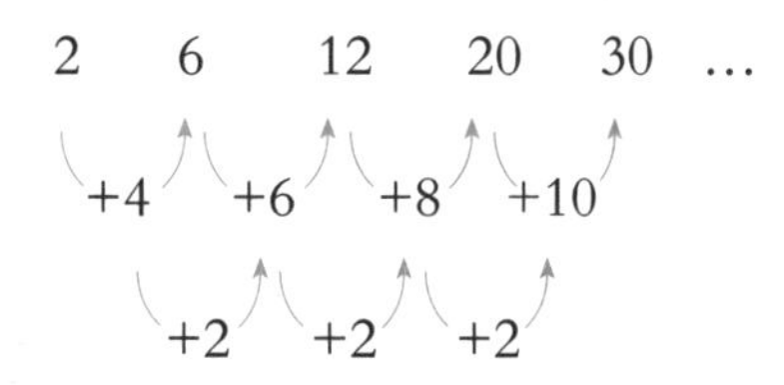

The *gap* increases by 2 each time.

"Starting with 2 you add on 4 and then each time add on 2 more than the last time."

or "Starting with 2 you add on consecutive even numbers beginning with 4."

If there is no obvious connection between gaps try looking for a **multiplier**.

E.g. Look at this sequence:

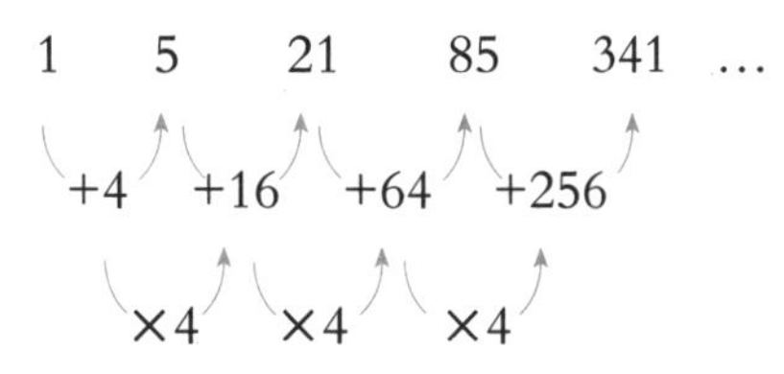

You multiply by 4 every time so the rule must include × 4.
Look at the original sequence. If you multiply 1 by 4 you get 1 less than you want so you need to multiply by 4 **and then add 1**.
Check next term: $(5 \times 4) + 1 = 21$.
So the rule is × 4 + 1 starting at 1.

4 Find the rules used to generate these sentences:
(a) 3, 4, 5, 6, 7, …
(b) 3, 6, 9, 12, 15, …
(c) 1, 3, 7, 15, 31, …
(d) 1, 3, 11, 43, 171, …

Note: They may have more than one part.

5.2 Sequence notation

Consider the sequence 4, 7, 10, 13, 16, ... The rule for this sequence is + 3 starting with 4. But this rule only tells you how to find a term if you know the term which comes before it. What if you wanted to find the hundredth term? Or the millionth term? You need to be able to generalise this statement by writing it *algebraically* so you can work out a term just from the number (position) of the term, without having to work out all the terms before it.

xaminer's tip

Being able to express a sequence symbolically is a higher level skill but it is often useful in investigational coursework.

To do this you number the terms. The first term is called u_1, the second is called u_2 and so on. Everything you need to know about the sequence is given by the **general term** or ***n*th term**, u_n.

E.g. Write down the first eight terms of the sequence with general term $u_n = 3n - 3$.

$u_1 = 3(1) - 3 = 0$
$u_2 = 3(2) - 3 = 3$
$u_3 = 3(3) - 3 = 6$
$u_4 = 3(4) - 3 = 9$
$u_5 = 3(5) - 3 = 12$
$u_6 = 3(6) - 3 = 15$
$u_7 = 3(7) - 3 = 18$
$u_8 = 3(8) - 3 = 21$

n	1	2	3	4	5	6	7	8
$3n - 3$	0	3	6	9	12	15	18	21

1 Write down the first five terms of the sequences with the following general terms:
(a) $3n^2$ (b) $4n - 1$ (c) $\frac{1}{2}n^2$ (d) $\frac{2}{3}n$

Note: Substitute in $n = 1, 2, 3, 4, 5$.

2 If $u_n = 5 \times 2^{n-1}$ calculate:
(a) the third term (b) the sixth term (c) u_{10}

Arithmetic sequences

Sequences which are generated by adding or subtracting the same number each time are called **arithmetic** sequences.

E.g. Look at this sequence:

Term number	1	2	3	4	5	...	n	...
Term	4	7	10	13	16	...	u_n	...

+3 +3 +3 +3

The gap between consecutive terms is always 3. **Multiplying** the term number **by 3** gives this sequence:

3 6 9 12 15 ...

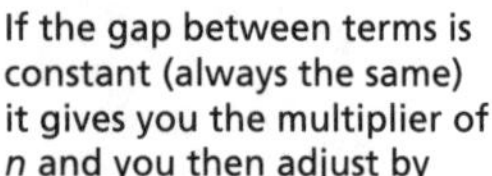

xaminer's tip

If the gap between terms is constant (always the same) it gives you the multiplier of *n* and you then adjust by adding or subtracting.

This is one less than you want each time. To correct this you **add 1**.

This gives the sequence you want:

4 7 10 13 16 ... $3n + 1$ ...

So this is the sequence $u_n = 3n + 1$ or simply $[3n + 1]$.

3 Write down the nth term in each of these sequences:
(a) 1, 4, 7, 10, 13, ...
(b) 3, 5, 7, 9, 11, ...
(c) 4, 9, 14, 19, 24, ...

4 Investigate the number of hidden faces when bricks are laid along the ground. Try making some sketches, tabulate your results and look for a sequence in them. Try to express the sequence algebraically.

5 In the first year of his new job Joe is paid a salary of £8500. At the end of each year his salary is increased by £900. What is his salary
(a) in his fifth year at work?
(b) in his eighth year in this job?
(c) after 12 years?
(d) if he works in the same place for 30 years?

Note: First write down Joe's salary for his nth year at work.

Geometric sequences

Sequences which are generated by multiplying or dividing by the same number each time are called **geometric** sequences.

E.g. Look at this sequence:

Term number	1	2	3	4	5	...	n	...
Term	1	4	16	64	256	...	u_n	...

×4 ×4 ×4 ×4

In this sequence you multiply by 4 an extra time for each new term.
Multiplying 4 by itself the same number of times as the term number gives this sequence:

Term number	1	2	3	4	5	...	n	...
Term	4	16	64	256	1024	...	4^n	...

You have multiplied 4 by itself one too many times so **divide by 4**.

Term number	1	2	3	4	5	...	n	...
Term	1	4	16	64	256	...	4^{n-1}	...

This gives the sequence you want. So the general term is $u_n = 4^{n-1}$

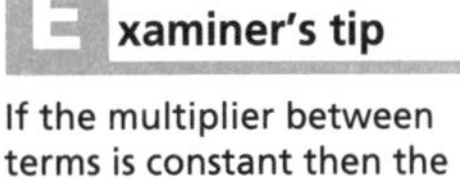
Examiner's tip

If the multiplier between terms is constant then the general term has this number raised to a power and you adjust by multiplying or dividing.

6 Write down the nth term for each of the following sequences:
(a) 1, 3, 9, 27, 81, ...
(b) 5, 25, 125, 625, 3125, ...
(c) 4, 20, 100, 500, 2500, ...
(d) 7, 21, 63, 189, 567, ...
(e) 1, $\frac{1}{3}$, $\frac{1}{9}$, $\frac{1}{27}$, $\frac{1}{81}$, ...

7 Consider the sequence 2, 4, 8, 16, 32, ...
(a) Write down the general term, u_n.
(b) Use your answer to part (a) to find the general term for this sequence:
6, 12, 24, 48, 96, ...

Other sequences

If the gaps between the terms are not constant and the multipliers between terms are not constant then we need to look for some other kind of pattern.
When this happens it is likely that the nth term will involve a power of n, with or without some addition, subtraction, multiplication or division to correct it.

E.g. Look at this sequence:

2 5 10 17 26 ...

+3 +5 +7 +9

You cannot use the examples above to write the general term of this sequence.
Try comparing it with this sequence:
1 4 9 16 25 ... n^2 ...
This gives you one less than you want each time so add 1.
The general term is $n^2 + 1$.

8 By comparing them with the sequence $[n^2]$, write the nth term for each of the following sequences:
(a) 0, 3, 8, 15, ...
(b) 4, 9, 16, 25, ...
(c) 2, 8, 18, 32, ...

Fractions

If you have a sequence involving fractions treat it as two separate sequences: the sequence of numerators (top numbers) and the sequence of denominators (bottom numbers).

E.g. Express $\frac{1}{2}, \frac{2}{3}, \frac{3}{4}, \frac{4}{5}, \ldots$ in general terms.
First consider the sequence of numerators:
1 2 3 4 ...
The general term for this sequence is clearly n.
Now consider the sequence of denominators:
2 3 4 5 ...
The general term for this sequence is $n + 1$.
Putting them together gives the general expression $\frac{n}{n+1}$.

9 Write the general expression for each of the following sequences:
(a) $\frac{1}{2}, \frac{2}{5}, \frac{3}{8}, \frac{4}{11}, \ldots$
(b) $\frac{2}{3}, \frac{4}{5}, \frac{8}{7}, \frac{16}{9}, \ldots$

5.3 Graphs of real-life situations

Graphs can be used to display many different types of information. But there are some things all graphs have in common.

Graphs in two dimensions have two axes which enable you to compare two variables.

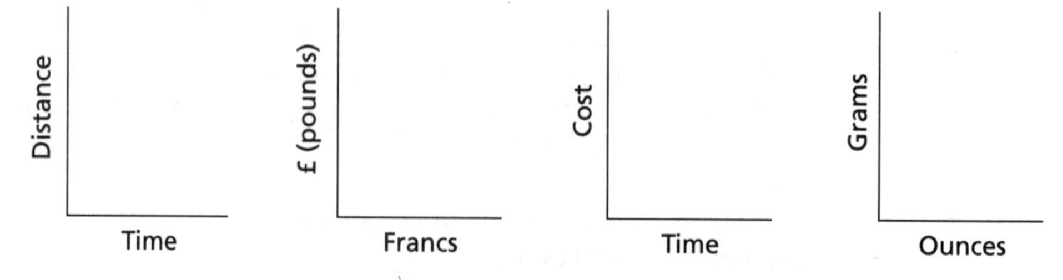

The line of the graph shows you the relationship between the two variables.

A horizontal or vertical line shows that one of the variables remains constant (unchanged) as the other variable changes.

E.g.

The horizontal parts of the line show periods when the time changes but the distance from the start does not. (The subject being graphed is therefore stationary.)

Distance

Time

A vertical break in the line represents a sudden jump in values.

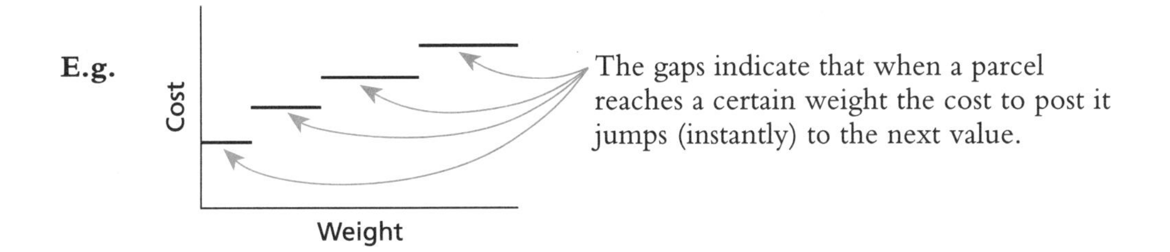

E.g.
Cost
Weight
The gaps indicate that when a parcel reaches a certain weight the cost to post it jumps (instantly) to the next value.

A diagonal line indicates that both variables are changing at the same time, at a steady rate.

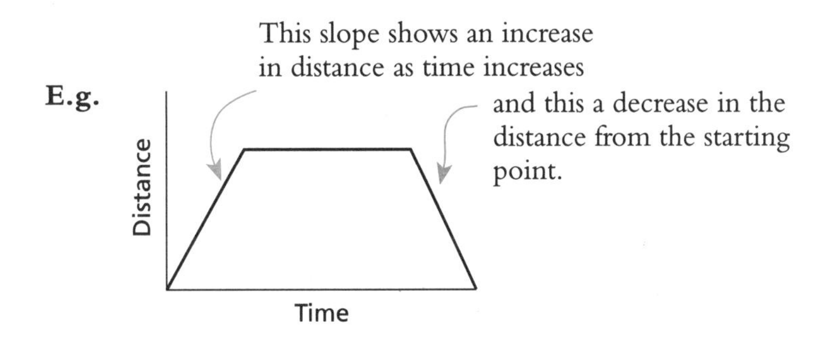

This slope shows an increase in distance as time increases
E.g.
and this a decrease in the distance from the starting point.
Distance
Time

This graph shows a rapid increase in noise level when my favourite record comes on.

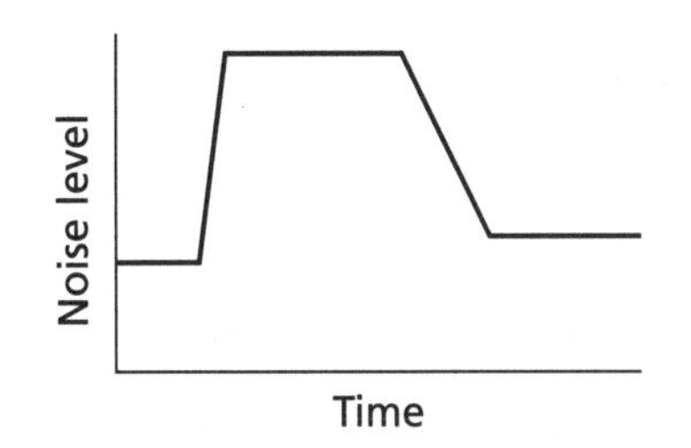

A curved graph means that the rate of change of one variable with respect to the other keeps varying.

E.g.

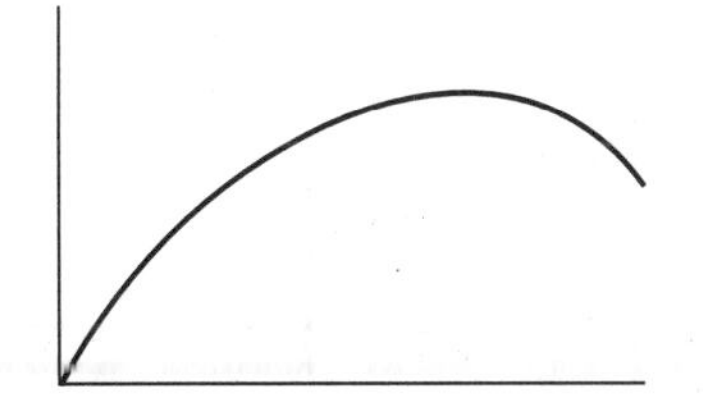

This curve shows the height of a ball being thrown up in the air, plotted against time. The ball starts off gaining height very rapidly so the curve starts off nearly vertical. As it travels the ball slows down so it gains height less and less quickly. This is shown by the gradient of the curve decreasing. Eventually the ball stops and begins to fall back down.

Graphing relationships

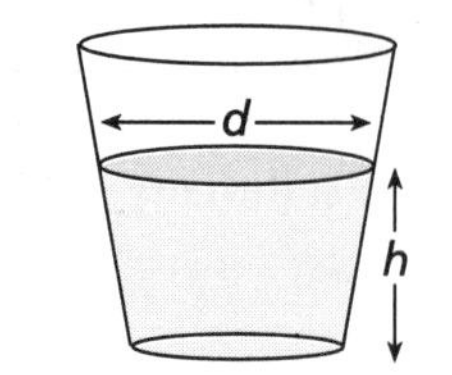

Examiner's tip

Students often draw the axes of graphs incorrectly– the first variable given is usually across.

This flask is being filled with water.

The graph of the diameter of the water's surface against the depth of water in the flask looks like this.

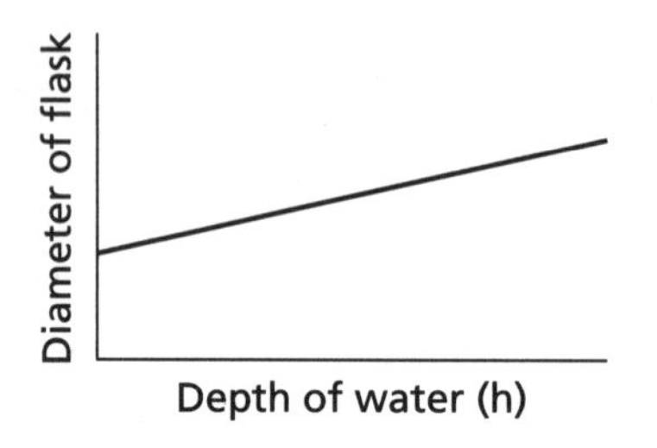

1 These flasks are also being filled with water.

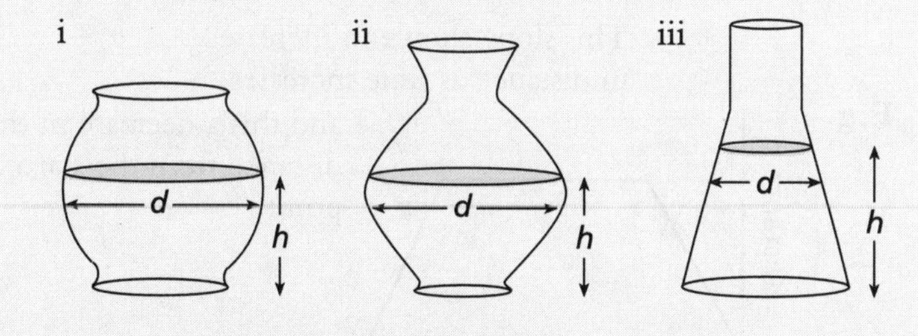

Match these graphs to the flasks above.

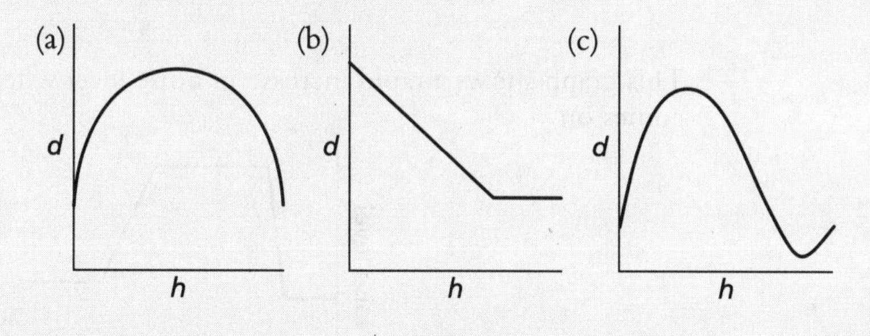

2 Look at these graphs which show William riding his bike.

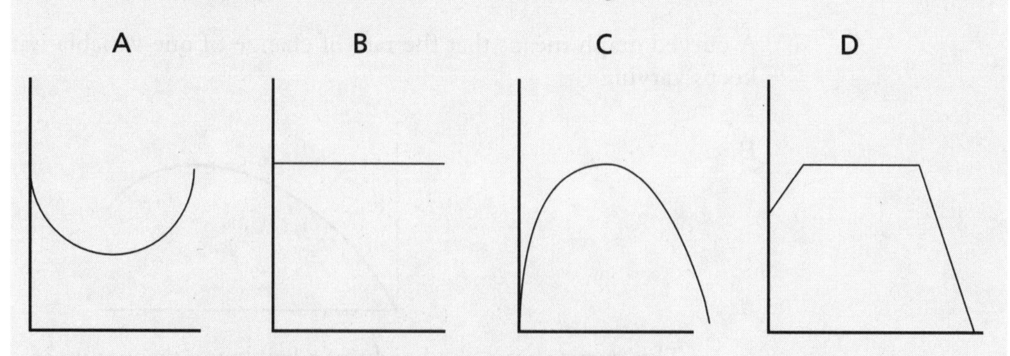

(a) Which of the graphs shows William travelling at a constant speed?
(b) Which shows William starting from a set of traffic lights when they go green and then stopping at the next red light?
(c) Which graph shows William accelerating, travelling at a constant speed and then quickly stopping?

3 Draw a graph to describe the following:
(a) I turned on the hot tap to fill the bath. When it was half full I turned on the cold tap as well. Then I turned both taps off.
(b) The exchange rate between the pound and the dollar was steady but now it's falling.
(c) I left home and walked slowly to the bus stop. I waited a short while for the bus and then travelled to town. The bus stopped twice on the way.

Travel graphs

The graph you drew in question 3(c) is a travel graph.

E.g. Mike has a meeting in London. This travel graph shows his journey by train from Milton Keynes to London, the time he spends in London and the return journey.

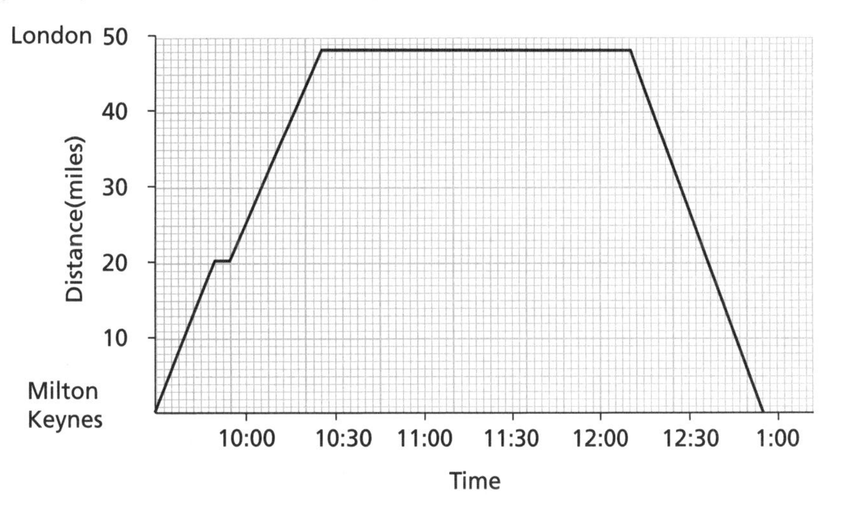

From the graph you can see that the train left Milton Keynes at 9:30 am.
The train stopped once for 5 minutes at Watford and arrived in London at 10:25.
Between 10:25 and 12:10 Mike got no further from Milton Keynes so the graph is horizontal.
At 12:10 Mike caught a train back to Milton Keynes which did not stop.

4 This graph shows a coach journey from London to Leeds (195 miles). The coach stops at a motor way service station on the way.
(The graph does not return to the bottom line because the journey is one-way.)

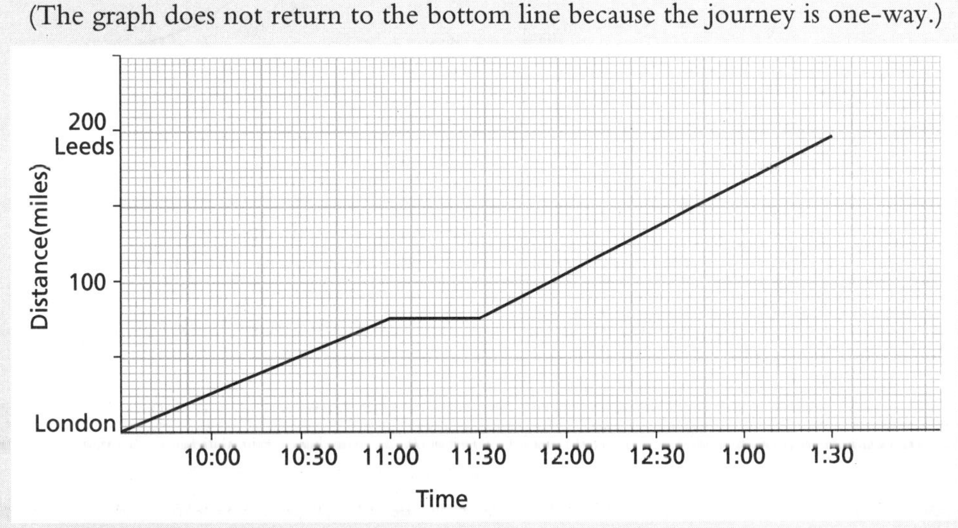

(a) How long does the journey from London to Leeds take?
(b) How far is the service station from London?
(c) How long does the coach stop at the service station?

A travel graph can be used to find the average speed for the journey or part of a journey.

The formula used is average speed $= \dfrac{\text{distance travelled}}{\text{time taken}}$

Note: The time taken must be in hours.

E.g. Looking at the travel graph of Mike's journey from Milton Keynes to London you can see that the return journey took 45 minutes and the distance travelled was 48 miles.
First convert the time taken to hours.
45 minutes = 0·75 hours

$$\text{average speed} = \frac{\text{distance travelled}}{\text{time taken}} = \frac{48}{0 \cdot 75} = 64 \text{ mph}$$

5 Using the graph in question 4 calculate the speed of the coach
(a) before it stopped at the service station.
(b) after it stopped at the service station.

Note: The time taken must be in hours.

Curved graphs

A curve is produced when the rate at which the variables change is no longer steady.

E.g. Linda's pulse rate is monitored while she is doing aerobics. This graph shows the results.
From this graph it is possible to find Linda's pulse rate at various times through the exercise and to say what is happening.

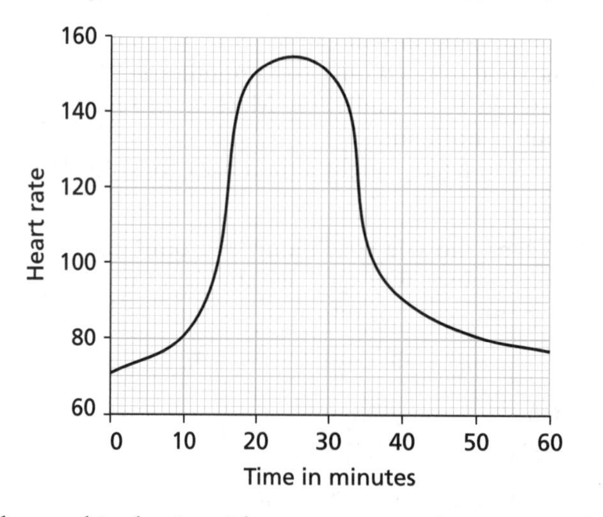

The aerobics begin with a warm up session.
The exercise gets harder during the middle period.
As the exercise continues Linda's pulse remains above its starting point and then in the last part of the session it drops back towards its normal rate.

6 Use the graph to answer the following questions.
(a) What was Linda's pulse rate at the start of the exercise session?
(b) About how long did the warm up last?
(c) For how long was Linda's pulse beat over 120?

5.4 Graphs of simple functions

Examiner's tip

You can recognise a quadratic expression because the highest power is 2.

Quadratics

You should recognise that these are all quadratic expressions:

$$2x^2 + 5x - 3, \qquad x + x^2 - 6, \qquad 2x^2 - 7, \qquad y^2 + 4$$

What shape is the graph of a quadratic?

E.g. Draw the graph of $y = x^2$.

Note: Do not use a ruler to join the points – the graph must be curved.

Examiner's tip

For a curve use at least 5 values, including negative ones, and then use extra values where you need to check the shape.

x	x^2
3	9
2	4
1	1
$\frac{1}{2}$	$\frac{1}{4}$
0	0
$^{-}\frac{1}{2}$	$^{-}\frac{1}{4}$
$^{-}1$	1
$^{-}2$	4
$^{-}3$	9

Now you can see that the y-axis needs to go from 0 to 9. Plot these points and join them with a smooth curve.

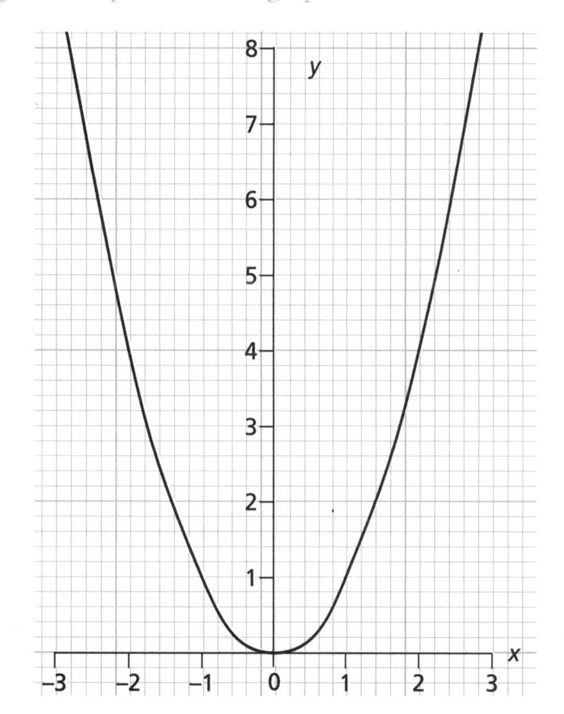

This curve is called a **parabola**.

1 Using a single pair of axes plot the graphs of the following quadratic expressions:

(a) $x^2 - 1$ (b) $x^2 + 1$ (c) $x^2 + 2$

(d) $x^2 + 3$ (e) $^{-}x^2$ (f) $^{-}x^2 + 2$

2 (a) What effect does the number added to or subtracted from the x^2 term have on the graph?

(b) What is the effect of making the x^2 term negative?

More complex quadratics still have the same shape.

E.g. Draw the graph of $y = x^2 - 2x - 3$.

x	4	3	2	1	0	$^{-}1$	$^{-}2$	$^{-}3$	$^{-}4$
x^2	16	9	4	1	0	1			
$-2x$	-8	-6	-4	-2	0	2			
-3	-3	-3	-3	-3	-3	-3			
y	5	0	$^{-}3$	$^{-}4$	$^{-}3$	0			

Note: You should notice that each row has a distinct pattern.

Complete the table yourself.

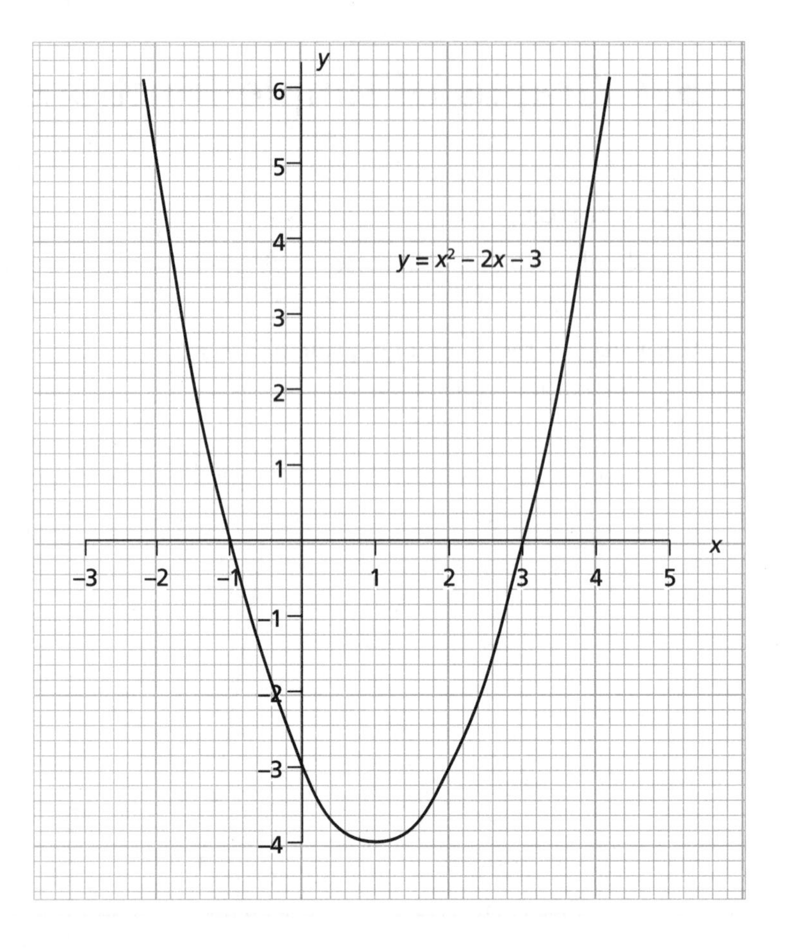

3 Draw the graphs of the following quadratics:
(a) $y = 5 - x^2$ (b) $y = 2x^2 - 3x - 2$ (c) $y = x^2 + 5x + 6$

Multiplying the x^2 term by 2 in question 3(b) makes the parabola thinner.

So you have seen that the graph of a quadratic equation is always a parabola.

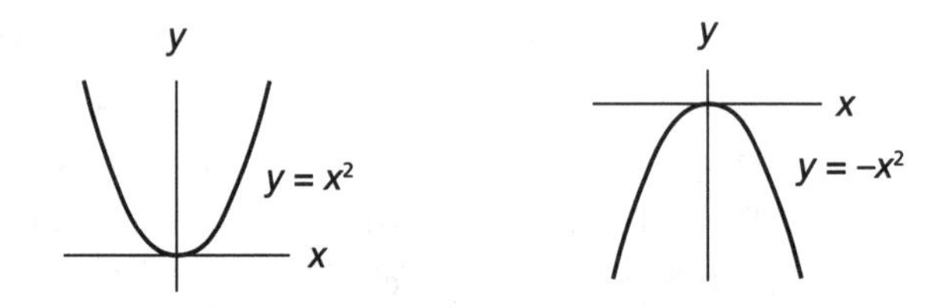

If the x^2 term is negative then the parabola is inverted (upside down).

Cubics

In a **cubic** expression the highest power is 3.

E.g. Draw the graph of $y = x^3$ (the simplest cubic function).

First calculate some values of y.

x	y
2	8
1	1
0	0
$^-1$	$^-1$
$^-2$	$^-8$

Plot these points.

These don't give you enough idea of the shape so calculate some more values to check the shape when $^-1 \leq x \leq 1$.

x	y
$\frac{3}{4}$	0·42
$\frac{1}{2}$	0·13
$\frac{1}{4}$	0·02
$^-\frac{1}{4}$	-0·02
$^-\frac{1}{2}$	-0·13
$^-\frac{3}{4}$	-0·42

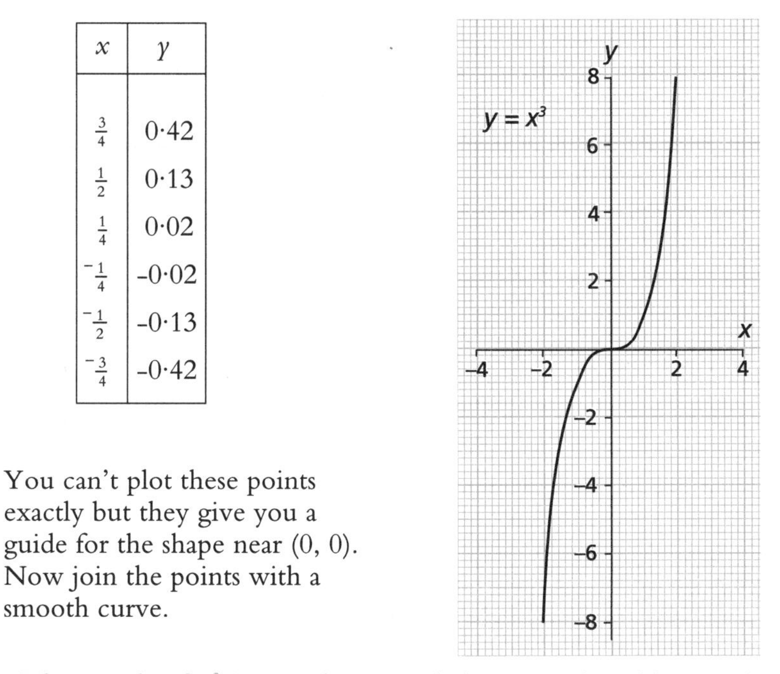

You can't plot these points exactly but they give you a guide for the shape near (0, 0). Now join the points with a smooth curve.

Note: The graph of x^3 is **not** the typical shape produced by a cubic. The graph of a cubic can have 1, 2 or 3 turning points.

4 Starting with values of x from $^-2$ to 2 draw the graphs of the following cubics:
(a) $\frac{1}{2}x^3$ (b) $2 - x^3$ (c) $x^3 - 4x^2 + 3x$

Note: Adding a number to the expression or making the x^3 term negative has the same effect as with a quadratic.

Reciprocals

Here are some examples of reciprocal expressions:

$$\frac{1}{x}, \frac{5}{x}, \frac{1}{x+12}, \frac{3}{x+a}$$

A reciprocal function has the form $y = \frac{a}{x+b}$, where a and b are any number (positive or negative).

E.g. Draw the graph of $y = \frac{1}{x}$.

This looks like x and y are inversely proportional. So y gets bigger as x gets smaller and y gets smaller as x gets bigger.
Let x be from $^-3$ to 3 ($^-3 \leq x \leq 3$).

x	$\frac{1}{x}$	y
3	$\frac{1}{3}$	0·3
2	$\frac{1}{2}$	0·5
1	1	1
$\frac{1}{2}$	2	2
$\frac{1}{4}$	4	4
$^-\frac{1}{4}$	$^-4$	$^-4$
$^-\frac{1}{2}$	$^-2$	$^-2$
$^-1$	$^-1$	$^-1$
$^-2$	$^-\frac{1}{2}$	$^-0·5$
$^-3$	$^-\frac{1}{3}$	$^-0·3$

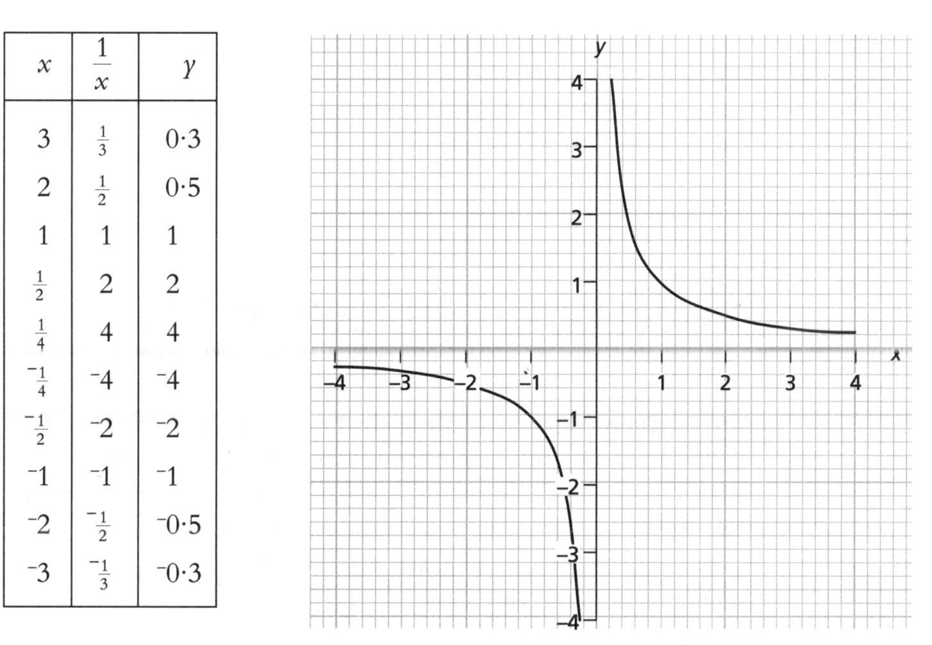

Note: When x is very small (either positive or negative), y gets very large, and as x gets very close to 0, y becomes infinite. So the graph never touches the y-axis. As x gets very large (either positive or negative), y gets very small but never reaches 0. So the graph never touches the x-axis.

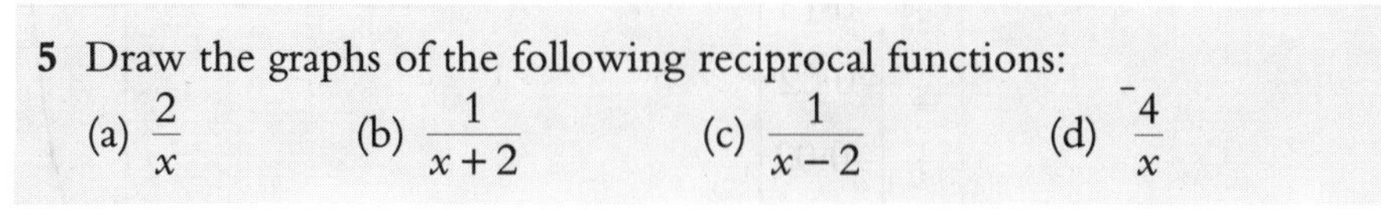

5 Draw the graphs of the following reciprocal functions:

(a) $\frac{2}{x}$ (b) $\frac{1}{x+2}$ (c) $\frac{1}{x-2}$ (d) $\frac{^-4}{x}$

Note: These are the shapes of the most common types of curve:

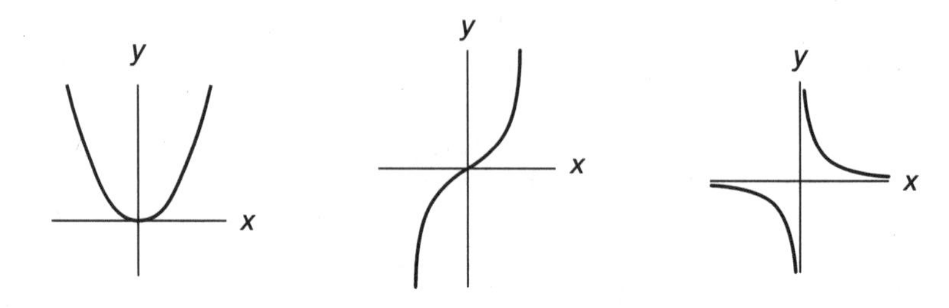

Making any of these expressions negative will reflect the curve in the x-axis. Adding or subtracting a constant will move the curve up or down the y-axis.

E.g. Choose the right equation from the following list for each of the graphs below.

(a) $y = 2x^2$	Positive parabola through (0, 0), steeper than x^2.
(b) $y = x^3$	Positive cubic which crosses x-axis at 0 only.
(c) $y = x^2 + 2$	Positive parabola which crosses y-axis at 2.
(d) $y = 4 - x^2$	Negative parabola which crosses y-axis at 4.
(e) $xy = 1$	Reciprocal. Look for 2 separate parts to the graph.
(f) $y = 2x^3 + x^2 - 3x$	Positive cubic with 2 or 3 turning points.

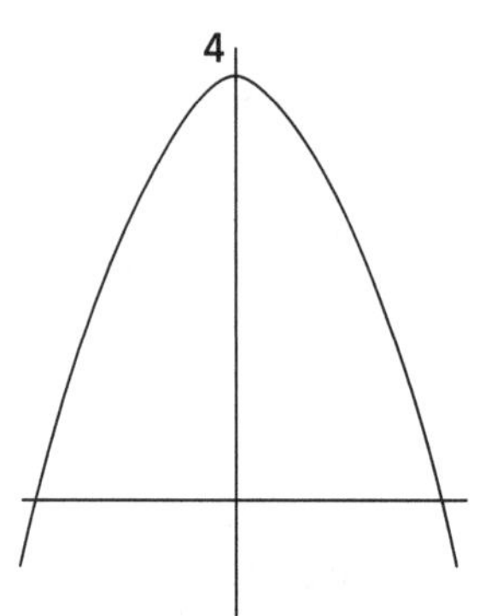

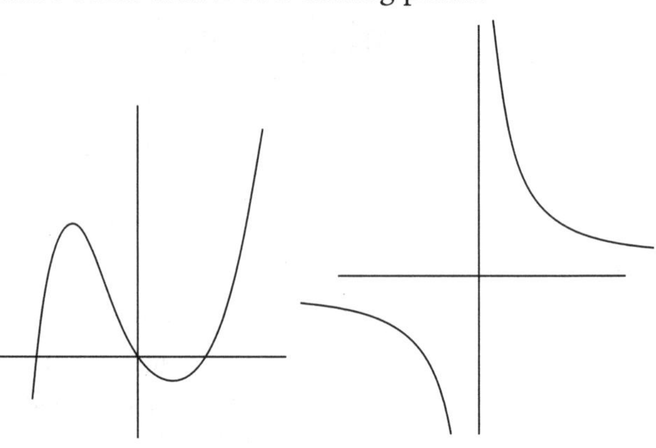

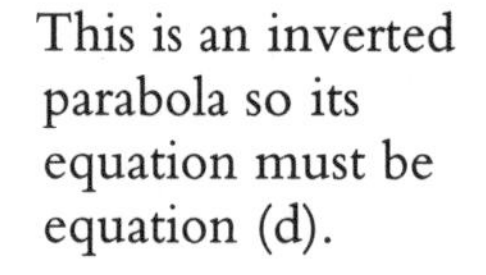

This is an inverted parabola so its equation must be equation (d).

This is the graph of a cubic. It has 3 turning points so it must be (f).

This is the graph of a reciprocal so the equation must be (e).

Examiner's tip

The largest power in an expression dictates the basic shape of a graph.

5.5 Gradient and y intercept ($y = mx + c$)

Any equation which gives a straight-line graph can be expressed in the form $y = mx + c$. By understanding the simple properties of an equation written in this form you can draw straight line graphs without needing to calculate values first. This can save you a lot of time and effort.

You should already know how to draw the graphs of simple expressions by substituting values of x into the equation.

1 Draw the graphs of the following equations:

(a) $y = 3x - 1$ (b) $y = x + 3$ (c) $y = 4x - 2$

Note: Substitute in 3 easy values of x for a line.

Now look at the **gradient** (or steepness) of the graph of $y = 3x - 1$ in question 1(a). The line goes up 3 squares for every 1 across. This means the gradient is 3.
The line crosses the y-axis at $y = ^{-}1$.
Compare the gradient and the point of intersection with the equation of the graph.

In the equation of a straight line expressed in the form $y = mx + c$, the m value gives you the gradient and the c value the point of intersection on the y-axis.
Now look back at your answers to 1(b) and 1(c) to check that this is true.

Note: When an equation is written in the form:

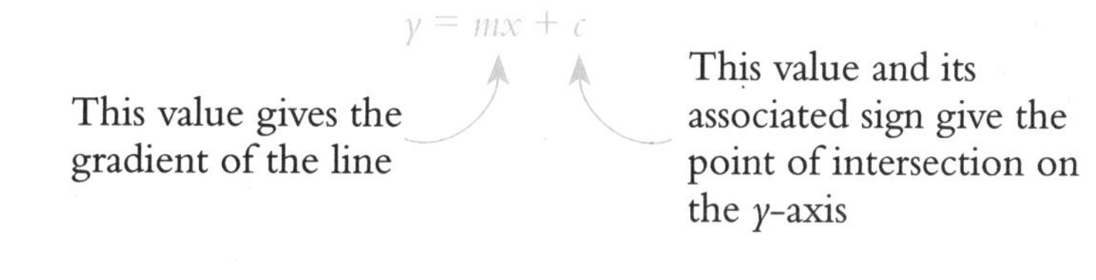

E.g. In the equation $y = 3x - 2$

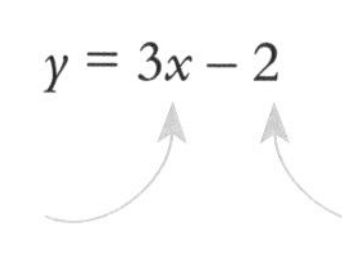

The gradient of this line will be 3 (3 up for each 1 across)

The point of intersection on the y-axis will be -2

Note: c is the crossing value.

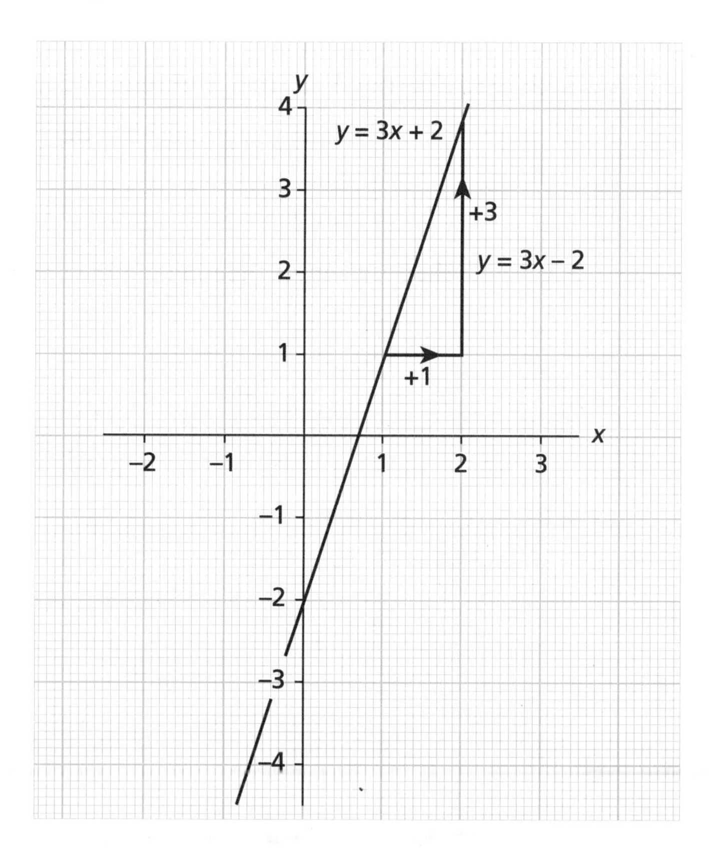

Note: Gradient is given by change in $y \div$ by change in x.

2 Sketch the graphs of the following equations:
(a) $y = 2x - 2$
(b) $y = 4x + 1$
(c) $y = x$ **Hint:** $c = 0$
(d) $y = {}^-2x$ **Hint:** The gradient is negative so the graph goes down.
(e) $y = x + 3$
(f) $y = {}^-2x + 3$

Equations are not always given to you in the form $y = mx + c$. You may have to do some rearranging to get the equation into this form.

E.g. Sketch the graph of $2x + 3y = 5$.

First rewrite the equation in the form $y = mx + c$.

$$2x + 3y = 5$$
$$3y = {}^-2x + 5$$
$$y = \tfrac{1}{3}({}^-2x + 5)$$
$$y = \tfrac{{}^-2}{3}x + \tfrac{5}{3}$$

So the gradient is $\frac{{}^-2}{3}$ and the y intercept is $\frac{5}{3}$.

3 (a) Rearrange the following equations in the form $y = mx + c$:
(i) $2x + 3y = 12$ (ii) $5x + y = 5$ (iii) $4x + 3y = 15$
(iv) $3x - 5y = 15$ (v) $2x - 3y = 12$
(b) Use your answers to part (a) to sketch the graph of each equation.

Note: This method of sketching a graph is a quick and useful way of checking any graph you have drawn.

The gradient of a line between two points

Given two points it is possible to calculate the gradient of a line joining them.

$$\text{Gradient} = \frac{\text{Change in } y}{\text{Change in } x}$$

E.g. Find the gradient of a line joining the points (3, 4) and (5, 8)

$$\text{Gradient} = \frac{8-4}{5-3} = \frac{4}{2} = 2$$

4 Find the gradient of the lines joining the following points:
(a) (2, 4) and (4, 2) (b) (1, 1) and (4, 2) (c) (1, 2) and (3, 5)

Chapter 6

Equations and formulae

6.1 Substituting into a formula

In various parts of your examination paper you will need to substitute numbers into given formulae. There is an order in which such processes are carried out:

brackets, powers, multiplication and division, addition and subtraction

E.g. Given that $v = u - at$, find the value of v when $a = {}^{-}2$, $t = 5$ and $u = 17$.

$v = 17 - {}^{-}2 \times 5$

$v = 17 + 10$

$v = 27$

1 If $s = n\ (a + b)$ find s when:

(a) $n = 6$, $a = 2$, $b = 5$ (b) $n = 4$, $a = {}^{-}3$, $b = 4$ (c) $n = 2{\cdot}5$, $a = 2{\cdot}4$, $b = {}^{-}1{\cdot}5$

Note: Do $a + b$ first because it is in brackets then $\times$ by n

2 If $v = \sqrt{(a-2b)}$ Find the value of v when a and b have the following values:

(a) $a = 36$, $b = 10$ (b) $a = 25$, $b = {}^{-}12$ (c) $a = 8.1$, $b = 1.6$

3 The focal length of a lens is given by $f = \frac{1}{u} + \frac{1}{v}$. Find the value of f when:

(a) $u = 5$, $v = 10$ (b) $u = 0{\cdot}6$, $v = 0{\cdot}4$ (c) $u = {}^{-}2{\cdot}5$, $v = 9{\cdot}3$

6.2 Collecting like terms

Once an expression has been multiplied out it will need to be simplified by collecting together.

E.g. Simplify the following expression $3x(2y + z) + 3xy + 4xz$

First multiply out the bracket $6xy + 3xz + 3xy + 4xz$

then put like terms together $9xy + 7xz$

Note: xy is the same as yx.

1 Simplify the following expressions:

(a) $6x + 3y + 3x + 4y$ (b) $9a + 7b + c - 6b - c - 2a$ (c) $5r + p - 3r - 4p$

2 Expand the following expressions to remove the brackets and simplify if possible:
(a) $4a(b+3c)+3a(b-3c)-6ab$ (b) $5ab+2a(4c-b)$ (c) $2(3x+4y)+3(5x+2y)$

6.3 Manipulating brackets

Brackets

Brackets are used to group like terms together.
$(x + 3) + (x + 3) = 2(x + 3)$

The bracket means that an operation applies to more than one term.
$2(x + 3)$ means $2 \times x$ **and** 2×3
$ab^2 = a \times b \times b$ but $(ab)^2 = a \times a \times b \times b$

You can remove the brackets from an expression by multiplying out (expanding) the contents.

If the value multiplying the bracket is negative it will change the sign of each term inside the bracket.

E.g. (a) $4(x + 2) = 4 \times x + 4 \times 2$
$= 4x + 8$

(b) $2y(x - 3) = 2y \times x - 2y \times 3$
$= 2xy - 6y$

(c) $^-3(2x - 5) = {}^-3 \times 2x - {}^-3 \times 5$
$= {}^-6x + 15$

Sometimes an expression has brackets within brackets.

E.g. Simplify $3a[(a + 3b) - 5(2b - a)]$

Deal with the inside brackets first:	$3a[(a + 3b - 10b + 5a)]$
Collect like terms:	$3a[a + 5a + 3b - 10b]$
Simplify:	$3a[6a - 7b]$
Multiply out:	$18a^2 - 21ab$

1 Expand (multiply out) the following expressions and fully simplify them:
(a) $3(x + 5)$ (b) $^-2(x + 5)$ (c) $^-3x(x - 4)$
(d) $x\,[4(3x + 2) - 3\,(2x - 4)]$ (e) $3(2x - y) - y$ (f) $4(2x + y) - 3(x - 2y)$

Multiplying two brackets

Be careful with the signs:
+ × + and − × − are +
and + × − and − × + are −

$(a + b)(c + d)$ means $(a + b) \times (c + d)$

Each term in the first bracket is multiplied by each term in the second bracket:

$(a + b)(c + d) = a(c + d) + b(c + d)$
$= ac + ad + bc + bd$

E.g. Expand $(x + 3)(x + 4)$

Step 1	$(x+3)(x+4)$	giving	$x \times x$
Step 2	$(x+3)(x+4)$	giving	$x \times 4$
Step 3	$(x+3)(x+4)$	giving	$3 \times x$
Step 4	$(x+3)(x+4)$	giving	3×4

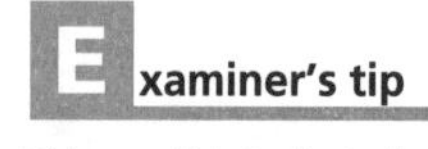

This result is typical of what happens when you multiply out two brackets of this form. Try to remember this pattern.
$(x + a)(x + b) =$
$x^2 + (a + b)x + ab$

Note: To help you remember, this is called the over and under method.

You then add the results together which gives

$(x + 3)(x + 4) = [x \times x] + [x \times 4] + [3 \times x] + [3 \times 4]$
$= x^2 + 4x + 3x + 12$

Collecting like terms $= x^2 + 7x + 12$

2 Multiply out the following and fully simplify:
(a) $(x + 2)(x + 3)$ (b) $(x - 2)(x + 3)$ (c) $(x - 4)(x - 2)$

The expression $(x + 3)(x + 3)$ can be simplified to $(x + 3)^2$.
To expand $(x + 3)^2$ first write it as $(x + 3)(x + 3)$ and then multiply out in the normal way.

3 Multiply out the following expressions. These are some common types of quadratics that you will probably have seen before.
(a) $(a + b)(a - b)$ (This is called the difference of two squares.)
(b) $(a + b)^2$
(c) $(a - b)^2$

4 Expand the following and fully simplify:
(a) $(x + 5)^2$ (b) $(x - 2)^2$ (c) $(x - y)(x + y)$
(d) $(2x + 3)(x + 2)$ (e) $(5x + 4)(3x + 7)$ (f) $(ax + b)(cx + d)$

6.4 Factorising

When the terms or parts of an expression have a common factor you can simplify the expression by **factorisation**. This is the reverse of the process you have just been using.

E.g. Factorise $ab + ac$

The terms ab and ac have a common factor a so you can take out the a.
$ab + ac = a(b + c)$

So the factors of $ab + ac$ are a and $(b + c)$.

Check: $a(b + c) = ab + ac$

Always check your answers by multiplying out or expanding the expression.

Always make sure that you have used the highest possible common factor. Also make sure that you have not changed any signs.

E.g. Factorise $3a + 4bx - 3b - 4ax$

Note: Do this in simple steps!

Write down each step so you can easily find any mistakes and so an examiner can see what you have done.

Step 1 Collect together similar terms
$3a - 3b + 4bx - 4ax$

Step 2 Take out the common factors
$3(a - b) + 4x(b - a)$

It would help to have $(a - b)$ and $(b - a)$ the same way round. Try again but this time put the letters in the same order.

Step 1 $3a - 3b - 4ax + 4bx$

Step 2 $3(a - b) - 4x(a - b)$

Now the brackets are the same. This is what you should always aim to do.
Now simplify further by taking out the common factor $(a - b)$

$3(a - b) - 4x(a - b) = (3 - 4x)(a - b)$

1 Factorise the following expressions:
(a) $2a + 4b$ (b) $2a^2 - 4a$ (c) $^-4a - 6b$
(d) $5y^3 + 10y^2 - 25y$ (e) $ax + 2a + 2bx + 4b$

Factorising simple quadratics

A quadratic equation is an equation whose greatest power is squared

E.g. $ax^2 + bx + c$

At the intermediate level you will need to factorise such expressions when $a = 1$

E.g. $x^2 + 3x + 2$ has been produced by multiplying $(x + 2)$ and $(x + 1)$ which are its factors together.

When you factorise quadratics of this type your solution should take a form similar to the example above.

Note: The number at the end of the quadratic is the product of multiplying the numerical values in each bracket together.

The value which multiplies the x value is the addition of the two numerical values from the brackets.

E.g. Factorise $x^2 + 2x - 8$. The -8 could be $1 \times {}^-8$, ${}^-1 \times 8$, $2 \times {}^-4$ or ${}^-2 \times 4$ but only $-2 + 4$ is equal to 2.

Hence $(x - 2)(x + 4)$

You can check this by multiplying out the brackets $(x - 2)(x + 4)$

$x^2 + 4x - 2x - 8$
$= x^2 + 2x - 8$

2 Factorise the following
(a) $x^2 + 5x + 6$ (b) $x^2 - x - 12$ (c) $x^2 - 6x + 8$ (d) $x^2 + 5x - 6$
(e) $x^2 - 9$
Note: the values in the brackets must multiply to give 9 and add up to 0.

Factorising expressions involving roots

You already know how powers and roots are related and how to use the rules of indices. You can use this knowledge to simplify individual expressions involving roots.

E.g. Simplify the following expressions:

(a) $\sqrt{a^6} = \sqrt{a^{(3\times2)}}$
$= \sqrt{(a^3)^2}$

The square and the square root cancel each other out so

$\sqrt{a^6} = a^3$

(b) $\sqrt{a^5} = \sqrt{(a^4 \times a)}$
$= \left(\sqrt{a^4}\right)\times\left(\sqrt{a}\right)$
$= \left(\sqrt{(a^2)^2}\right)\times\left(\sqrt{a}\right)$
$= a^2\times\left(\sqrt{a}\right)$
$= a^2\sqrt{a}$

When terms involving roots are added or subtracted you can simplify each term and then take out common factors.

E.g. Factorise $\sqrt{a^3} + \sqrt{a}$

$\sqrt{a^3} = \sqrt{a^2 \times a}$
$= \sqrt{a^2} \times \sqrt{a}$
$= a\sqrt{a}$

So $\sqrt{a^3} + \sqrt{a} = a\sqrt{a} + \sqrt{a}$

$= \sqrt{a}\,(a+1)$

3 Factorise each of the following:

(a) $\sqrt{a^3} + \sqrt{a^2}$ (b) $\sqrt{a^9} + \sqrt{a^7}$ (c) $\sqrt{a^5} + \sqrt{a^4}$ (d) $\sqrt{8a^3} + \sqrt{2a}$

6.5 Indices (powers)

You know that 2 to the power 6 means 2 multiplied by itself 6 times.

$2 \times 2 \times 2 \times 2 \times 2 \times 2 = 2^6$

The power is also called the **index**.

Using indices (powers) allows you to shorten expressions in algebra.

$a \times a \times a \times a$ can be shortened to a^4

$y \times y \times y \times x \times x$ can be shortened to y^3x^2

Adding and subtracting

When you have numbers raised to a power you can always add or subtract them by first writing them as ordinary numbers (or using your calculator).

E.g. $3^4 + 2^3 = 3 \times 3 \times 3 \times 3 + 2 \times 2 \times 2 = 81 + 8 = 89$
$4^3 - 2^4 = 4 \times 4 \times 4 - 2 \times 2 \times 2 \times 2 = 64 - 16 = 48$

Expressions with **different** indices cannot be added ~~a^3+a^2~~ or subtracted ~~a^5-a^2~~

Only terms with the same letter and the same power can be added or subtracted.

E.g. $x^2 + x^2 = 2x^2$
$3a^4 - a^4 = 2a^4$

When terms can be added or subtracted a question may ask you to *collect like terms* or to *simplify* the expressions.

1 Simplify the following expressions where possible:

(a) $3a^2 + 5a^2$ (b) $4x^3 + 4x^2$ (c) $2x^3 + 4y^2 + x^3 + 3y^2$ (d) $5b^5 - b^5$

Examiner's tip

When you multiply expressions involving indices the indices appear to be added.

Multiplying

When you multiply expressions with indices together this is what happens:

$a^3 \times a^2 = (a \times a \times a) \times (a \times a) = a \times a \times a \times a \times a = a^5 = a^{(3+2)}$

E.g. $2n^4 \times 5n^3 = (2 \times 5) \times n^4 \times n^3 = 10 \times n^{(4+3)} = 10n^7$

You can use this rule to simplify expressions which contain more than one unknown. First collect the letters together.

E.g. Simplify $a^2b^3 \times ab^2c$
$a^2b^3 \times ab^2c = (a^2 \times a) \times (b^3 \times b^2) \times c$
$= a^{(2+1)} \times b^{(3+2)} \times c$
$= a^3b^5c$

Examiner's tip

Remember the numbers are multiplied and the indices appear to be added.

2 Simplify the following:
(a) $2x^2 \times 4x^5$ (b) $3a^5 \times 6a^4$ (c) $5y^4 \times 8y^7$ (d) $x^2y \times 3xy^4$

3 Work out the following, leaving your answer as a power:
(a) $10^{27} \times 10^4$ (b) $7^2 \times 7^{12}$ (c) $(3 \times 5^4) \times (2 \times 5^{11})$

Dividing

When you divide expressions involving indices this happens:

$$a^8 \div a^2 = \frac{a^8}{a^2}$$
$$= \frac{a \times a \times a \times a \times a \times a \times \not{a} \times \not{a}}{\not{a} \times \not{a}}$$
$$= a^6$$
$$= a^{(8-2)}$$

Examiner's tip

When you divide expressions involving indices the indices appear to be subtracted.

E.g. $10n^6 \div 2n^4 = \frac{10}{2} \times (n^6 \div n^4)$
$= 5 \times n^{(6-4)}$
$= 5n^2$

4 Simplify the following:
(a) $a^6 \div a^2$ (b) $3x^5 \div 2x^2$ (c) $4x^5 \div x^2$ (d) $4a^3b \div 2a^2$

5 Work out the following, leaving your answer as a power:
(a) $7^4 \div 7^2$ (b) $9^5 \div 9^2$ (c) $\frac{5^2 \times 2^5}{2^3}$ (d) $10^{17} \div 10^4$

Powers of powers

In an expression like $5ab^2$ only the b is to the power 2. If a whole expression is to the power then **brackets** are used.

Examiner's tip

When you raise a power to another power you multiply the indices (powers).

E.g. Simplify $(3y^2)^3$
That means the 3 is cubed **and** the y^2 term is cubed.
$(3y^2)^3 = 3^3 \times (y^2)^3$
$= 27 \times y^{(2 \times 3)}$
$= 27y^6$

6 Simplify the following expressions:
(a) $(a^2)^4$ (b) $(3x^3)^2$ (c) $(4n^3)^4$ (d) $(a^2b^3c)^4$

7 Simplify the following expressions:
(a) $(a^2b \times a^3)^2$ (b) $(xy)^3 \times x^2y$ (c) $\left(\frac{4a^7b^2}{a^2b}\right)^3$

6.6 Rearranging formulae

Transforming a formula or equation means rearranging to change the subject of the formula or equation.

E.g. $A = l \times w$ (Area = length × width)
A stands alone on one side of the equation so the **subject** of this formula is A.

You can make either l or w the subject of the formula:

$$l = \frac{A}{w} \text{ or } w = \frac{A}{l}$$

To change the subject of the formula we use **inverse operations**.
Suppose you want to make w the subject of the formula. You can see that w is multiplied by l.
To get w on its own you need to do the opposite (inverse) of multiplying by l.
The inverse of multiplication is division so you divide both sides by l.
This has the effect of leaving the w on one side of the equation and the other parts of the expression on the other.

$$A = l \times w$$

Dividing both sides by l you get $\frac{A}{l} = \frac{l \times w}{l}$

Since l divided by l is 1 you get $\frac{A}{l} = 1 \times w$ or $\frac{A}{l} = w$

You need to know the inverse of each operation to be able to transform an equation or formula.

Operation	Inverse operation
$+$	$-$
$-$	$+$
$\times$	$\div$
$\div$	$\times$
x^n (x to the power n)	$\sqrt[n]{x}$ (the nth root of x)
$\sqrt[n]{x}$ (the nth root of x)	x^n (x to the power n)

Examiner's tip

Take care over + and – signs when you are taking roots.

These operations must be carried out in the correct order.
Suppose you want to make x the subject of a formula.

Step 1 If the x term is contained in a bracket or root sign, deal with anything outside the bracket or root sign. (Remember that an expression like $\frac{x+2}{3}$ is another way of writing $\frac{1}{3}(x + 2)$, so think of this as having a bracket.)

First remove any terms added to or subtracted from the bracket, and then deal with any multiplier or divisor.

E.g. $y = 2\sqrt{x+1} - 7$ Add 7 to both sides

$y + 7 = 2\sqrt{x+1}$ Then divide by 2

$\frac{y+7}{2} = \sqrt{x+1}$

Step 2 Deal with the root sign or the power (if the bracket is raised to a power).
Remember you can think of an expression like $\frac{1}{x+7}$ as $(x + 7)^{-1}$ so this counts as a power.

Step 3 Now remove any terms added to or subtracted from the term involving x.

Step 4 Deal with any value multiplying or dividing the x term.

Step 5 Deal with any powers or roots.

Here is an example to show you all the steps. You won't usually have to use all of them.

E.g. $y = \sqrt{2x^2 + 3} - 1$

Step 1 $y + 1 = \sqrt{2x^2 + 3}$

Step 2 $(y + 1)^2 = 2x^2 + 3$

Step 3 $(y + 1)^2 - 3 = 2x^2$

Step 4 $\frac{(y+1)^2 - 3}{2} = x^2$

Step 5 $\sqrt{\frac{(y+1)^2 - 3}{2}} = x$

Examiner's tip

The object of rearranging an equation is to get the variable you want by itself on one side of the equation and positive if possible.

1 Make the highlighted letter the subject in each of the following equations:

(a) $y = a - bx$ (b) $w = \frac{u - v}{x}$ (c) $s = ut + \frac{1}{2}at^2$

(d) $z = \frac{ax}{by}$ (e) $m = 4n^2 - p$ (f) $y = \sqrt{\frac{3}{x+2}}$

There are a wide range of formulae and functions which you may be expected to understand and use.

Temperatures

The formula used to change temperatures given in degrees Celsius (Centigrade) into temperatures in degrees Fahrenheit is:

$$f = 1{\cdot}8c + 32$$

This formula can be transformed (rearranged) to give you temperatures in degrees Celsius:

$$f - 32 = 1{\cdot}8c$$

$$\frac{f - 32}{1{\cdot}8} = c$$

E.g. If the temperature is 46°F what is it in degrees C?

Substituting $f = 46$ into the formula gives

$$c = \frac{46 - 32}{1{\cdot}8} = \frac{14}{1{\cdot}8} = 7{\cdot}777\,°\text{C}$$

so the temperature is 7·8 °C (to 1 d.p.).

2 Convert the following temperatures into degrees Celsius:

(a) 80 °F (b) 110 °F (c) 20 °F

6.7 Solving inequalities

Some expressions are equal $x = y$ and some are unequal $x > y$.
The inequalities $>$ and $<$ can be read in either direction.
Left to right ($6 < 7$) reads six is less than seven and right to left reads seven is greater than six.
Often two inequalities are used to define a set of values which form the solution to a problem.

E.g. Give the set of integers which satisfy the expression $3 \leqslant x < 10$ (integers are positive and negative whole numbers)

This reads x is greater than or equal to 3 and x is less than 10. Hence the solution set is 3,4,5,6,7,8,9.

1 Give the integer values which satisfy the following inequalities.

(a) $1 \leqslant x \leqslant 4$ (b) $^-6 < x \leqslant {^-1}$

Linear inequalities

When you are solving linear inequalities (inequations) you deal with them in a similar way to the way you deal with linear equations.

You may add and subtract from both sides of the statement and multiply and divide both sides by positive values without changing the inequality.

E.g. (a) Solve the inequality $2x + 3 < 11$.

Subtracting 3 from both sides $\quad 2x + 3 - 3 < 11 - 3$

$$2x < 8$$

Dividing both sides by 2 $\quad \frac{2x}{2} < \frac{8}{2}$

Therefore $\quad x < 4$

(b) Solve $3x - 1 > x + 9$

Adding 1 to both sides $\quad 3x - 1 + 1 > x + 9 + 1$

$$3x > x + 10$$

Subtracting x from both sides $\quad 3x - x > x - x + 10$

$$2x > 10$$

Dividing both sides by 2 $\quad \frac{2x}{2} > \frac{10}{2}$

Therefore $\quad x > 5$

Examiner's tip

Always treat inequalities in the same way as equations.

2 Solve the following inequalities:

(a) $6x + 3 < 33$ (b) $4(3x + 5) < 32$

(c) $3x + 6 < x + 2$ (d) $\frac{x+9}{2} > 3$

When multiplying or dividing both sides of the statement by a negative value it is very important that you remember that the inequality reverses.
Think of what happens with numbers.

$$7 > 3$$

Multiplying both sides by $^-1$ gives $\quad ^-7 < ^-3$

There are two ways of dealing with this.

E.g. Solve the inequality $7 - 3x < 13$.

Method 1

$$7 - 3x < 13$$
$$7 - 3x + 3x < 13 + 3x$$
$$7 < 13 + 3x$$
$$7 - 13 < 13 - 13 + 3x$$
$$^-6 < 3x$$

This method is longer but avoids dividing by $^-3$ and the change of sign.

$$\frac{^-6}{3} < \frac{3x}{3}$$
$$^-2 < x$$

Examiner's tip

$^-2 < x$ and $x > ^-2$ mean the same. The arrow always points to the smaller quantity.

3 Solve the following inequalities:

(a) $12 - x > 8$ (b) $15 - 3x < 2(x - 5)$

Non-linear inequalities

Inequalities may also involve higher powers of x.

E.g. Solve the inequality $x^2 + 3 < 12$.

Subtracting 3 from both sides $x^2 + 3 - 3 < 12 - 3$

$$x^2 < 9$$

Since $^-x \times ^-x = x^2$ and $x \times x = x^2$ you obtain two inequalities.

$(x)^2 < 9$ gives $x < 3$ and $(^-x)^2 < 9$ gives $^-x < 3$

So $x < 3$ and $x > ^-3$

This is usually written $^-3 < x < 3$.

Solve the inequality using the positive root of x^2 and then remember that in the negative root the inequality changes direction.

E.g. Solve the inequality $x^2 + 1 > 50$.

$x^2 + 1 - 1 > 50 - 1$
$x^2 > 49$
$x > 7$

Changing the sign and reversing the inequality gives $x < {}^{-}7$.
So the solutions are given by $x > 7$ or $x < {}^{-}7$.

4 Solve the following inequalities:
(a) $2x^2 - 1 > 1$ (b) $x(x - 2) < 2(2 - x)$

6.8 Graphs of linear inequalities

1 Draw the graphs of the following equations. (Draw the lines very lightly. You will see why later.)
(a) $y = x$ (b) $y = 2x$ (c) $y = 3$
(d) $x = 2$ (e) $y = {}^{-}x$ (f) $y = 2x - 3$

Look at the graph of $y = x$ in question 1(a). On one side of the line, $y < x$ and on the other side, $y > x$.

So we can use a region or area of the graph to illustrate $y < x$ or $y > x$. The region includes all the points which make the inequality true.

With $<$ and $>$ the points on the line are not included in the region so the line is dotted to show that it's not part of the region.

With $\leq$ (less than or equal to) or $\geq$ (greater than or equal to) the line is drawn solid to show that it's included in the region.

E.g. Draw a graph to illustrate the region $x < 2$.

First draw the graph of $x = 2$. Then on one side of the line you will have $x < 2$. Make the line dotted because it's not part of the region.

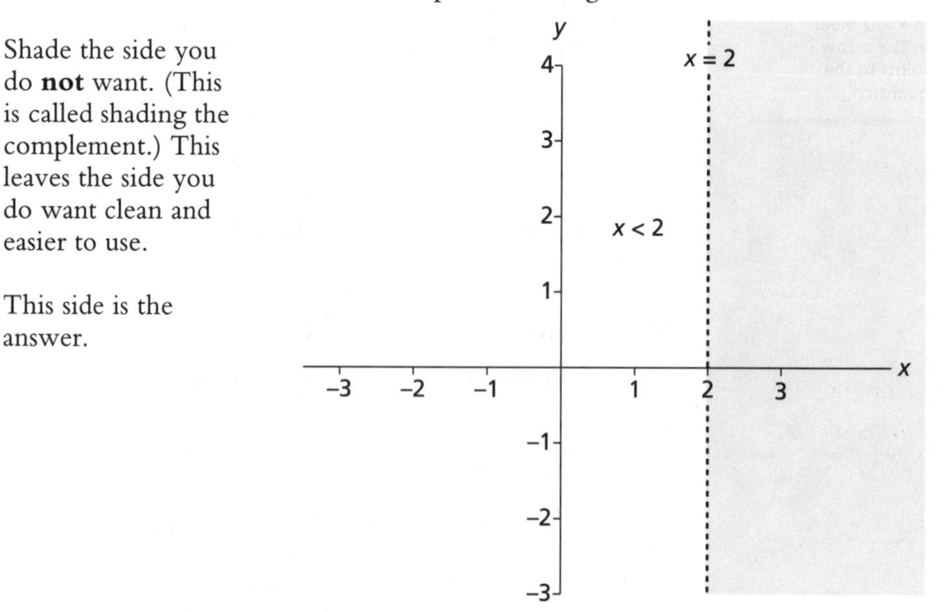
Shade the side you do **not** want. (This is called shading the complement.) This leaves the side you do want clean and easier to use.
This side is the answer.
y
4
3
2
1
x = 2
x < 2
–3
–2
–1
1
2
3
x
–1
–2
–3

Examiner's tip

Shade the area you do not want. Make it clear in your diagram which you have shaded.

When the line is vertical or horizontal deciding which side to shade is relatively easy. If the line is diagonal you can decide which side to shade by choosing an easy point on one side of the line and seeing whether it satisfies the inequality (makes the inequality true).

> **Examiner's tip**
>
> For < and > the line at the edge of the region is dotted. For ≤ and ≥ it is solid.

2 Illustrate the following inequalities using the graphs you drew in question 1.
(a) $y > x$ (b) $y \leq 2x$ (c) $y > 3$
(d) $x \geq 2$ (e) $y < {}^{-}x$ (f) $y > 2x - 3$

In each of these cases the region which satisfies the inequality only has one boundary (edge). In every other direction it goes on forever.

By using three or more inequalities you can locate a region which is bounded on every side.

E.g. Illustrate $x < 2$, $y > {}^{-}x - 1$ and $y < 2$ on the same pair of axes.

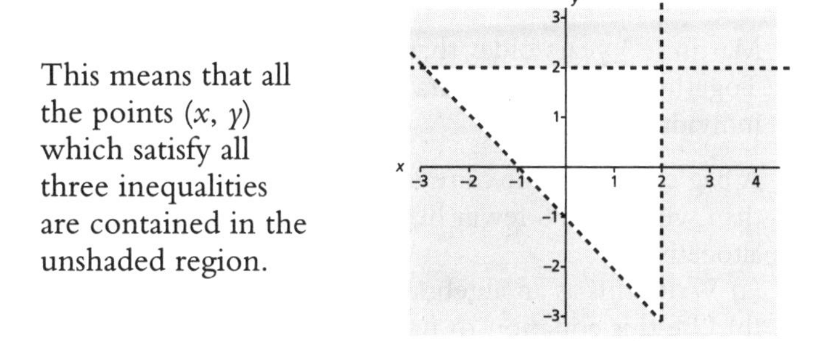

This means that all the points (x, y) which satisfy all three inequalities are contained in the unshaded region.

3 Illustrate the regions given by the following inequalities:
(a) $x < 2$, $y > {}^{-}1$ and $y < 2x + 2$
(b) $y > {}^{-}3$, $y < x - 1$ and $y < {}^{-}x$

6.9 Forming equations

You will often be given information in written form or on a diagram and asked to find an unknown quantity. You need to form your own equation and then solve it to find the answer.

E.g. (a) When x is doubled and 8 is added the result is 26. Find the value of x.

Express the statement algebraically:
$$2x + 8 = 26$$
Now solve it:
$$2x = 18$$
$$x = 9$$

(b) Trebling a number and then taking away 5 gives the same result as doubling it and adding 2. What is the number?

Call the number x (or any other letter).

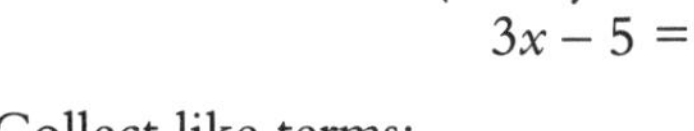

$$3x - 5 = 2x + 2$$

Collect like terms:
$$3x - 2x = 5 + 2$$
$$x = 7$$

Check: LHS $= (3 \times 7) - 5 = 21 - 5 = 16$
RHS $= (2 \times 7) + 2 = 14 + 2 = 16$

> **Examiner's tip**
>
> Always check your answer by substituting it back into the equation.

1 Express the following statement algebraically and hence find the number:
If you subtract 6 from a number and then multiply the answer by 5 you get the same result as subtracting 4 and then multiplying by 3.

E.g. Jane, Gurjit and Richard have been collecting money for charity. Gurjit has collected 3 times as much as Jane and Richard has collected £6 more than Jane. Altogether they have collected £41. How much did each collect?

If you let Jane's money = £x, then Gurjit's will be £$3x$, and Richard's will be £$(x + 6)$.

Since this adds up to £41 you can write the equation as:

$$x + 3x + x\ (x + 6) = 41$$

Simplifying gives $5x + 6 = 41$

$$5x = 35$$

$$x = 7$$

So Jane collected £7, Gurjit £21 and Richard £13.

Check: $7 + 21 + 13 = 41$

2 Martin is 3 years older than Sandra and Abdul is two years younger than Sandra. Together Martin's, Sandra's and Abdul's ages add up to 43 years. Find their individual ages.

3 A bag contains white, grey and black counters. There are 14 more grey counters than white, and 6 fewer black counters than white. There are 44 counters altogether.
(a) Write this as an algebraic equation.
(b) Use this equation to find the number of white counters.

You may also be asked to find missing angles. You can use the properties you know (such as the angles of a triangle add to 180°) to form an equation.

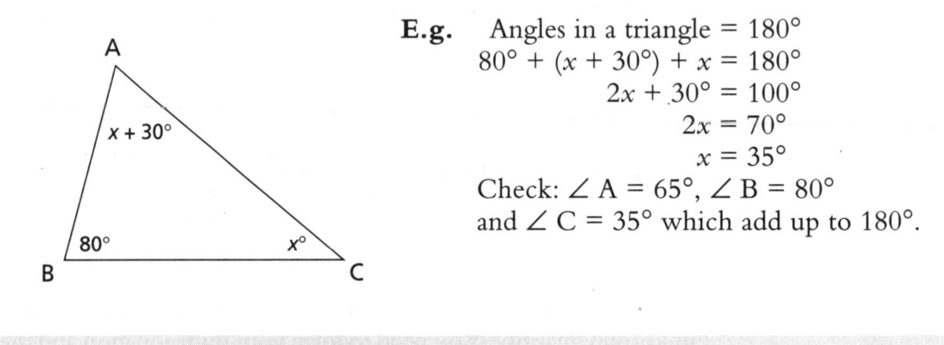

E.g. Angles in a triangle = 180°

$$80° + (x + 30°) + x = 180°$$

$$2x + 30° = 100°$$

$$2x = 70°$$

$$x = 35°$$

Check: $\angle$ A = 65°, $\angle$ B = 80° and $\angle$ C = 35° which add up to 180°.

4 Find the value of x in the following diagrams:

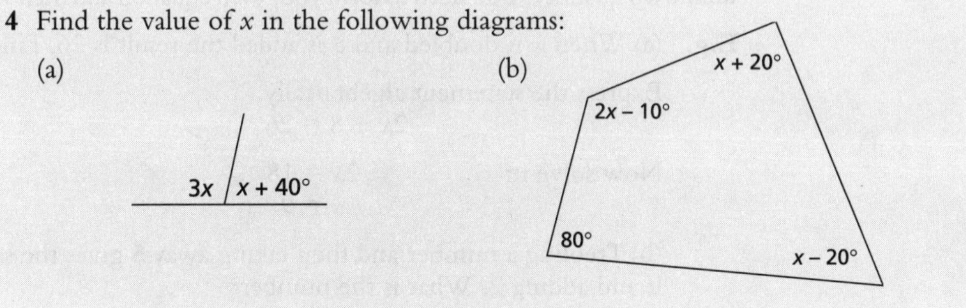

Note: The angles in a quadrilateral add to 360°.

You can apply the same technique in work on length or area.

E.g. Find the value of x in this diagram if the perimeter of this shape is 38 m.

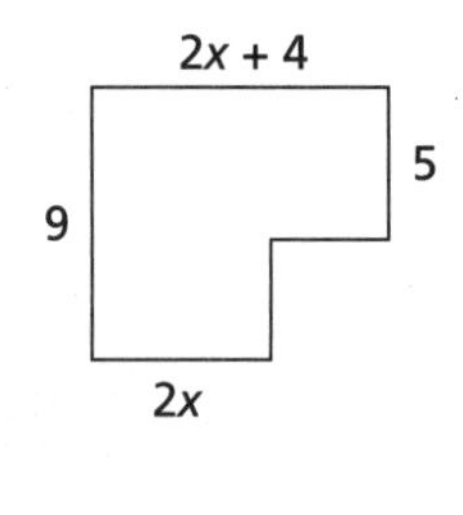

First find the lengths of the sides which are not marked.
Since the sides are parallel both unmarked sides must be 4 m.
Perimeter = total length of all sides

$$9 + (2x + 4) + 5 + 4 + 4 + 2x = 38$$

$$26 + 4x = 38$$

$$4x = 12$$

$$x = 3$$

5 Four identical triangles and a square are to be used to construct a pyramid. The base of each triangle is 5 cm wide and its height is $(4x - 3)$ cm.

If the total surface area including the base is 115 cm^2 find the value of x.

6.10 Simultaneous equations

xaminer's tip

Remember that the objective is to remove one of the two variables.

You know how to solve a linear equation involving one unknown. When you have more than one unknown you need to have more than one equation in order to get a solution. To get a solution when you have **two** unknowns you need to have **two** equations.

You need to find a value of x and a value of y which make both equations true *at the same time*. Another way of saying 'at the same time' is 'simultaneously' so these equations are called **simultaneous equations**.

You can find a solution either algebraically or by drawing the line given by each equation and finding the point where they cross.

Solving simultaneous equations algebraically

There are two algebraic methods which can be used to solve simultaneous equations. In either case the main thing to remember is that you have to eliminate (get rid of) one of the variables as a first step.

Method 1 This method involves multiplying one or both of the equations so that one of the variables appears the same number of times in both equations. You then add or subtract the equations so that this variable is removed.

E.g. Solve $2x + y = 7$ (A)
$3x + 2y = 11$ (B)

Label the equations (A) and (B)

By multiplying (A) by 2 you get $2y$ in both equations.
$2\times$(A) $4x + 2y = 14$
(B) $3x + 2y = 11$

Take equation (B) from 2(A).
2(A) – (B) $4x - 3x = 14 - 11$
$x = 3$

xaminer's tip

Always check your answers by substituting them into the equation you did not use to find the second unknown.

You now know $x = 3$. Put this back into one of the equations.
Putting $x = 3$ into (A):
$(2 \times 3) + y = 7$
$y = 1$
Therefore $x = 3$ and $y = 1$
Check your answers by substituting them back into the other equation, (B):
$(3 \times 3) + (2 \times 1) = 11$

1 Solve the following pairs of simultaneous equations:

(a) $a + 2b = 9$
$3a + b = 7$

(b) $7x + 3y = 27$
$2x + y = 8$

Sometimes you have to multiply both equations to make one of the variables appear the same number of times.

E.g. Solve $3x + 2y = 7$ (A)
$2x + 5y = 12$ (B)

You could make either the x or y coefficients (this means the numbers in front of x and y) the same size.
By multiplying equation (A) by 2 and equation (B) by 3 the x coefficients become the same.

2(A) $6x + 4y = 14$
3(B) $6x + 15y = 36$

3(B) – 2(A) $15y - 4y = 36 - 14$
$11y = 22$
$y = 2$

Put this into one of the equations to find the value of x.
Putting $y = 2$ into (A):
$3x + (2 \times 2) = 7$
$3x + 4 = 7$
$3x = 3$
$x = 1$
Therefore $y = 2$ and $x = 1$
Check by substituting into (B): $(2 \times 1) + (5 \times 2) = 12$

2 Solve the following pairs of simultaneous equations. Remember to check your answers by substituting them back into the equations.

(a) $2m + 3n = 27$
$3m + 2n = 28$

(b) $2a + 5b = 13$
$5a + 3b = 23$

If one of the variables has a negative coefficient then you can make the coefficients the same size (but one negative and one positive) and then add the equations.

E.g. Solve $2x + y = 40$ (A)
$3x - 2y = 4$ (B)

2(A) $4x + 2y = 80$
(B) $3x - 2y = 4$
2(A) + (B) $7x = 84$
$x = 12$
Substituting $x = 12$ into (A):
$(2 \times 12) + y = 40$
$24 + y = 40$
$y = 16$

Therefore $x = 12$ and $y = 16$
Check these values satisfy (B): $(3 \times 12) - (2 \times 16) = 4$

3 Solve each of the following pairs of simultaneous equations:

(a) $2a + 3b = 16$
$3a - b = 13$

(b) $7p + 3q = 61$
$4p - 2q = 20$

(c) $4m + 3n = 93$
$3m - 4n = 1$

Method 2 An alternative method is to rearrange one of the equations so that one variable is expressed in terms of the other and then substitute this into the second equation.

E.g. Solve the pair of equations (A) $2x + 3y = 14$ and (B) $3x - y = 10$.

(B) can easily be rewritten as $y = 3x - 10$
You now have a value of y which can be substituted into equation (A) which you can now solve because there is only one unknown.

Substituting you get
$$2x + 3(3x - 10) = 14$$
$$2x + 9x - 30 = 14$$
$$11x = 44$$
$$x = 4$$

You can now substitute $x = 4$ back into one of the equations to find the value of y.

Substituting into (B):
$(3 \times 4) - y = 10$
$y = 2$

Check by substituting both answers back into (A): $(2 \times 4) + (3 \times 2) = 14$

4 Use this method to solve the following: $2r - 3s = 19$
$3r - s = 11$

5 Emma buys 4 ham rolls and 1 cheese roll and pays £7·35.
Wayne buys 3 ham rolls and 2 cheese rolls and pays £7·20.
(a) Write down an equation for Emma's rolls and one for Wayne's.
(b) Solve the equations simultaneously to find the cost of each type of roll. (Use whichever method you prefer.)

6 The Taylors and the Hannons have booked the same holiday. The Taylor family have to pay £1880 for two adults and three children. The Hannon family will pay £2110 for three adults and two children.
(a) Write down the equation for each family.
(b) Work out the cost of the holiday for each adult and each child.

Using graphs to solve simultaneous equations

You can solve simultaneous equations by drawing a graph of the two equations. The x and y coordinates of the point where the two lines cross give you the solution to the equations.

E.g. Solve the following pair of simultaneous equations by drawing a graph.
(A) $y - x = 2$
(B) $2x - y = 2$

The first step is to rearrange each equation in the form $y = mx + c$.
(A) $y = x + 2$
(B) $y = 2x - 2$

Next substitute x values into each equation to calculate some coordinates.

Note: Three points for a line.

Here are two of the ways to set this out

x	$x + 2$
0	2
1	3
2	4

x	0	1	2
$2x$	0	2	4
–2	-2	-2	-2
y	-2	0	2

Plot the points for equation (A) and join them to form a line.

Then do the same for equation (B).

The point of intersection is (4, 6).

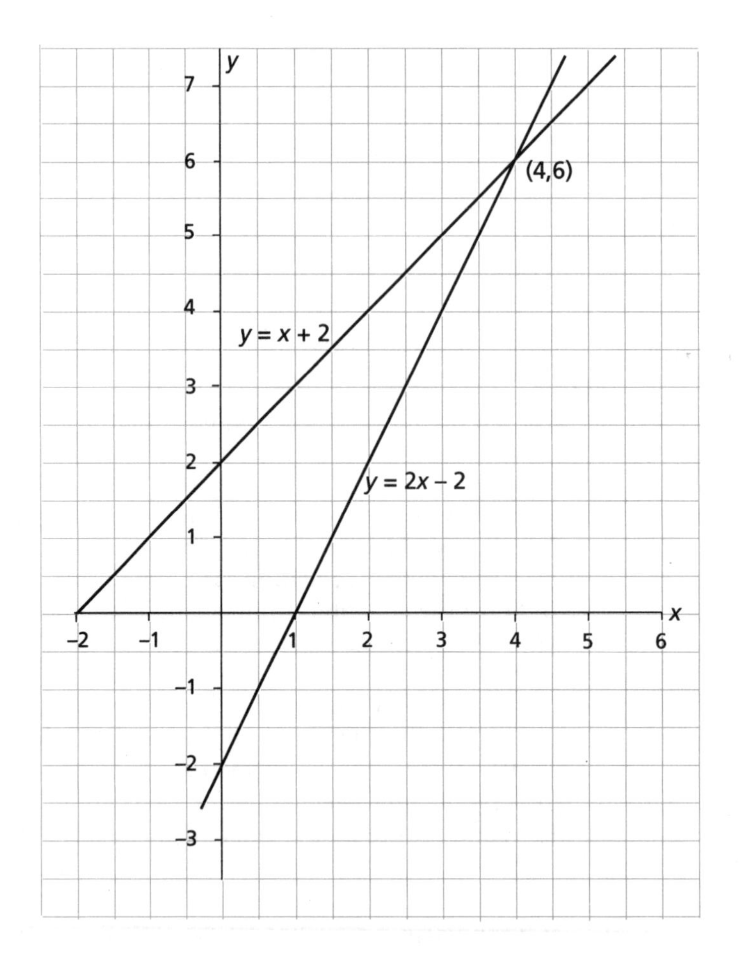

Check that this solution is correct by putting these values back into the equations.

Substituting $x = 4$ and $y = 6$ into (A): $6 - 4 = 2$

Check that (B) also works.

7 The following pairs of equations have been drawn for you. What are their solutions?

(a) 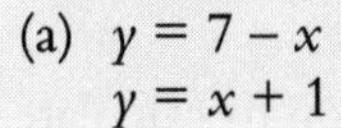

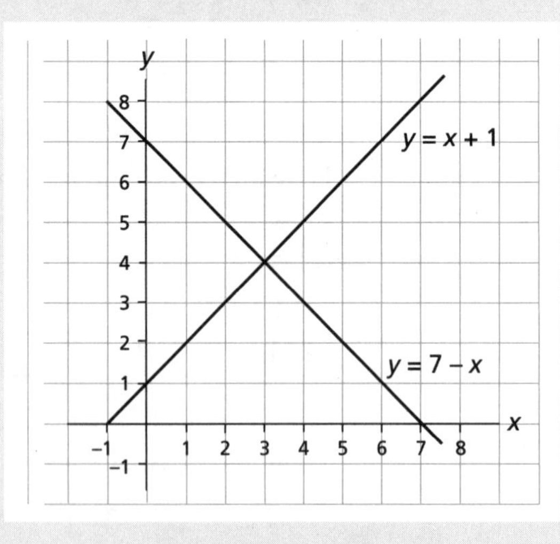

(b) $y = 2x + 1$
$y = \frac{1}{2}x + 4$

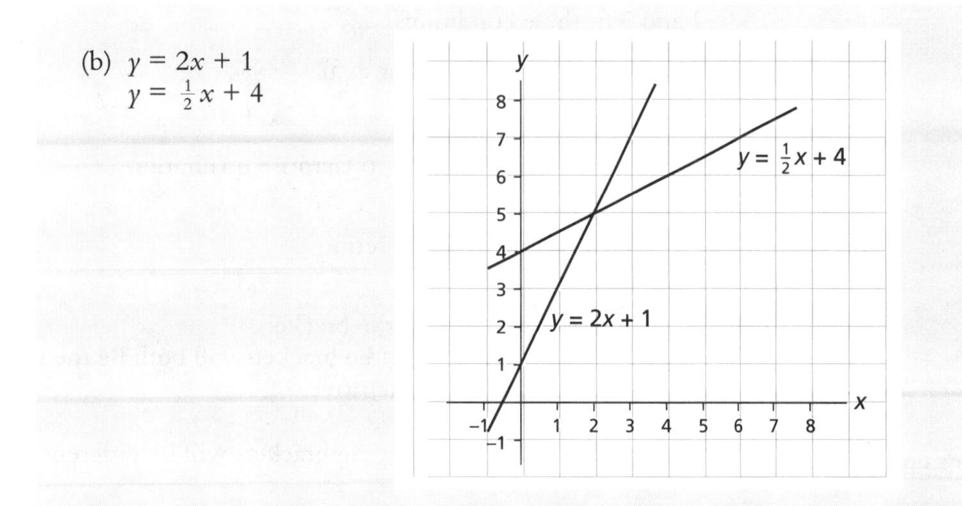

8 Solve these pairs of simultaneous equations by graphical methods.
(a) $y = x - 1$, $y = 7 - x$
(b) $3x - y = 2$, $x - 2y = {}^{-}6$

9 The milk lady in Dickens Road has worked out the bills for two houses for a week.

Address	Skimmed Milk	Gold Top Milk	Total Cost
36 Dickens Road	18	2	610p
38 Dickens Road	25	5	925p

(a) Using S = Skimmed milk and G = Gold top write down an equation for the cost of the milk at each house.
(b) Rewrite the equations in the form $G = mS + c$.
(c) Draw the graphs of both equations on the same pair of axes.
Hint: The solutions must be positive so you only need positive axes. (G on the vertical axis goes to 350 and S goes to 40.)
(d) Use your graph to work out the cost of each type of milk.

Examiner's tip

Always check your solutions by substituting them back into the equations.

6.11 Factorising quadratics

A **quadratic** is a polynomial in which the highest power is 2. The general form of a quadratic equation is $ax^2 + bx + c$ with $a \neq 0$.

You have seen above that when expressions of the form $(x + p)$ and $(x + q)$ are multiplied together the result is a quadratic.

$$(x + p)(x + q) = x^2 + (p + q)x + pq$$

Turning this around tells you that quadratics can be factorised into a pair of brackets.

$$x^2 + (p + q)x + pq = (x + p)(x + q)$$

E.g. Factorise $x^2 + 7x + 10$

Suppose $x^2 + 7x + 10 = (x + p)(x + q)$
$x^2 + 7x + 10 = x^2 + (p + q)x + pq$

So you need to find values for p and q such that $p + q = 7$ and $pq = 10$.
In other words, look for two factors of 10 which add to give 7.

2 and 5 fit these conditions.

So $x^2 + 7x + 10 = (x + 2)(x + 5)$

Check: $(x + 2)(x + 5) = x^2 + 5x + 2x + 10 = x^2 + 7x + 10$

The following steps will help you to factorise quadratics.
Factorise $x^2 + bx + c$

Step 1 First deal with the x^2 term.
$(x \quad)(x \quad)$

Step 2 Sort out the signs in the brackets.

(a) If c is positive then the signs in the brackets will both be the same. The signs will be + if b is positive and – if b is negative.
$(x + \quad)(x + \quad)$ or $(x - \quad)(x - \quad)$

(b) If c is negative then the signs in the brackets will be different.
$(x + \quad)(x - \quad)$

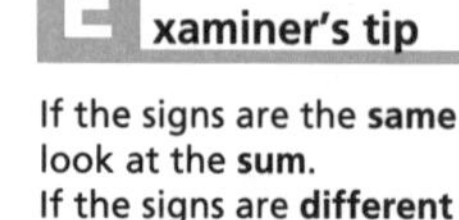
Examiner's tip

If the signs are the **same** look at the **sum.**
If the signs are **different** look at the **difference.**

Step 3 Now look for the numbers to go in the brackets.
The two numbers must multiply to give c (c is the *product* of the two numbers) and they must add or subtract to give b (b is the *sum* or *difference*).

(a) In the quadratic $x^2 + 5x + 6$ you are looking for two numbers which multiply together to give 6 and add up to 5.

(b) In the quadratic $x^2 + x - 6$ the c term is negative so the signs in the brackets will be different. You are looking for two numbers whose product is 6 and whose **difference** is 1.

E.g. Factorise $x^2 - 5x + 6$

Step 1 $(x \quad)(x \quad)$ x^2 factorises into x in each bracket.

Step 2 $(x - \quad)(x - \quad)$ The sign in front of the c value is + so both signs are the same. The sign in front of the b value is – so both signs in the brackets must be –.

Step 3 $(x - 2)(x - 3)$ The numerical values in the brackets must multiply together to give 6 and add up to give 5. So the values must be 2 and 3.

Check: $(x - 2)(x - 3) = x^2 - 3x - 2x + 6 = x^2 - 5x + 6$

If you have a quadratic with a number a in front of the x^2 term then factorising is a bit more difficult but the steps above are still applied.

Step 1 The factors of a go in front of the xs in each bracket.

Step 2 As above.

Step 3 The factors of c are now multiplied by the factors of a to give b.

1 Factorise each of the following:

(a) $x^2 + 6x + 8$ (b) $x^2 + 6x - 7$ (c) $x^2 + 8x + 15$
(d) $x^2 - 9x + 20$ (e) $x^2 - 2x - 3$ (f) $x^2 - 13x - 30$

The difference of two squares

A quadratic in the form $a^2 - b^2$ represents a difference of two squares.
In question 3 above you saw that $(a + b)(a - b) = a^2 - b^2$.
Turning this around shows you how to factorise the difference of two squares:

$$a^2 - b^2 = (a + b)(a - b)$$

E.g. Factorise $4x^2 - 25$

$$4x^2 - 25 = (2x)^2 - 5^2 = (2x + 5)(2x - 5)$$

Check: $(2x + 5)(2x - 5) = 4x^2 - 10x + 10x - 25 = 4x^2 - 25$

2 Factorise each of the following:

(a) $x^2 - 4$ (b) $9x^2 - 1$

6.12 Solving simple quadratics and cubics using graphs

Quadratics

A quadratic equation is an equation of the form $ax^2 + bx + c = 0$, with $a \neq 0$.

You can solve an equation of this form by plotting the graph of $y = ax^2 + bx + c$ and finding the value of x when $y = 0$. This means finding the values of x where the graph crosses the x-axis.

E.g. Solve the equation $x^2 - x - 2 = 0$ by drawing the graph of $y = x^2 - x - 2$.

First produce a table of results.

x	$^-3$	$^-2$	$^-1$	0	1	2	3
x^2	9	4	1	0	1	4	9
$-x$	3	2	1	0	$^-1$	$^-2$	$^-3$
-2	$^-2$	$^-2$	$^-2$	$^-2$	$^-2$	$^-2$	$^-2$
y	10	4	0	$^-2$	$^-2$	0	4

Plot the points and join them with a smooth curve. Do not use a ruler.

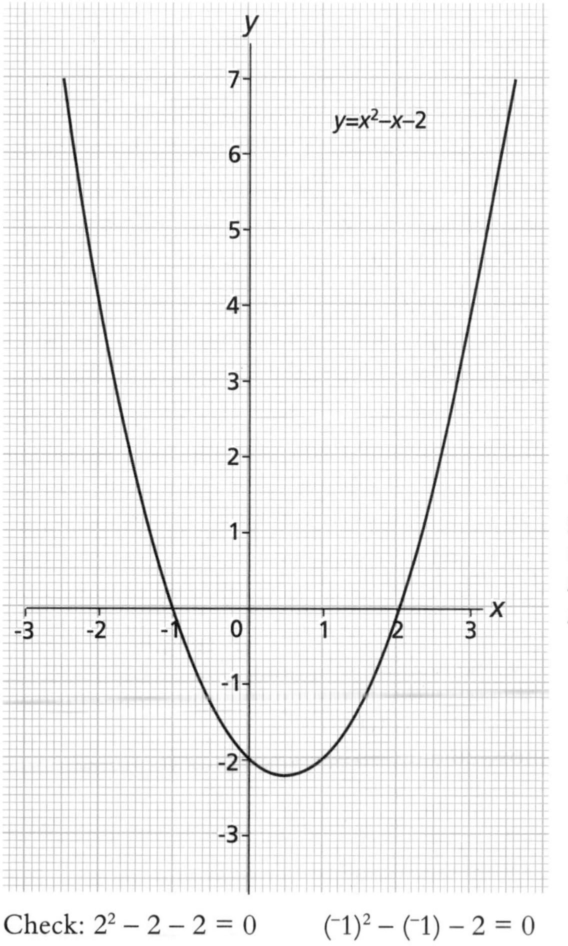

The solution of the equation is given by the points at which the curve crosses the x-axis.

$x^2 - x - 2 = 0$ when $x = {}^-1$ and when $x = 2$

Check: $2^2 - 2 - 2 = 0$ $\quad (^-1)^2 - (^-1) - 2 = 0$

Always check your results by substituting your solutions back into the equation.

1 Where you can, solve the following equations by drawing their graphs. (One of the equations has no solution.)
(a) $x^2 - 5x + 4 = 0$ $(0 \le x \le 5)$
(b) $x^2 - 3x + 2 = 0$ $({}^-1 \le x \le 4)$
(c) $2 + x - x^2 = 0$ $({}^-2 \le x \le 3)$
(d) $x^2 - 4x + 4 = 0$ $({}^-1 \le x \le 4)$
(e) $x^2 + 3 = 0$ $({}^-2 \le x \le 2)$

A quadratic equation has two solutions if the curve crosses the x-axis, it has one solution if the curve just touches the x-axis and it has no solution if the curve does not cross or touch the x-axis.

Another way to find the solutions of a quadratic equation is by drawing a curve and a straight line. The solutions are given by the points where the line crosses the curve.

E.g. A gardener wants to build a flower bed in her garden. She has 10 m of edging to construct a rectangular bed.
(a) Find the maximum area of flower bed she can make with this edging.
(b) If the gardener wants the area of the flower bed to be 4·5 m^2 what should the length be?

Draw a graph of area against length for the flower bed.

Copy and complete this table of values:

Length	0	0·5	1	1·5	2	2·5	3	3·5	4	4·5	5
Width	5	4·5	4	3·5	3						
Area	0	2·25	4	5·25	6						

Copy and complete the graph.

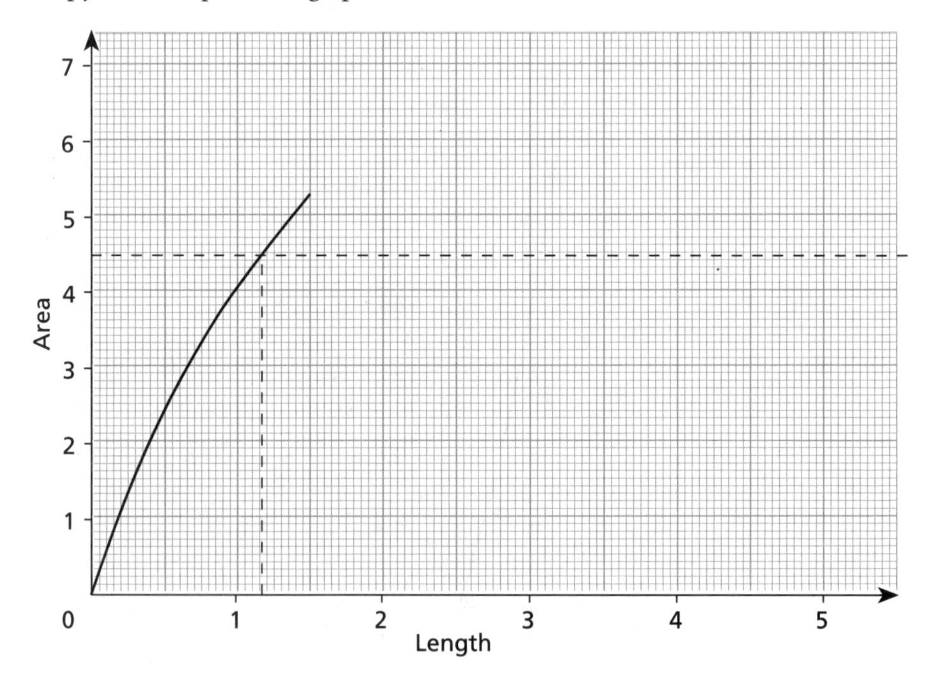

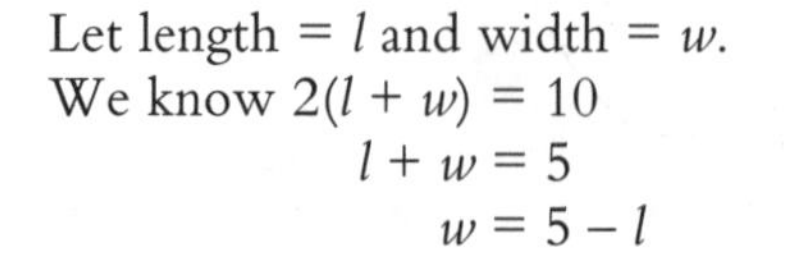
Let length = l and width = w.
We know $2(l + w) = 10$
$l + w = 5$
$w = 5 - l$

Let the area of the bed = A.

$A = lw$
$= l(5 - l)$
$= 5l - l^2$

So the equation of the curve is $A = 5l - l^2$.

(a) From the graph, the maximum area is 6·25 m^2.

(b) Draw a horizontal line across the graph with the equation $A = 4{\cdot}5$.
This line crosses the curve at two points. At these points you draw a vertical line to the l-axis.
This gives you two possible lengths for the flower bed.
To 1 decimal place, the length is 1·2 m or 3·8 m.

These points are the solutions of the equation $5l - l^2 = 4{\cdot}5$.

E xaminer's tip

The accuracy of the answers depends on how carefully the graph is drawn.

Note: Always check your answers.

If length = 1·2 then width = 3·8 and area = 1·2 × 3·8 = 4·56m^2.
Similarly if length = 3·8 (with width and length swapped over).
4·56m^2 is near enough 4·5m^2 so the answers are correct to 1 d.p.

2 Draw the graph of $y = x^2$ ($^-3 \le x \le 3$) and then use it to solve the following equations.
(a) $x^2 = 4$
(b) $x^2 = 2x + 3$ (Draw the line given by the equation $y = 2x + 3$ and find where it crosses the curve.)
(c) $x^2 = {}^-x$

3 Draw the graphs of $y = x^2 + 2x - 4$ ($^-4 \le x \le 3$) and $y = x + 2$ on the same pair of axes. Use the graph to solve the equation $x^2 + 2x - 4 = x + 2$.

Cubics

A cubic equation is one in which the highest power is 3.

One way to solve a cubic equation is to draw the graph of the equation and then find the points of intersection with the x-axis (where $y = 0$).

E.g. Solve the equation $x^3 - 3x^2 - x + 3 = 0$ by drawing its graph. ($^-2 \le x \le 4$)

Let $x^3 - 3x^2 - x + 3 = y$

x	4	3	2	1	0	$^-1$	$^-2$
x^3	64	27	8	1	0	$^-1$	$^-8$
$-3x^2$	$^-48$	$^-27$	$^-12$	$^-3$	0	$^-3$	$^-12$
$-x$	$^-4$	$^-3$	$^-2$	$^-1$	0	1	2
$+3$	3	3	3	3	3	3	3
y	15	0	$^-3$	0	3	0	$^-15$

Plot these points and join them with a smooth curve.

The solutions to the equation
$x^3 - 3x^2 - x + 3 = 0$
are given by the points where the graph crosses the x-axis.
These points are
$x = {}^-1$, $x = 1$ and $x = 3$.

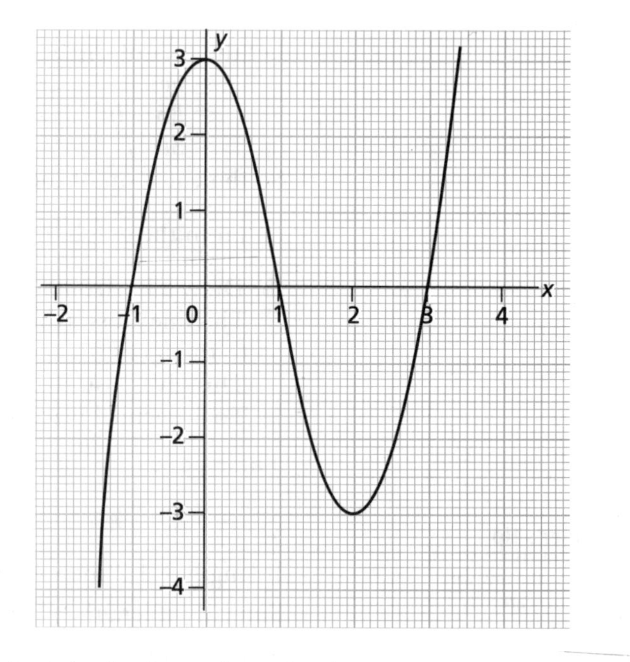

A cubic equation can always be written in the form $x^3 = ax^2 + bx + c$.

You can then solve the equation by plotting the curves $y = x^3$ and $y = ax^2 + bx + c$ and finding their points of intersection.

E.g. Solve the equation $x^3 = 3x^2 - 2x$ by drawing a graph of $y = x^3$ and $y = 3x^2 - 2x$.

x	$^-1$	0	1	2
x^3	$^-1$	0	1	8

x	$^-1$	0	1	2
$3x^2$	3	0	3	12
$-2x$	2	0	$^-2$	$^-4$
y	5	0	1	8

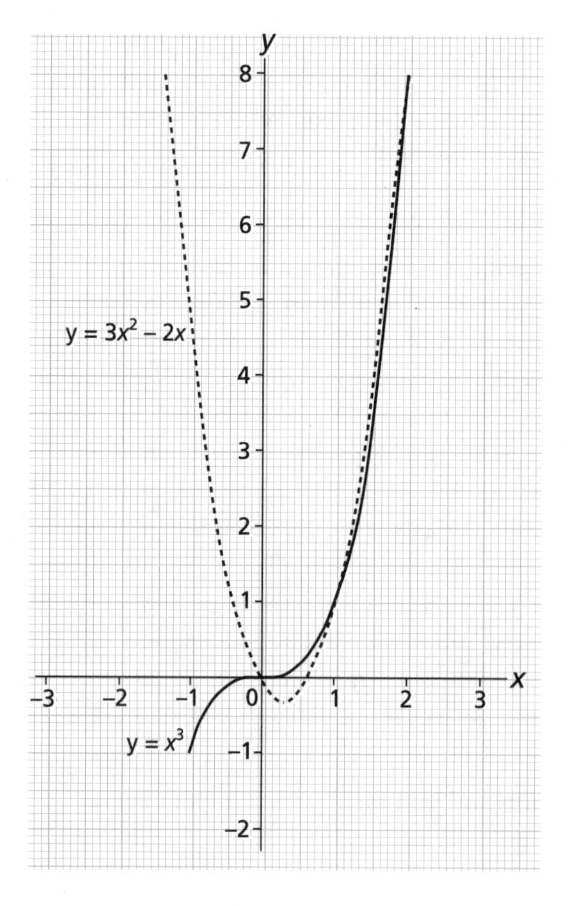

You can see from the graph that $y = x^3$ and $y = 3x^2 - 2x$ cross at the points (0, 0), (1, 1) and (2, 8).
So the x values which satisfy the equation $x^3 = 3x^2 - 2x$ are $x = 0$, $x = 1$ and $x = 2$.

4 Draw the graphs of the following cubics and find their solutions.
(a) $x^3 + 1 = 0$ ($^-2 \leq x \leq 1$)
(b) $x^3 - 6x^2 + 9x = 0$ ($^-1 \leq x \leq 4$)

5 Draw the graph of $y = x^3$ ($^-2 \leq x \leq 2$) and use it to solve the following equations.
(a) $x^3 = 0$
(b) $x^3 = x^2 - x + 1$
(c) $x^3 = 2x - 4$
(d) $x^3 + x = 0$
(e) $x^3 - x^2 - 2x = 0$

A cubic equation may have 1, 2 or 3 solutions. It must always have at least 1 solution.

6.13 Solving polynomials by trial and improvement

Complicated polynomials can be solved by making an estimate of the solution and then improving it until you get the required degree of accuracy.

E.g. Solve the equation $x^3 + x = 8$ to 2 d.p.

First look for the nearest whole numbers to the solution.
$2^3 + 2 = 10$ which is too small
$3^3 + 3 = 30$ which is too large

So x must be between 2 and 3 so try a value between them.

$2{\cdot}5^3 + 2{\cdot}5 = 18{\cdot}125$ which is just a little too large so try 2·49
$2{\cdot}49^3 + 2{\cdot}49 = 17{\cdot}928249$ which is too small

Check which is closer by trying 2·495
If this is above 18 then the answer will be closer to 2·49, if it is below then 2·5 will be closer.

$2{\cdot}495^3 + 2{\cdot}495 = 18{\cdot}02643737$

Hence $x = 2{\cdot}49$ (to 2 d.p.)

Examiner's tip

When you are asked to solve to 2 d.p. it means the value of *x* should be to 2 d.p. not the answer to the equation.

1 Solve the following equations to 2 d.p.:
(a) $x^3 + x = 12$ (b) $x^3 + 2x = 20$

Chapter 7
Further algebra

7.1 Expressing general laws in symbolic form

You may be given a set of data or a graph and asked to express the relationships displayed in an algebraic form.

If you are given a set of data you may be able to see a constant relationship between the two variables but it is often far easier if you graph the relationship.

Note: Rates of change are given by the gradient of the graph.

E.g. This table shows the cost of gas for cooking and heating.

Therms used	10	20	30	40	50
Cost (£)	17·00	21·50	26·00	30·50	35·00

Try to find a connecting rule between the cost and the number of therms used.

$$\text{Gradient} = \frac{\text{Change in } y}{\text{Change in } x} = \frac{(35 - 17)}{(50 - 10)} = \frac{18}{40} = £0{\cdot}45 \text{ per therm}$$

Cost intercept = £12·50

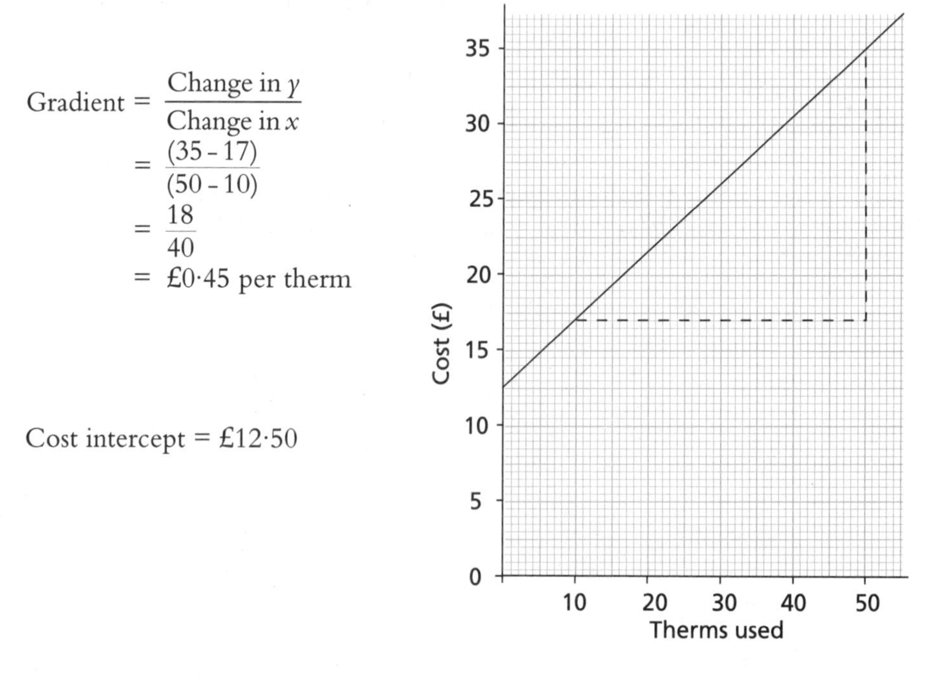

Since this is a straight-line graph the gradient will give you a rate per therm.
And the intercept on the cost axis will give you a standing charge.
Therefore the connecting formula is

$$\text{Cost} = 0{\cdot}45 \times \text{therms used} + 12{\cdot}50$$

1 A printer is producing a circular. The following is a table of charges.

Charges (£)	130	180	230	280	330
Number of copies	1000	2000	3000	4000	5000

By drawing a graph or otherwise, work out an equation to give you the cost of any number of circulars.

The same basic principles can be used to tackle more difficult examples. It is always better to get a straight-line graph if possible. Then you can be sure of the shape so your answers will be more accurate. And a straight line is much easier to draw!

E.g. Rita and Gurbash have recorded the following results for an experiment in science.

Area (A)	1	4	9	16	25	36
Result (R)	20	30	40	50	60	70

The results go up in equal steps but the areas don't, so plotting area against the results would not give a straight line.
Looking at the table they can see that all the areas are squares. So they try constructing a table of width ($\sqrt{A}$) and results.

Width (w)	1	2	3	4	5	6
Result (R)	20	30	40	50	60	70

Now the results go up in equal steps **and** the widths go up in equal steps which means a linear relationship between width and the results obtained.

By graphing this relationship they obtain the graph on the right.

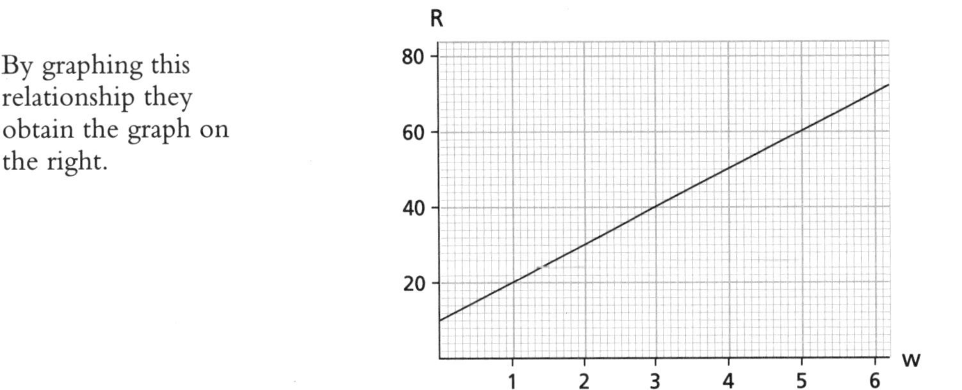

Since this relationship gives a straight line they know they can express it in the form

$R = mw + c$

From the graph, the gradient $m = 10$ and the R intercept $c = 10$.
This gives them $R = 10w + 10$

Substituting in $w = \sqrt{A}$ gives

$R = 10\sqrt{A} + 10$

Note: By putting $w = \sqrt{A}$ you get a straight line instead of a curve.

Some questions involve more complicated relationships. But the graphs involved should be graphs you are familiar with. This type of question usually has several parts to lead you through to the result.

E.g. Isobel is trying to work out a rule to help her calculate stopping distances. She has this data from the highway code.

Speed in miles per hour	0	30	50	70
Stopping distance in feet	0	75	175	315

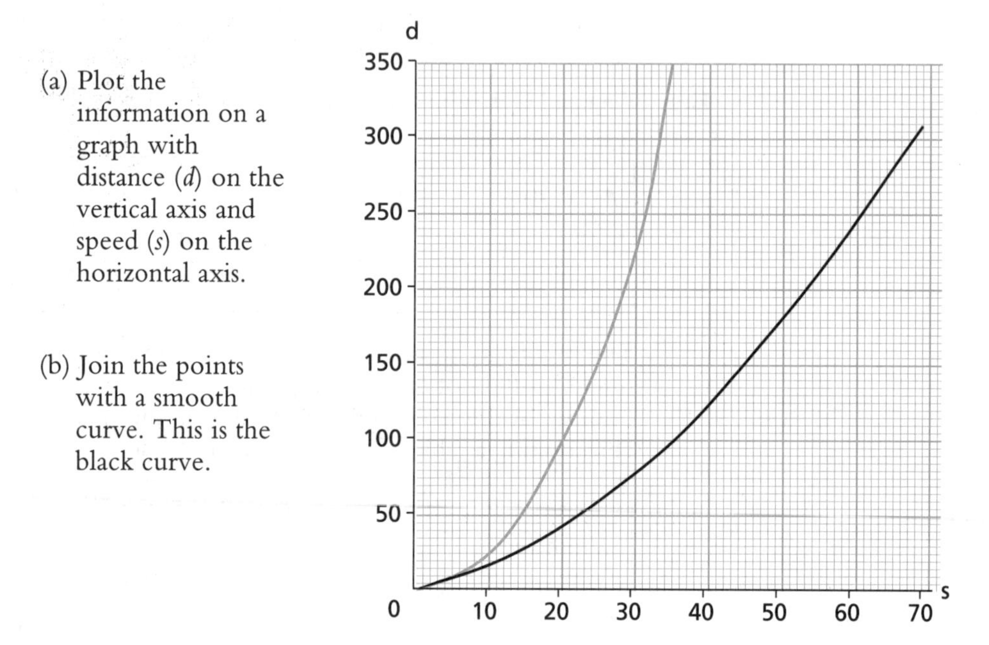

(a) Plot the information on a graph with distance (d) on the vertical axis and speed (s) on the horizontal axis.

(b) Join the points with a smooth curve. This is the black curve.

Note: This curve looks like a quadratic with a fractional coefficient of s^2.

(c) Complete this table.

Speed (s)	0	10	20	30	40	50	60	70
s^2	0	100	400	900				
$\frac{s^2}{4}$	0	25	100	225				

(d) Plot the values of $\frac{s^2}{4}$ on your graph and join them with a smooth curve. This has been done in green on the original graph above.

(e) Use your graph to help you find an approximate equation linking speed and stopping distances.

The graph of $\frac{s^2}{4}$ is similar to the graph of speed against stopping distance. By dividing s^2 by numbers larger than 4 the values of $\frac{s^2}{n}$ become closer to the original graph.

The graph $d = \frac{s^2}{15}$ is very close to the graph of speed against stopping distance. So an approximate relationship is $d = \frac{s^2}{15}$.

2 A paper rocket is fired into the air.
The following heights are recorded over the rocket's flight.

Height (m)	2	6	8	8	6	2
Time (s)	0	1	2	3	4	5

(a) Draw the graph of the rocket's flight. (Put time on the horizontal axis.)
(b) What is the maximum height reached by the rocket?
(c) Plot the graph of $h = {}^{-}(t - 2{\cdot}5)^2$ on the same axes.
(d) Use this to help you work out an equation for the rocket's flight.

7.2 Quadratic equations

You have already seen how to solve quadratic equations by drawing graphs and finding points of intersection. This unit covers various algebraic methods for solving quadratic equations.

Factorisation (harder quadratics)

You already know how to factorise quadratic expressions into two brackets of the form $(ax + b)(cx + d)$.
So given a quadratic equation you can write it in the form

$$(ax + b)(cx + d) = 0$$

When two numbers multiply together to give zero then at least one of the numbers must itself equal zero.

Therefore $(ax + b) = 0$ or $(cx + d) = 0$ or both.

If $(ax + b) = 0$ then $x = {}^{-}\frac{b}{a}$ and if $(cx + d) = 0$ then $x = {}^{-}\frac{d}{c}$

so the solutions (roots) of the quadratic equation are $x = {}^{-}\frac{b}{a}$ and $x = {}^{-}\frac{d}{c}$.

E.g. Solve the equation $6x^2 + 5x - 6 = 0$ by factorising.

First factorise $6x^2 + 5x - 6$.
You need to find two factors of 6 which combine with another two factors of 6 to give 5. Because the number term is negative you are looking for the **difference** to equal 5.

Note: Start by trying the factors which are closest together.

The closest factors of 6 are 2 and 3. Try the factor pairs (2, 3) and (2, 3).
$3 \times 3 - 2 \times 2 = 5$ which gives the result you want.

One factor pair gives the coefficients of x so start with

$(2x \quad)(3x \quad)$

The other factor pair goes at the ends of the brackets. To get 5 you need to multiply the 3's together and the 2's together so this tells you which bracket to put each number in.

$(2x \quad 3)(3x \quad 2)$

Because the number term in the original expression is negative the signs in the brackets will be different. To get 5 you subtracted the 2×2 so the – goes in front of the 2.

$(2x + 3)(3x - 2)$

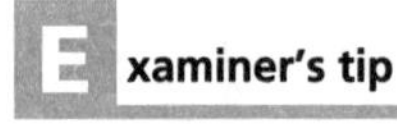

xaminer's tip

Always check your answer by multiplying the brackets.

Check: $(2x + 3)(3x - 2) = 6x^2 - 4x + 9x - 6 = 6x^2 + 5x - 6$
So $6x^2 + 5x - 6 = (2x + 3)(3x - 2)$
Putting $(2x + 3)(3x - 2) = 0$
gives $(2x + 3) = 0$ or $(3x - 2) = 0$
So the solutions are $x = {}^{-}\frac{3}{2}$ and $x = \frac{2}{3}$.

E xaminer's tip

If a question asks you to solve a quadratic to a given number of decimal places then you can't do it by factorising!

1 Solve the following quadratics by factorising:
(a) $8x^2 + 16x + 6 = 0$ (b) $9x^2 + 27x + 20 = 0$ (c) $6x^2 - 40x - 14 = 0$

Not all quadratics can be factorised into brackets with integer (whole number) coefficients (e.g. $x^2 - 7$) so we need an alternative method.

The formula

If you are asked to solve a quadratic equation to any number of decimal places you will have to use the formula:

$$x = \frac{-b \pm \sqrt{b^2 - 4ac}}{2a}$$

E.g. Solve the quadratic $3x^2 + 2x - 4 = 0$ to 2 decimal places.

Comparing with $ax^2 + bx + c = 0$ you have $a = 3$, $b = 2$ and $c = {}^{-}4$.
Substituting into the formula

$$x = \frac{{}^{-}2 \pm \sqrt{2^2 - 4 \times 3 \times {}^{-}4}}{2 \times 3}$$

$$= \frac{{}^{-}2 \pm \sqrt{4 + 48}}{6}$$

$$= \frac{{}^{-}2 \pm \sqrt{52}}{6} \quad \left(\text{or} \quad \frac{{}^{-}2 + \sqrt{52}}{6} \quad \text{and} \quad \frac{{}^{-}2 - \sqrt{52}}{6} \right)$$

To 2 decimal places the roots are $x = 0{\cdot}87$ and $x = {}^{-}1{\cdot}54$.

E xaminer's tip

The clue to using this method lies in the question asking for solutions to a number of decimal places.

2 Solve the following quadratics to 2 decimal places using the formula:
(a) $2x^2 - 3x - 7 = 0$ (b) $3x^2 - 5x - 1 = 0$

Note: You will be given the formula in an exam.

Completing the square

One method which works for all quadratic equations (unless they don't have any solutions – see below) is completing the square. This is a way of getting x to appear only once in the equation so that you can then simply rearrange it to find the values of x.

Note: This method is not popular and it is not used as frequently as the two above.

E.g. (a) Solve the quadratic $x^2 - 7x - 12 = 0$ to 2 decimal places.

First get the terms involving x on one side and the number on the other.

$$x^2 - 7x = 12$$

Then write the expression on the left hand side (LHS) in the form of a square. To do this you divide the coefficient of x (the number in front of x) by 2.

$$(x - \tfrac{7}{2})^2$$

Expanding this bracket gives $x^2 - 7x + \frac{49}{4}$ or $x^2 - 7x + 12{\cdot}25$

So by adding 12·25 to the LHS you can complete the square. To preserve the equation you must also add 12·25 to the RHS.

$$x^2 - 7x = 12$$
$$x^2 - 7x + 12{\cdot}25 = 12 + 12{\cdot}25$$
$$(x - 3{\cdot}5)^2 = 24{\cdot}25$$

Taking square roots,

$$x - 3{\cdot}5 = \pm\sqrt{24\cdot25}$$
$$x = 3{\cdot}5 \pm\sqrt{24\cdot25}$$

To 2 decimal places the solutions are $x = 8{\cdot}42$ and $x = {}^{-}1{\cdot}42$.

(b) Solve the quadratic $3x^2 + 2x - 4 = 0$ to 2 decimal places.
First get all the terms involving x on the left hand side (LHS).

$$3x^2 + 2x = 4$$

Then divide through by the coefficient of x^2.

$$x^2 + \tfrac{2}{3}x = \tfrac{4}{3}$$

Divide the coefficient of x by 2 then square it and add to both sides.

$$x^2 + \tfrac{2}{3}x + \tfrac{1}{9} = \tfrac{4}{3} + \tfrac{1}{9}$$

This can now be factorised.

$$\left(x + \tfrac{1}{3}\right)^2 = \tfrac{13}{9}$$

Taking the square root of both sides

$$x + \tfrac{1}{3} = {}^{\pm}\sqrt{\tfrac{13}{9}}$$

To 2 decimal places the solutions are $x = 0{\cdot}87$ and $x = {}^{-}1{\cdot}54$.

3 Solve the following equations to 2 decimal places by completing the square:
(a) $x^2 + 3x - 5 = 0$ (b) $x^2 - 2x - 34 = 0$

Quadratics with no real solutions

If the graph of a quadratic equation does not cross the x-axis then the equation has no real solutions. (If you go on to do Maths at a higher level you will find that 'imaginary' solutions exist.)

By looking at the formula you can see that there will be no real solutions of the equation $ax^2 + bx + c = 0$ if

$$b^2 - 4ac < 0$$

Note: If you are asked to solve a quadratic it will have a solution.

7.3 Using graphs to solve equations

If you are asked to solve an equation using a graph the two expressions will be related.

E.g. Use the graph of $y = x^2 + 5x$ to solve the equation $x^2 + 5x - 6 = 0$.

The first step is to make the equation look like the graph $y = x^2 + 5x$

Rearranging the equation gives $x^2 + 5x = 6$

Hence $y = 6$ which you can graph

Graphing $y = x^2 + 5x$ and $y = 6$ gives two solutions where the graphs cross.

Solutions are at $x = 1$ and $x = {}^{-}6$

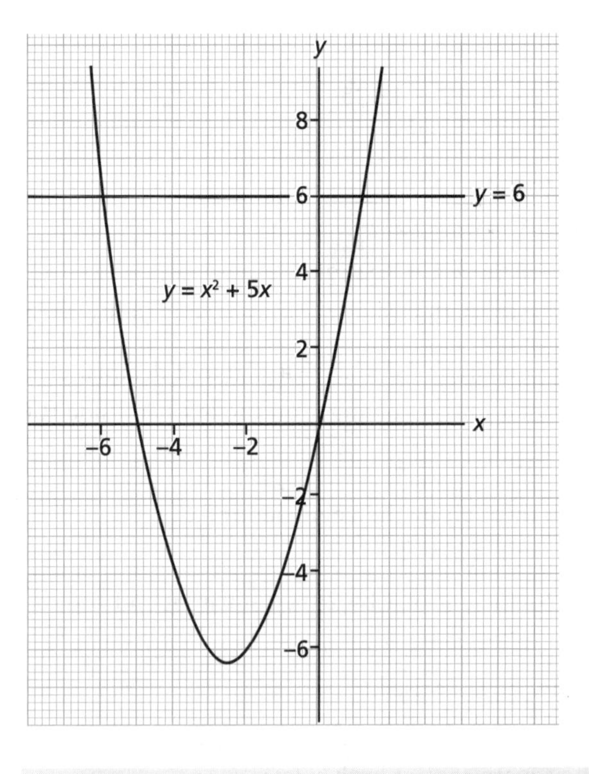

1 Solve the following equations by graphing both sides of each equation:

(a) $x^2 - 2x = 3$ (b) $x^2 - 2x - 1 = x - 1$

2 Draw the following pairs of equations on the same axes and use them to solve the given equations:

(a) Use the graphs of $y = x^2 - 2$ and $y = 2x + 1$ to solve $x^2 - 2 = 2x + 1$.

(b) Use the graphs of $y = x^2 - x - 2$ and $y = x + 1$ to solve $x^2 - x - 2 = x + 1$.

(c) Use the graphs of $y = x^2 - 2x - 1$ and $y = 2$ to solve $x^2 - 2x - 1 = 2$.

(d) Explain why the graphs drawn above have the same solutions.

7.4 Algebraic fractions

Common factors

By taking out common factors from the numerator and denominator of an algebraic fraction you can simplify the expression in the same way you would with an ordinary fraction.

E.g. Simplify $\dfrac{(x^2 - x - 6)(x^2 + 4x + 3)}{(x^2 - 9)(x + 1)}$

$(x^2 - x - 6)$ can be factorised to give $(x - 3)(x + 2)$

$(x^2 + 4x + 3)$ can be factorised to give $(x + 3)(x + 1)$

$(x^2 - 9)$ can be factorised to give $(x + 3)(x - 3)$

Putting each of these back into the original expression you can then cancel like terms that appear on the top and bottom.

$$\frac{\cancel{(x-3)}(x+2)\cancel{(x+3)}\cancel{(x+1)}}{\cancel{(x-3)}\cancel{(x+3)}\cancel{(x+1)}} = (x+2)$$

1 Simplify $\dfrac{(x^2 - 2x - 8)(x^2 + 5x + 4)}{(x^2 - 16)(x + 2)}$

Adding and subtracting

To add or subtract any fractions you first have to find a common denominator. With algebraic fractions the common denominator is usually found by multiplying the denominators together.

E.g. Simplify $\dfrac{1}{x} - \dfrac{2}{x+2}$

$\dfrac{1}{x} - \dfrac{2}{x+2}$ becomes $\dfrac{(x+2)}{x(x+2)} - \dfrac{2x}{x(x+2)}$

$$\frac{x + 2 - 2x}{x(x+2)} = \frac{2 - x}{x^2 + 2x}$$

2 Simplify the following:

(a) $\dfrac{1}{x+1} - \dfrac{1}{x-1}$ (b) $\dfrac{3}{3x^2} - \dfrac{2}{3x}$ (c) $\dfrac{3}{x^2 - x} - \dfrac{5}{x^2 - 1}$

Equations

E.g. Solve the equation $\dfrac{2x+1}{x-1} = \dfrac{6x+1}{3x-2}$

The first step is to multiply both sides of the equation by both denominators.

$$\frac{(3x-2)(x-1)(2x+1)}{(x-1)} = \frac{(6x+1)(3x-2)(x-1)}{(3x-2)}$$

Cancelling gives $(3x - 2)(2x + 1) = (6x + 1)(x - 1)$

$$6x^2 - 4x + 3x - 2 = 6x^2 + x - 6x - 1$$

$$^{-}x - 2 = {}^{-}5x - 1$$

Hence $4x = 1$

giving $x = \frac{1}{4}$

Note: Always substitute this value back into the equation to check it works.

3 Solve the following equations:

(a) $\dfrac{2}{x} = \dfrac{3}{x+1}$ (b) $\dfrac{x}{3} - \dfrac{x}{4} = 1$ (c) $\dfrac{1}{x-1} + \dfrac{2}{x+1} = \dfrac{3}{x}$

7.5 Rearranging more difficult formulae

You have already rearranged formulae to make a particular variable the subject of the equation. If the variable you have to find appears in the expression more than once the rearrangement is more difficult.

E.g. Make the given letter the subject of the following formulae:

$zx + zy = t$ make z the subject

factorising by z gives $z(x + y) = t$

hence $z = \dfrac{t}{(x+y)}$

E.g. Make b the subject of the following equation:

$$a = \sqrt{\left(\frac{b}{b+c}\right)}$$

First square both sides to remove the root $a^2 = \left(\dfrac{b}{b+c}\right)$

Multiply both sides by $b + c$ $a^2(b + c) = b$

Expand the brackets $a^2b + a^2c = b$

Collect the b's $a^2c = b - a^2b$

Factorising the right side of the equation $a^2c = b(1 - a^2)$

Hence $\dfrac{a^2c}{(1-a^2)} = b$

Note: The methods used here are a variety which can be used to solve this type of problem.

1 In each of the following make the letter given in brackets the subject of the equation.

(a) $Pt = mv + mu$ (m)

(b) $\dfrac{1}{v} - \dfrac{1}{u} = f$ (v)

(c) $xy = \dfrac{w}{y} + ty$ (y)

(d) $P = \dfrac{Ay}{x(A+t)}$ (A)

7.6 The rules of indices for negative and fractional indices

Negative indices

You have used the rules of indices for positive whole number indices. These same rules can be extended to negative indices.

Note: A negative index gives the inverse (reciprocal) of the positive index.

$$x^{-n} = \frac{1}{x^n}$$

E.g. $2x^{-2} \times 3x^{-3} = \dfrac{2}{x^2} \times \dfrac{3}{x^3}$

$= \dfrac{2 \times 3}{x^2 \times x^3}$

When you multiply you add the indices:

$$= \frac{6}{x^{(2+3)}}$$
$$= \frac{6}{x^5}$$
$$= 6x^{-5}$$
$$= 6x^{(-2+-3)}$$

So the same rule applies for negative indices: when you multiply expressions you add the indices.

1 Simplify the following:

(a) $x^{-4} \times x^{-3}$ (b) $3x^{-2} \times 2x^{-4}$ (c) $2x^{-1} \times 2x^{-2}$

(d) $3a^{-6} \times 2a^{-4}$ (e) $5b^7 \times 12b^{-4}$ (f) $x^{-3}y^2 \times 7x^{-2}y^{-4}$

Dividing expressions involving negative indices takes a bit more care.

E.g. (a) $x^{-5} \div x^{-3} = \frac{1}{x^5} \div \frac{1}{x^3}$

To divide by a fraction you multiply by its inverse:

$$= \frac{1}{x^5} \times \frac{x^3}{1}$$
$$= x^3 \div x^5$$

When you divide you subtract the indices:

$$= x^{(3-5)}$$
$$= x^{-2}$$
$$= x^{(-5--3)}$$

(b) $6x^{-4} \div 3x^{-1} = (6 \div 3) \times (x^{-4} \div x^{-1})$

$$= 2x^{(-4--1)}$$
$$= 2x^{(-4+1)}$$
$$= 2x^{-3}$$

2 Simplify the following:

(a) $x^{-6} \div x^{-2}$ (b) $8x^{-6} \div 2x^{-2}$ (c) $7x^{-5} \div x$ (d) $5x^3 \div x^{-4}$

(e) $21a^{-3}b^{-1}c \div 3a^2b^{-4}c^{-8}$

You also need to take care with the + and – signs when you raise a power to a negative power.

E.g. $(z^{-2})^{-3} = (\frac{1}{z^2})^{-3}$

$$= (\frac{z^2}{1})^3$$

When you raise a power to a power you multiply:

$$= z^{(2\times 3)}$$
$$= z^6$$
$$= z^{(-2\times -3)}$$

3 Simplify the following expressions:

(a) $(a^{-3})^7$ (b) $(2b^4)^{-1}$ (c) $(4n^{-3})^{-4}$ (d) $(x^2y^{-3}z^{-1})^{-5}$

Fractional indices

The rules for indices can also be extended to fractional indices.

Note: A fractional index represents a root.

$$x^{\frac{1}{n}} = \sqrt[n]{x}$$

Where the index is of the form $\frac{a}{b}$ with $a \neq 1$ it gives the bth root of x^a which can also be written $\sqrt[b]{x^a}$.

4 Express the following in the form $\sqrt[b]{x^a}$:

(a) $x^{\frac{2}{5}}$ (b) $x^{\frac{3}{7}}$ (c) the cube root of x^2 (d) the square root of x cubed

E.g.
$$\begin{aligned} x^{\frac{1}{2}} \times x^{\frac{1}{4}} &= x^{\frac{2}{4}} \times x^{\frac{1}{4}} \\ &= \sqrt[4]{x^2} \times \sqrt[4]{x} \\ &= \sqrt[4]{x^2 \times x} \\ &= \sqrt[4]{x^3} \\ &= x^{\frac{3}{4}} \\ &= x^{\left(\frac{1}{2}+\frac{1}{4}\right)} \end{aligned}$$

So the rules of indices apply to fractional values in exactly the same way.

5 Simplify the following:

(a) $x^{\frac{1}{3}} \times x^{\frac{1}{2}}$ (b) $x^{\frac{2}{3}} \times x$ (c) $x^{\frac{2}{7}} \times x^{\frac{3}{4}}$

E.g.
$$\begin{aligned} x^{\frac{1}{2}} \div x^{\frac{1}{6}} &= x^{\left(\frac{1}{2}-\frac{1}{6}\right)} \\ &= x^{\left(\frac{3}{6}-\frac{1}{6}\right)} \\ &= x^{\frac{1}{3}} \end{aligned}$$

6 Simplify the following:

(a) $x^{\frac{3}{5}} \div x^{\frac{1}{5}}$ (b) $a^{\frac{4}{3}} \div a^{\frac{1}{6}}$

E.g. (a)
$$\begin{aligned} \left(x^{\frac{1}{5}}\right)^2 &= x^{\frac{1}{5}} \times x^{\frac{1}{5}} \\ &= x^{\left(\frac{1}{5}+\frac{1}{5}\right)} \\ &= x^{\frac{2}{5}} \\ &= x^{\left(2\times\frac{1}{5}\right)} \end{aligned}$$

(b)
$$\begin{aligned} \left(x^{\frac{1}{7}}\right)^{\frac{1}{2}} &= x^{\left(\frac{1}{7}\times\frac{1}{2}\right)} \\ &= x^{\frac{1}{14}} \end{aligned}$$

7 Simplify the following:

(a) $\left(a^{\frac{2}{3}}\right)^3$ (b) $\left(x^{\frac{1}{2}}\right)^7$ (c) $\left(x^2y\right)^{\frac{1}{5}}$

7.7 Finding the area under a curve

There are various methods that can be used to calculate the approximate area under a curve. One way is by approximating the area to a series of rectangles.

E.g. To calculate its insurance premiums a firm needs to calculate the volume of a warehouse with a curved roof. To calculate the volume they first need to find the area of the end wall.

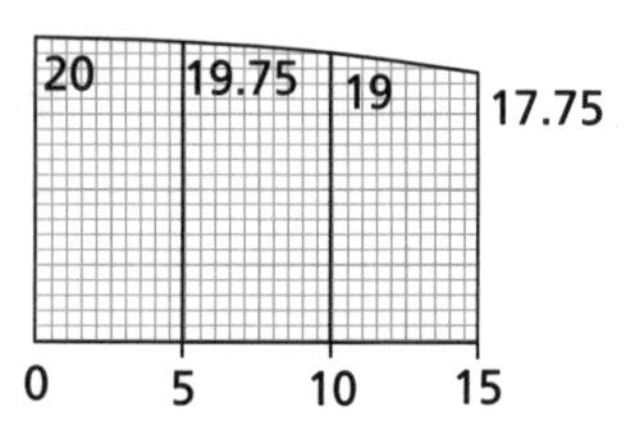

The end wall is 15 m wide and the curve of the roof is given by the equation $y = 20 - 0{\cdot}01x^2$.

First divide the area of the wall into vertical strips of equal width.
Use the equation $y = 20 - 0{\cdot}01x^2$ to calculate the height of the roof at the edge of each strip.

You can now approximate each strip to a rectangle.

x	0	5	10	15
y	20	19·75	19	17·75

Method 1 Using the longer edge for each strip, draw a step-graph above the curve. You can work out the area under the step-graph since you know the height and width of each column.

The area under the step-graph is given by:

$(5 \times 20) + (5 \times 19{\cdot}75) + (5 \times 19)$
$= 5 \times 58{\cdot}75$
$= 293{\cdot}75\ \text{m}^2$

Since the step-graph is always above the curve this gives an **upper bound** for the area under the curve.

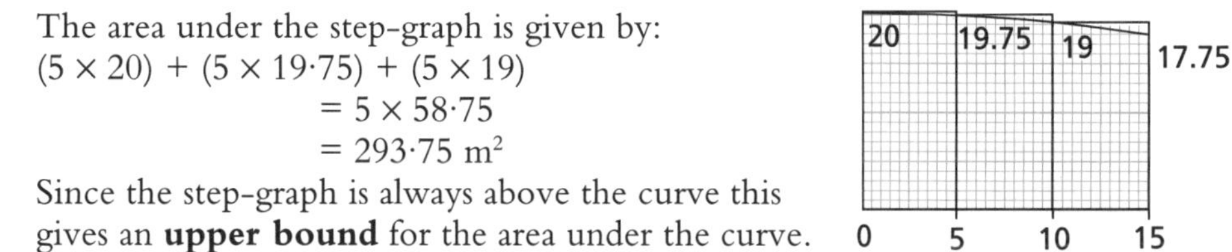

Area of the wall $\leq 293{\cdot}75\ \text{m}^2$

So $293{\cdot}75\ \text{m}^2$ is an approximate value for the area but you know it's too big.

Method 2 Using the shorter edge of each strip, draw a step-graph under the curve.
The area of this step-graph is given by:

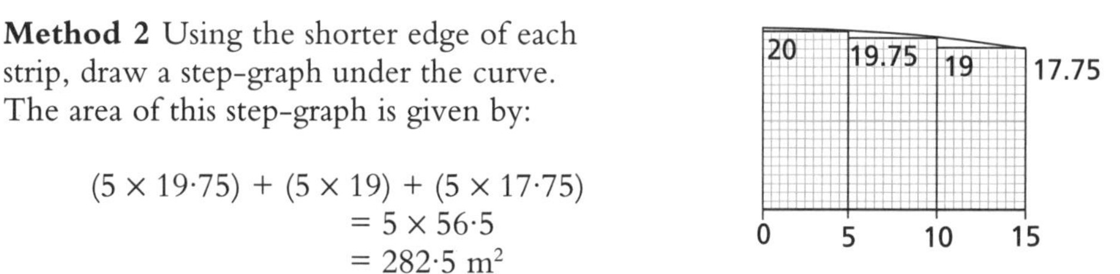

$(5 \times 19{\cdot}75) + (5 \times 19) + (5 \times 17{\cdot}75)$
$= 5 \times 56{\cdot}5$
$= 282{\cdot}5\ \text{m}^2$

This gives a **lower bound** for the area under the curve.

So the area of the warehouse wall is between $282{\cdot}5\ \text{m}^2$ and $293{\cdot}75\ \text{m}^2$.

Since the roof curves outwards, the area under the curve will be closer to the upper bound than to the lower bound, so a first approximation to the area is $293{\cdot}75\ \text{m}^2$.

To get a more accurate approximation for the area under a curve you can take the average of the upper and lower bounds.

$$\frac{293 \cdot 75 + 282 \cdot 5}{2} = 288 \cdot 125$$

So the area of the wall is approximately $288\ \text{m}^2$.

1 (a) Calculate the upper and lower bounds for the area under this curve.
(b) Which value is a better approximation?
(c) Calculate the average of the upper and lower bounds.

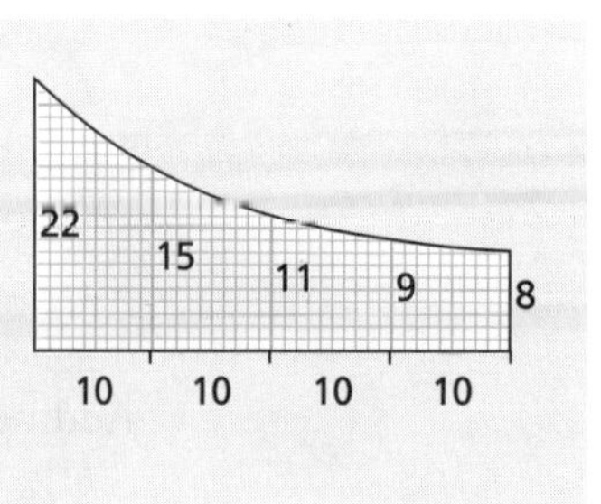

2 Calculate the approximate area under the graph of $y = x^2(4 - x)$ between $x = 0$ and $x = 4$ by drawing a step-graph above the curve with steps of $0{\cdot}5$.

This method of approximating using rectangles becomes more accurate if the width of the strips is reduced. The disadvantage is that when you have a large number of strips to calculate it becomes very long-winded. However, a computer can make an approximation very quickly.

E.g. Calculate the approximate area under the curve $y = 3 + 0{\cdot}1\,x^2$ between $x = 0$ and $x = 2$.

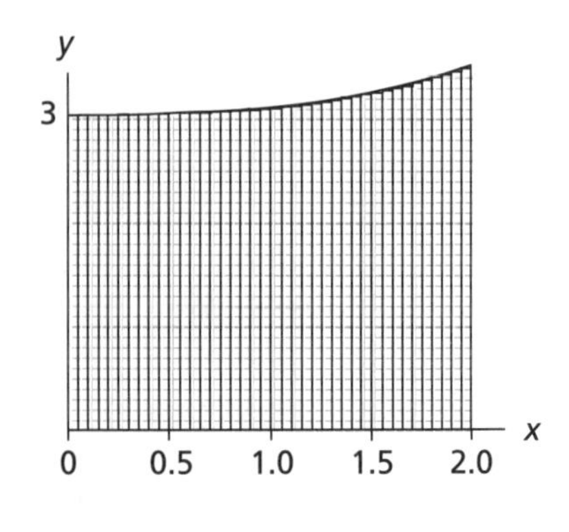

The following program in BASIC can be used to calculate the lower bound. The width of each strip in this case is 0·05.

```
10 Let W = 0·05
20 For X = 0 to 2 – W step W
30 Let Y = 3 + 0·1 * X * X
40 Let A = W * Y
50 Let S = S + A
60 Next X
70 Print S
```

For the upper bound replace line 20 with

```
20 For X = W to 2 step W
```

Finding the upper and lower bounds and then taking the average means doing two calculations. By approximating each strip to a trapezium you can average out the upper and lower bounds in one single calculation.

The trapezium rule

Divide the area under the curve into strips in the same way but this time join up the points where the edges of the strips meet the curve. Now each strip is a trapezium (or a triangle if the value at one end is 0).

The area of each strip is $\frac{1}{2}h(a + b)$, where a and b are the heights at the edge of the strip and h is the width.

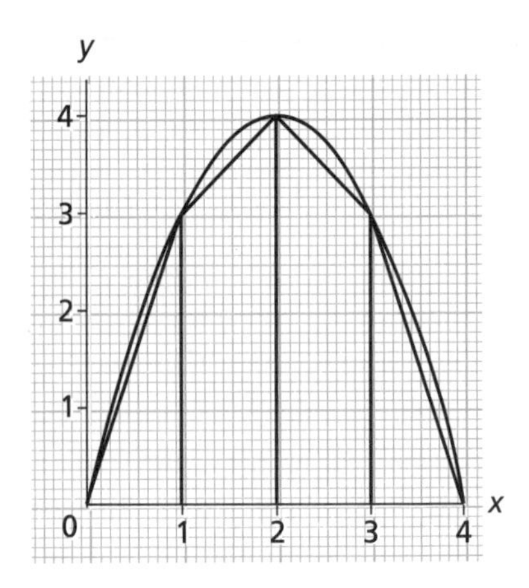

If you divide the area under a curve into n strips of width h and the values of y at the edges of the strips are $y_0, y_1, y_2, \dots, y_n$ then

Area of $T_1 = \frac{1}{2}h(y_0 + y_1)$

Area of $T_2 = \frac{1}{2}h(y_1 + y_2)$

Area of $T_3 = \frac{1}{2}h(y_2 + y_3)$

.

.

.

Area of $T_{n-1} = \frac{1}{2}h(y_{n-2} + y_{n-1})$

Area of $T_n = \frac{1}{2}h(y_{n-1} + y_n)$

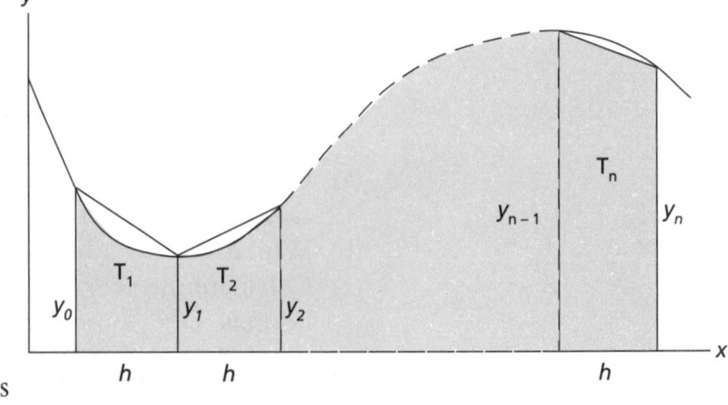

Adding the areas together gives $\frac{1}{2}h(y_0 + 2y_1 + 2y_2 + \dots + 2y_{n-1} + y_n)$

Note: Each height is added in twice apart from those at the ends.

So the trapezium rule says that the approximate area under the curve is

$\frac{1}{2}h[y_0 + y_n + 2(y_1 + y_2 + \ldots + y_{n-1})]$ or $h[\frac{1}{2}(y_0 + y_n) + y_1 + y_2 + \ldots + y_{n-1}]$

3 Use the trapezium rule to approximate the area under the curve with equation $y = 10 - x^2$ between $x = {}^-3$ and $x = 3$ using strips of width 1.

Area under a speed/time graph

If you draw a graph of speed against time then the area under the graph gives the distance travelled.
This is easiest to see when the speed is constant.

E.g. This graph shows a car travelling at a constant speed of 5 m/s for 6 seconds.

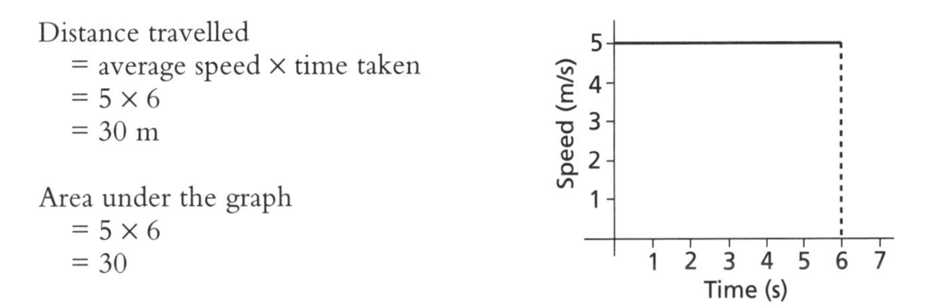

Distance travelled
= average speed × time taken
= 5 × 6
= 30 m

Area under the graph
= 5 × 6
= 30

4 The graph below shows an imaginary car travelling at 1 m/s for 1 second then 1·5 m/s for the next second, 2 m/s in the third second … up to 6 seconds.
Calculate the distance travelled by the car.

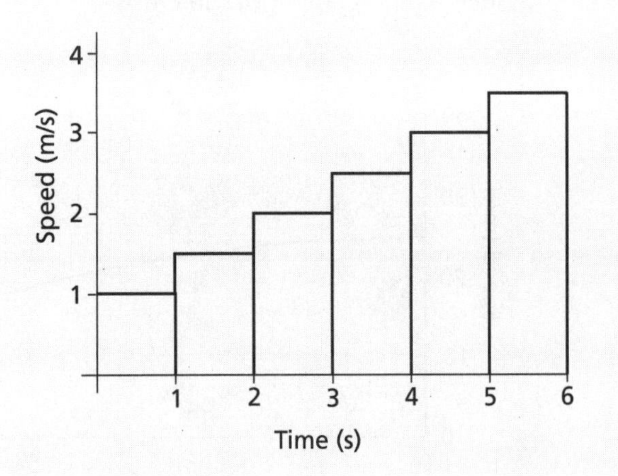

To see what would happen for a curved graph, imagine making the widths of the steps in question 4 smaller and smaller. You would eventually get a smooth curve, which would represent the motion of a real car. The area under the curve would still give you the distance travelled.

Other graphs

The area under other types of graph can also represent a particular quantity. Multiplying together the units on each axis may help you to decide what that quantity is.

E.g. The rate of water flowing through a hosepipe over a 20 second period is shown on page 98.

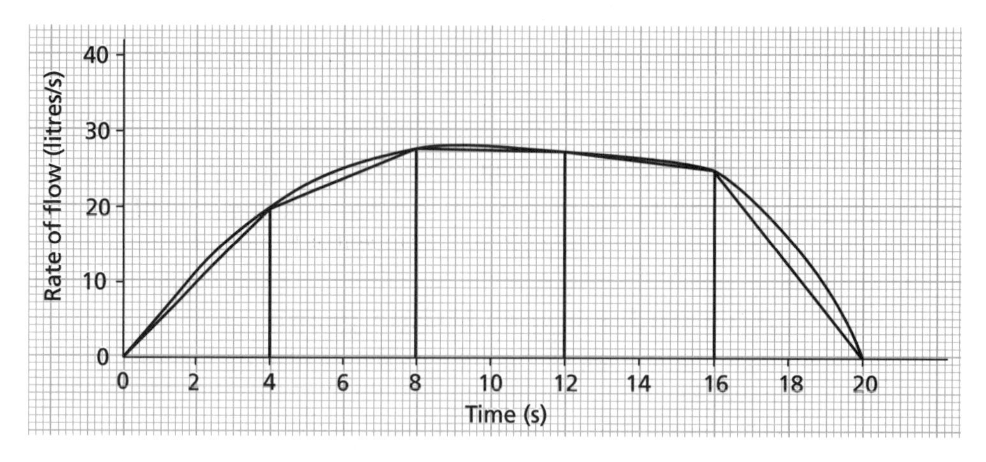

The area under the curve represents the volume of water which flowed through the pipe.

Check: Multiplying units gives (litres/seconds) × seconds = litres

Use the trapezium method with strips of width 4 seconds to calculate the total volume of water which flowed through the hosepipe.

Area under curve $\approx 4\left(\frac{1}{2}(0+0) + 20 + 28 + 27 + 25\right)$
$\approx 4 \times 100$
≈ 400

So the volume of water which flowed through the hosepipe in 20 seconds was approximately 400 litres.

5 A lorry is travelling at 25 m/s when the driver applies the brakes. t seconds after applying the brakes the lorry's speed is given by the equation $25 - 0{\cdot}25\,t^2$. The speed/time graph looks like this.

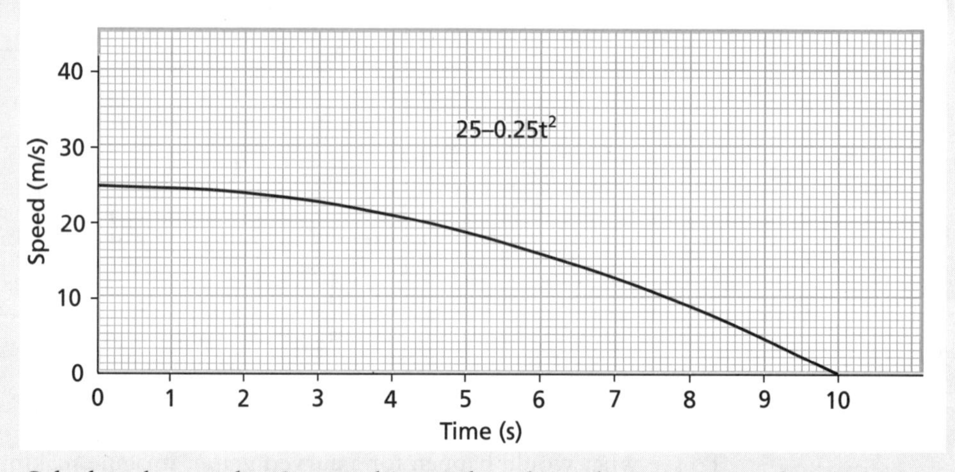

Calculate the speed at 2-second intervals and use the trapezium rule to calculate the distance travelled by the lorry before it stops.

7.8 Finding gradients using tangents

The gradient of a line is the same for every point on the line. So the gradient of a straight line graph can be found by choosing a suitable part of the line and calculating

$$\frac{\text{change in } y}{\text{change in } x}.$$

The gradient of a curve varies from point to point along the curve so you can only find the gradient at a point.

An approximate value for the gradient of a curve at a particular point is given by the gradient of the **tangent** to the curve at that point.

A **tangent** to a curve at a particular point is a straight line through the point following the direction of the curve at that point.

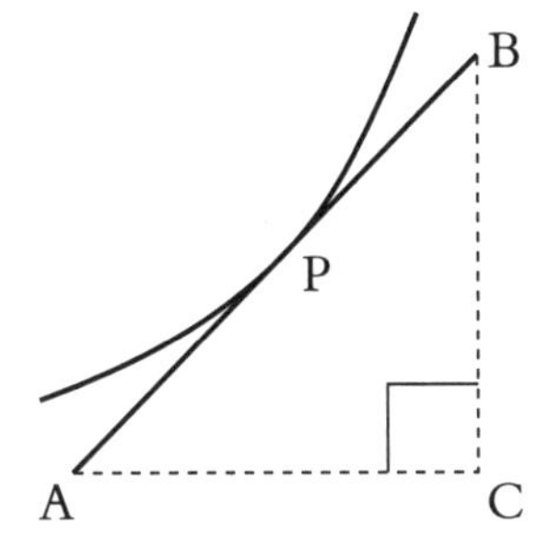

So to find the gradient of this curve at point P you construct a tangent at P and then find the gradient of the tangent AB by drawing in the horizontal line AC and the vertical line BC and calculating $\frac{BC}{AC}$.

It is important to remember that this method only gives you an approximation of the gradient of the curve at the point P. To make your answer as accurate as possible draw a long tangent and use large values of AC and BC.

1 Copy and complete the following table of values and use it to draw a graph of $y = x^2$ with as large a scale as possible.

x	0	0.4	0.5	0.7	0.9	1	1.1	1.5	2.0
y	0								

By drawing tangents to your graph find the gradients when x has the following values:

(a) $x = 0{\cdot}5$ (b) $x = 1$

E.g. This graph shows the speed of a car accelerating over a period of 10 seconds. Use the graph to find the acceleration of the car after 5 seconds.

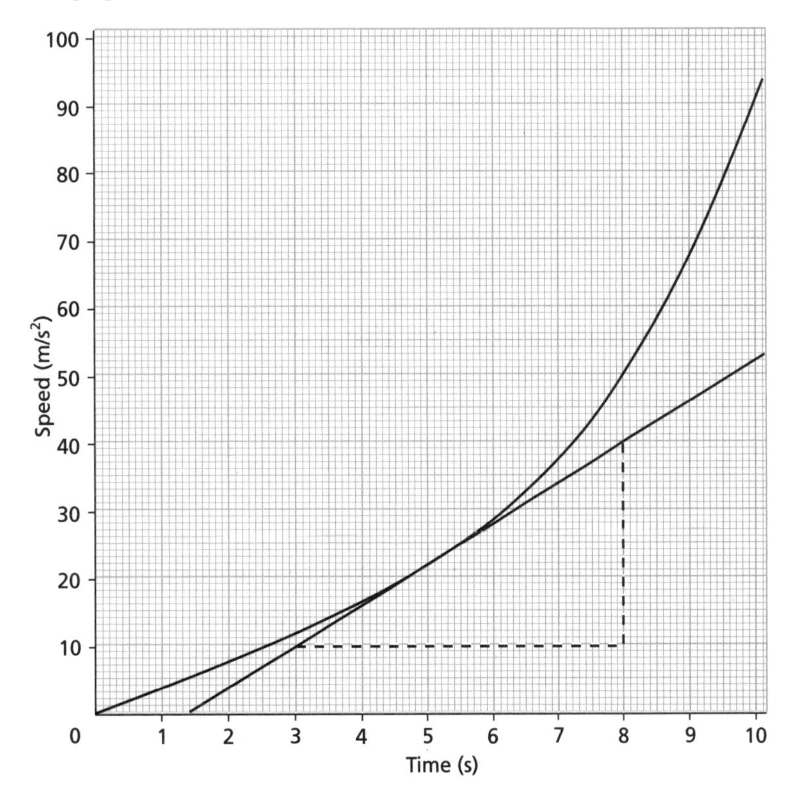

Acceleration is rate of change of speed so the acceleration is given by the tangent of the curve at 5 seconds.

$$\text{Gradient} = \frac{\text{change in } y}{\text{change in } x}$$

$$= \frac{40 - 10}{8 - 3}$$

$$= 6$$

The units of the gradient are given by $\frac{\text{units on the vertical axis}}{\text{units on the horizontal axis}}$.

The units are $\frac{\text{m/s}}{\text{s}} = \text{m/s}^2$

So the acceleration after 5 seconds is 6 m/s^2 (to 2 d.p.).

Examiner's tip

Make your tangents as long as possible.

2 Use the graph to calculate the acceleration of the car after the following times:
(a) 3 seconds
(b) 7 seconds
(c) 9 seconds

7.9 Sketching the graphs of functions derived from other functions

You are already familiar with the graphs of common functions. Looking at the function $f(x) = x - x^2$ you can say that the shape will be a parabola because the function is a quadratic, and that the parabola will be upside down because the coefficient of x^2 is negative.

This is the graph of the function $f(x) = x - x^2$.

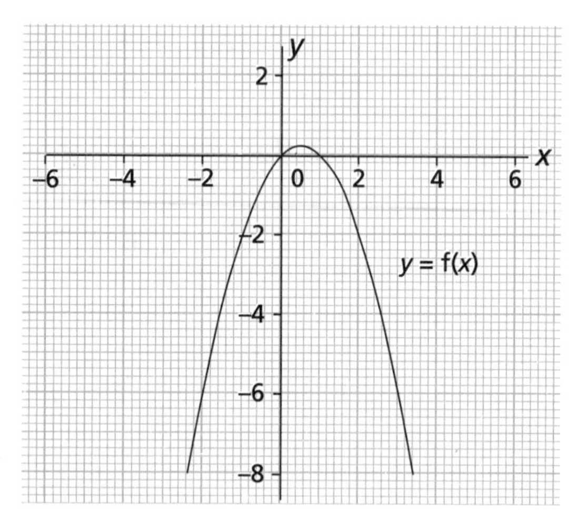

It is very useful to be able to sketch the graph of a function by relating it to a function whose graph you already know.

To do this you need to understand what effect changes to a function will have on the shape of the graph.

Translations in the y-direction

Adding a number to or subtracting a number from a function has the effect of moving the curve up or down the y-axis.

E.g. Sketch the graph of $y = f(x) - 8$, where $f(x) = x - x^2$.

We can call this new function $f'(x) = f(x) - 8$.

To calculate values of y for the graph $y = f'(x)$ you simply subtract 8 from the y values for the graph $y = f(x)$ so the curve moves down the Cartesian plane 8 places.

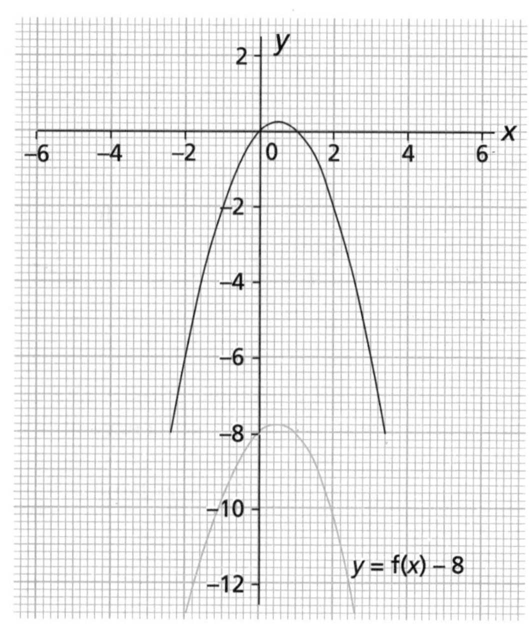

Translations in the x-direction

Adding a number to or subtracting a number from x before you substitute it into the function has the effect of moving the curve to the left or right.

E.g. Sketch the graph of $y = f(x - 3)$, where $f(x) = x - x^2$.

Call the new function $f'(x) = f(x - 3)$.

You have to look 3 places to the left on the curve $y = f(x)$ to find the value of $f'(x)$.

$f'(0) = f({}^-3)$ etc.

Therefore plotting $y = f'(x)$ has the effect of moving the graph 3 places to the right.

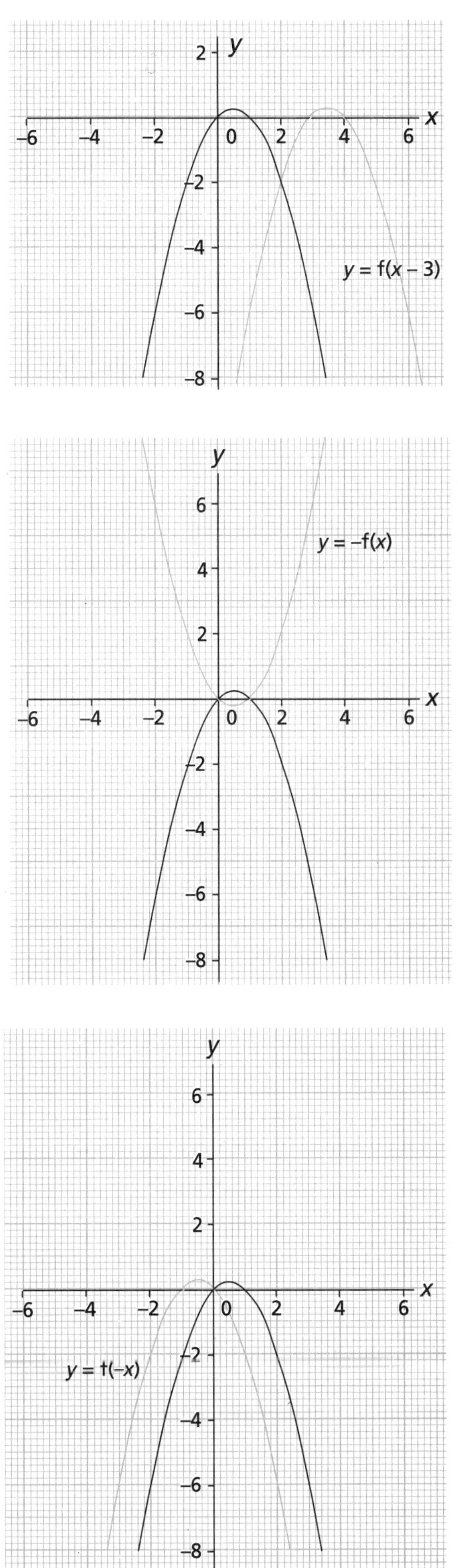

Reflections

Making the function negative has the effect of reflecting the graph in the x-axis.

E.g. Sketch the graph of $y = {}^-f(x)$, where $f(x) = x - x^2$.

x	–2	–1	0	1	2
f(x)	–6	–2	0	0	–2
$^-$f(x)	6	2	0	0	2

Replacing x with ^-x has the effect of reflecting the graph in the y-axis.

E.g. Sketch the graph of $y = f({}^-x)$, where $f(x) = x - x^2$.

x	$^-2$	$^-1$	0	1	2
f(x)	$^-6$	$^-2$	0	0	$^-2$
f(^-x)	$^-2$	0	0	$^-2$	$^-6$

Stretches

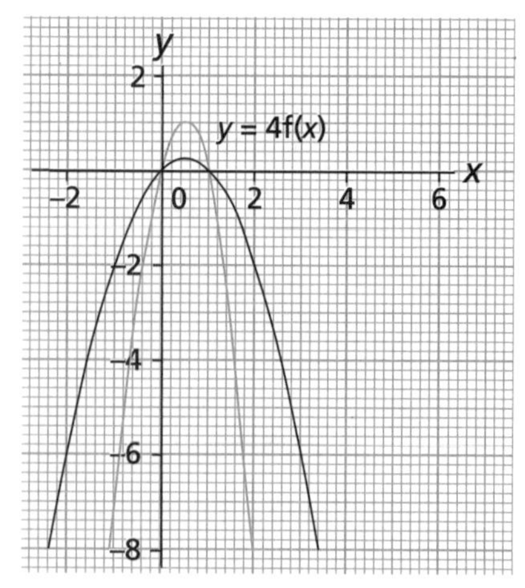

Multiplying a function by a constant has the effect of stretching the graph parallel to the y-axis.

E.g. Sketch the graph of $y = 4f(x)$, where $f(x) = x - x^2$.

Every y value is multiplied by 4 so this has the effect of stretching the graph parallel to the y-axis by a factor of 4.

Note: Points on the x-axis are fixed.

Replacing x with kx has the effect of a stretch parallel to the x-axis but the stretch factor is $1/k$ so if $k > 1$ then the graph gets thinner.

You could describe this is as telescoping $f(x)$ by a factor of k in the x-direction.

E.g. Sketch the graph of $y = f(4x)$, where $f(x) = x - x^2$.

$f(x)$ has roots 0 and 1.

$f(4x) = 4x(1 - 4x)$ has roots 0 and ¼ .

The graph of $f(4x)$ is $\frac{1}{4}$ of the width of $f(x)$.

Note: Points on the y-axis are fixed.

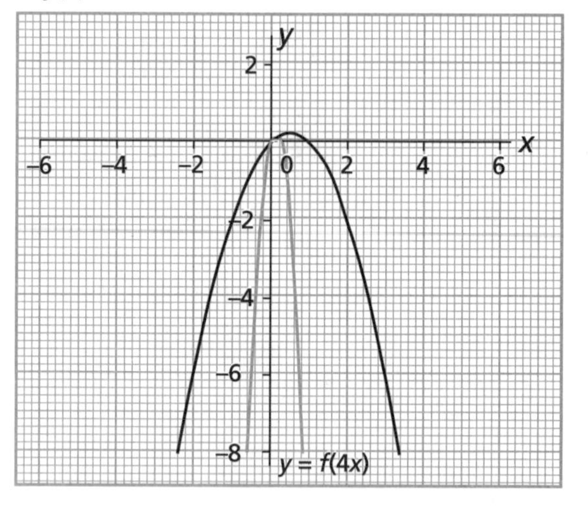

Examiner's tip

- $f(x) + a$ moves the graph a places up (down if a is negative).
- $f(x + a)$ moves the graph a places to the left (right if a is negative).
- $^-f(x)$ reflects the graph in the x-axis.
- $f(^-x)$ reflects the graph in the y-axis.
- $kf(x)$ stretches the graph by a factor of k parallel to the y-axis.
- $f(kx)$ telescopes the graph by a factor of k parallel to the x-axis.

1 Draw the graph of the function $f(x) = x^2 - x - 2$ for $^-3 \le x \le 3$.
Use this to sketch the graphs of the following, and describe how the graph has been transformed in each case.

2 (a) $y = f(x) + 3$
(b) $y = x^2 - x - 3$

3 (a) $y = f(x + 3)$
(b) $y = (x - 2)^2 - (x - 2) - 2$

4 (a) $y = f(^-x)$
(b) $y = {^-f(x)}$

5 (a) $y = 2f(x)$
(b) $y = 4x^2 - 2x - 2$

You can use a combination of these ideas to sketch the graphs of different functions.

6 Sketch the graph of $y = f(x + 1) + 2$.

Reciprocal functions

Knowing the shape of a function $f(x)$ does not tell you the exact shape of the graph of the reciprocal function $\dfrac{1}{f(x)}$ but it does tell you certain characteristics of the graph of $\dfrac{1}{f(x)}$.

Where $f(x)$ is large $\dfrac{1}{f(x)}$ will be small and where $f(x)$ is small $\dfrac{1}{f(x)}$ will be large.

7 (a) Draw the graphs of $y = x$ and $y = \dfrac{1}{x}$ on the same pair of axes.

(b) Draw the graphs of $y = x^2$ and $y = \dfrac{1}{x^2}$ on the same pair of axes.

8 By investigating the graphs of various functions and their reciprocals, answer the following questions:

(a) What do you notice about the graph of $\dfrac{1}{x^a}$ when a is even and when a is odd?

(b) What happens to the graph of $\dfrac{1}{f(x)}$ at points where $f(x) = 1$?

(c) What happens to the graph of $\dfrac{1}{f(x)}$ at points where $f(x) = 0$?

7.10 Growth and decay rates

A quantity which grows by being multiplied by the same value at regular intervals is described as growing **exponentially**.

E.g. A young tree grows 20% in height each year. If the tree is 1 m tall when it is planted how tall will it be after 4 years? Draw a graph to show its growth over these 4 years.

The height increases by 20% so height at end of year = $1{\cdot}20 \times$ height at start of year. The height is given by repeatedly multiplying by 1·2. After n years the height is $1 \times 1{\cdot}2^n$ m.

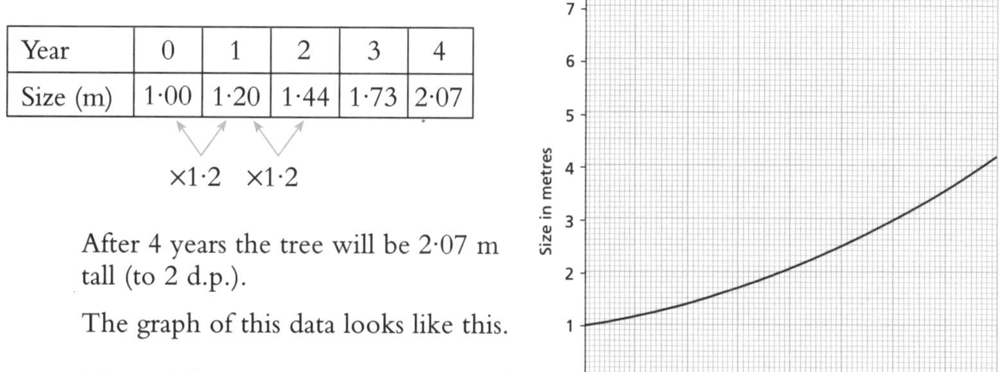

Year	0	1	2	3	4
Size (m)	1·00	1·20	1·44	1·73	2·07

×1·2 ×1·2

After 4 years the tree will be 2·07 m tall (to 2 d.p.).

The graph of this data looks like this.

Note: The curve gets progressively steeper.

1 A microscopic organism reproduces itself by splitting into two at the end of each minute. Assuming that you start with only one organism complete a table of the number of micro-organisms at the end of each minute over a period of 15 minutes.

2 When a child was born her grandparents invested £100 in an account that guaranteed to pay a fixed rate of 12% per annum (per year). She is to be given the contents of the account when she is 18.
(a) Draw a table of the results to show how the account grows over the 18 years.
(b) Draw a graph to illustrate these results.

3 One litre of a salt solution contains 25 grams of salt. 30% of the solution is tipped away and replaced with water. This process is repeated several times.
(a) Draw a table to show the amount of salt (to 2 d.p.) left in the solution as the process is repeated 10 times.
(b) Draw a graph of your results.

Chapter 8
Properties of shape

8.1 Triangles

Constructing triangles

To draw any triangle given three sides.

E.g. To draw a triangle with sides length 9 cm, 8 cm and 6 cm:

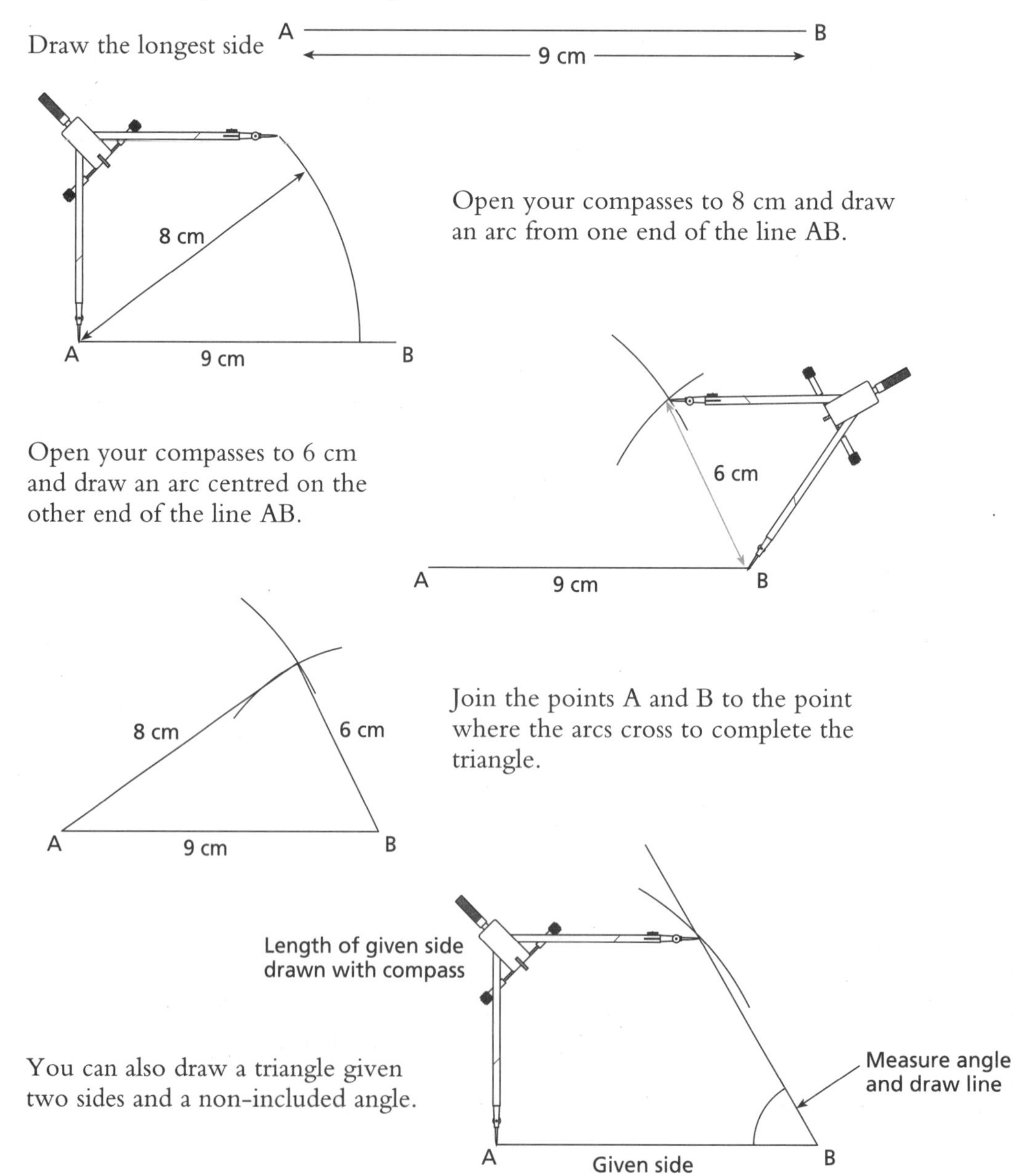

Draw the longest side

Open your compasses to 8 cm and draw an arc from one end of the line AB.

Open your compasses to 6 cm and draw an arc centred on the other end of the line AB.

Join the points A and B to the point where the arcs cross to complete the triangle.

You can also draw a triangle given two sides and a non-included angle.

1 Construct a triangle with sides 10 cm, 7 cm, and 9 cm.

2 Construct a triangle with sides AB length 8 cm, BC length 7 cm and included angle $A\hat{B}C$ of 60°.

3 A regular tetrahedron is a solid triangular-based pyramid where all faces are equilateral triangles.

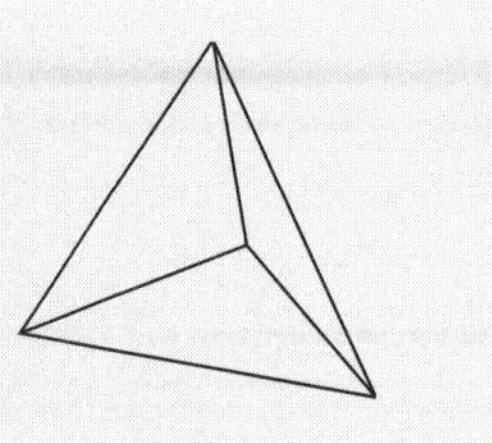

(a) Construct a net of a regular tetrahedron with sides of length 4 cm.

Angles in triangles

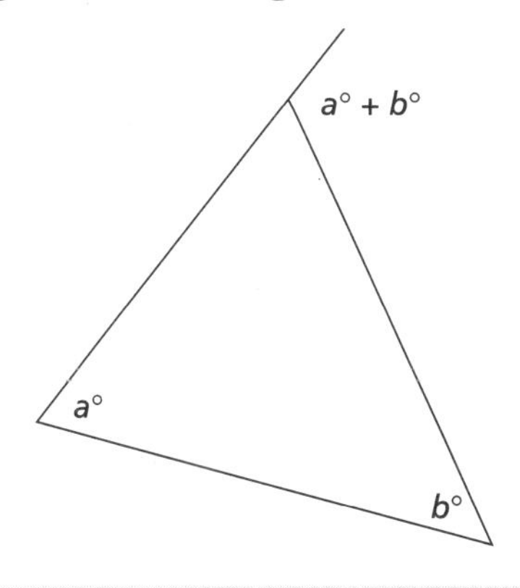

The external angle of a triangle = the sum of the opposite internal angles.

Examiner's tip

Angles which make a straight line (supplementary angles) = 180°.

4 Calculate the external angles x, y and z in the following triangle.

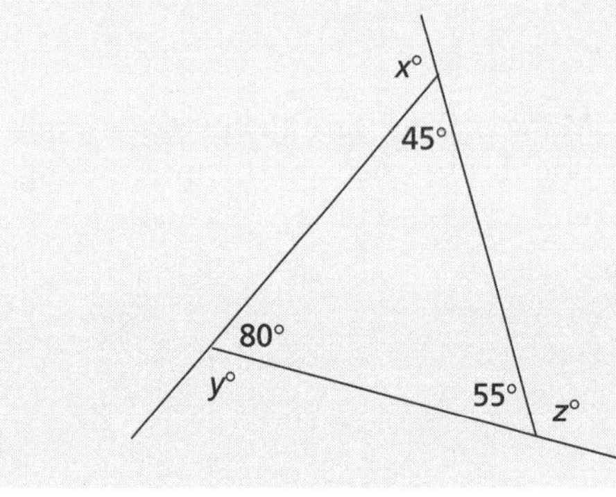

8.2 Regular polygons

A regular polygon is a geometric shape with all its sides and all its angles equal. Here is a list of the first ten regular polygons. You should know the names of the ones which are most frequently used. These have been highlighted in bold type for you.

No. of sides	Name
3	**equilateral triangle**
4	**square**
5	**pentagon**
6	**hexagon**
7	heptagon or septagon
8	**octagon**
9	nonagon
10	decagon
11	undecagon
12	dodecagon

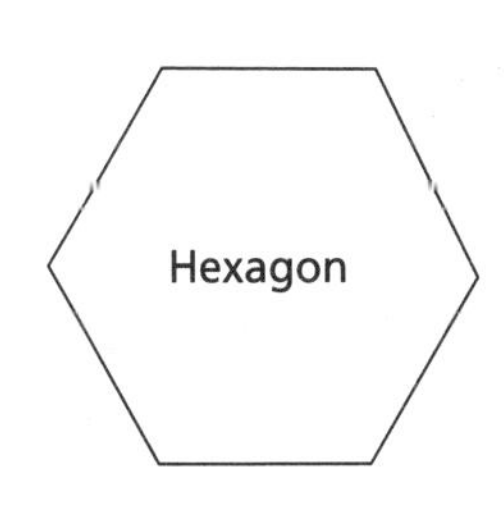

There are three types of angle in a regular polygon.

Note: The angle at the centre is the same size as the external angle.

The **angle at the centre** is found by dividing 360° by the number of sides.
The **interior** or **internal angle** is 180° minus the angle at the centre.
The **exterior** or **external angle** is supplementary to the interior angle (they add to 180°) and equal to the angle at the centre.

Looking at the hexagon above you can see that OAB is an isosceles triangle so the angles OAB and OBA are equal. Together they add to 180° minus the angle at the centre (angle sum of a triangle is 180°). But each of these angles is half of an internal angle so internal angle = 180° – angle at the centre.

You can see from the diagram that the exterior and interior angles add up to 180° because they are on a straight line.

Note: Angles which add up to 180° are called supplementary angles.

1 (a) Mark and measure the exterior angle of each of the following polygons.
(b) Use this to calculate the interior angle of each polygon.

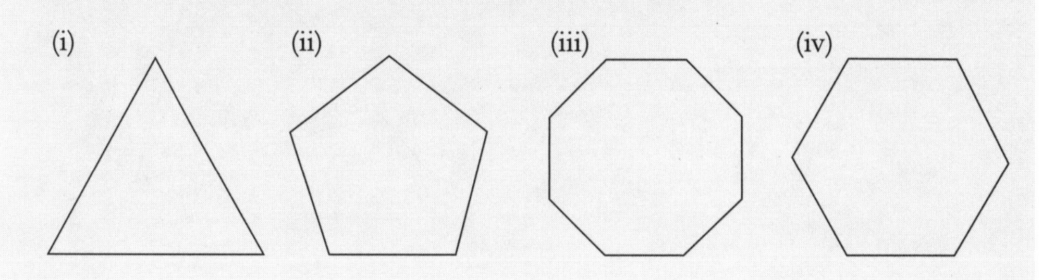

There is another way to find the internal angle: by first finding the sum (total) of all the internal angles.

Divide the polygon into the smallest number of triangles possible. For a polygon with n sides this gives $n - 2$ triangles. The sum of the angles in each triangle is 180°. So the sum of the internal angles is given by 180° $(n - 2)$.

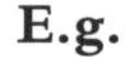

E.g.

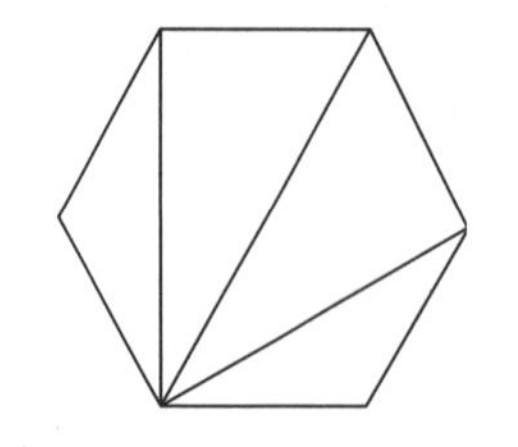

In this case there are 4 triangles. Hence the sum of the internal angles is 4 × 180° = 720°.
Alternatively, using the formula $S = 180° (n - 2)$ for the sum of the internal angles, $S = 180° (6 - 2) = 180° \times 4 = 720°$.
Dividing by 6 internal angles gives you 120° for each internal angle.

You can use these angle properties to work out how many sides a polygon has given one of its angles.

E.g. If the angle at the centre of a regular polygon is 15° calculate how many sides the polygon has.
Angle at the centre = 360° ÷ n, where n is the number of sides.
So n = 360° ÷ angle at the centre = 360° ÷ 15° = 24
Hence the figure has 24 sides.

2 (a) Calculate the number of sides of a polygon with an external angle of 18°.
(b) Calculate the sum of the internal angles of this polygon.

Drawing polygons

To draw a regular polygon the first thing you need to do is to work out the size of each angle at the centre of the polygon.

E.g. Draw a regular octagon (8 sides).
Divide 360° by the number of sides: 360° ÷ 8 = 45°
Mark off each 45° around the circle using a protractor or angle measurer.
Join up the points you have marked.

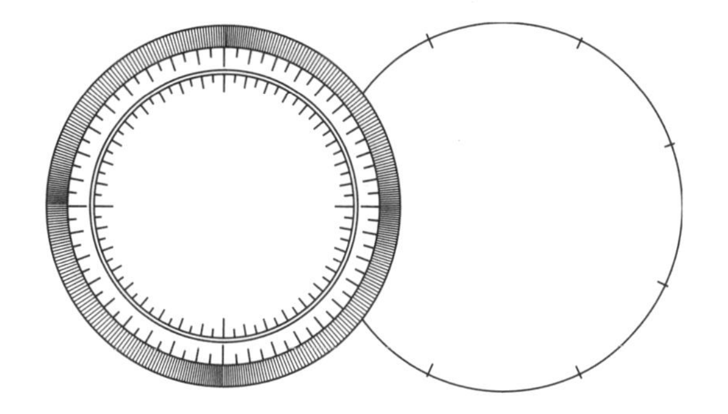

3 To construct a regular octagon using logo you must turn through the external angle. Calculate the external angle of an octagon.

8.3 Pythagoras' theorem

Pythagoras' theorem states that if a square is drawn on the longest side of a right-angled triangle (the **hypotenuse**), its area will be equal to the sum or total of the areas of the squares drawn on the other two sides.

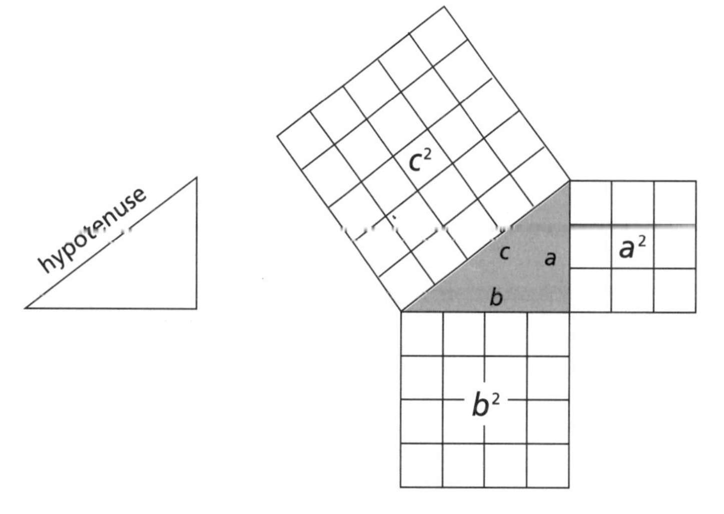

Examiner's tip

This formula is given in the information at the front of your exam paper.

Note: The square on the hypotenuse is equal to the sum of the squares on the other two sides, i.e. $a^2 + b^2 = c^2$.

If you call the hypotenuse c and the other sides a and b Pythagoras' theorem can be expressed as

$$c^2 = a^2 + b^2$$

There are two ways in which this information can be used:

1. Given any two sides of a right-angled triangle you can use the rule to find the third.
2. Given all three sides of a triangle you can check whether it is right-angled.

E.g. Find the missing side in the following right-angled triangle.

$a^2 + b^2 = c^2$
$3^2 + 4^2 = c^2$
$9 + 16 = c^2$
$25 = c^2$
$\sqrt{25} = c$
$5 \text{ m} = c$

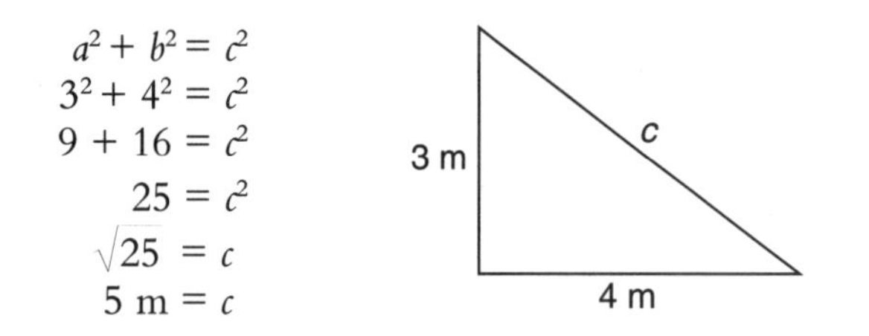

Note: Remember to include the correct units on the length of the missing side, e.g. m.

Examiner's tip

The (3, 4, 5) triangle often appears on exam papers – look out for it.

The (3, 4, 5) triangle is the smallest right-angled triangle with whole number sides. Any triangle with sides in the ratio 3 : 4 : 5 is called a (3, 4, 5) triangle e.g. (6, 8, 10) and (15, 20, 25). Any set of whole numbers which gives the sides of a right-angled triangle is called a **Pythagorean triple**. (5, 12, 13) and (8, 15, 17) are two other examples.

When you are calculating one of the shorter sides and not the hypotenuse the formula needs to be rearranged.

E.g. Find the length of side a in this triangle.

Rearranging the formula gives
$a^2 = c^2 - b^2$

Putting in the values of c and b gives
$a^2 = 7^2 - 5^2$
$a^2 = 49 - 25$
$a^2 = 24$
$a = \sqrt{24}$
$a = 4{\cdot}90$ (to 2 d.p.)

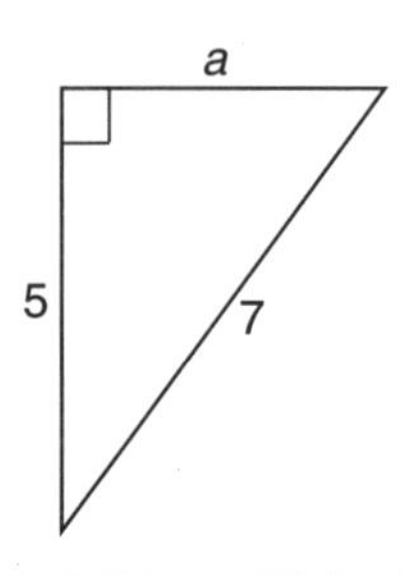

1 Calculate the length of the missing side in each of these triangles:

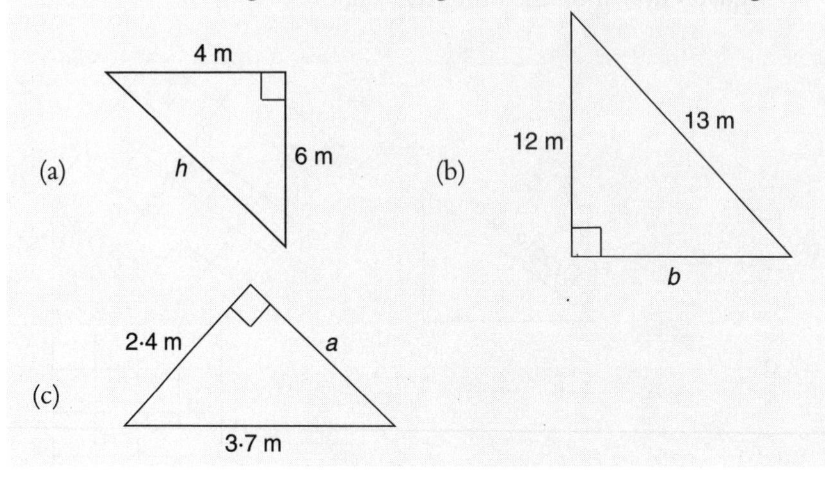

2 Look carefully at the following diagram. How many triangles in the 3, 4, 5 family can you find?

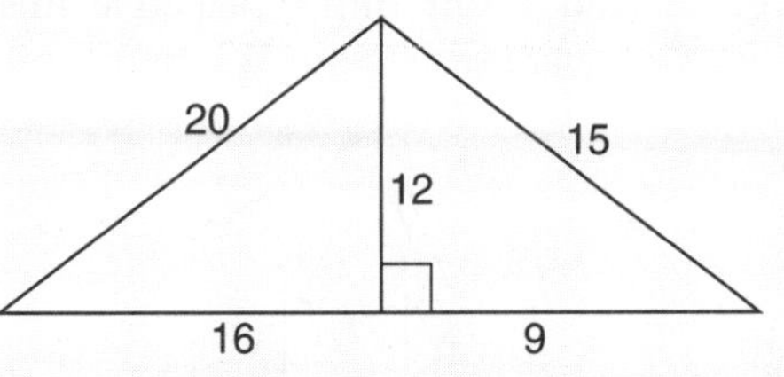

Examiner's tip

Diagrams often help.

3 A ladder 5 m long is placed against a vertical wall. The foot of the ladder is 2·5 m horizontally from the bottom of the wall. How high up the wall will the ladder reach?

4 Use Pythagoras' theorem to find out which of the following triangles are right-angled. (They have not been accurately drawn.)

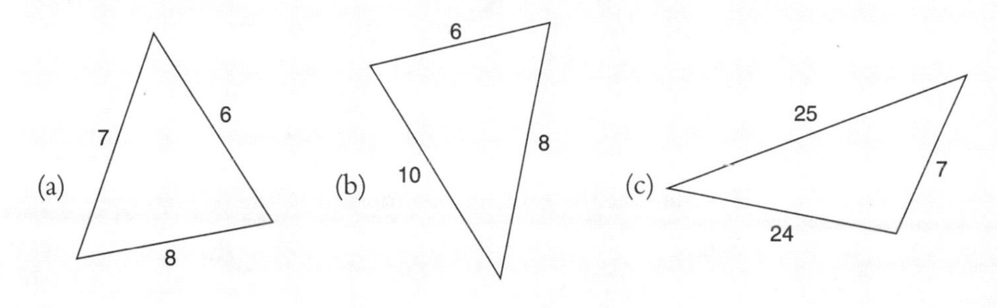

Applying Pythagoras' theorem

Pythagoras' theorem can be used to calculate the length of a vector or the distance between two points expressed as coordinates.

E.g. Calculate the distance between the points (2, 3) and (7, 6).

Examiner's tip

Draw a sketch or diagram if it helps.

The distance between the x values is $7 - 2 = 5$ and the distance between the y values is $6 - 3 = 3$.

Using Pythagoras, $h^2 = x^2 + y^2$

$h^2 = 5^2 + 3^2$

$h^2 = 25 + 9 = 34$

$h = \sqrt{34}$

$h = 5{\cdot}83$ (to 2 d.p.)

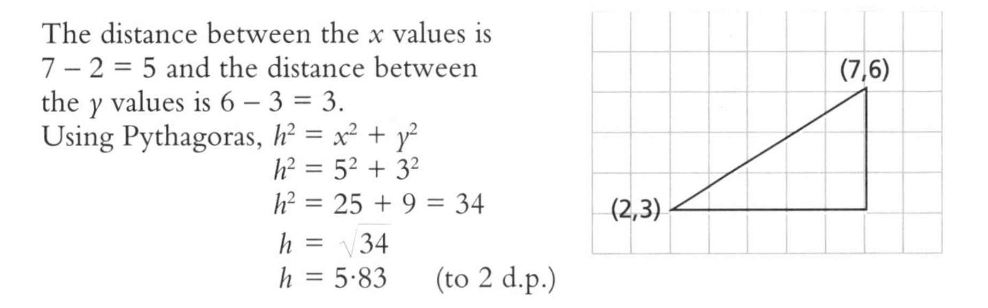

5 Calculate the distance of the point (6, 8) from the origin (0, 0).

6 A ski lift takes skiers from the top of Mount Windsor, which is 2500 m high, to the top of Mount Henry, which is 3200 m high. The horizontal distance between the two peaks is 4 km. Calculate the length of the cable between the peaks.

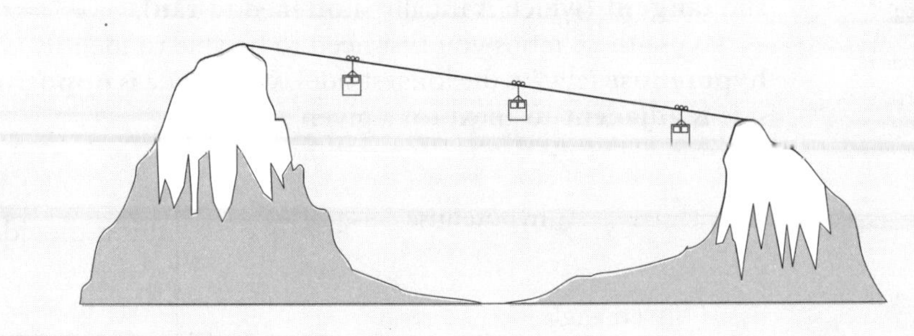

To find the shorter sides using Pythagoras' theorem

E.g. A ladder 8 m long is placed against a wall 3 m from its base. Calculate the height reached by the ladder.

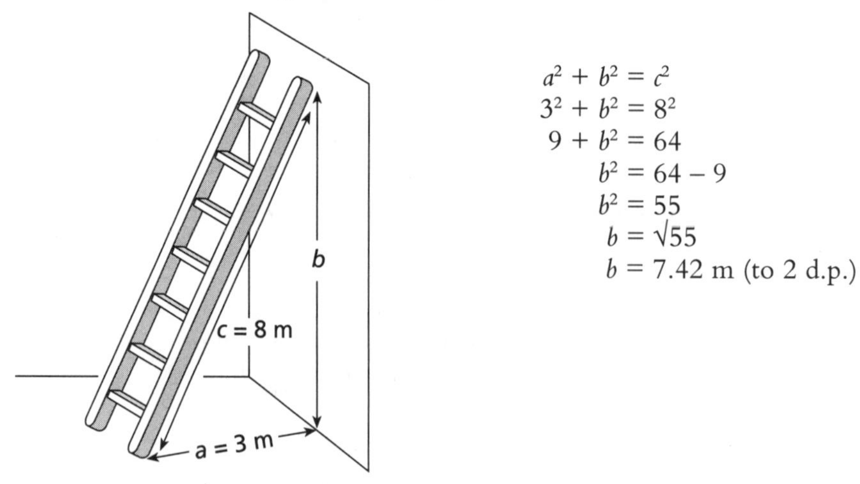

$a^2 + b^2 = c^2$
$3^2 + b^2 = 8^2$
$9 + b^2 = 64$
$b^2 = 64 - 9$
$b^2 = 55$
$b = \sqrt{55}$
$b = 7.42$ m (to 2 d.p.)

Note: You can also do this by arranging the formula first, i.e. $a^2 = c^2 - b^2$

7 Calculate the missing side in each of the following triangles:

(a) (b)

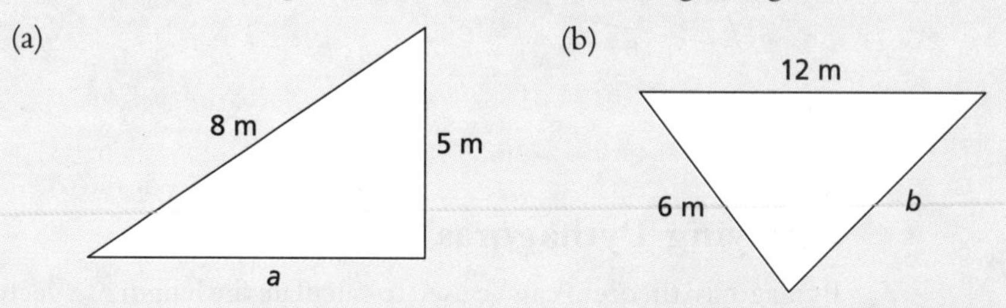

8 The diagonal of a gate is 4.5 m long. If the gate is 4 m wide, what is its height?

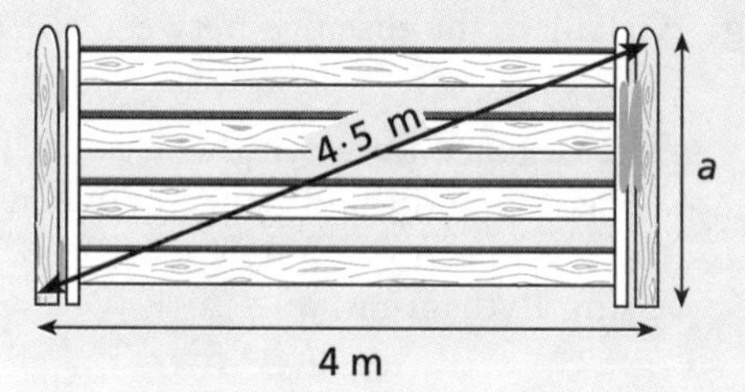

8.4 Sin, cos and tan

Examiner's tip

Make sure your calculator is working in degrees (deg) not (rad) or (gra). You will need to change the mode if it is not in degrees.

In a right-angled triangle the sides and angles are related by three trigonometrical (trig) ratios: **sine** (which is usually shortened to **sin**), **cosine** (which is usually shortened to **cos**) and **tangent** (which is usually shortened to **tan**).

To use these ratios you first need to be able to identify which side of a triangle is the **hypotenuse** (always the longest side), which side is **opposite** to a given angle and which side is **adjacent** to (next to) a given angle.

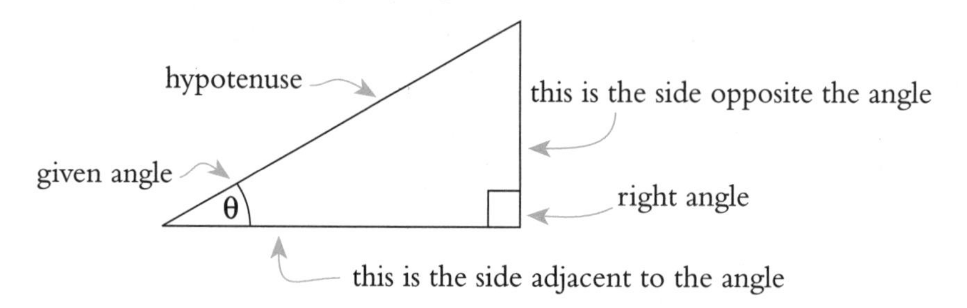

1 Write down the hypotenuse, opposite and adjacent sides to the angle θ (theta) in each of the following triangles:

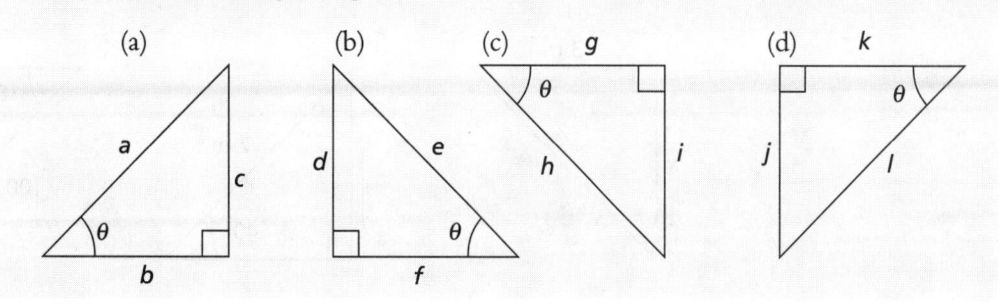

The trig ratios relate an angle θ to the hypotenuse, opposite and adjacent sides in the following ways:

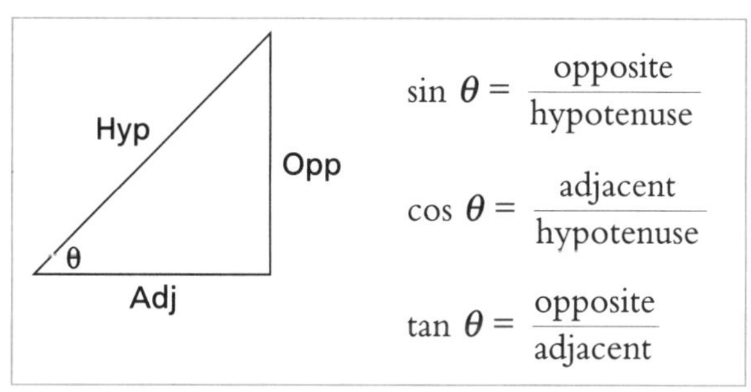

Examiner's tip

These formulae and the triangle are given on the formula sheet at the front of your exam paper.

It is useful to learn these formulae (although most examination boards give them to you). There are several mnemonics (memory aids) which can help you to remember them. Here is an example:

S O H C A H T O A

Sin = Opp/Hyp Cos = Adj / Hyp Tan = Opp/Adj

You may have been taught the ratios in the following form:

Examiner's tip

These formulae are also given.

hypotenuse × sin θ = opposite side	(hyp × sin θ = opp)
hypotenuse × cos θ = adjacent side	(hyp × cos θ = adj)
adjacent × tan θ = opposite side	(adj × tan θ = opp)

Finding missing sides

First you need to decide which ratio to use. Look at which two sides are involved in the question.

E.g. Find the length to 2 d.p. of side x in this triangle.

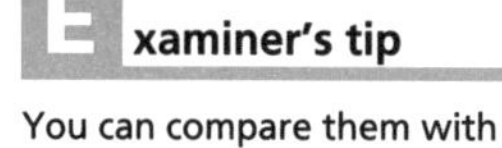

Examiner's tip

You can compare them with the triangle and formulae given on the formulae sheet.

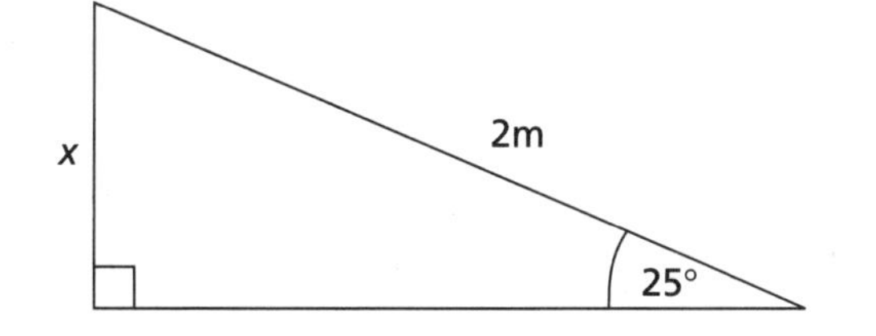

You have been given an angle and the *hypotenuse* and asked to find the side *opposite* the angle. The ratio which links angle, hypotenuse and opposite is *sin*.

Examiner's tip

Always show all your working out.

Choose the correct formula from the formulae sheet,

opposite = hypotenuse × sin

$x = 2 \times \sin 25°$

$= 2 \times 0{\cdot}422618261$

$= 0{\cdot}845236523$

$x = 0{\cdot}85$ m (to 2 d.p.)

2 Use sin, cos or tan to find the missing side x in each of the following triangles. (Give your answer to 2 d.p.)

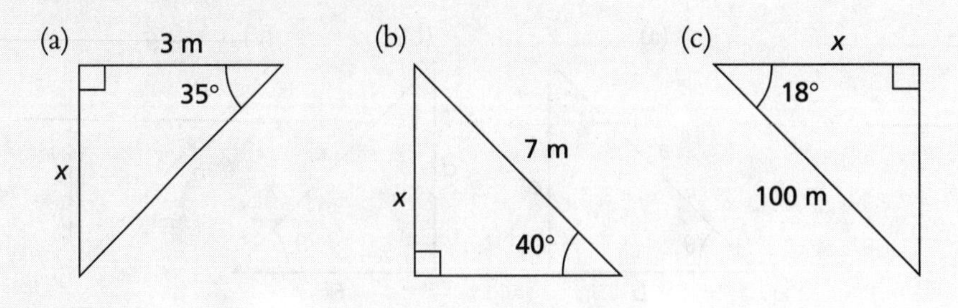

Note: Sometimes you will be asked to find the side which appears on the bottom of a formula. Then you have to rearrange the formula.

3 Find the side marked x in each of the following triangles. (Give your answer to 2 d.p.)

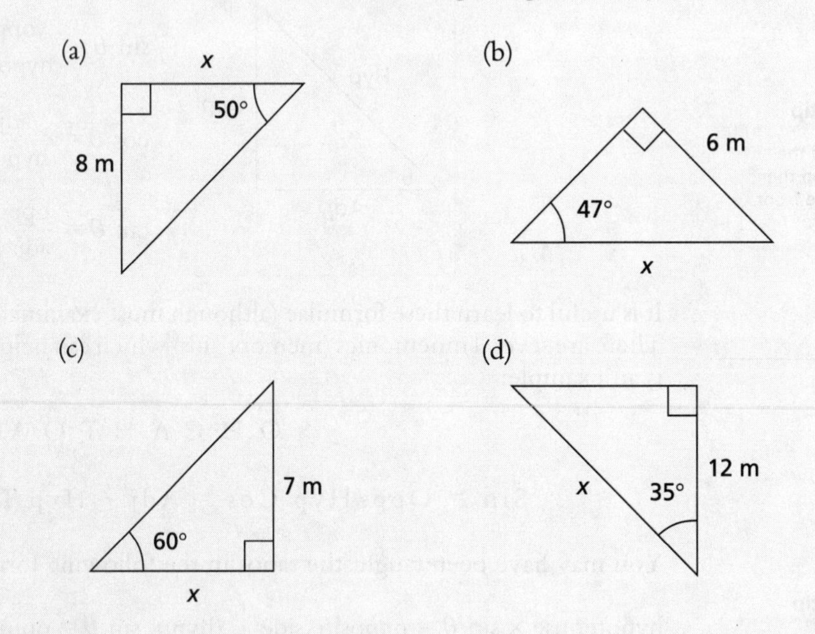

Examiner's tip

If you know two sides you can use Pythagoras' theorem to find the third side.

4 In the following diagrams the line AB bisects the circle. Calculate the lengths of the missing side, x, in each case.

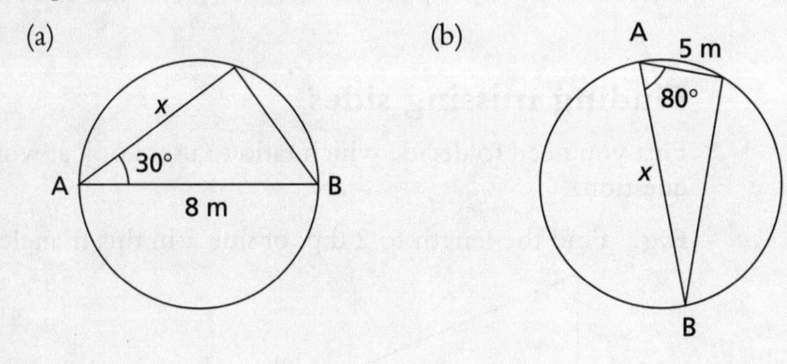

Examiner's tip

The angle of a triangle drawn inside a circle with the hypotenuse equal to the diameter will always be right angled.

Diameter

Finding missing angles

Given two of the sides you can calculate the angles.

E.g. Find the angle θ in this triangle.

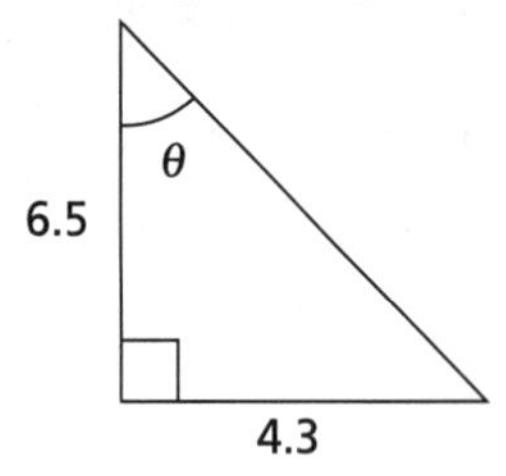

You have been given the *opposite* side and the *adjacent* side to θ so this must be a *tan* problem.

$$\tan\theta = \frac{\text{opposite}}{\text{adjacent}}$$

$$\tan\theta = \frac{4\cdot3}{6\cdot5} = 0\cdot6615$$

Note: To find the angle you have to use the INV (inverse) or 2nd function key on your scientific calculator:

The inverse of tan is written $\tan^{-1}$.

$\tan^{-1} 0\cdot6615 = 33\cdot486°$
$\theta = 33\cdot49°$ (to 2 d.p.)

Examiner's tip

Once you have found the angle θ the remaining angle is 90° – θ.

You already know that one angle is a right angle so now you know two of the angles in the triangle. You can find the third by using the fact that the three angles of a triangle always add to 180°.

5 Find the angle θ in each of the following triangles. (Give your answer to 2 d.p.)

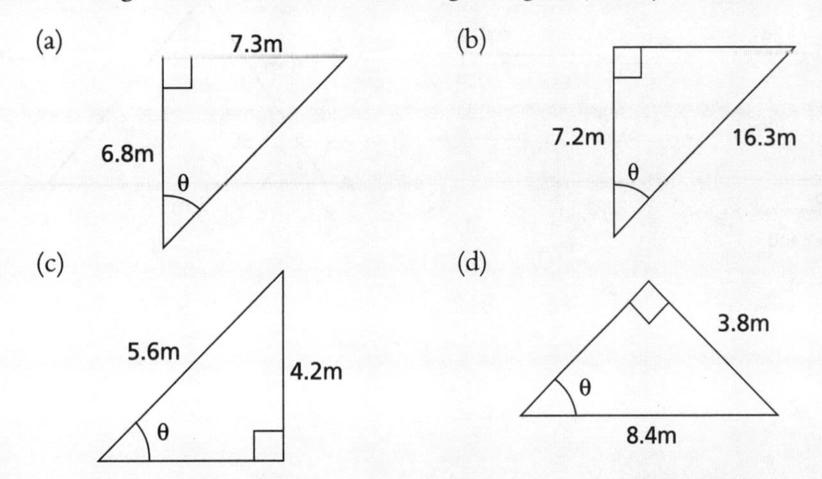

6 These questions are a mixture of the different types covered in this section. Find the side marked x or the angle θ in each case. (Give your answer to 2 d.p.)

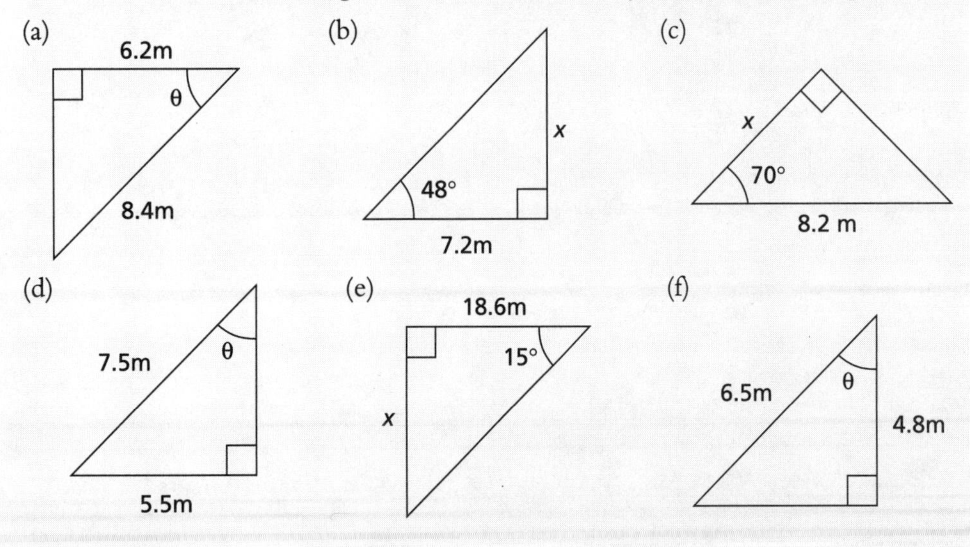

7 A glider flies from X to Y to Z. The journey from X to Y is 16·5 km on a bearing of 040° and the journey from Y to Z is 9·8 km on a bearing of 085°. Answer the following to 2 d.p.

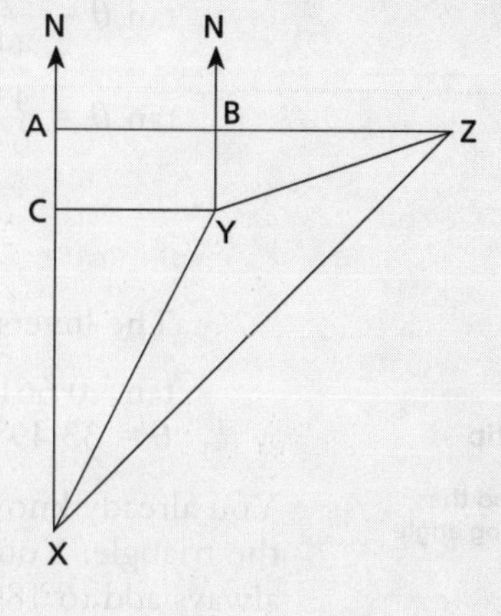

(a) Calculate how far C is north of X.

(b) How far east of C is Y?

(c) How far north of Y is Z?

(d) How far east of Y is Z?

(e) Calculate the distance of the glider from its starting point.

(f) Calculate the bearing from X to Z to the nearest degree.

8 Calculate the area of this triangle.

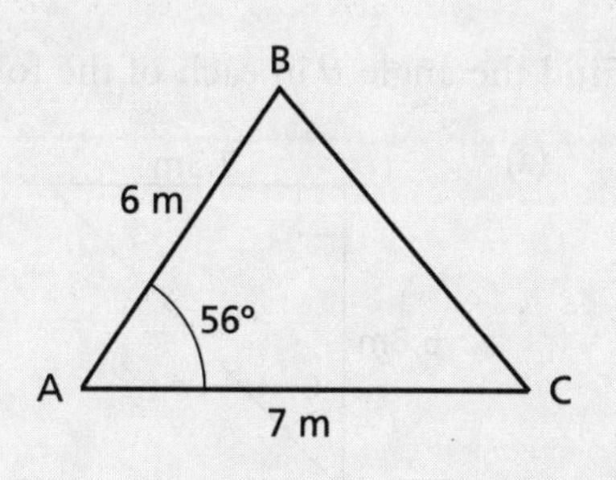

Note: First calculate its height by dropping a perpendicular from B to AC.

Examiner's tip

Use the formulae sheet and check your calculator is working in degrees (deg).

Chapter 9

Position, movement and transformation

9.1 Recognising simple transformations

The simplest reflections are those in the horizontal lines $y = c$, vertical $x = c$ and diagonal lines $y = x$ and $y = {}^{-}x$.

E.g. This diagram shows the lines $x = 1$ and $y = 2$. The figure ABC is shown reflected in each line.

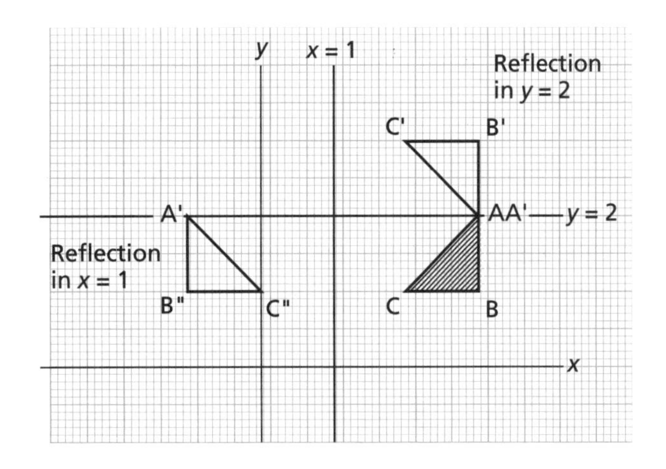

1 (a) Draw the following lines on graph paper:

(i) $x = 2$ (ii) $y = {}^{-}1$ (iii) $x = {}^{-}1$ (iv) $y = 3$

(b) Plot the points A (2,3), B(2,1), C(1,1) and join them to form a triangle.

(c) Reflect the triangle in each of the lines drawn in part (a) labelling them (I) to (IV).

2 (a) Draw the following lines on graph paper:

(i) $y = x$ (ii) $y = {}^{-}x$

Note: In the equation $y = x$ if $x = 2$ then $y = 2$. Try substituting other values into the equations and plot the results.

(b) Plot and then join the following points A(1,1), B(3,1), C (3,0), D(1,0).

(c) Reflect the rectangle ABCD in each line.

Examiner's tip

Horizonal lines → have equations giving only a y value.
Vertical lines ↑ have equations giving only a x value.

9.2 Vector notation and translations

A **vector** is a quantity which has both *magnitude* (size) and *direction*. Vectors can be used to represent displacement, velocity, force, momentum, acceleration.

In a diagram a vector can be represented in two ways:

1. By using capital letters at each end and an arrow showing the direction.

This is the vector $\overrightarrow{AB}$. The arrow above the letters tells you the direction.

A B

The magnitude of the vector is written as $|\overrightarrow{AB}|$ (sometimes called the modulus or mod of AB) or AB (the length of the line).

2. By using a small letter and an arrow showing the direction.

This is the vector **a**.
In handwriting this is written as $\underline{a}$ or $\underset{\sim}{a}$.

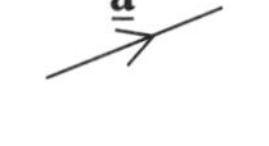

The magnitude (length) of the vector is written as $|\mathbf{a}|$ or $|\underset{\sim}{a}|$ or a.

A vector with magnitude 0 is called the zero vector, written **0**. A vector with magnitude 1 is called a unit vector. Vectors are equal or equivalent if they have the same magnitude and the same direction.

$\underline{a} = \underline{b}$

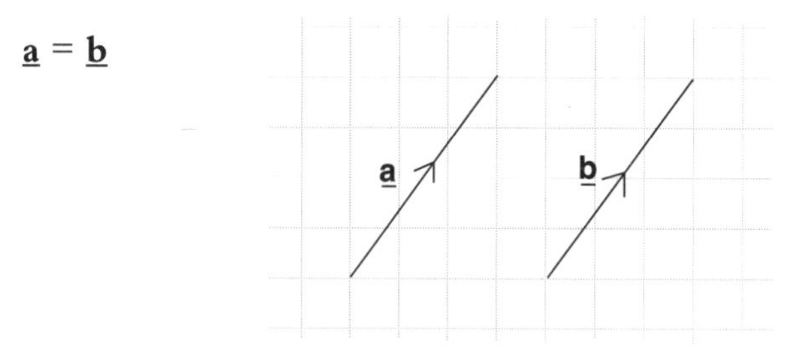

Using vectors to describe movement

A vector can be used to represent a move from one place to another or to describe a translation. The move represented by the vector **a** can be written as a **column vector**

$\mathbf{a} = \begin{bmatrix} x \\ y \end{bmatrix}$ or $\begin{pmatrix} x \\ y \end{pmatrix}$

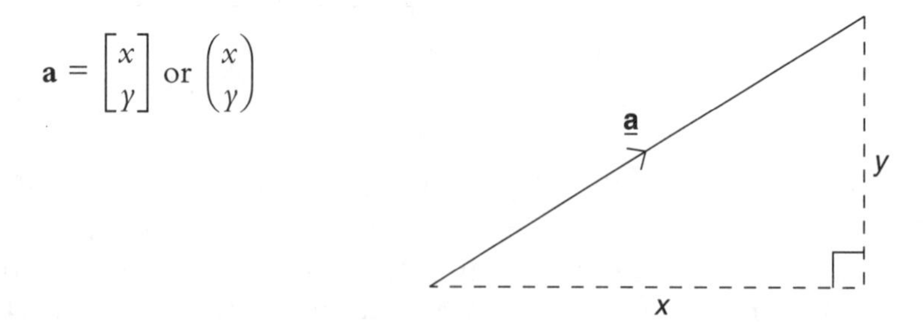

x and y are called the **components** of **a**. The x component gives you the horizontal move and the y component gives you the vertical move.

Imagine a pair of axes with their origin at the start of the vector. The horizontal component is + to the right and – to the left. The vertical component is + up and – down.

1 A knight on a chess board moves either 1 space horizontally and 2 spaces vertically or 2 spaces horizontally and 1 vertically. Write the following moves as column vectors:

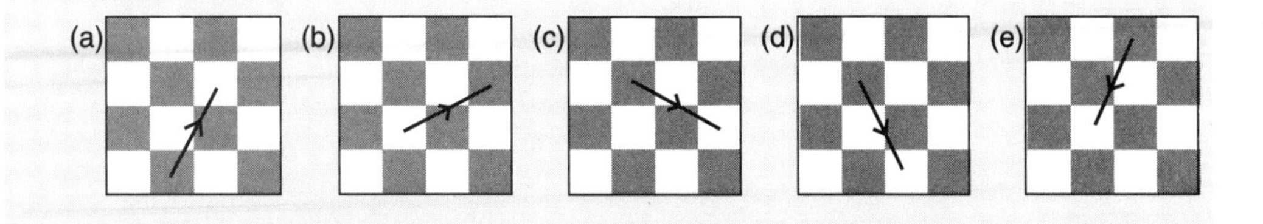

2 Draw the following vectors, remembering to mark the direction:

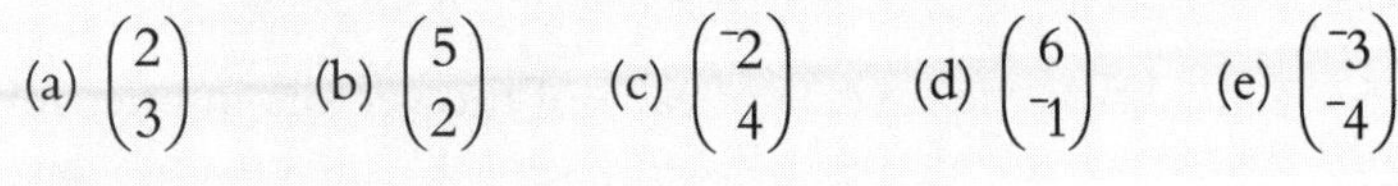

(a) $\begin{pmatrix}2\\3\end{pmatrix}$ (b) $\begin{pmatrix}5\\2\end{pmatrix}$ (c) $\begin{pmatrix}^-2\\4\end{pmatrix}$ (d) $\begin{pmatrix}6\\^-1\end{pmatrix}$ (e) $\begin{pmatrix}^-3\\^-4\end{pmatrix}$

3 In each of the following, write the translation which takes A to A′ as a column vector.

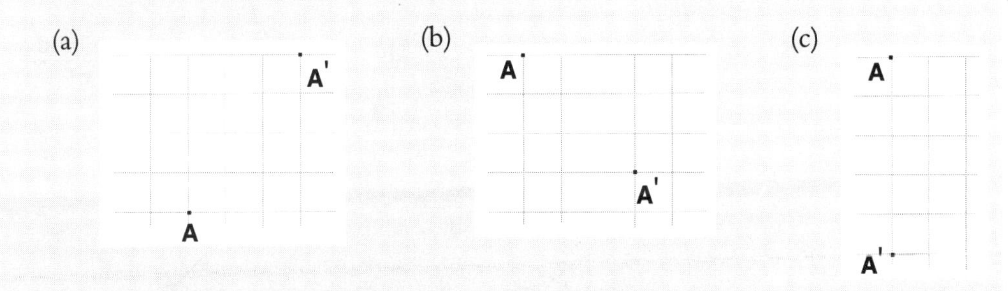

4 Translate the quadrilateral ABCD using the following vectors:

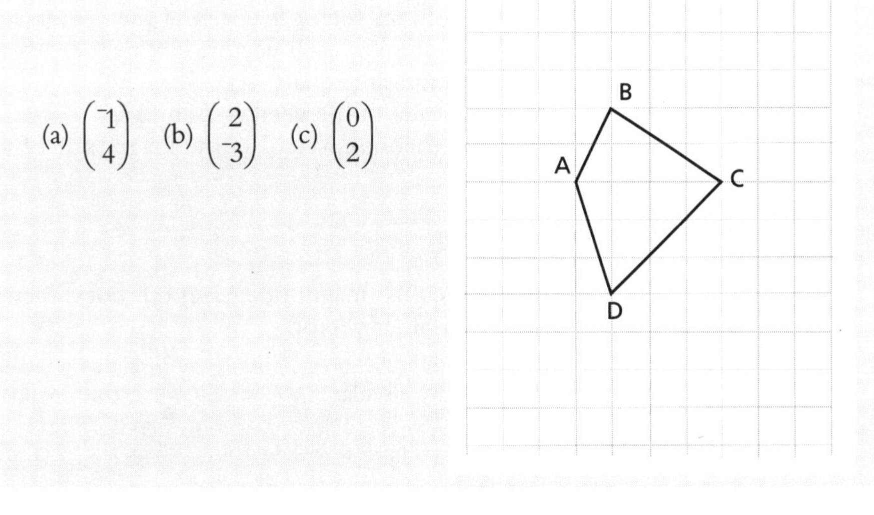

(a) $\begin{pmatrix}^-1\\4\end{pmatrix}$ (b) $\begin{pmatrix}2\\^-3\end{pmatrix}$ (c) $\begin{pmatrix}0\\2\end{pmatrix}$

The **position vector** of a point A (x, y) represents the move from the origin O to A. It can be written like this:

$$\vec{OA} = \begin{pmatrix}x\\y\end{pmatrix}$$

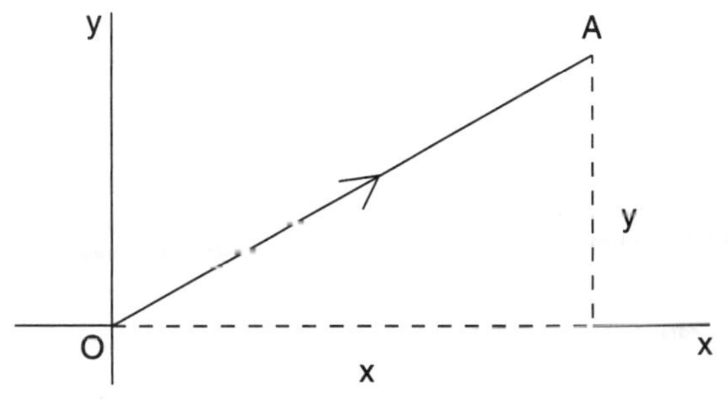

Using Pythagoras' theorem, the magnitude of OA is

$$|\vec{OA}| = \sqrt{x^2 + y^2}$$

Inverse vectors

The **inverse** of a vector is a vector of equal magnitude (size) but in the opposite direction. The inverse of $\vec{AB}$ is $^-\vec{AB}$ or $\vec{BA}$.

The inverse of **a** is ⁻**a**.

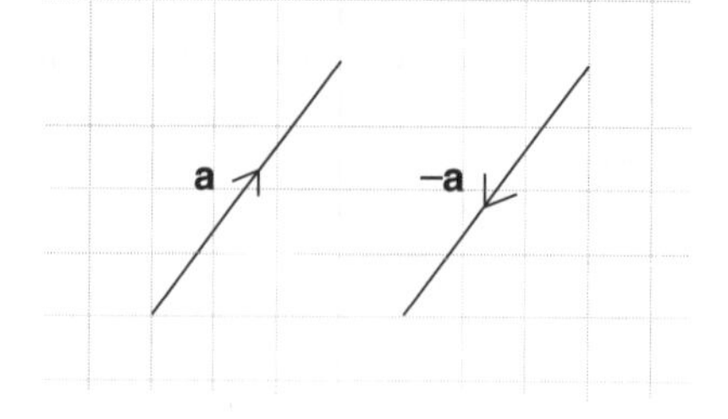

If $\mathbf{a} = \begin{pmatrix} x \\ y \end{pmatrix}$ then $^{-}\mathbf{a} = \begin{pmatrix} ^{-}x \\ ^{-}y \end{pmatrix}$.

5 Write down the inverse of each of the vectors in question 2.

6

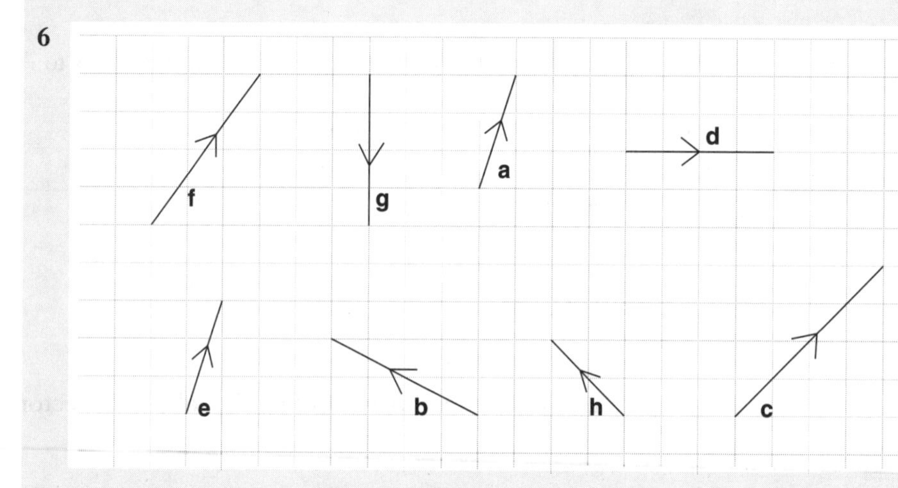

(a) Write down the column vector for each of the vectors **a** to **h**.
(b) Write down the inverse of each vector.
(c) Which pairs of vectors are equal?
(d) What is the magnitude of the vectors **d** and **g**?
(e) Using Pythagoras' theorem, calculate the magnitude of vectors **c** and **f**.

Scalars

A **scalar** is a quantity which has magnitude (size) but not direction. You can multiply a vector by a scalar to get another vector.

If a vector **a** is multiplied by a scalar k we get k**a**.

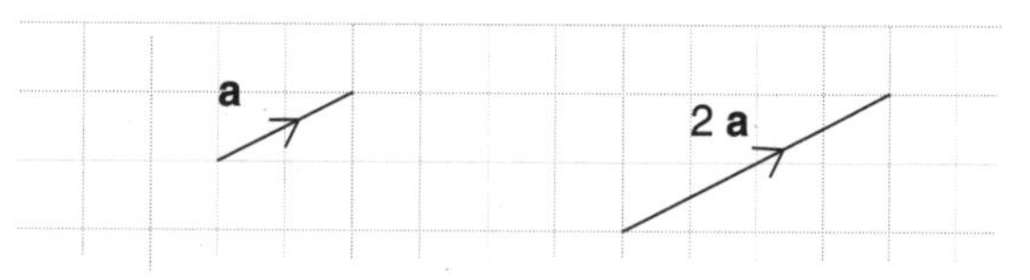

k**a** is parallel to **a**, in the same direction if k is positive and in the opposite direction if k is negative. The length of k**a** is k times the length of **a**.

To multiply a column vector by a scalar you simply multiply each component by the scalar.

$$k\begin{pmatrix} x \\ y \end{pmatrix} = \begin{pmatrix} kx \\ ky \end{pmatrix}$$

Examiner's tip

A vector has magnitude and direction. If you multiply a vector by a scalar the magnitude of the vector changes but the direction stays the same, unless the scalar is negative.

7 Multiply $\begin{pmatrix} 2 \\ 4 \end{pmatrix}$ by each of the following scalars. Write your answers as column vectors.

(a) 3 (b) $\frac{1}{2}$ (c) $^{-}2$ (d) $^{-}\frac{1}{2}$

9.3 Combinations and inverses of transformations

To combine two transformations you perform the first transformation on an object, which gives you an image, and then apply the second transformation to the image.

E.g. Let transformation I be a rotation of 90° anticlockwise about the origin and let transformation II be a reflection in the y-axis. Carry out the combined transformation given by I followed by II on this flag.

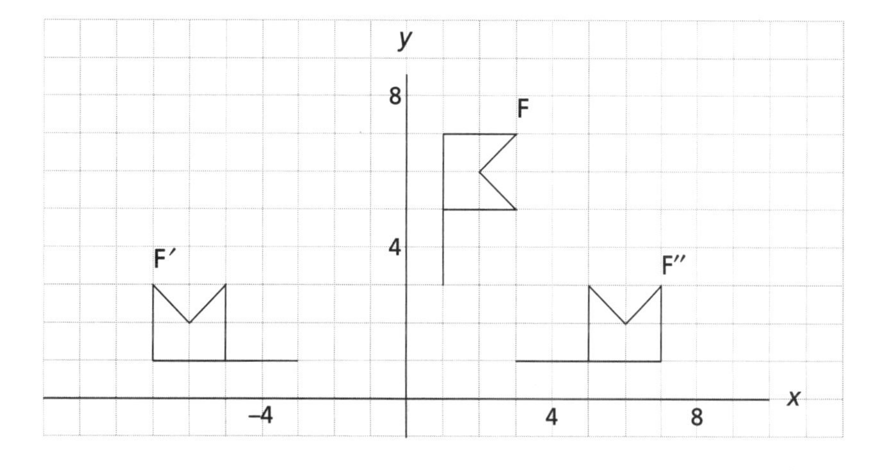

Examiner's tip

The *order* in which you combine two transformations is important. Sometimes combining two transformations in the opposite order would give the same result but often it gives a completely different result.

1 Carry out the transformations in the example above in the opposite order.

Translations

The **combination** of two translations is always another translation.

E.g.
(a) Translate the triangle ABC using the vector $\begin{pmatrix}4\\2\end{pmatrix}$.
Label the result A'B'C'.
(b) Now translate the figure A'B'C' using the vector $\begin{pmatrix}2\\5\end{pmatrix}$.
Label the result A"B"C".
(c) Give a single transformation that will have the same effect as the two carried out in (a) and (b).
The combined transformation is given by $\begin{pmatrix}4\\2\end{pmatrix} + \begin{pmatrix}2\\5\end{pmatrix} = \begin{pmatrix}6\\7\end{pmatrix}$

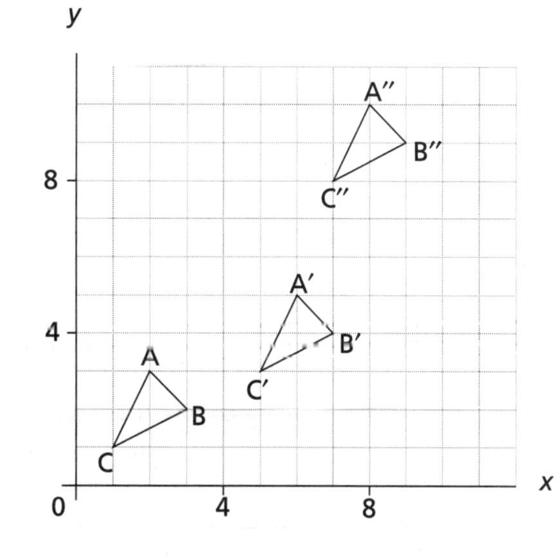

Note: Vectors are used to describe translations.

Note: Shapes which have been translated will be congruent.

(d) Give a single transformation which will transform A"B"C" back onto ABC.
The work you have done on vectors should tell you that to return to the original position you need a vector of equal magnitude in the opposite direction.
The translation $\begin{pmatrix} ^-6 \\ ^-7 \end{pmatrix}$ is the **inverse** of the translation $\begin{pmatrix} 6 \\ 7 \end{pmatrix}$.

2

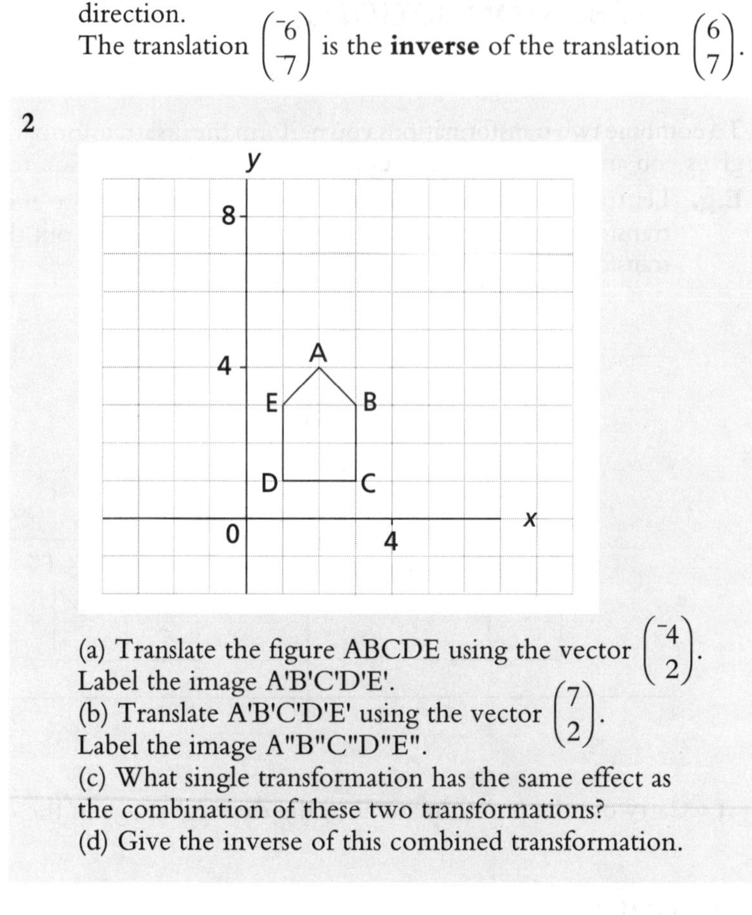

(a) Translate the figure ABCDE using the vector $\begin{pmatrix} ^-4 \\ 2 \end{pmatrix}$.
Label the image A'B'C'D'E'.
(b) Translate A'B'C'D'E' using the vector $\begin{pmatrix} 7 \\ 2 \end{pmatrix}$.
Label the image A"B"C"D"E".
(c) What single transformation has the same effect as the combination of these two transformations?
(d) Give the inverse of this combined transformation.

Rotations

Examiner's tip

If two rotations with the **same centre** are combined then the result is equivalent to a single rotation about the same centre.

Shapes which have been rotated are congruent.

Note: To describe a rotation you need: 1. the centre; 2. the direction of rotation; 3. the distance rotated through.

E.g.

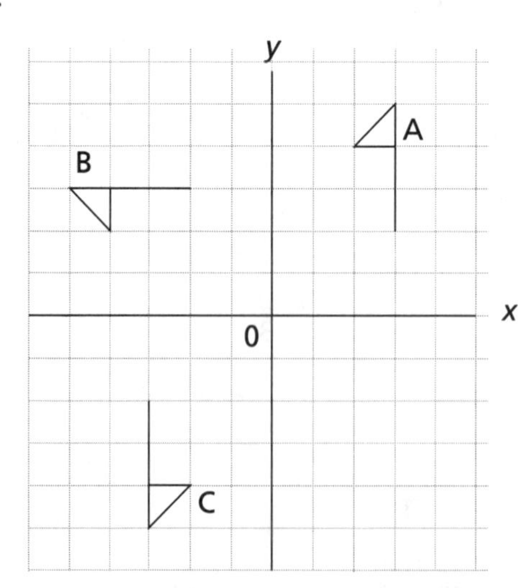

(a) Rotate the flag A $^+90°$ (anticlockwise) about the origin. Label the image B.
(b) Rotate B $^+90°$ about the origin. Label the image C.
(c) What single rotation will transform A onto C?
Since the two rotations performed were both about (0, 0) this will be the centre of rotation for the single equivalent rotation. The angle of rotation is the sum of the two angles turned through: $90° + 90° = 180°$.

(d) What rotation will transform C onto A?
There are two rotations which will take C back onto A.
(i) A rotation in the *opposite* direction to the rotation from A to C but of an equal magnitude about the same centre.
A rotation of $^-180°$ (clockwise) about (0, 0).
(ii) A rotation which *completes* a full circle about the same centre.
A rotation of $^+180°$ (in an anticlockwise direction) about (0, 0).
In this case the angles are both 180° so we can just say the rotation is 180° about (0, 0) without specifying direction.
This gives the **inverse** of the rotation from A to C.

3

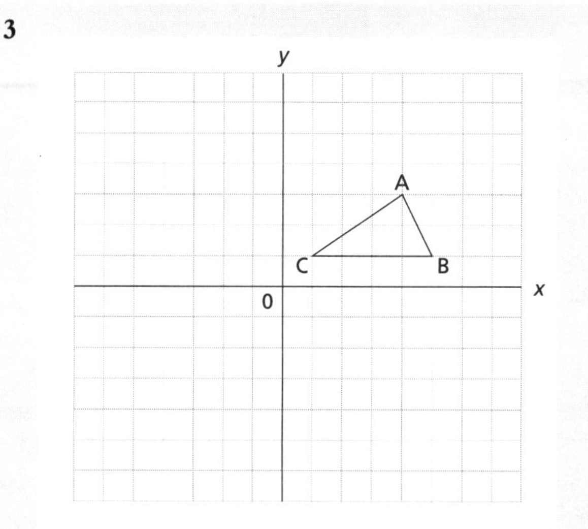

(a) Rotate the triangle ABC $^-90°$ (clockwise) about (0, 0).
Label the image of this rotation A'B'C'.
(b) Rotate A'B'C' 180° about (0, 0).
(c) What single transformation has the same effect as the combination of these two rotations?
(d) Give the two alternatives for the inverse of this combined transformation.

Note: Remember centre, direction, distance.

When two rotations with **different centres** are combined the effect is very different.
If the equivalent transformation is a rotation then it has a different centre from either of the other two. To find this centre you can use the following property of rotation:
If you draw a line joining a point to its image under a rotation then the perpendicular bisector of this line passes through the centre of rotation.

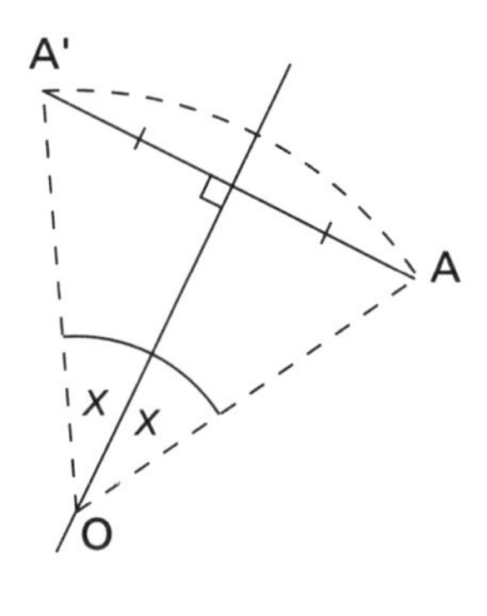

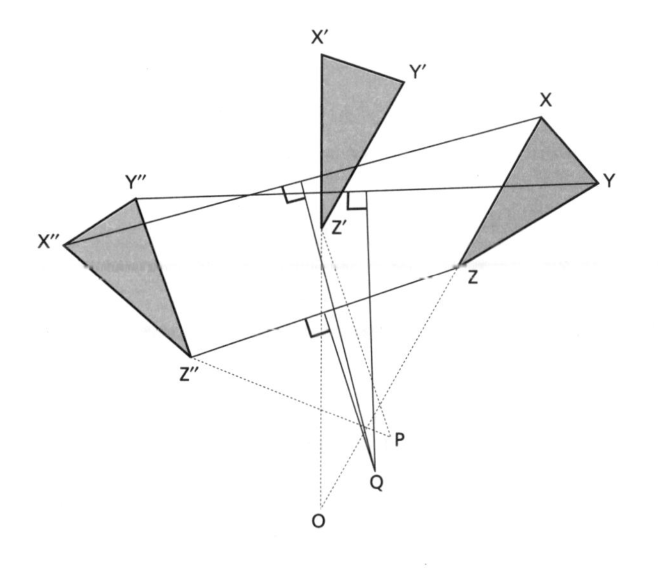

E.g. Rotate triangle XYZ 30° about the point O. Label the image X'Y'Z'. Rotate X'Y'Z' 50° about the point P. Label the image X"Y"Z". Find a single rotation which takes XYZ to X"Y"Z".

Draw lines joining X to X", Y to Y" and Z to Z". Construct the perpendicular bisectors of these lines. Where the perpendicular bisectors meet will give you the centre of the single equivalent rotation, marked Q. To find the angle of rotation measure the angle ZQZ".

4

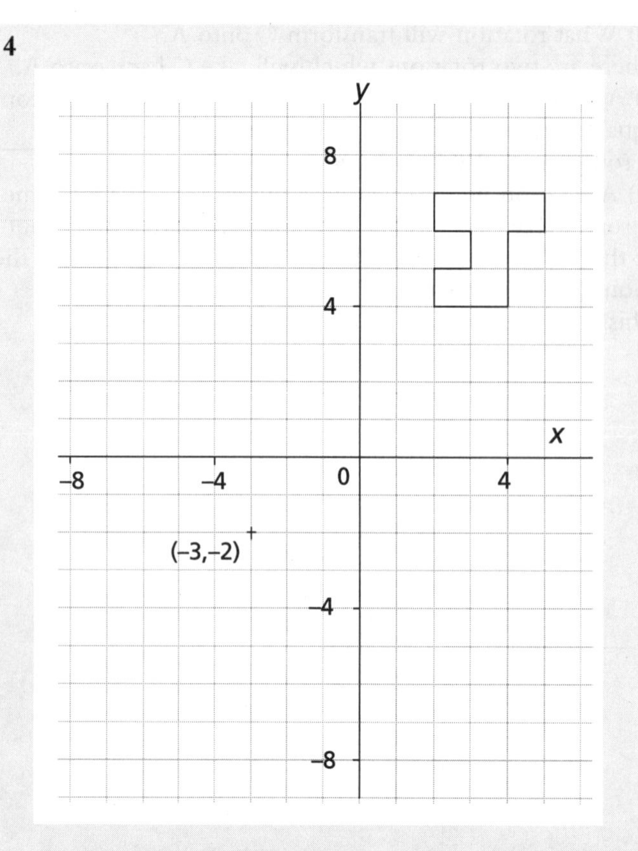

(a) Rotate the letter J 90° about (0, 0).
(b) Rotate the image of J 180° about the point (⁻3, ⁻2).
(c) Find a single transformation equivalent to the combination of these two rotations.
(d) Give the inverse of this transformation.

5 Draw a triangle with vertices D (5, 8), E (7, 5), F (5, 5). By rotating DEF 90° about (2, 2) and then rotating its image ⁻90° about (⁻1, ⁻3), find a single transformation equivalent to the combination of these two rotations.

Examiner's tip

To define a rotation you must give the centre of rotation, the direction of rotation and the distance you have rotated through.

Reflections

Reflecting a figure twice in the same line takes it back onto itself so a reflection is always its own **inverse**.
When you **combine** two reflections, the figure you are reflecting ends up back the right way up so the combination is equivalent to a single translation or a single rotation. The effect of reflecting in two **parallel** lines is a translation. Shapes which have been reflected remain congruent.

E.g.

(a) Reflect the letter F in the line $x = 3$.
Call the image F'.
(b) Reflect F' in the line $x = 0$ (the y-axis).
Call this image F".
(c) What is the effect of combining these reflections?

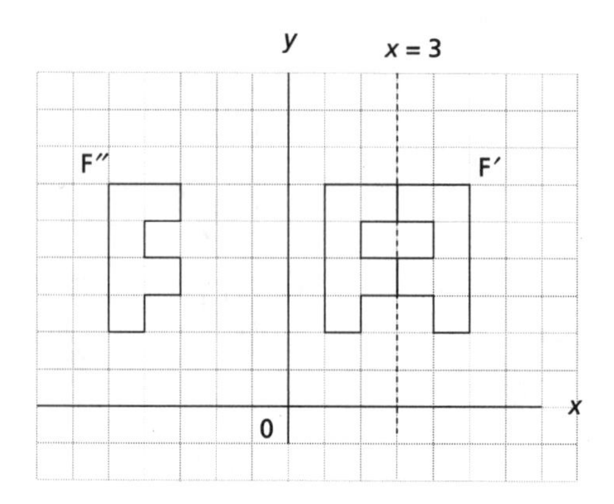

The figure has been translated 6 places to the left.

Describing this translation using a vector gives $\begin{pmatrix} ^{-}6 \\ 0 \end{pmatrix}$.

6 (a) Reflect the letter N in the x-axis ($y = 0$) and label the image N'.

(b) Reflect N' in the line $y = 2$. Label this image N".

(c) What single transformation has the same effect as the combination of these two parallel reflections?

(d) Give the inverse of this combined transformation.

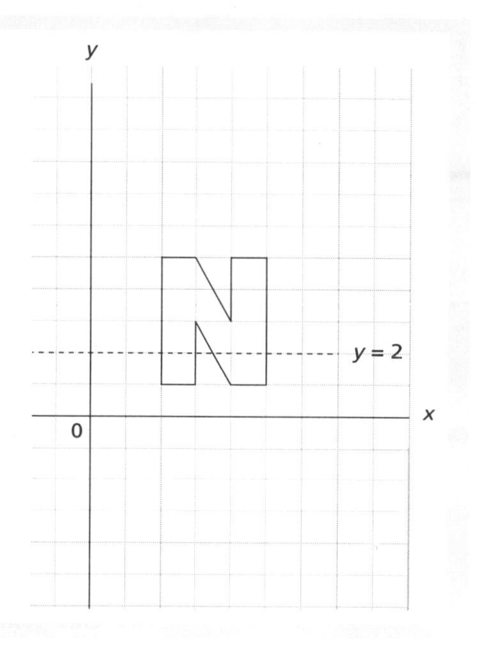

Note: To describe a reflection you must give the equation of the mirror line.

Examiner's tip

To define a reflection you need to give the line of reflection.

When a figure is reflected in lines which are **not parallel** (skew) the combination of the reflections will be equivalent to a single rotation.
The centre of the rotation is the point of intersection of the two lines and the angle of rotation is twice the angle between them.

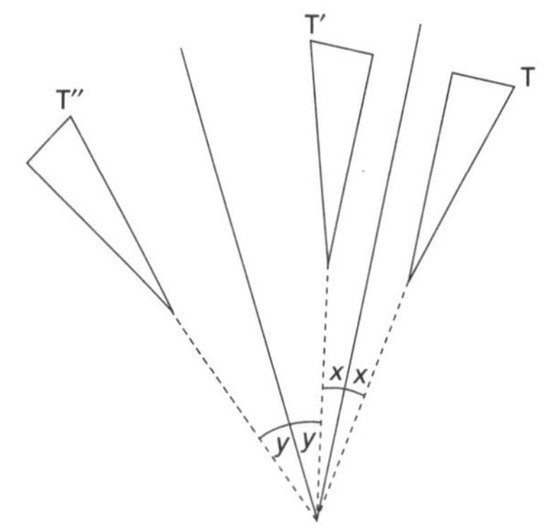

7 (a) Reflect the figure V in the line $x = 0$. Label this reflection V'.

(b) Reflect V' in the line $y = x$. Label this reflection V".

(c) Find a single rotation which would take V to V".

(d) Give the inverse of this rotation.

Enlargements

The effect of **combining** two enlargements is a single enlargement with a scale factor given by multiplying the scale factors of the two individual enlargements together. If the two enlargements have the **same centre** then the centre of enlargement of the combination is the same. Enlargement produces 'similar' figures that are not congruent.

E.g. (a) Enlarge the rectangle ABCD by a factor of $\frac{1}{3}$ using the centre of enlargement O.
Label the image of this enlargement A'B'C'D'.
(b) Enlarge A'B'C'D' by a factor of 2 using the same centre of enlargement.
Label the image of this enlargement A"B"C"D".

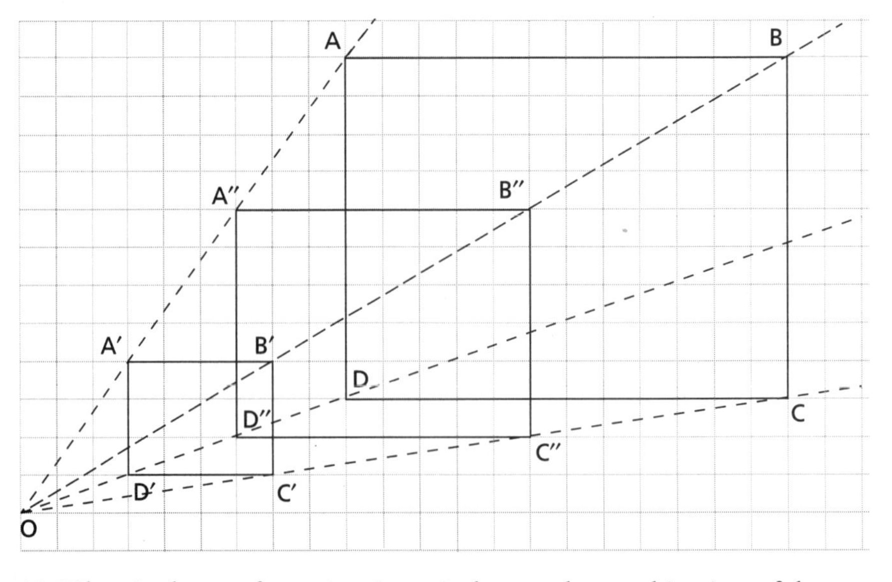

(c) What single transformation is equivalent to the combination of these two enlargements?

The single transformation which takes ABCD onto A"B"C"D" is clearly an enlargement with centre O. The scale factor is given by $\frac{1}{3} \times 2 = \frac{2}{3}$

(d) Give the inverse of the combined transformation.

The **inverse** of an enlargement is another enlargement with the same centre with the inverse (reciprocal) scale factor. In this case, the inverse transformation is an enlargement centre O with scale factor $\frac{3}{2}$.

xaminer's tip

To define an enlargement you need to give the centre of enlargement and the scale factor.

If two enlargements with **different centres** are combined then you can use what you already know about finding a centre of enlargement to find the centre for the single equivalent enlargement.

Finding a centre of enlargement

Join up corresponding points on the object and the image. Extend the lines you have drawn until they meet. The point of intersection is the centre of enlargement. You will need to draw at least two lines. Draw a third line to check the first two are right.

8 Find the centres of the following enlargements:

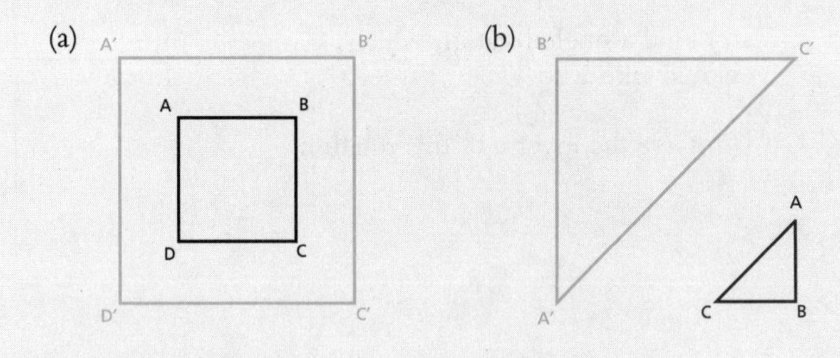

(c) Find the scale factor used for each enlargement.

You may be asked to enlarge a shape to fit into a given space.

Finding a scale factor

If a shape has been enlarged you can find the scale factor by dividing a length on the image (enlarged shape) by the corresponding length on the object (original shape).

$$\text{Scale factor} = \frac{A'B'}{AB}$$

If a centre of enlargement has been used then the scale factor is also given by

$$\text{Scale factor} = \frac{OA'}{OA}$$

Note: If the object and the image are on opposite sides of the centre of enlargement then the scale factor is negative.

E.g. Julie wants to enlarge a photograph so that it will fit into a larger frame.
The photograph is 6 cm wide and 10 cm high.
The frame is 42 cm wide and 60 cm high.

What is the largest factor of enlargement Julie can use if she wants the shape of the photograph to remain the same?

Divide the width of the frame by the width of the photograph.
$42 \div 6 = 7$

So the frame is 7 times the width of the photograph.

Divide the height of the frame by the height of the photograph.
$60 \div 10 = 6$

So the frame is 6 times the height of the photograph.

If Julie used a scale factor of 7 then the photograph would be too tall for the frame so she must use the smaller of the two scale factors, 6. The photograph will fill the height of the frame but not its width.

9 Find the scale factor of enlargement needed to fit each of these photographs into their new frames.

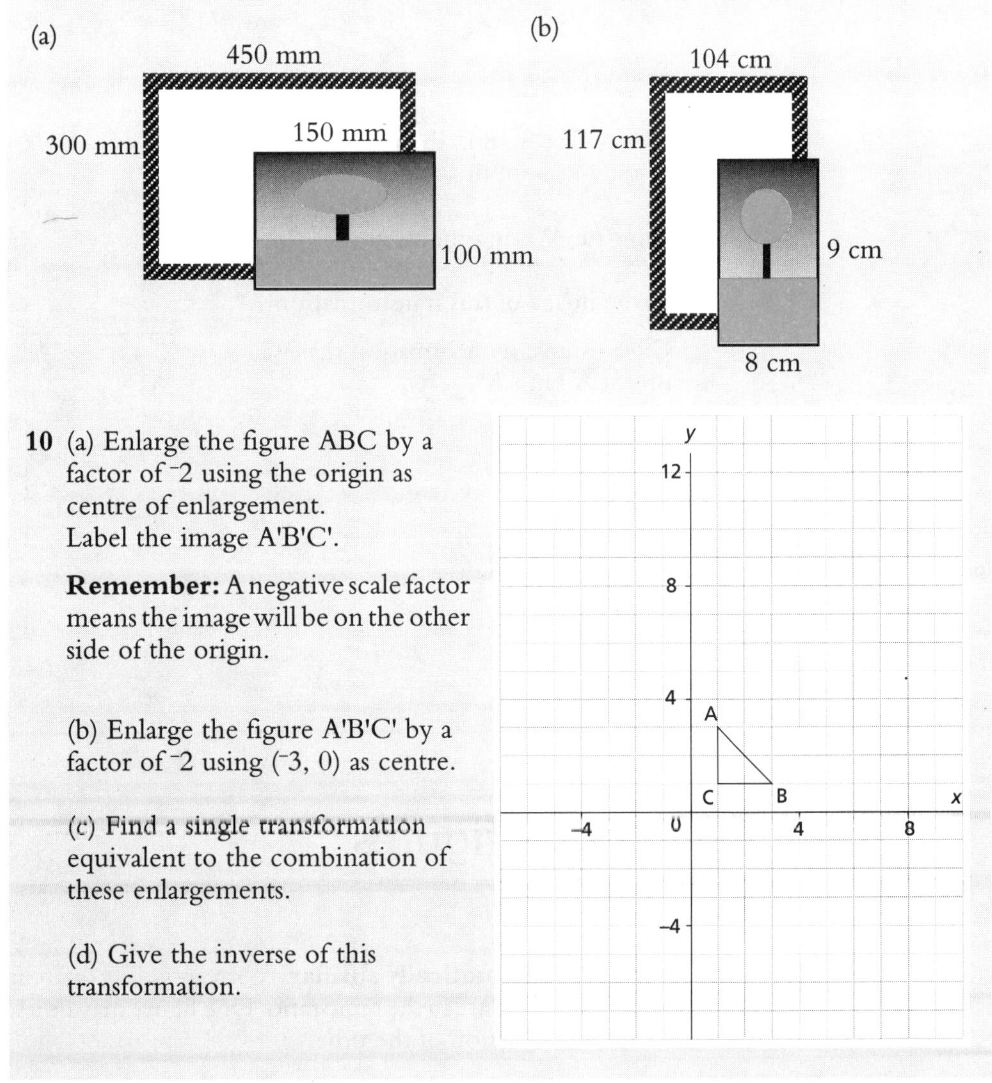

10 (a) Enlarge the figure ABC by a factor of $^{-}2$ using the origin as centre of enlargement.
Label the image A'B'C'.

Remember: A negative scale factor means the image will be on the other side of the origin.

(b) Enlarge the figure A'B'C' by a factor of $^{-}2$ using ($^{-}3$, 0) as centre.

(c) Find a single transformation equivalent to the combination of these enlargements.

(d) Give the inverse of this transformation.

Combinations of congruent transformations

Translations, reflections and rotations are all called **congruent** transformations because the object and image are congruent (the same size and shape).
When you combine two congruent transformations the result must be a congruent transformation.
You have seen above what happens when congruent transformations of the same type are combined.
When two congruent transformations of different types are combined you can use this simple checklist to help you find the equivalent transformation:

Is the final image	Then it must be a
reversed?	reflection
rotated?	rotation
neither?	translation

11 (a) Rotate the letter L 180° about (0, 0).
Label the image of this transformation L'.

(b) Reflect L' in the line $x = 0$.
Label the image L".

(c) What single transformation has the same effect as the combination of these transformations?

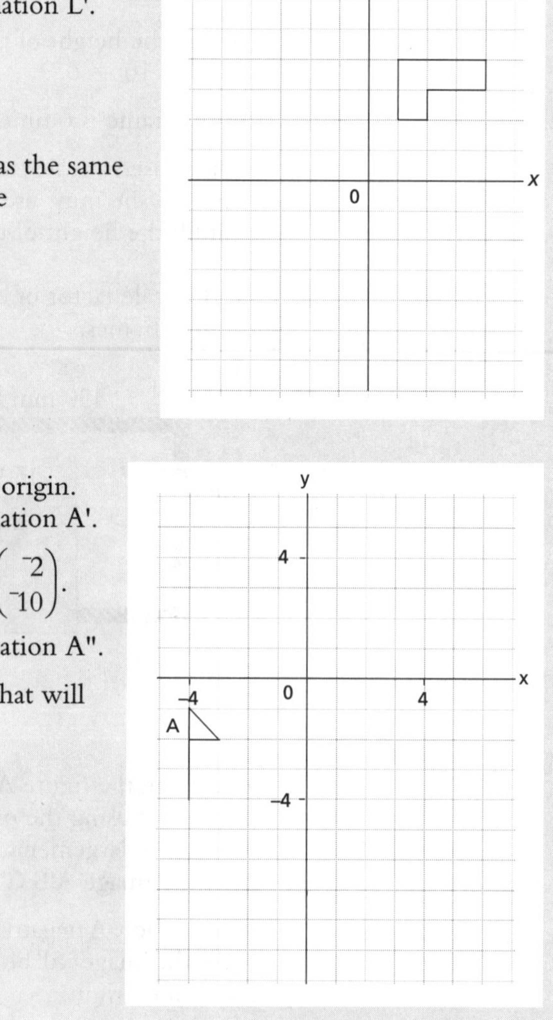

12 (a) Rotate flag A 180° about the origin.
Label the image of this transformation A'.

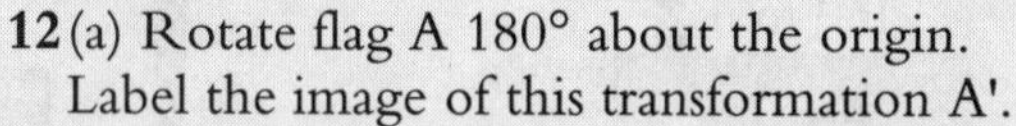

(b) Translate A' using the vector $\begin{pmatrix} ^-2 \\ ^-10 \end{pmatrix}$.

Label the image of this transformation A".

(c) Give a single transformation that will transform A onto A".

9.4 Similar figures

Two figures are **mathematically similar** if corresponding (matching) angles are all equal and corresponding sides are in the same ratio. One figure may be a scaled up, scaled down, rotated or reflected version of the other.

1 Using a pair of compasses and a ruler construct a triangle that has sides 3 cm, 4 cm and 5 cm long. Use the same method to construct a triangle with sides twice as long. Measure the angles in each of the triangles.

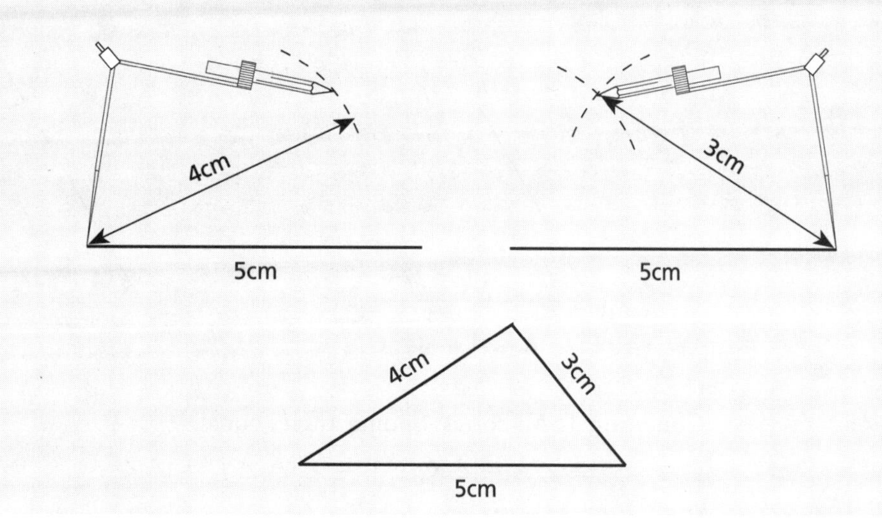

You should have found that, although the sides of the second triangle are twice as long as the first, the angles are the same.

2 Try constructing a triangle with sides half as long as the first triangle. What can you say about the angles?

The triangles you have drawn are mathematically similar.

When you are checking for similarity look for the points which correspond to (match) each other and then label them in the same order on each figure to make it easier to see which angles and sides are corresponding.

E.g. Show that the following quadrilaterals are similar.

A corresponds to W

B corresponds to X

C corresponds to Y

D corresponds to Z

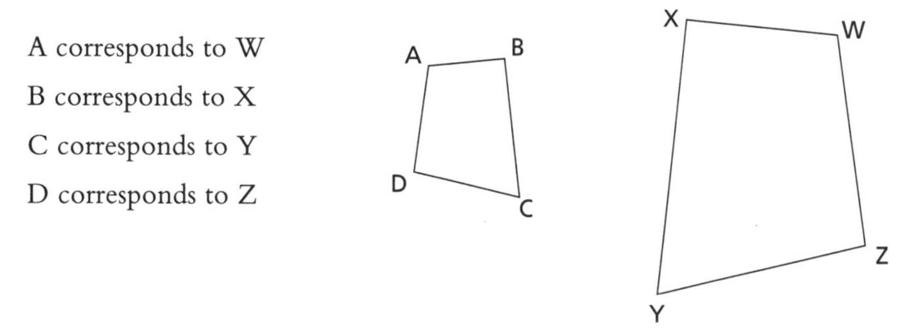

To prove that two quadrilaterals are similar it is enough to show that corresponding angles are equal. Then the sides must be in the same ratio.

Measure the angle at A and the corresponding angle at W. They are the same. The angles at B and X are also equal, and so are the angles at C and Y. The angles of a quadrilateral add to 360° so the remaining angles must be equal. So ABCD and WXYZ are similar.

Check: Measure the lengths of the sides.
WX = 2 AB, XY = 2 BC, YZ = 2 CD, WZ = 2 AD
Corresponding sides are in the same ratio (1 : 2).

Similar triangles

To prove that triangles are similar you don't have to check all the angles and all the sides. If two triangles satisfy *one* of the following conditions then they are similar.

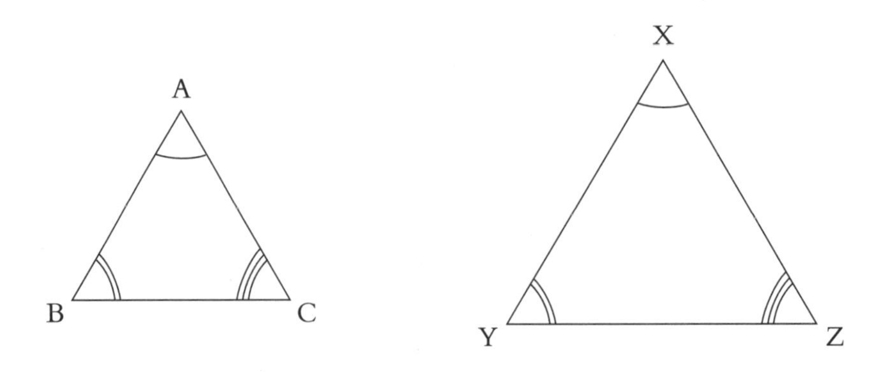

Condition 1: All corresponding angles equal.

$$\angle A = \angle X, \angle B = \angle Y, \angle C = \angle Z$$

You may have realised that it is only necessary to show that two pairs of corresponding angles are equal. The third pair of angles will have to be equal because the angles of a triangle always add up to 180°.

Condition 2: All corresponding sides in the same ratio.

$$\frac{AB}{XY} = \frac{AC}{XZ} = \frac{BC}{YZ}$$

Condition 3: Two corresponding sides in the same ratio and the angles between them equal.

$$\frac{AB}{XY} = \frac{AC}{XZ} \text{ and } \angle A = \angle X$$

Finding missing sides and angles

If you know that two shapes are similar then you can use this to find missing sides or angles.

E.g. Triangles AXY and ABC are similar. Calculate the length of the sides AB and AC.

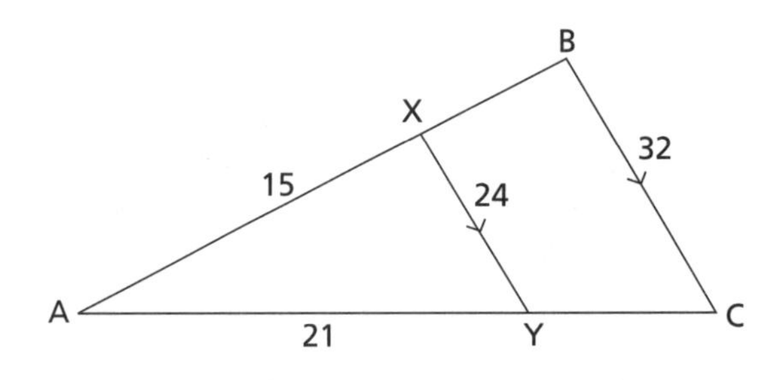

The ratio of BC to XY is $\frac{32}{24} = \frac{4}{3}$

Because the triangles are similar, AB and AX, and AC and AY, are in the same ratio.

$$\frac{AB}{AX} = \frac{4}{3} = \frac{AC}{AY}$$

$$\frac{AB}{15} = \frac{4}{3} = \frac{AC}{21}$$

Using equivalent ratios (or fractions),
AB = 20 and AC = 28

Examiner's tip

If you have not been told that shapes are similar you must prove it before you can use the properties of similar shapes.

3 (a) Show that the triangles ABC and CDE are similar.
Use the similarity of the triangles to calculate the length of the following sides:
(b) DE (c) BC

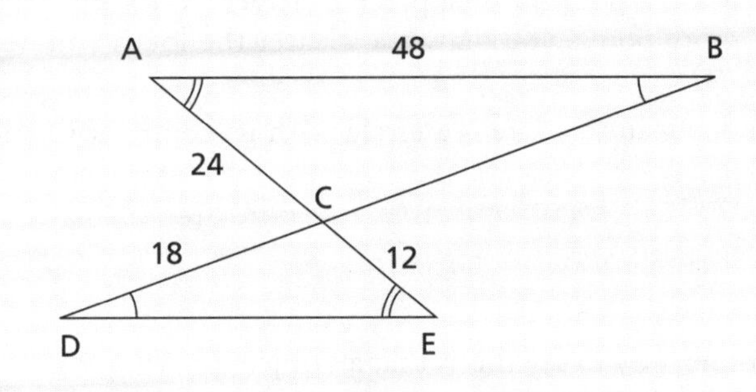

4 (a) Show that the triangles ABC and ADE are similar.
(b) Calculate the length of BC.

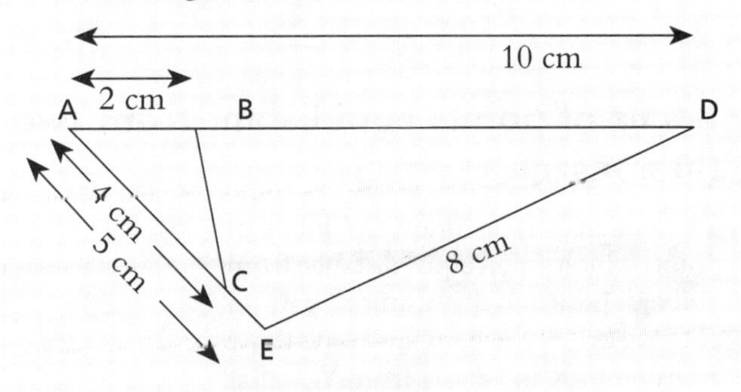

5 Which of the following quadrilaterals is not similar to the other three?

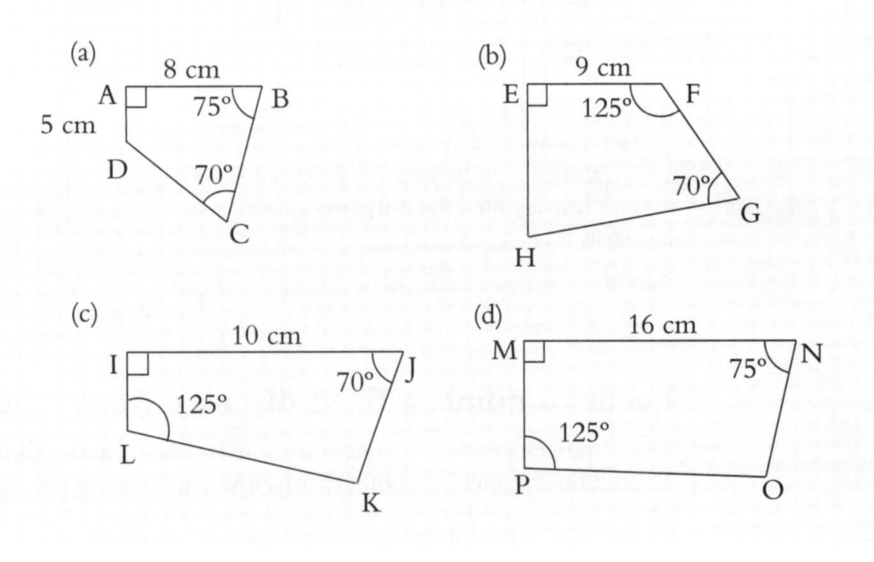

Examiner's tip

In similar figures corresponding angles are equal and corresponding sides are in the same ratio.

9.5 Loci

A **locus** is the path traced out as an object moves according to a rule. Another way to describe a locus is as the set of points which satisfy the rule. The points are all the different positions of the object as it moves. The plural of locus is **loci**.

Locus of points a fixed distance from a fixed point

1 Mark a point O on a piece of paper. Mark in points that are 2 cm from O. The more points you draw the clearer the locus will become.

The locus in this case is a circle with its centre at O and a radius of 2 cm.

Note: The locus of points a fixed distance from a single fixed point is a circle.

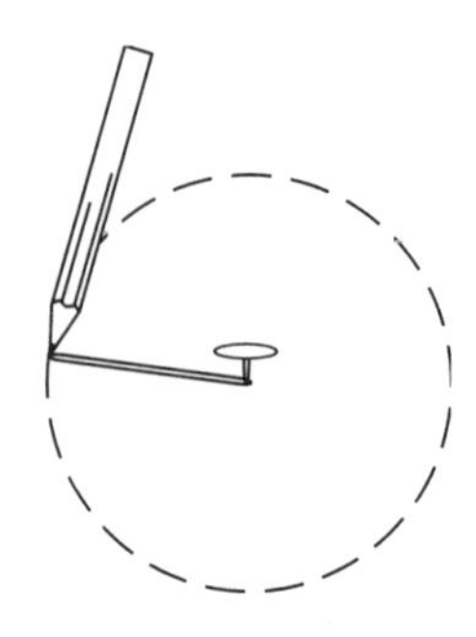

Another way to say this is that an object moving at a constant (fixed) distance from a fixed point will always follow a circular path.

Locus of points equidistant from two fixed points (line bisector)

The easiest way to draw the locus of points which are an equal distance from 2 fixed points is by using a pair of compasses. Set the compasses and draw an arc from X and an arc from Y so that the arcs intersect. The point of intersection is the same distance from X and Y. Change the radius of the compasses and repeat the operation to find more points until you are sure of the shape of the locus.

The locus in this case is the line which cuts XY in half and is at 90° to it. This line is called the perpendicular bisector.

Note: The locus of points equidistant from two fixed points is the perpendicular bisector of the line joining the two points.

Locus of points a fixed distance from a line

The distance between a point and a line is defined as the shortest distance between them. To find the distance of a point from a line you measure the distance *at right angles to the line.*

If you have a line with end points X and Y, then where XY is a straight line the locus will form two parallel lines, on each side of XY.

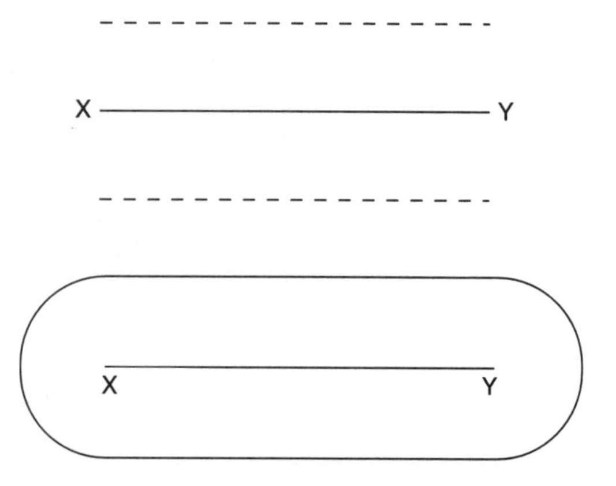

The ends of the line act like fixed points. You have seen that the locus of points at a fixed distance from a fixed point is a circle. So at the ends the locus will form semicircles around the points X and Y.

Note: The locus of points a fixed distance from a line is two parallel lines, one on either side.

Locus of points equidistant from two intersecting lines (angle bisector)

To draw the locus of points equally distant from two intersecting lines you can use a pair of compasses.

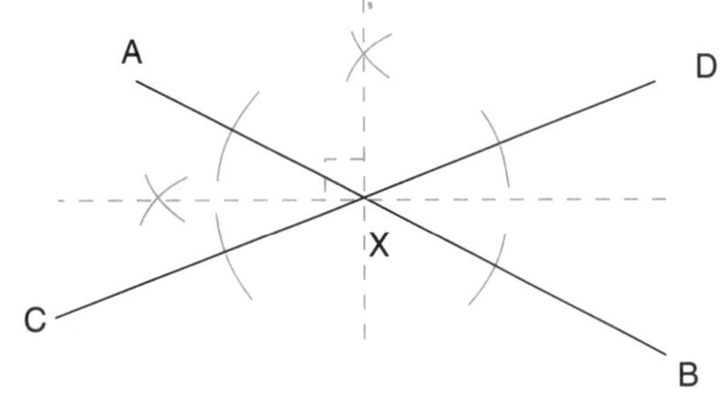

Use your compasses to mark points on AB and CD which are equally distant from X. Then draw intersecting arcs by putting the point of the compasses on each of these points in turn. The points where the arcs intersect are the same distance from both lines. Repeat this process until you have enough points to describe the locus.

This locus forms two lines perpendicular to each other which bisect (cut in half) each of the angles between AB and CD.

Note: The locus of points equidistant from two intersecting lines is the bisector of the angles between the lines.

Locus of points whose total distance from two fixed points is fixed

You can draw this locus using a pin board (or a thick newspaper on a flat surface), two pins and a loop of string.

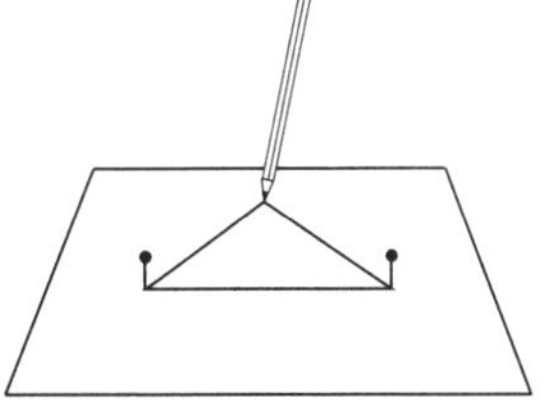

Put some paper on the board and place the pins in the board at a distance apart which is shorter than the loop. Now place your pencil in the loop and pull it tight. Keeping the string tight, draw a line all the way around the two pins. Try changing the distance between the pins and repeating the process.

You can also draw this locus using a pair of compasses. First you need to calculate some distances.

Distance from A	$5\frac{1}{2}$	5	4	3	2	1	$\frac{1}{2}$
Distance from B	$\frac{1}{2}$	1	2	3	4	5	$5\frac{1}{2}$
Total	6	6	6	6	6	6	6

You can now set your compasses and plot the points.

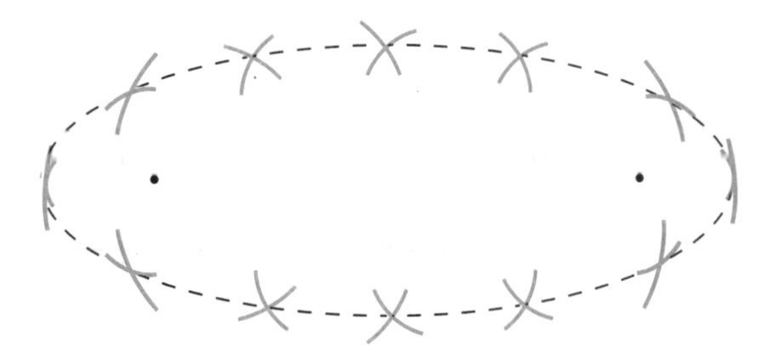

2 Draw the locus of points with a total distance from two points A and B of 10 cm. Start with A and B 7cm apart.

Note: The locus of an object moving so that the sum of its distances from two fixed points is constant is an ellipse.

Examiner's tip

If you find this difficult to picture then trace the shape, marking A, B, C and D, put a pen in point C and rotate the tracing paper.

3 Two radio stations 70 km apart broadcast over distances of 45 km and 55 km. Using a scale of 1 cm to 10 km draw the loci of the limits of their broadcasting ranges. Shade the area where both stations can be heard.

4 A large rectangular crate is to be moved by rotating it about one edge. This diagram shows the side view of the crate which will rotate about corner C .

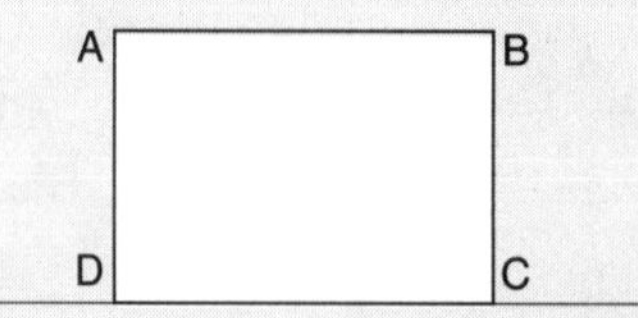

Draw the locus of the corner A as the crate is rotated. Clearly label the vertices (corners) once the crate has been rotated. Mark the new position of A as A′, B as B′ etc.

5 This diagram shows a garden drawn to scale. In the garden there are already two trees marked A and B and the gardener wishes to plant a third. There are a number of rules he wishes to apply.

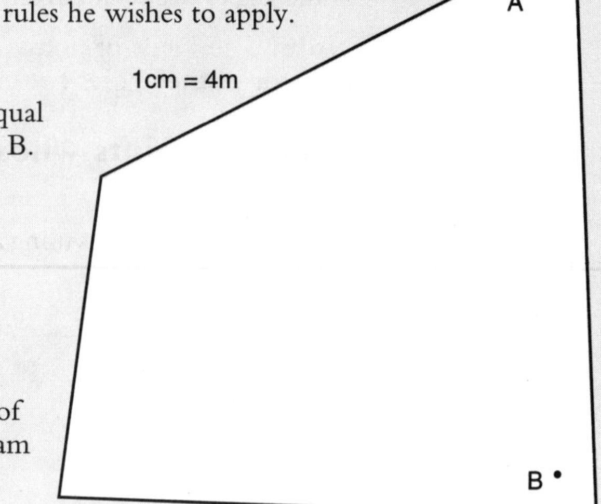

(a) The new tree must be an equal distance from both trees A and B.

(b) The new tree must be at least 4 m from the edge of the garden.

(c) The new tree must not be within 14 m of tree B.

Draw the locus given by each of these rules clearly on the diagram and show the possible planting sites for the new tree.

Chapter 10
Measure

10.1 Estimating measurements

You will be expected to use the correct measurements with your answers to calculations.

Note: Your answers must be sensible.

You should be familiar with metric units of length, mass (weight), area and volume so that your answers will be of the right order.

Grams	Kilograms	Tonnes	
Millimetres	Centimetres	Metres	Kilometres
Millilitres	Centilitres	Litres	

Examiner's tip

You should learn these conversions as a minimum

1 km = $\frac{5}{8}$ miles

1 kg = 2.2 lb

1 litre = $1\frac{3}{4}$ pints

You should also be familiar with the imperial measures which are in everyday use.

Ounces	Pounds		
Pints	Gallons		
Inches	Feet	Yards	Miles

You also need to be able to do approximate conversions from metric units to imperial and back.

1 (a) What is the approximate length of a bicycle in centimetres?
(b) Approximately how long is a football pitch in metres?
(c) Approximately how heavy is a newborn baby in kilograms?
(d) What is the approximate height of a house in feet?
(e) Approximately how many litres of water will a bucket hold?
(f) What is the approximate area of your classroom floor in square metres?
(g) What is the approximate area of your classroom floor in square feet?

10.2 Discrete and continuous measures

Discrete measures are those which are recorded by counting. A discrete measure will have a fixed value.

Continuous measures are those which are recorded by measuring. Continuous measures are approximations to the value of an object expressed to a given degree of accuracy.

1 Decide whether the following statements contain discrete or continuous measures.
(a) The weight of a group of people.
(b) The time taken to run 100 metres.
(c) The number of brothers each person in a class has.
(d) The number of books in your bag.
(e) The temperature in your classroom.
(f) The shoe sizes of the people in your class.

10.3 Recognising that a measurement is in possible error of half a unit

You know that all measurements are approximations. Measurements cannot be given exactly so they are given to the nearest practical units.

Measuring a value to the nearest unit means deciding that it is nearer to one mark than another, in other words it is within half a unit of that mark.

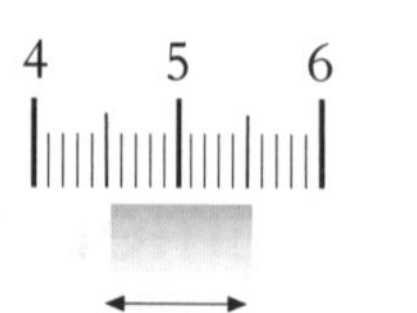

Anything within the shaded area is 5 to the nearest unit.

If David's age is 14 to the nearest year that means he is actually between $13\frac{1}{2}$ and $14\frac{1}{2}$.

E.g. In a class survey the following information was recorded.

David Carter	
Height	158 cm
Weight	48 kg
Waist	67 cm
Neck	32 cm
Leg	70 cm

David's height is given as 158 cm. Since this has been measured to the nearest cm David's height could be anywhere within 0·5 cm either side of 158 cm.

The *smallest* he could be is 157·5 cm because this is the smallest measurement which rounds up to 158 cm.

What is the tallest David could be?

He must be less than 158·5 cm because this rounds up to 159 cm. But anything under 158·5 cm would be 158·49999… cm so it would round down to 158 cm.

The possible range of heights (h) for David is $157{\cdot}5\text{ cm} \le h < 158{\cdot}5\text{ cm}$.

Note: At the upper end a less than sign is used. Although h can come very close to 158·5 cm it will never equal it.

1 Complete the following table for David's measurements.

	Minimum possible measurement	Maximum possible measurement	Range
Height			
Weight			
Waist			
Neck			
Leg			

10.4 Areas of plane shapes and volumes of prisms

You should already know and be able to use these formulae.

Note: These formulae will be given to you in the exam on the formulae sheet.

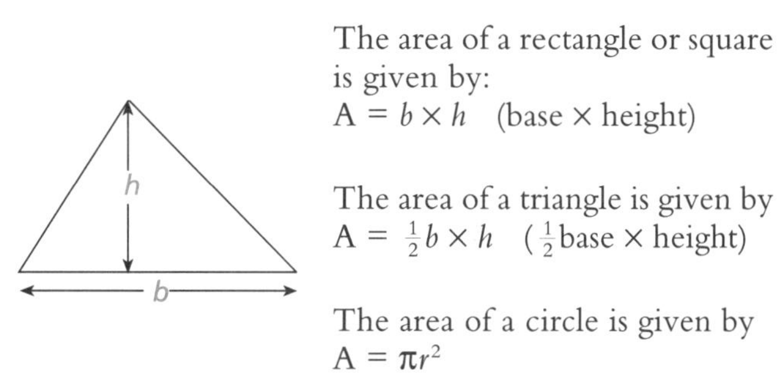

The area of a rectangle or square is given by:
A = $b \times h$ (base × height)

The area of a triangle is given by
A = $\frac{1}{2}b \times h$ ($\frac{1}{2}$base × height)

The area of a circle is given by
A = πr^2

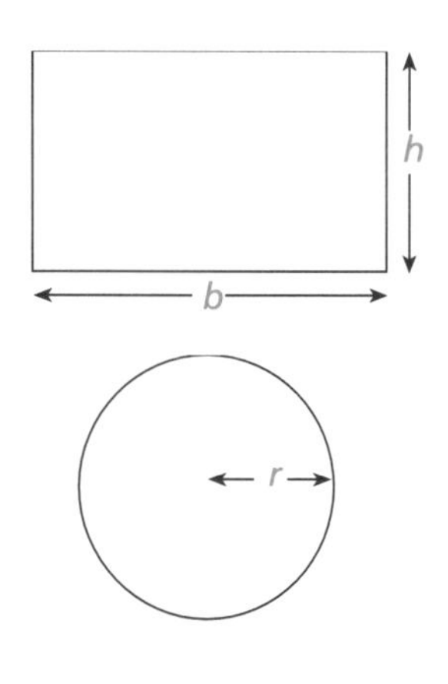

Note: Height is always perpendicular to the base.

Parallelogram

A parallelogram is a quadrilateral with opposite sides parallel.

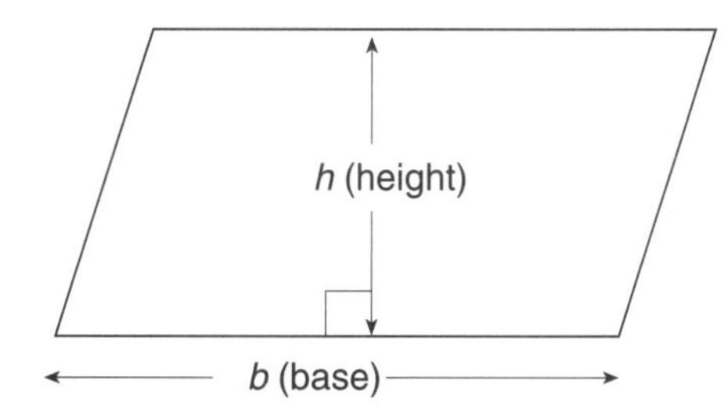

The area of a parallelogram is base × height = bh

This is because you can cut off a triangle at one end and move it to the other to get a rectangle.

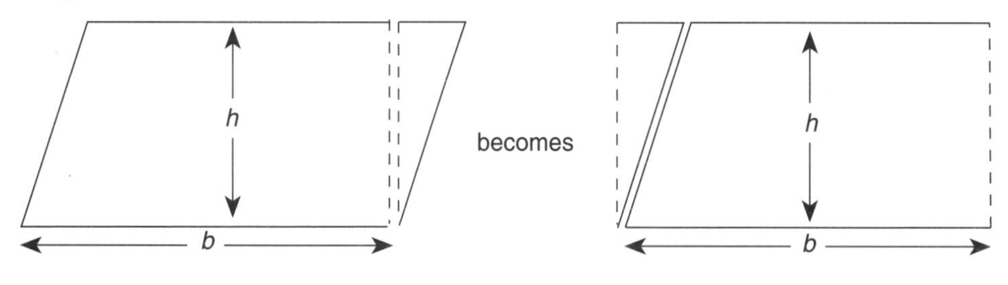

Rhombus

A rhombus is a quadrilateral with all its sides equal.

The area of a rhombus can be calculated using the same method as for a parallelogram or by multiplying the diagonals together.

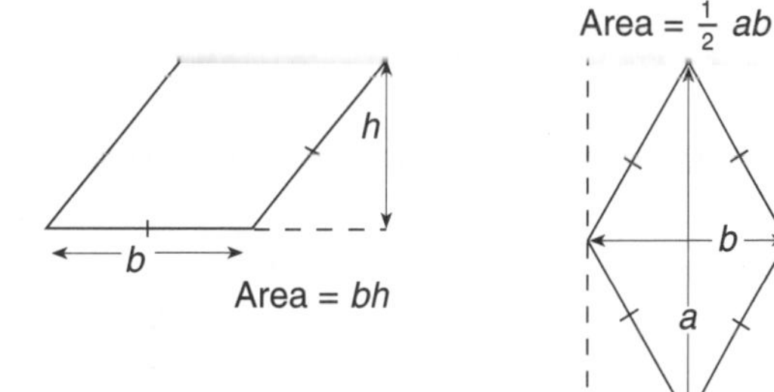

Trapezium

A trapezium is a quadrilateral with one pair of parallel sides.

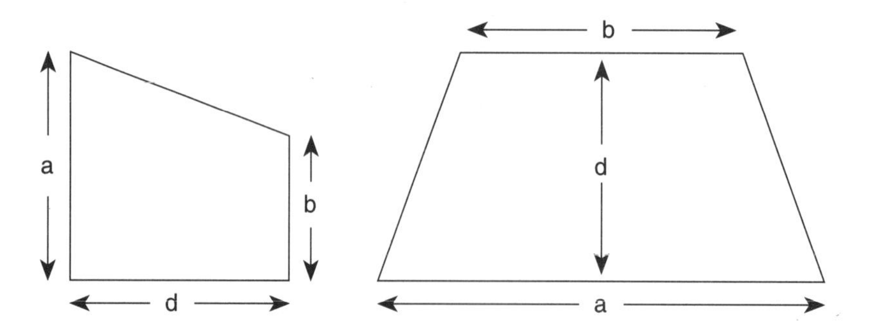

Note: d is the distance between the parallel sides.

The area of a trapezium is $\frac{1}{2} \times$ (sum of parallel sides) $\times$ height $= \frac{1}{2}(a + b)d$

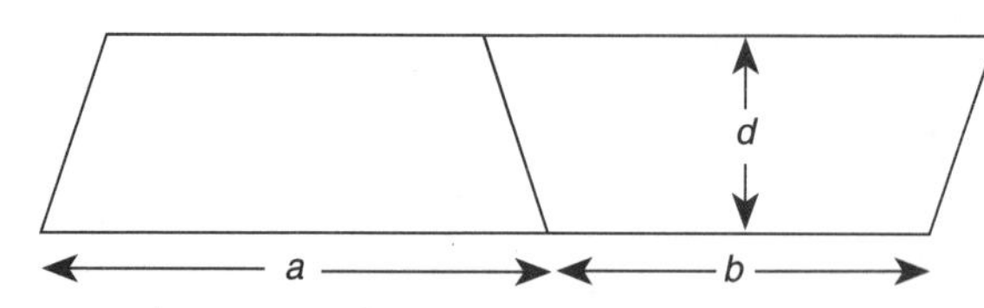

This is because you can take a second trapezium congruent to (the same shape and size as) the first and fit them together to make a parallelogram with sides of length $a + b$. The area of one trapezium will be half the area of the parallelogram.

1 This is the plan of a plot of building land drawn to a scale of 1 cm to 10 m. Calculate its area. Give your answer to the nearest square metre.

C D A B

Examiner's tip

It is best to divide the plot into triangles, as shown in green. Measure the base and height of each triangle, convert them to their real lengths and work out the area of each triangle.

2 This diagram shows the side view of a staircase.
(a) Calculate the area under the stairs.
(b) Calculate the area of the banisters.

1 m
3 m
3·5 m

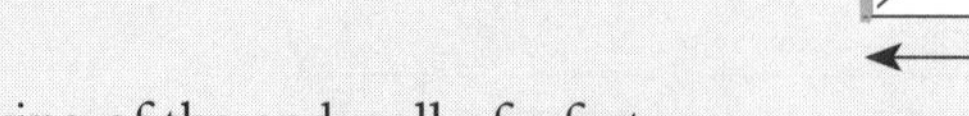

3 This is a drawing of the end wall of a factory.
(a) Calculate the area of each section marked A, B, C and D.
(b) Calculate the areas of the doors and windows.
(c) Calculate the total area of wall excluding doors and windows.

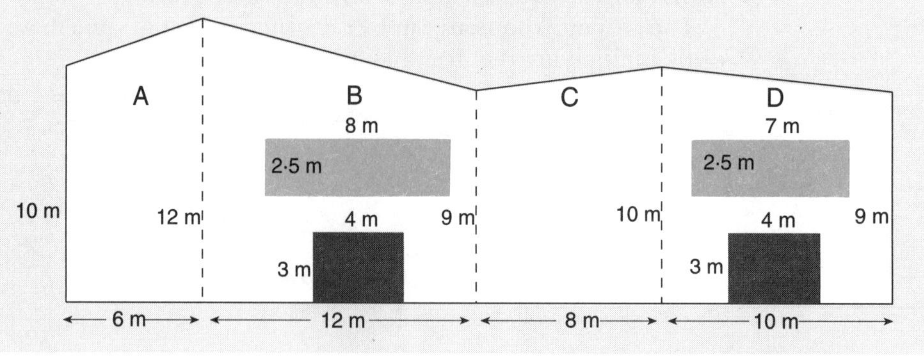

Calculating volumes of prisms

If a solid has a uniform cross-section (the area is the same throughout its length) then the volume is given by

Volume = cross-sectional area × length

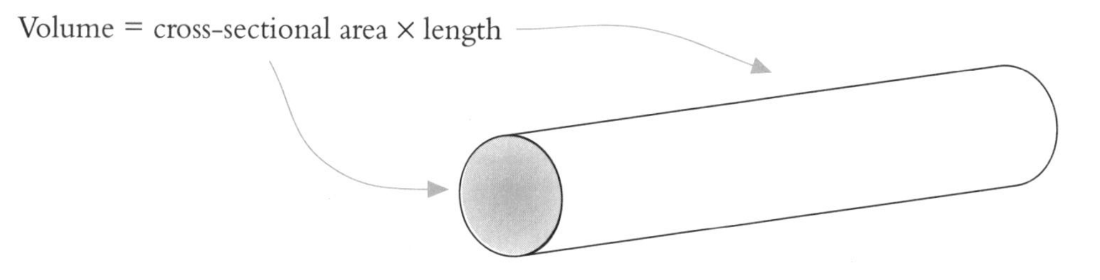

Such a solid is sometimes called a **prism**.

E.g. Calculate the volume of water in this swimming pool.

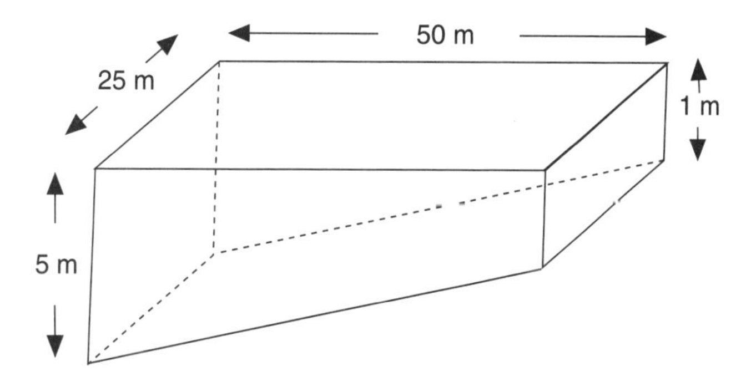

The cross-section of the swimming pool is a trapezium with $h = 50$ m, $a = 1$ m and $b = 5$ m.

$$\begin{aligned}\text{Area of cross-section} &= \tfrac{1}{2}(a + b)h \\ &= \tfrac{1}{2}(1 + 5) \times 50 \\ &= 150 \text{ m}^2\end{aligned}$$

Multiplying the cross-section by the length gives

$$150 \times 25 = 3750$$

Therefore the pool holds 3750 m^3 of water.

Note: Volume is in cubic units.

4 The track for a new high speed train is to be in a cutting for its entire length to reduce environmental impact. This diagram shows the cross-section of the cutting.

(a) Calculate the area of the cross-section of the cutting.

(b) Use your answer to (a) to calculate the volume of material to be removed for each kilometre of cutting.

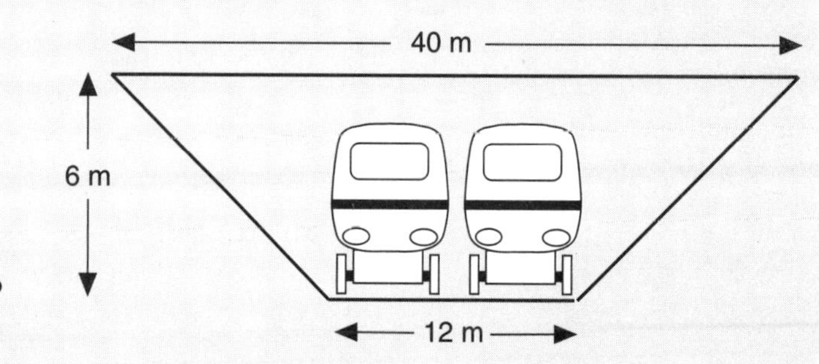

5 A syringe is to be used to draw a sample of blood from a patient in hospital. If the radius of the syringe is 3·5 mm and the length is 25 mm calculate the volume of blood in the syringe when it is full.

6 A manufacturer needs to produce rectangular based boxes with a volume of 1200 cm^3. The boxes must pack neatly into crates 50 cm wide, 60 cm long and 50 cm high.
(a) How many boxes will fit into each crate?
(b) Investigate some possible dimensions for the box.

10.5 Distinguishing between formulae for 2-D and 3-D figures

xaminer's tip

The key to knowing whether the units are length, area or volume lies in the number of lengths multiplied together.

To carry out this process you need to look carefully at the formula you are working with. The method you use is to determine the number of dimensions, length, width and height that you have multiplied together.

A formula involving one dimension, e.g. **height** is a measurement of **length**.
A formula involving two dimensions, e.g. **width** × **height** is a measurement of **area**.

Note: Area is measured in squared units.

A formula involving three dimensions, e.g. **width** × **height** × **length** is a measurement of **volume**.

Note: Volume is measured in cubed units.

E.g. Is $\frac{4}{3}\pi r^3$ a formula for volume or surface area?

In this case you have $r^3 = r \times r \times r$ Since radius, r, is a length this formula must give you a volume.

1 Which of the following are length, which are area and which are volume?

(a) $\frac{1}{2}bh$ (b) $4\pi r^2$ (c) bh (d) $2\pi r$
(e) $\frac{1}{2}(a + b)h$ (f) $\frac{4}{3}\pi r^3$ (g) $2(l + w)$ (h) $4l + 4w + 4h$
(i) $\frac{1}{3}\pi r^2 h$ (j) $\frac{1}{2}ab \sin c$ (k) $2\pi r^2 + 2\pi rh$ (l) $a^2 + b^2 = c^2$

Chapter 11
Further shape, space and measure

11.1 Enlargement by a negative scale factor

When you are using a negative scale factor you measure the distance to the point on the original shape in the same way but to find the image point you measure in the opposite direction. So the image will be on the other side of the centre of enlargement.

E.g. Enlarge the following figure by a scale factor of $^{-}3$.

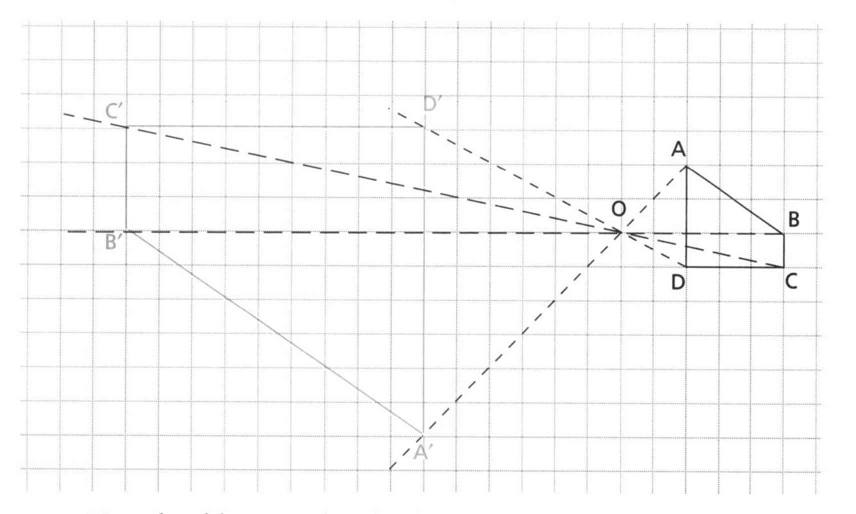

You should notice that the figure has been inverted. It is upside down and back to front. It looks like it has been rotated about the centre of enlargement.

1 Enlarge the triangle XYZ by a factor of $^{-}2$.

11.2 Enlargment by a fraction

You know how to enlarge a shape by a whole number scale factor. The same method can be used to enlarge by a fractional scale factor. For a fraction less than 1 the effect is to make the shape smaller.

E.g. Enlarge the figure ABCD by a scale factor of $\frac{1}{2}$.

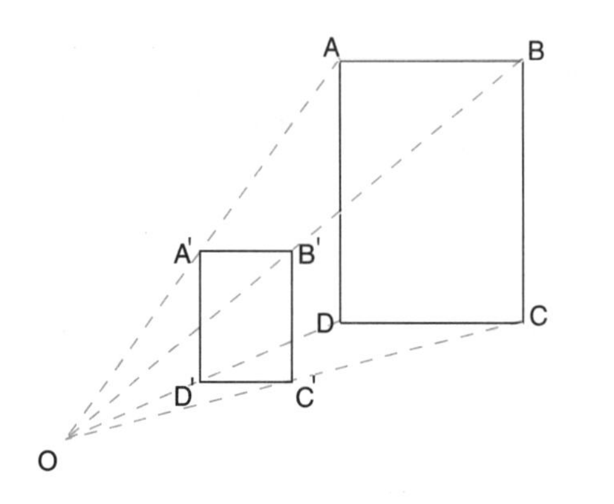

Draw guidelines from O through each corner A, B, C, D of the rectangle.
Measure the distance from O to A (OA) and halve it.
Mark the new point A′ on the line so that OA′ is $\frac{1}{2}$ OA.
Repeat this process for each corner. This gives the figure A′B′C′D′.

1 Enlarge each of the following shapes by the given scale factor using the centre of enlargement which has been marked for you.

(a) scale factor $\frac{1}{2}$

(b) scale factor $\frac{1}{3}$

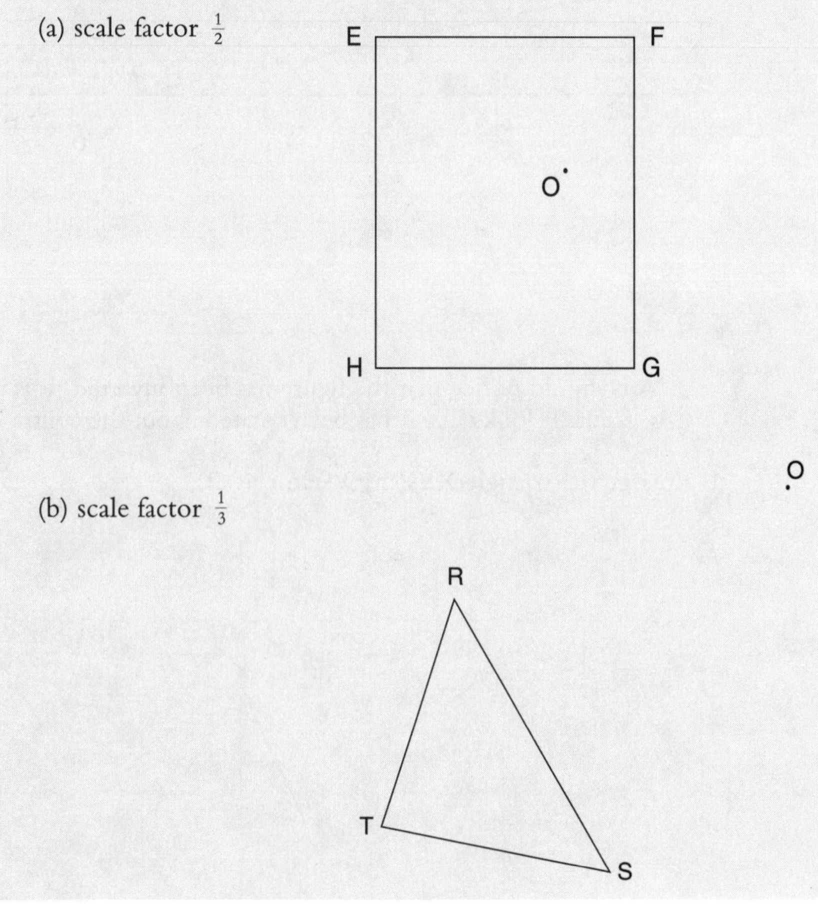

Note: A scale factor less than 1 will make your figure smaller.

11.3 Calculating distances and angles in solids

Finding distances and angles in solids involves solving right-angled triangles viewed in different planes, making use of Pythagoras' theorem and the trigonometrical ratios sin, cos and tan.

It is very important to draw a simple diagram that helps you to see clearly the part of the solid that you are working on and the type of operation you need to perform. Your drawing should include all the information you need to answer the question and you should clearly label the things you need to find. Ignore what you don't need. Draw vertical lines up and down the page, and if one point is vertically below another then draw it that way. Make all parallel lines parallel.

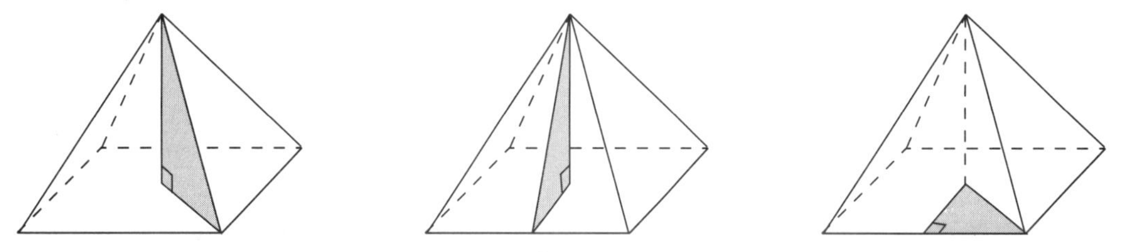

Note: 'A good picture is worth a thousand words.'

In sketches of three-dimensional solids right angles are not always obvious. There are often words in the question which will help you to identify the right angles: one line may be *perpendicular* to another, a point may be *vertically below* or *vertically above* another point.

E.g. In a regular square based pyramid ABCDE the edge AB = 8 cm and the vertical height to the apex point E = 7 cm. Let X be the point on the base directly below E and let Y be the mid-point of AB.

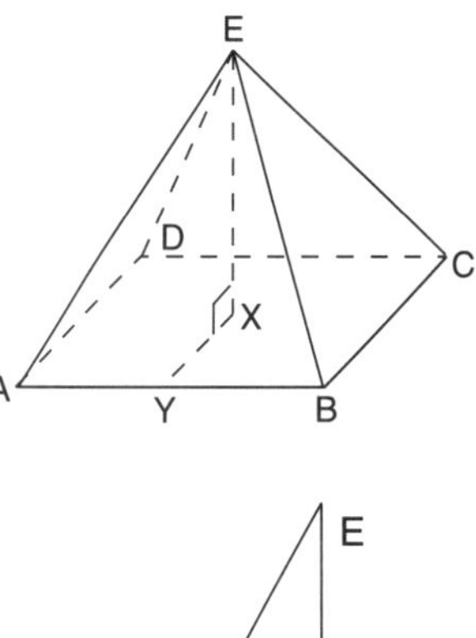

(a) Calculate the angle $E\hat{Y}X$.
(b) Calculate the length of the slope EY.
(c) Calculate the area of the face ABE.

Note: An angle is often indicated by using 3 corners or vertices. Angle $E\hat{Y}X$ is the angle made by joining these points.

(a) To calculate $E\hat{Y}X$ you need to draw the triangle $E\hat{X}Y$.

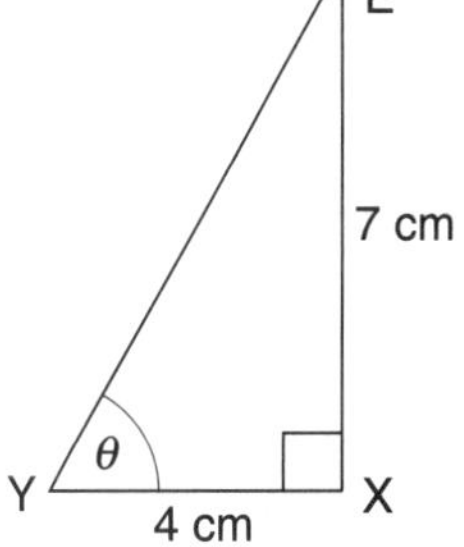

You know that EX = 7 cm. Because EX is vertical the angle $E\hat{X}Y$ is a right angle. Because the pyramid is regular, X is in the middle of the base so XY is half the length of the base. Therefore XY = 4 cm.

Looking at the diagram you can see that you know the opposite and adjacent sides to the angle you want to find. So use tan.

Let $E\hat{Y}X = \theta$

$$\tan \theta = \frac{\text{opposite}}{\text{adjacent}} = \frac{7}{4}$$

$E\hat{Y}X = 60{\cdot}26°$ (to 2 d.p.)

(b) To calculate the length of the slope EY you can use Pythagoras' theorem in the triangle already drawn. (You could use the angle you have just found to calculate EY but if you got the angle wrong then you'd get the length of EY wrong too.)

Using Pythagoras, $EY^2 = EX^2 + XY^2$
$= 4^2 + 7^2$
$= 16 + 49$
$= 65$
$EY = \sqrt{65}$
$EY = 8{\cdot}06$ cm (to 2 d.p.)

(c) To find the area of the triangle ABE you need a new diagram.

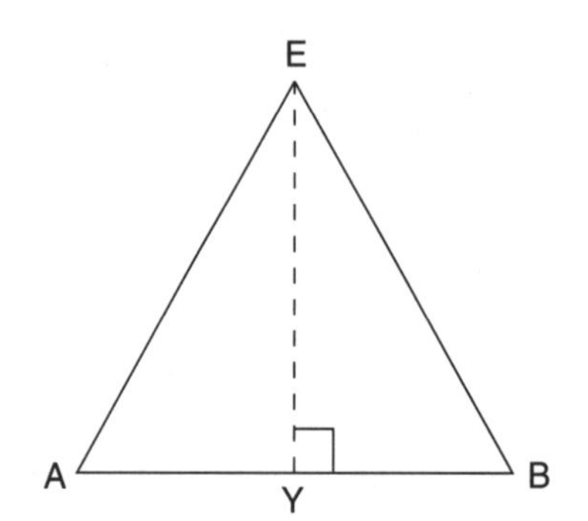

You know the length of EY from part (b).

Note: Do not use the rounded answer. It may create a rounding error. Use the **exact** value.

The exact value of EY is $\sqrt{65}$ cm. You know that AB = 8 cm.

Examiner's tip

If possible always use information that you have been given rather than your own answers.

Area of ABE $= \frac{1}{2}$ base × height
$= \frac{1}{2} \times 8 \times \sqrt{65}$
$= 32{\cdot}249031$

The area of ABE = $32{\cdot}25$ cm² (to 2 d.p.)

1 ABCDEFGH is a regular cuboid with AB = 25 cm, BC = 10 cm and BF = 7 cm.

(a) Find the length EG.

Note: Draw triangle EFG.

(b) Find the length AG.

Note: Draw triangle AEG.

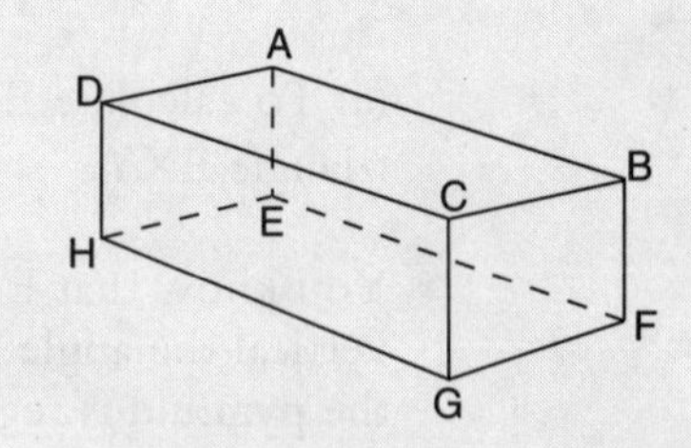

(c) Calculate the angle AGE.
(d) Find the length BG.
(e) Calculate the angle AGB.
(f) Calculate the area of the triangle ABG.

2 A snail is moving on a brick represented by the cuboid in question 1. The snail travels in a straight line from A to G along the shortest route.
(a) Calculate the length of the snail's trail.

Note: Imagine the box opened out.

(b) Find the angle from AB that the snail will travel along.
(c) How far from the corner D will the snail cross the edge CD?

3 A flag pole stands exactly in the centre of a courtyard 3·6 m wide and 4·5 m long. The flag pole is supported by three cables attached to the pole at a point 7·6 m above the ground. The other ends of the cables are attached to points A, B and C on the ground. A and B are each half way along a side of the courtyard, and C is at one corner.

(a) Calculate the length of the cable attached to point A.

(b) Calculate the length of the cable attached to point B.

(c) Calculate the length of the cable attached to point C.

7.6 m
C
B
A
4.5 m
3.6 m

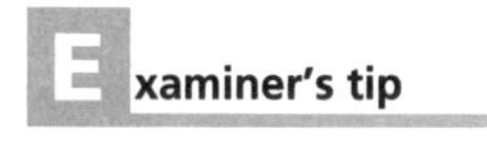

Examiner's tip

The most important thing to do in any 3D work is to draw a good diagram.

11.4 Polar coordinates

You should already be familiar with the ordinary (Cartesian) coordinate system. Polar coordinates use distance (r) from the origin and angle (θ) measured from the horizontal in a anti-clockwise direction to define a location.

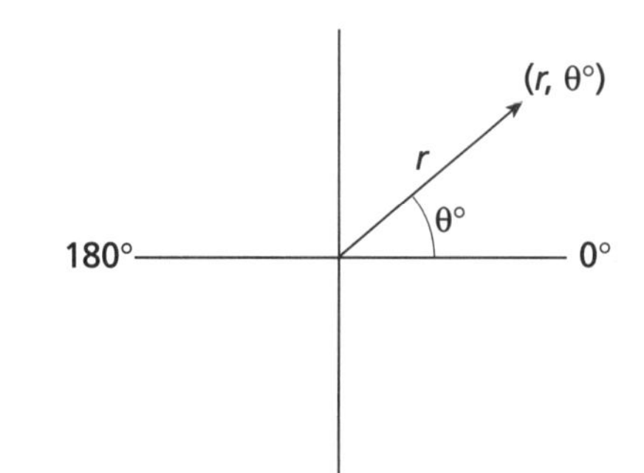

Note: Polar coordinates might be used to describe a location after using the sine or cosine rules.

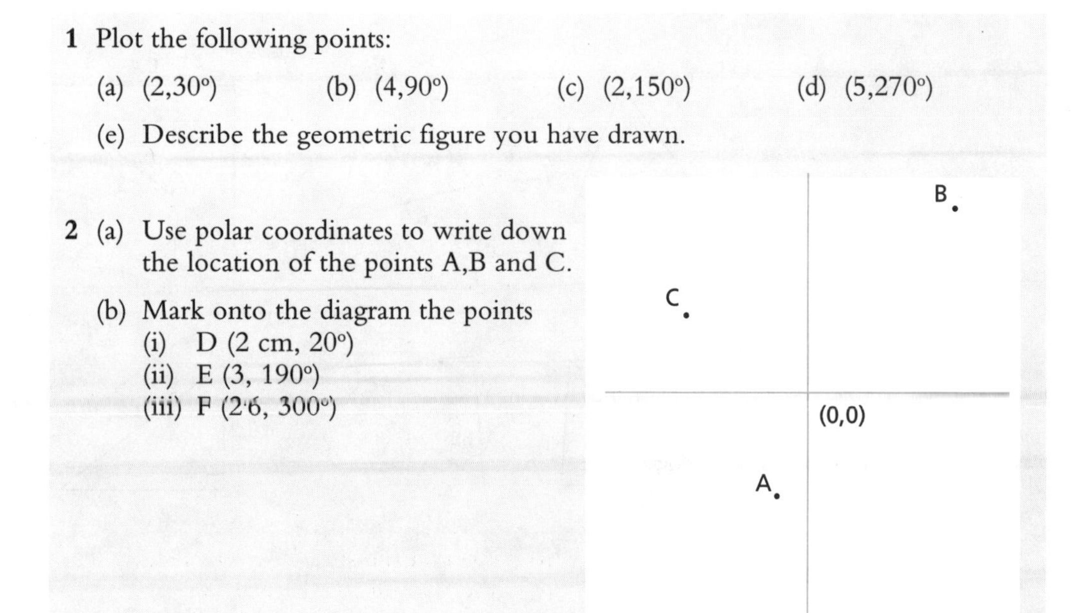

1 Plot the following points:

(a) (2,30°) (b) (4,90°) (c) (2,150°) (d) (5,270°)

(e) Describe the geometric figure you have drawn.

2 (a) Use polar coordinates to write down the location of the points A,B and C.

(b) Mark onto the diagram the points
(i) D (2 cm, 20°)
(ii) E (3, 190°)
(iii) F (2·6, 300°)

11.5 Congruent triangles

For any two shapes to be **congruent** to each other they must be *the same shape* and *the same size*. This means they fit onto each other exactly when rotated or reflected. For two polygons to be congruent all corresponding (matching) angles must be equal and all corresponding sides must be equal.
For two triangles to be congruent they must have:
3 pairs of corresponding equal angles and
3 pairs of corresponding equal sides

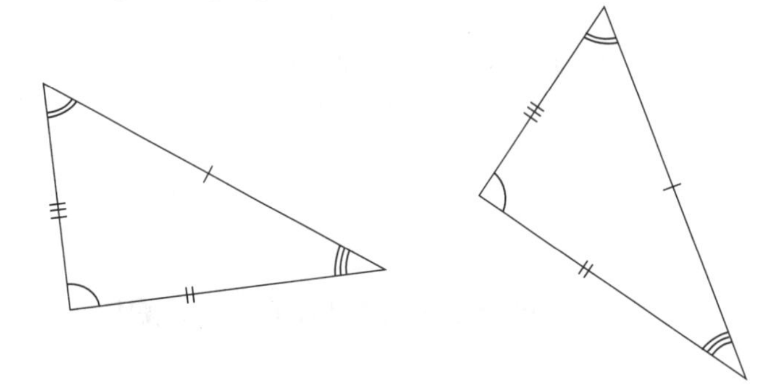

Note: Congruent shapes are exactly the same but they may be reflected or rotated.

1 Which of these triangles are congruent? (They are not drawn accurately.) Explain in each case why you have or have not decided a pair are congruent.

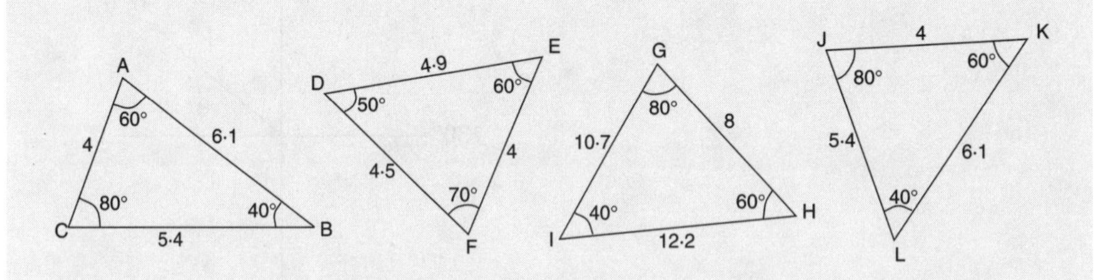

2 Which of the following pairs of triangles are congruent? (They are not drawn accurately.) Explain in each case why you have or have not decided a pair are congruent

(a)

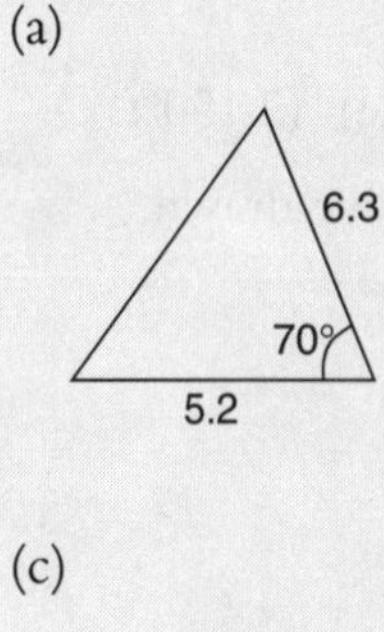

(b)

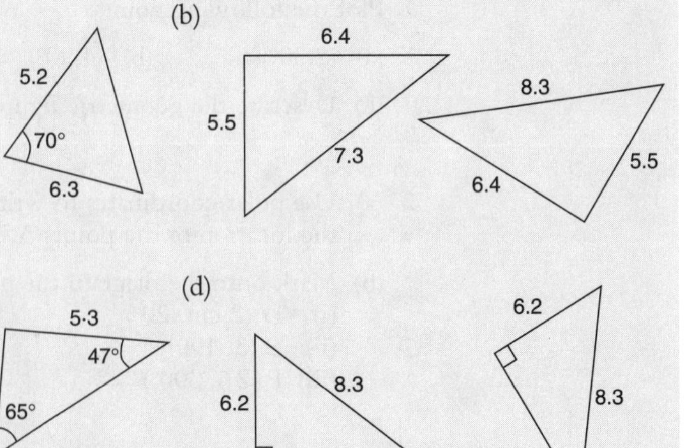

(c)

47°
65°
5·3
5·3
47°
65°

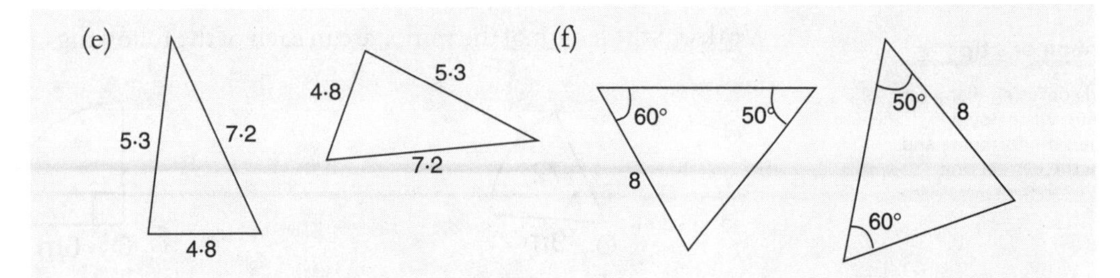

3 Draw a pair of triangles to show that two sides and an angle being equal does not prove congruence if the angle is not the included angle.

4 Jonathan has a windmill which he says is made of two congruent triangles.

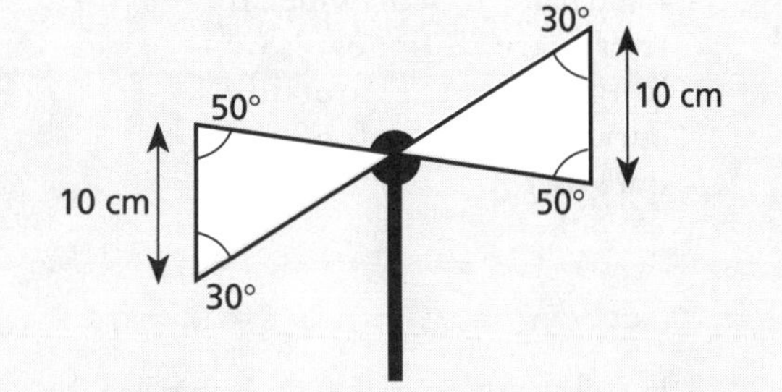

His brother says the triangles are not congruent. Who is correct and why?

11.6 Lengths, areas and volumes in shapes involving circles

Note: Any formulae you need will be given.

Arcs

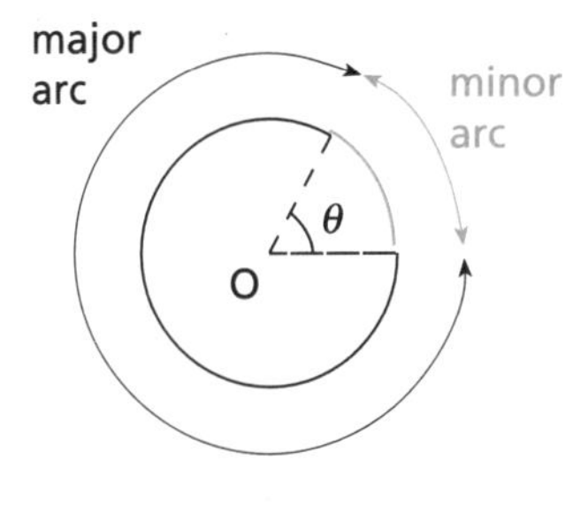

An **arc** is part of the circumference of a circle. If the circumference is cut in two then the arc which makes the larger angle at the centre is called the *major arc* and the arc which makes an angle of less than 180° at the centre is called the *minor arc*. If the circumference is cut exactly in half then two semicircular arcs are formed.

The length of the arc depends on the radius of the circle and the size of the angle turned through at the centre of the circle. If the angle turned through to produce the arc is θ and the diameter $= d$, radius $= r$, then

$$\text{Arc length} = \frac{\theta}{360} \times \pi d \quad \text{or} \quad \frac{\theta}{360} \times 2\pi r$$

E.g. Calculate the length of the minor arc AB given that $\angle$ AOB = 60° and $r = 4$ cm ($\pi = 3{\cdot}142$).

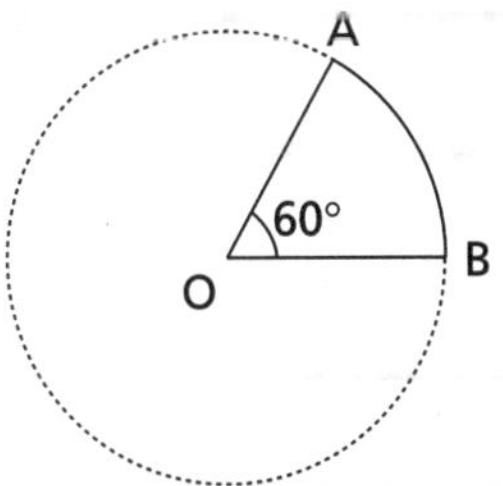

$$\text{Length of arc AB} = \frac{\theta}{360} \times 2\pi r$$

$$= \frac{60}{360} \times 2 \times 3{\cdot}142 \times 4$$

$$= 4{\cdot}1893333$$

$$\text{AB} = 4{\cdot}19 \text{ cm (to 2 d.p.)}$$

Examiner's tip

To avoid confusing diameter and radius, write down both, then the formulae and then use the correct one.

1 Work out the length of the minor arc in each of the following circles. (Answer to 2 d.p.)

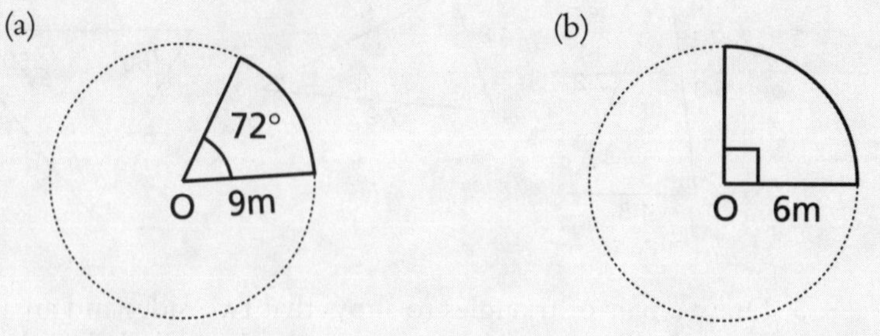

2 A groundsman has to set out a running track at a sports ground. The bends on the track are semicircles. The radius of the inner lane is 30 m.

Each lane is 1 m wide. If there are 8 lanes how long will the outside curve at one end of the track be?

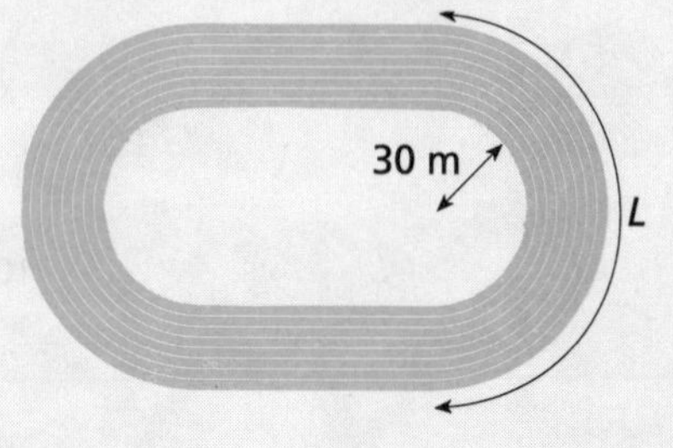

3 Hazel wants to make a witch's hat for a fancy dress party using this pattern.

If Hazel's head measures 54 cm around and she has enough black card to draw a circle of radius 30 cm, calculate the angle θ of the piece of card she needs to cut out.

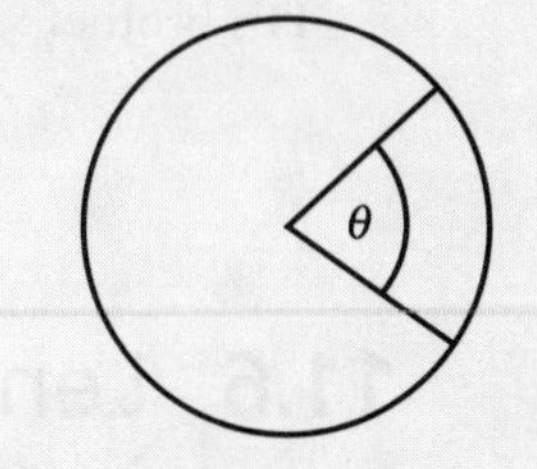

Note: The arc length has to go round Hazel's head.

Sectors of circles

A **sector** of a circle is an area bounded (edged) by an arc and two radii. You can think of a sector as being the shape of a slice of pizza.

A *minor sector* is bounded by a minor arc and a *major sector* is bounded by a major arc.
In the same way that the length of an arc is a fraction of the circumference of the circle, the area of a sector is a fraction of the area of the circle.

Area of sector $= \dfrac{\theta}{360} \times \pi r^2$

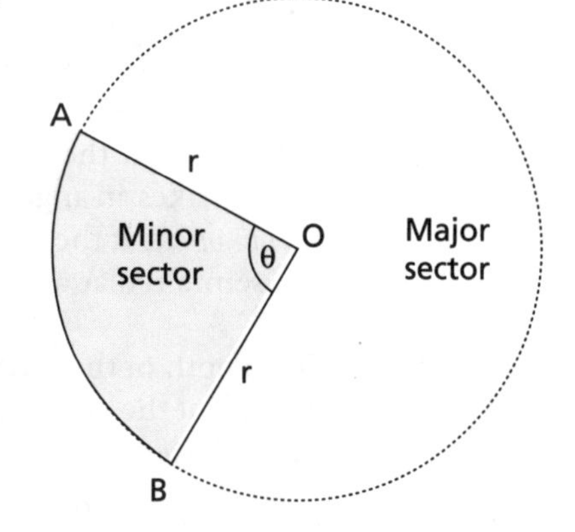

E.g. Calculate the area of the sector AOB where $\angle$ AOB = 90° and r = 10 m (π = 3·142).

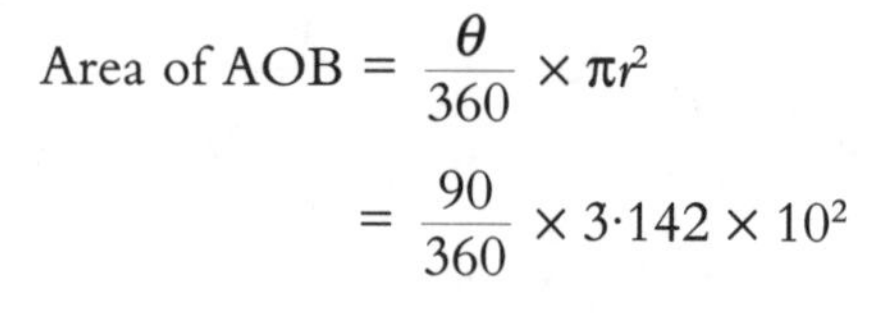

Area of AOB $= \dfrac{\theta}{360} \times \pi r^2$

$= \dfrac{90}{360} \times 3{\cdot}142 \times 10^2$

Area of AOB = 78·55 m²

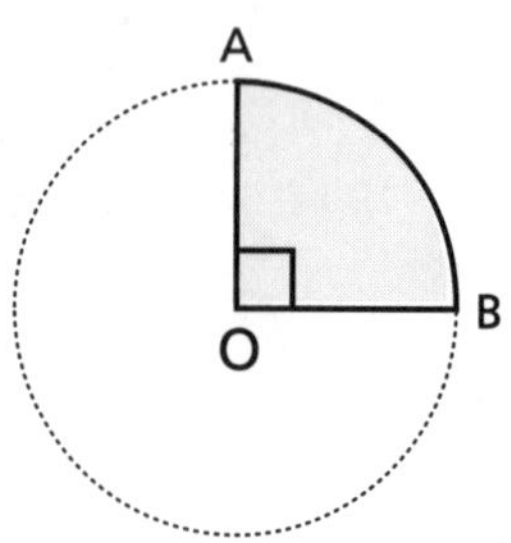

4 Calculate the area of the shaded sector AOB in each of the following circles. (Answer to 2 d.p.)

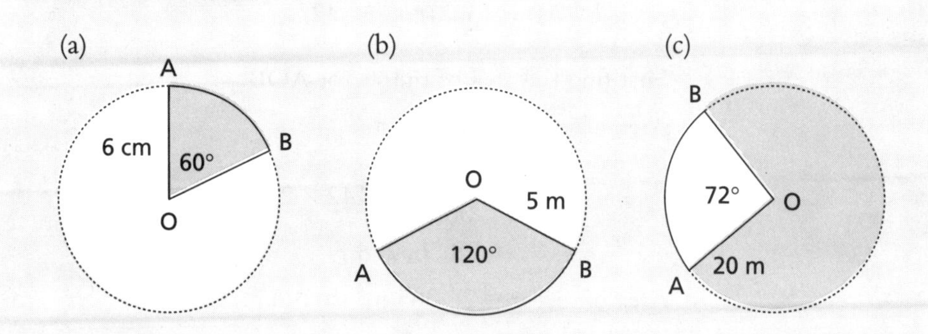

5 The rear windscreen wiper of a car rotates on an arm 45 cm long. The rubber wiper blade is 32 cm long. The wiper arm rotates through an angle of 110°. Calculate the area of windscreen cleared.

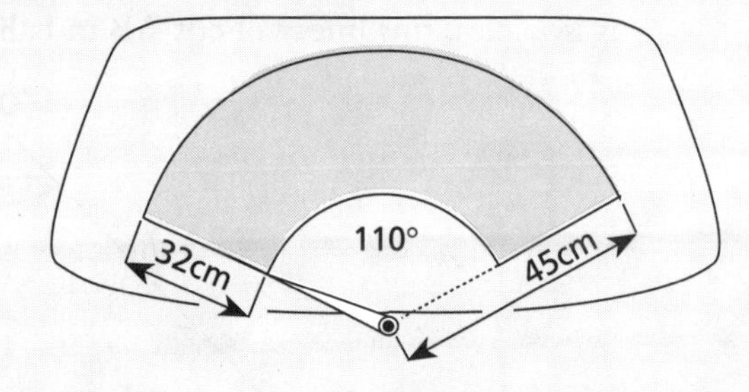

Note: Calculate the area covered by the whole length of the arm then take away the area not cleared by the wiper blade.

Segments of a circle

A **segment** is an area of a circle bounded by a chord and an arc.

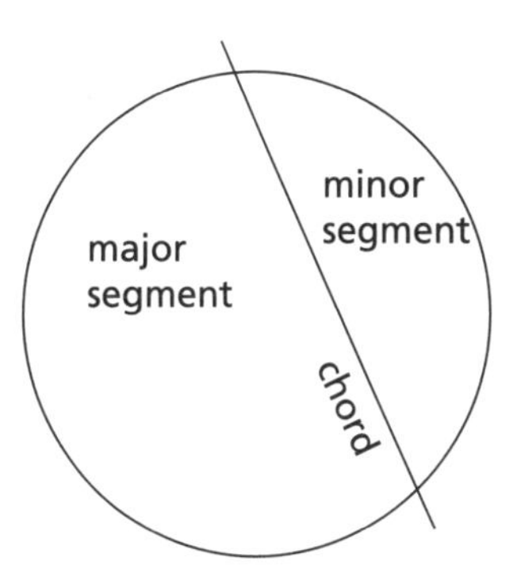

To calculate the area of a *minor segment* you first work out the area of the minor sector and then take away the area of the triangle formed by the chord and the two radii.

To calculate the area of a *major segment* you calculate the area of the major sector and then add on the area of the triangle.

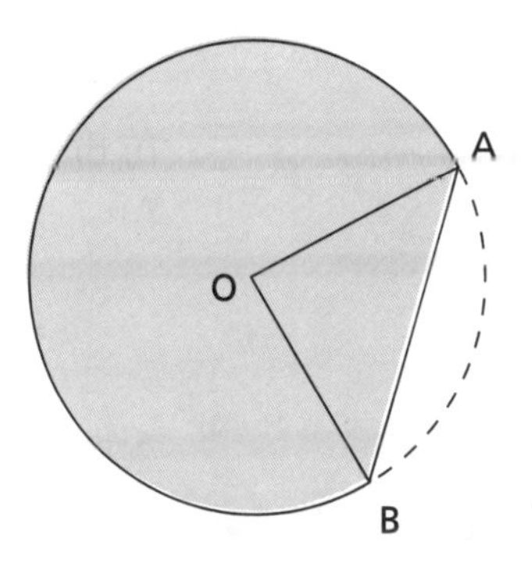

Area of segment = area of sector ± area of triangle

E.g. A gardener wishes to calculate the area of a flower bed which she knows forms a segment AB of a circle with radius 5 m. The angle subtended at the centre of the circle by AB is 130° ($\pi = 3{\cdot}142$).

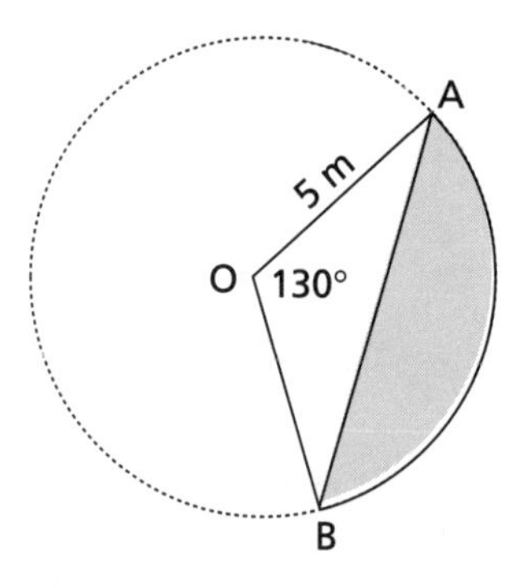

First find the area of the sector AOB.

$$\text{Area of sector} = \frac{\theta}{360} \times \pi r^2$$

$$= \frac{130}{360} \times 3{\cdot}142 \times 25$$

$$= 28{\cdot}365278$$

Area of sector = 28·365 m² (to 3 d.p.)

Now find the area of the triangle.
There are two ways to do this.

Method 1 Drop a perpendicular from O to the point X on AB. Since the triangle is isosceles, this line will cut AB in half at X.

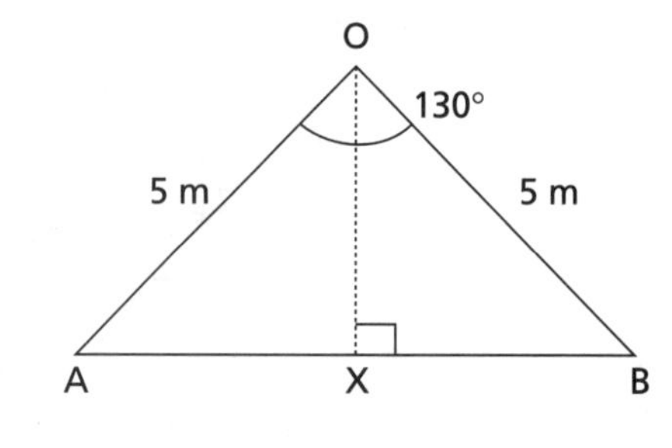

To calculate AX use sine in the triangle AOX with angle $\frac{1}{2}\theta$ and hypotenuse r.

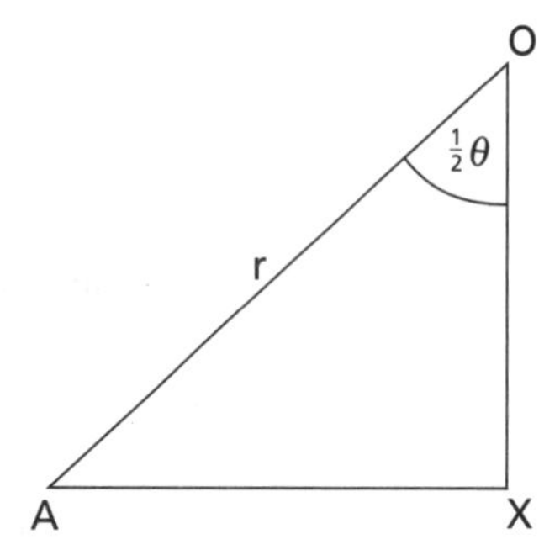

$AX = r \sin \frac{1}{2}\theta$

To calculate OX use cosine in the same triangle.

$OX = r \cos \frac{1}{2}\theta$

$$\text{Area of triangle} = \tfrac{1}{2}\, AB \times OX$$

$$= AX \times OX$$

$$= r^2 \sin \tfrac{1}{2}\theta \cos \tfrac{1}{2}\theta$$

$$= 5^2 \sin 65° \cos 65°$$

$$= 9{\cdot}5755555$$

Area of triangle = 9·576 m² (to 3 d.p.)

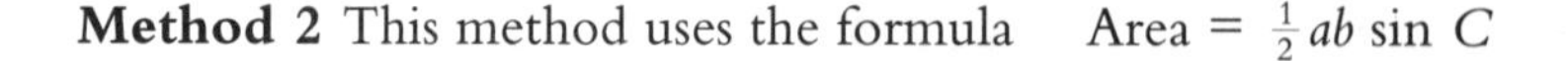

Method 2 This method uses the formula Area = $\frac{1}{2}ab \sin C$

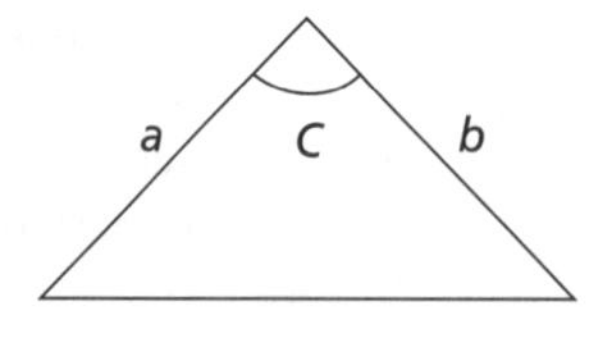

In this case the formula becomes

$$\text{Area} = \tfrac{1}{2} r^2 \sin \theta$$

$$= \tfrac{1}{2} \times 5^2 \sin 130°$$

$$= 9{\cdot}5755555$$

Area of triangle = 9·576 m² (to 3 d.p.)

Area of segment = area of sector − area of triangle
$= 28{\cdot}365\ \text{m}^2 - 9{\cdot}576\ \text{m}^2$
$= 18{\cdot}789\ \text{m}^2$
The area of the flower bed is $18{\cdot}8\ \text{m}^2$ (to 1 d.p.).

6 Water flows through a circular pipe of radius 20 cm. A flow indicator floats on the surface of the water. The indicator shows a swing of 50° from the vertical.

(a) Calculate the cross-sectional area of the water in the pipe.

(b) What volume of water in litres would there be in a section of pipe 15 m long?

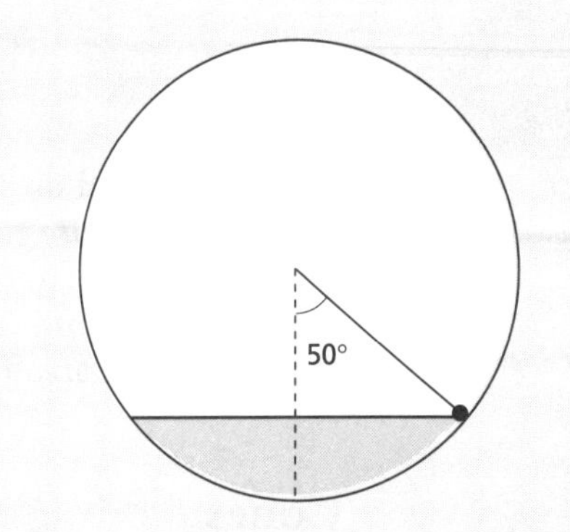

Note: $1000\ \text{cm}^3 = 1$ litre

Examiner's tip

GCSE exams might deal with this type of problem but not lead you through it in the way question 7 does.

7 A flat surface is to be milled (cut) on a steel bar with a radius of 25 mm. The width of the flat surface is to be 40 mm. This diagram shows a cross-section of the bar.

(a) Calculate the angle AOB.
(b) Calculate the area of the sector AOB.
(c) Calculate the area of the triangle AOB.
(d) Calculate the area of the segment to be removed from the bar.

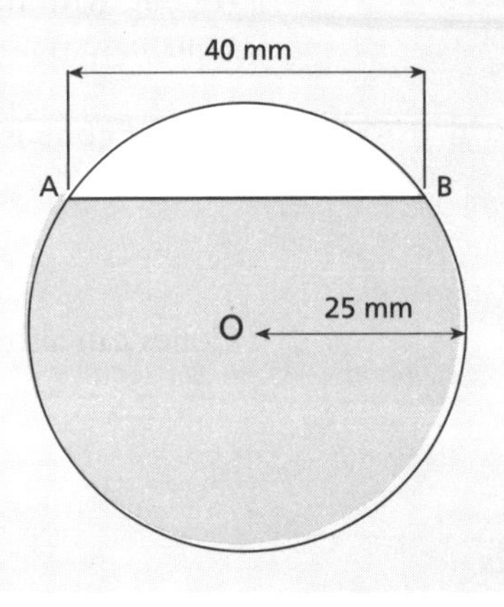

Cylinders

You already know how to calculate the volume of a cylinder.
Volume of a cylinder = $\pi r^2 h$

Now we will look at the surface area of a cylinder. Imagine a hollow cylinder opened out. Each end of the cylinder becomes a circle and the curved surface of the cylinder becomes a rectangle.

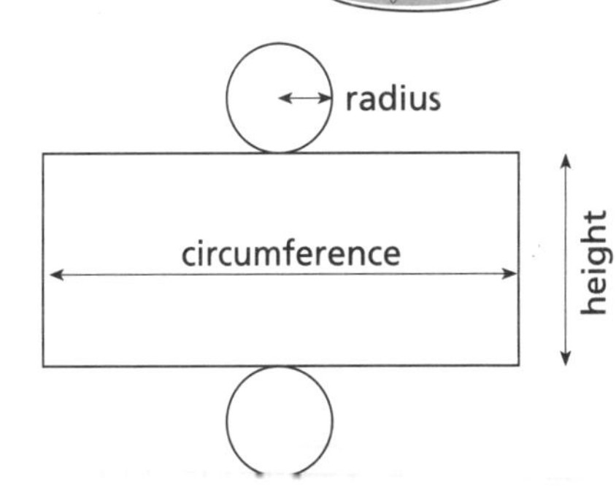

Curved surface area of a cylinder = circumference × height
Curved surface area of a cylinder = $2\pi rh$
Adding on the area of the ends gives:
Total surface area of a cylinder = $2\pi r^2 + 2\pi rh$ or $2\pi r(r + h)$

E.g. Work out the total surface area of a cylinder with a radius of 20 cm and a height of 40 cm ($\pi = 3{\cdot}142$).

Surface area $= 2\pi r^2 + 2\pi rh = 2\pi r(r + h)$
$= 2 \times 3{\cdot}142 \times 20\ (20 + 40)$
$= 7540{\cdot}8$
Total surface area of cylinder $= 7540{\cdot}8\ \text{cm}^2$

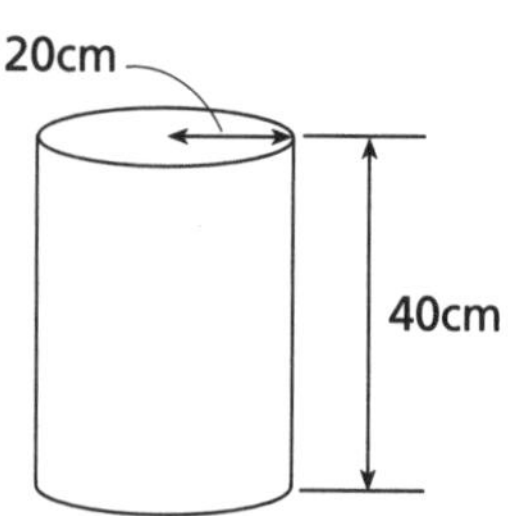

8 A steel band uses oil drums with a diameter of 80 cm and a height of 100 cm. The drums are to be painted a new colour for a carnival.
(a) Calculate the curved surface area of each drum to be painted.
(b) If the band decides to paint the bottom ends of the drums as well, what surface area of each drum will need to be painted?

Cones

A **cone** is a circular based pyramid.

A cone with its point (apex) above the centre of its base is a *right cone.*

A right cone is usually just called a cone.

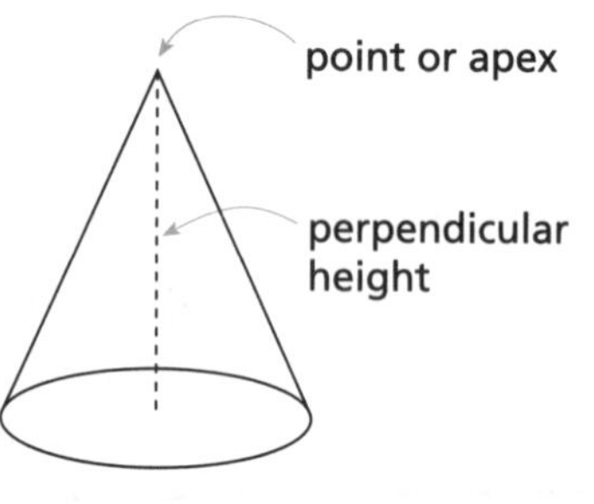

Cones can also be skewed (pushed over).

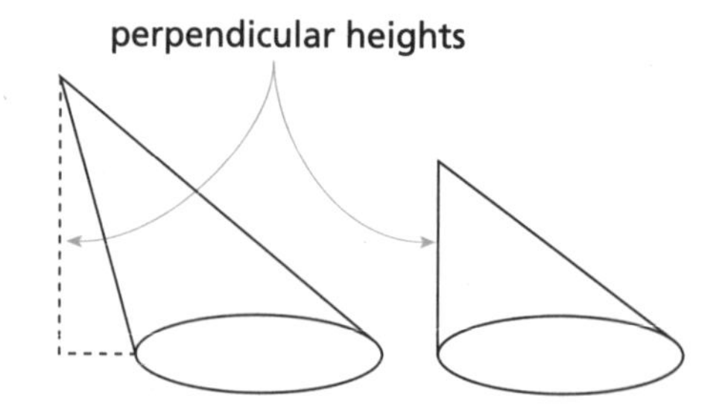

The volume of a cone (or any pyramid) is one third of the area of the base × the perpendicular height.
Volume of a cone $= \frac{1}{3}\pi r^2 h$

Note: A cone is a circular base pyramid.
The volume of a pyramid $= \frac{1}{3}$ base × height.

E.g. A pile of sand has been tipped in the shape of a cone. The diameter at the base of the pile is 1·8 m and the height is 0·6 m. Calculate the volume of sand to 1 decimal place ($\pi = 3{\cdot}14$).

Volume of a cone $= \frac{1}{3}\pi r^2 h$
$= \frac{1}{3} \times 3{\cdot}14 \times 0{\cdot}9^2 \times 0{\cdot}6$
$= 0{\cdot}50868$
Volume of sand $= 0{\cdot}5\ \text{m}^3$ (to 1 d.p.)

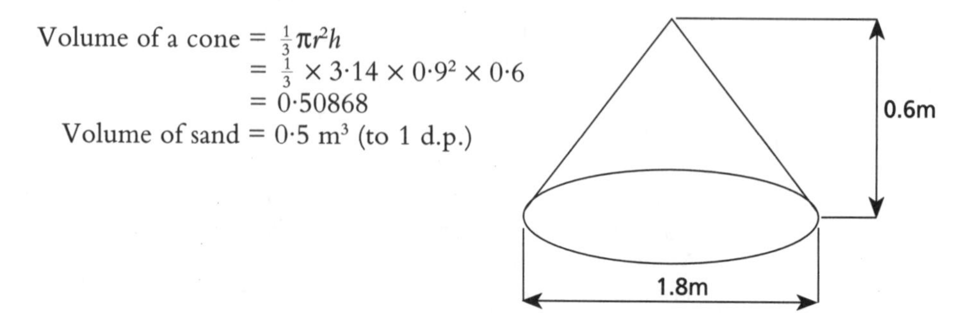

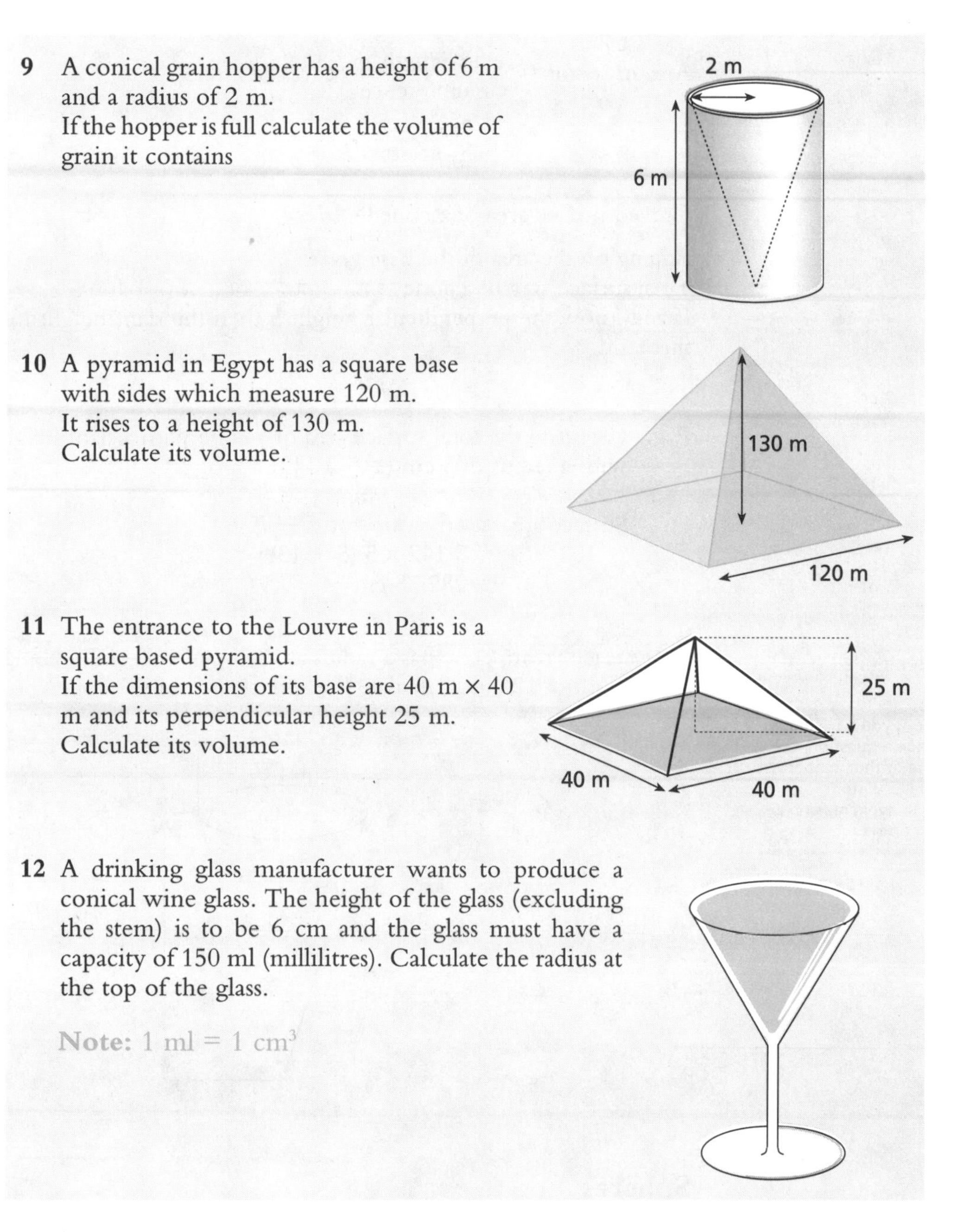

9 A conical grain hopper has a height of 6 m and a radius of 2 m.
If the hopper is full calculate the volume of grain it contains

10 A pyramid in Egypt has a square base with sides which measure 120 m.
It rises to a height of 130 m.
Calculate its volume.

11 The entrance to the Louvre in Paris is a square based pyramid.
If the dimensions of its base are 40 m × 40 m and its perpendicular height 25 m.
Calculate its volume.

12 A drinking glass manufacturer wants to produce a conical wine glass. The height of the glass (excluding the stem) is to be 6 cm and the glass must have a capacity of 150 ml (millilitres). Calculate the radius at the top of the glass.

Note: 1 ml = 1 cm^3

If you open out a hollow cone the base is a circle and the curved surface forms a sector of a larger circle.

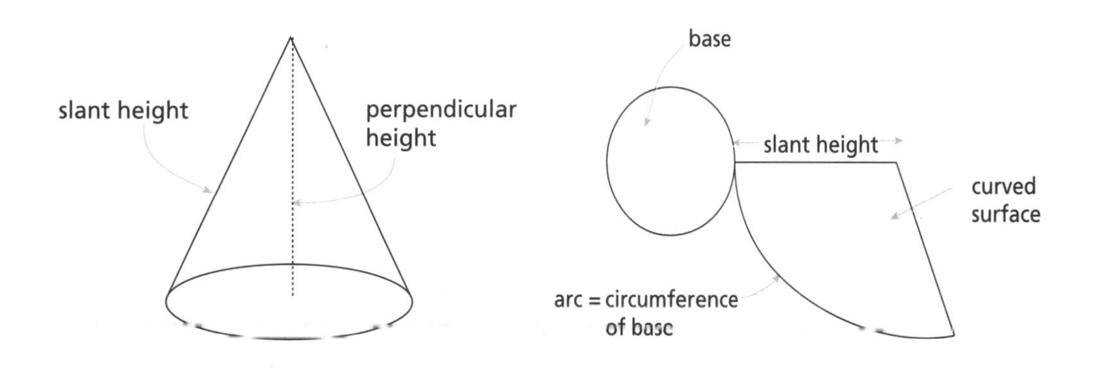

The arc length of this sector is equal to the circumference of the base and the radius of the sector is equal to the slant height *l*.

$$\text{Area of sector} = \frac{\text{arc length}}{\text{circumference}} \times \text{area of circle}$$
$$= \frac{2\pi r}{2\pi l} \times \pi l^2$$

Curved surface area of a cone = πrl

Adding on the area of the base gives:
Total surface area of a cone = $\pi r^2 + \pi rl$ or $\pi r(r + l)$
If you know the perpendicular height h then the slant height l is given by Pythagoras' theorem:

$$l = \sqrt{r^2 + h^2}$$

E.g. Calculate the total surface area of a cone with a slant height of 13 cm and a base with a radius of 5 cm ($\pi = 3{\cdot}142$).

Surface area $= \pi r^2 + \pi rl = \pi\, r(r + l)$
$= 3{\cdot}142 \times 5\,(5 + 13)$
$= 282{\cdot}78\ \text{cm}^2$

Examiner's tip

When you are using calculations you have made to continue a question, use the whole of the number and your calculator's memory to avoid making rounding errors.

13 An ice cream cone has a radius at the open end of 3 cm and a perpendicular height of 12 cm. Calculate the surface area of the cone.

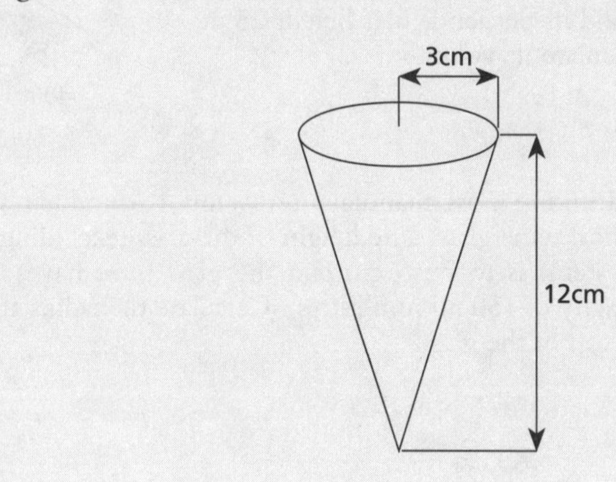

Spheres

Volume of a sphere = $\frac{4}{3}\pi r^3$

Surface area of a sphere = $4\pi r^2$

E.g. Find the volume and surface area of a football with a radius of 10 cm ($\pi = 3{\cdot}142$).

Volume $= \frac{4}{3}\pi r^3$
$= \frac{4}{3} \times 3{\cdot}142 \times 10^3$
$= 4189{\cdot}33\ \text{cm}^3$ (to 2 d.p.)

Surface area $= 4\pi r^2$
$= 4 \times 3{\cdot}142 \times 10^2$
$= 1256{\cdot}8\ \text{cm}^2$

A **hemisphere** is half a sphere.

Volume of a hemisphere = $\frac{2}{3}\pi r^3$

Curved surface area of a hemisphere = $2\pi r^2$
Adding on the area of the flat circular face of a hemisphere gives:
Total surface area of a hemisphere = $3\pi r^2$

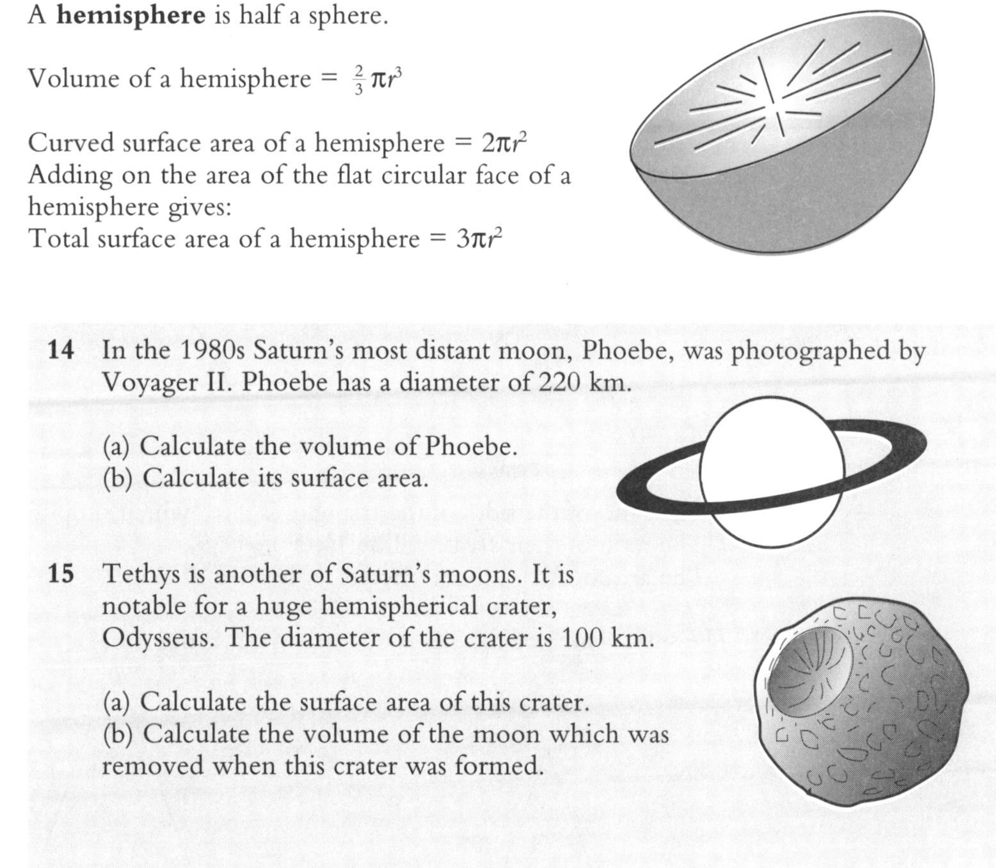

14 In the 1980s Saturn's most distant moon, Phoebe, was photographed by Voyager II. Phoebe has a diameter of 220 km.

(a) Calculate the volume of Phoebe.
(b) Calculate its surface area.

15 Tethys is another of Saturn's moons. It is notable for a huge hemispherical crater, Odysseus. The diameter of the crater is 100 km.

(a) Calculate the surface area of this crater.
(b) Calculate the volume of the moon which was removed when this crater was formed.

16 If the cone in question 13 is completely filled with ice cream and a hemispherical scoop is added on top, calculate the total volume of ice cream.

11.7 Areas and volumes of similar figures

If two figures are similar then corresponding edges on the two figures are always in the same ratio.

The ratio of the lengths of the sides of these cubes is 2 : 3.

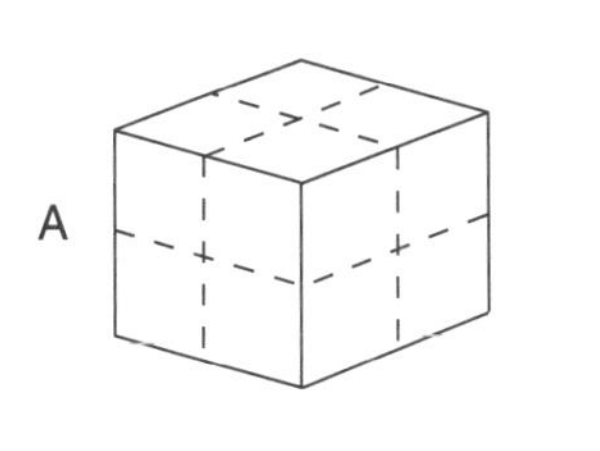

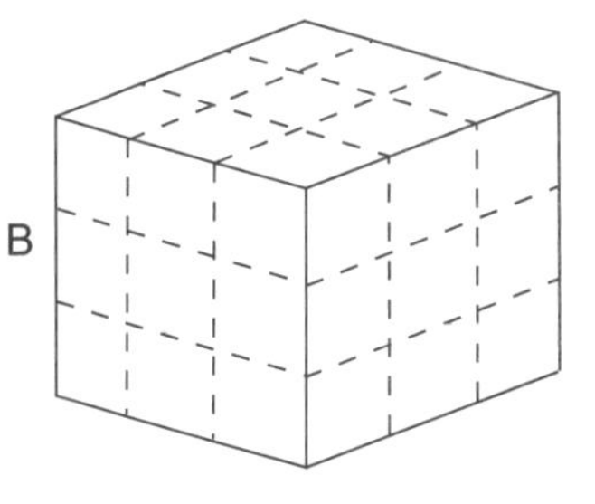

Ratio of areas

The area of a face on cube A is $2 \times 2 = 4$ square units.
The area of a face on cube B is $3 \times 3 = 9$ square units.
So the areas of the faces are in the ratio 4 : 9.
A cube has 6 faces so the surface area of A is $6 \times 4 = 24$ cm^2 and the surface area of B is $9 \times 4 = 54$ cm^2. The ratio of the surface areas is 24 : 54.
This can be simplified by dividing both numbers by 6 to give a ratio for the total surface areas of 4 : 9.

If you compare this result with the ratio of the lengths you should notice that the ratio of the **surface areas** of these two similar solids is the ratio of the **square** of the lengths of their sides.

If the ratio of the lengths is $A : B$
then the ratio of the areas is $A^2 : B^2$

Note: Area is measured in **square** units. The ratio of the areas is the ratio of the **squares** of the lengths.

E.g. Triangles A and B are similar (they have the same angles). If the area of triangle A is 1·8 cm^2 what is the area of triangle B?

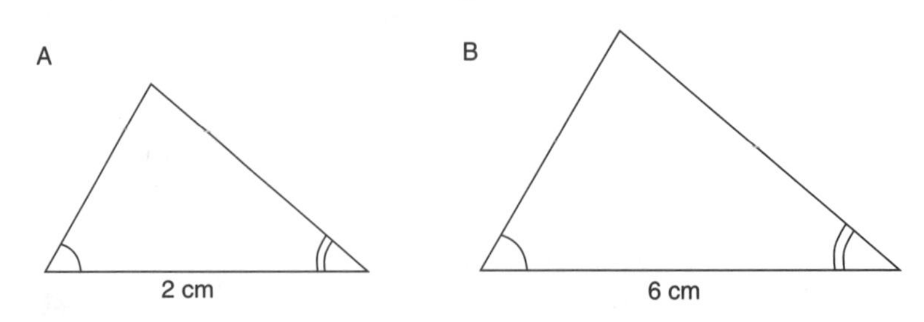

The ratio of the sides of the triangles is 2 : 6 which simplifies to 1 : 3.
The ratio of their areas will be $1^2 : 3^2 = 1 : 9$.
The area of A = 1·8 cm^2 therefore the area of B = 9 × 1·8 = 16·2 cm^2.

1 The surface area of cone C is 600 m^2. What is the surface area of cone D?

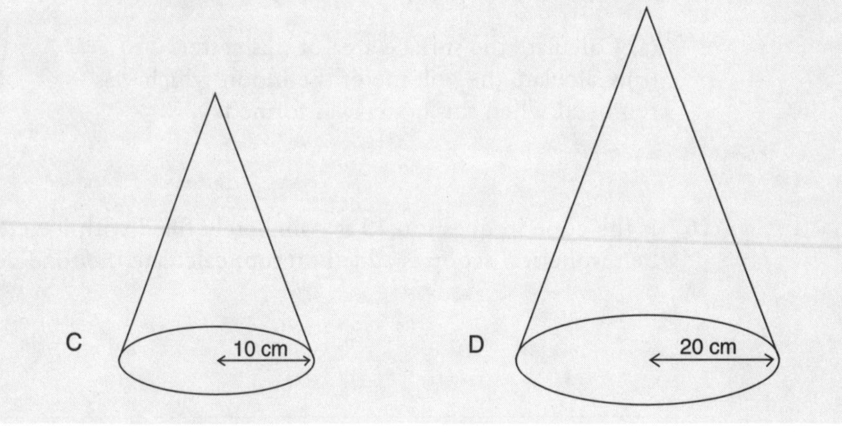

Ratio of volumes

Now consider the volume of the cubes A and B.
Volume of A = $2 \times 2 \times 2 = 2^3 = 8$ cubed units
Volume of B = $3 \times 3 \times 3 = 3^3 = 27$ cubed units
The ratio of the volumes is $2^3 : 3^3$ or 8 : 27.

If the ratio of the lengths is $A : B$
then the ratio of the volumes is $A^3 : B^3$

Note: Volume is measured in **cubed** units. The ratio of the volumes is the ratio of the **cubes** of the lengths.

2 The radius of a small moon is 100 km. The moon orbits a planet with a radius of 5000 km.
(a) Calculate the ratio of the radius of the moon to the radius of the planet.
(b) Calculate the ratio of their surface areas.

Note: You do not need to calculate the surface areas.

(c) Calculate the ratio of their volumes.

3 In a museum there is an exact replica of a steam locomotive. The model is 240 cm long and the real locomotive is 24 m long.
(a) Calculate the scale of the model in the form 1 : *k*.
(b) If it took 2 litres of paint to paint the model, how much paint would be needed to paint the real locomotive? (Ignore the thickness of the paint.)
(c) The real locomotive has a tank which holds 15 000 litres of water. How much water does the model tank hold?

11.8 Vectors

Two vectors can be added or subtracted to produce a third vector, called the **resultant**. On a diagram the resultant vector is marked with a double arrow head.

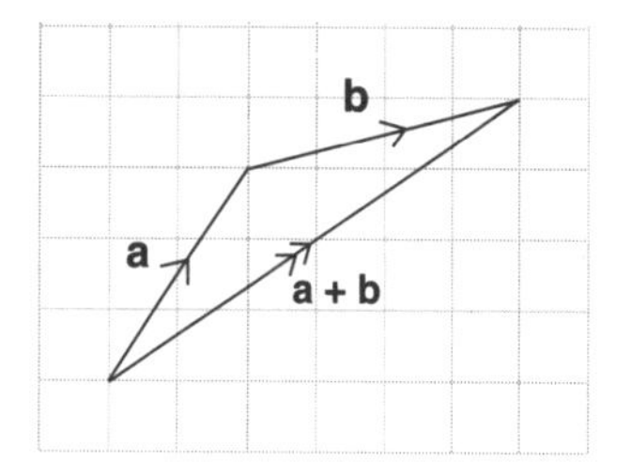

Addition

Adding two vectors means applying one vector and then applying the second. The second vector is drawn beginning at the end of the first. There are two laws governing the addition of vectors. One law says that going from A to B and then from B to C is the same as going directly from A to C. This is called the **triangle law**.

$\overrightarrow{AB} + \overrightarrow{BC} = \overrightarrow{AC}$

or

$\mathbf{a} + \mathbf{b} = \mathbf{c}$

Note: The second vector begins at the end of the first when you use the triangle law.

The second law says that going from A to C via D is the same as going from A to C via B. This is called the **parallelogram law**.

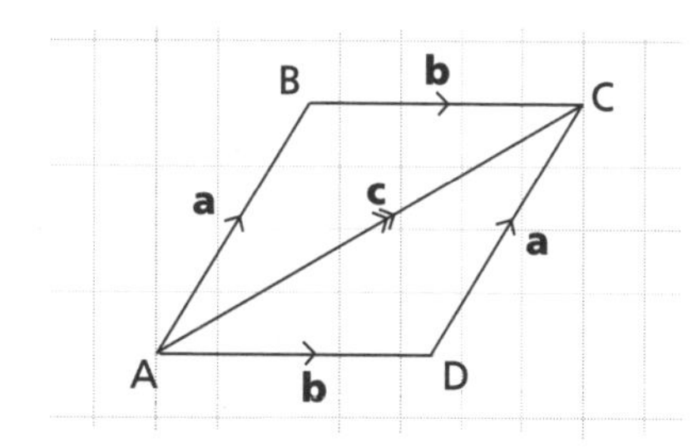

$\overrightarrow{AB} + \overrightarrow{BC} = \overrightarrow{AC}$

is the same as

$\overrightarrow{AD} + \overrightarrow{DC} = \overrightarrow{AC}$

The parallelogram law shows that the order in which you add vectors doesn't matter.

$\mathbf{a} + \mathbf{b} = \mathbf{c} = \mathbf{b} + \mathbf{a}$

Subtraction

Subtracting a vector is the same as adding its inverse.

$\mathbf{a} - \mathbf{b}$ is the same as $\mathbf{a} + (-\mathbf{b})$

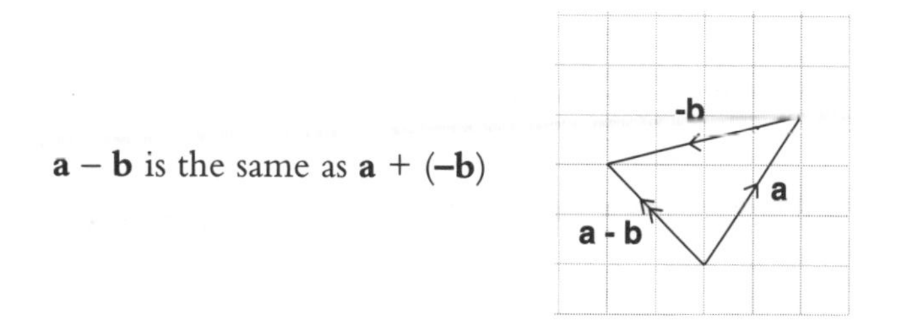

Note: The inverse of a vector has the same magnitude (length) but goes in the opposite direction.

1 Given **a** and **b** as shown in the diagram, draw the following vectors:

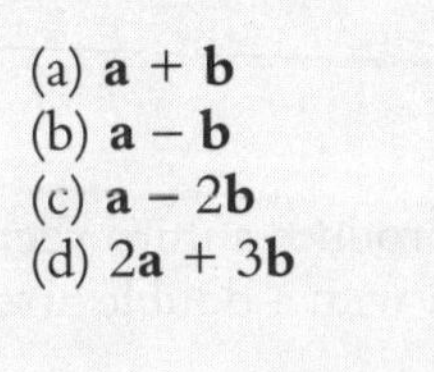

(a) **a** + **b**
(b) **a** – **b**
(c) **a** – 2**b**
(d) 2**a** + 3**b**

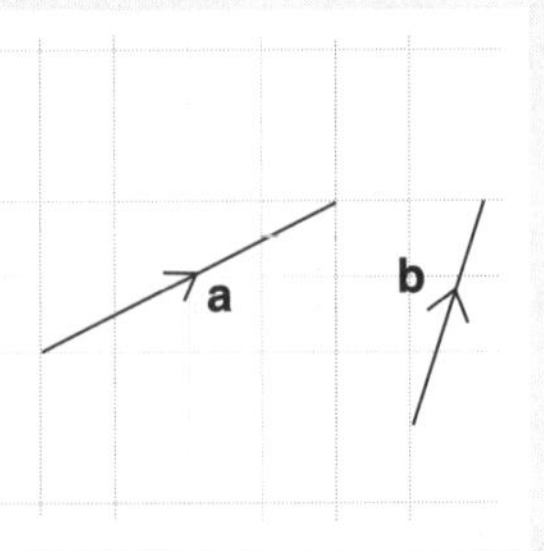

2 A quadrilateral ABCD has diagonals which intersect at E. Write each of the following as a single vector:

(a) $\overrightarrow{AB} + \overrightarrow{BC}$
(b) $\overrightarrow{AE} + \overrightarrow{ED}$
(c) $\overrightarrow{DC} + \overrightarrow{CA}$
(d) $\overrightarrow{EC} + \overrightarrow{AE}$
(e) $\overrightarrow{AE} - \overrightarrow{AD}$
(f) $\overrightarrow{BE} - \overrightarrow{BC}$
(g) $\overrightarrow{DA} + \overrightarrow{AB} + \overrightarrow{BC}$
(h) $\overrightarrow{CE} + \overrightarrow{BC} + \overrightarrow{EB}$

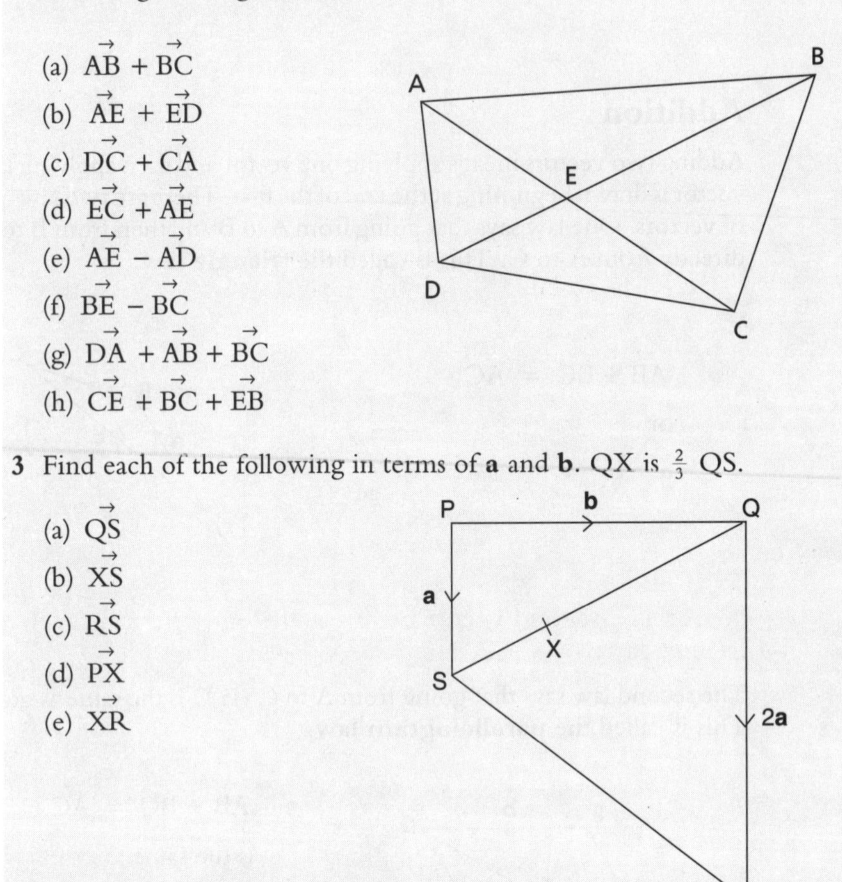

3 Find each of the following in terms of **a** and **b**. QX is $\frac{2}{3}$ QS.

(a) $\overrightarrow{QS}$
(b) $\overrightarrow{XS}$
(c) $\overrightarrow{RS}$
(d) $\overrightarrow{PX}$
(e) $\overrightarrow{XR}$

Column vectors

To add or subtract column vectors you simply add or subtract each component.

$$\begin{pmatrix} a \\ b \end{pmatrix} + \begin{pmatrix} c \\ d \end{pmatrix} = \begin{pmatrix} a+c \\ b+d \end{pmatrix}$$

4 Add the following vectors to find their resultants. (Draw the diagrams if it helps.)

(a) $\begin{pmatrix} 4 \\ 2 \end{pmatrix} + \begin{pmatrix} 1 \\ 3 \end{pmatrix}$ (b) $\begin{pmatrix} 3 \\ 1 \end{pmatrix} + \begin{pmatrix} 1 \\ 2 \end{pmatrix}$ (c) $\begin{pmatrix} 4 \\ 1 \end{pmatrix} + \begin{pmatrix} ^{-}1 \\ 6 \end{pmatrix}$

(d) $\begin{pmatrix} 3 \\ 4 \end{pmatrix} + \begin{pmatrix} 1 \\ ^{-}2 \end{pmatrix}$ (e) $\begin{pmatrix} 6 \\ 1 \end{pmatrix} + \begin{pmatrix} ^{-}2 \\ 2 \end{pmatrix}$ (f) $\begin{pmatrix} 3 \\ 2 \end{pmatrix} + \begin{pmatrix} 1 \\ 4 \end{pmatrix} + \begin{pmatrix} ^{-}2 \\ 2 \end{pmatrix}$

5 Find the resultants of the following. (Draw the diagrams if it helps.)

(a) $\begin{pmatrix}2\\3\end{pmatrix}-\begin{pmatrix}3\\2\end{pmatrix}$ (b) $\begin{pmatrix}4\\1\end{pmatrix}-\begin{pmatrix}3\\2\end{pmatrix}$ (c) $\begin{pmatrix}3\\^-4\end{pmatrix}-\begin{pmatrix}5\\1\end{pmatrix}$

(d) $\begin{pmatrix}3\\4\end{pmatrix}-\begin{pmatrix}^-2\\1\end{pmatrix}$ (e) $\begin{pmatrix}2\\2\end{pmatrix}-\begin{pmatrix}3\\^-1\end{pmatrix}$ (f) $\begin{pmatrix}3\\5\end{pmatrix}-\begin{pmatrix}^-2\\^-3\end{pmatrix}$

6 Given $\mathbf{r}=\begin{pmatrix}4\\1\end{pmatrix}$ and $\mathbf{s}=\begin{pmatrix}^-2\\3\end{pmatrix}$ write down the following vectors:

(a) $\mathbf{r}+\mathbf{s}$ (b) $\mathbf{r}-\mathbf{s}$ (c) $^-2\mathbf{s}$ (d) $2\mathbf{r}+3\mathbf{s}$

Geometry and vectors

Vectors can be used to prove certain properties and results in geometry. Because vectors have direction as well as length, they are particularly useful for showing that lines are parallel.

E.g. In the triangle ABC the points X and Y are the mid-points of AB and AC respectively. Show that the line XY is parallel to BC and half its length.

In terms of vectors, you need to show that

$\vec{BC}=2\vec{XY}$.

Then XY and BC must be parallel and

$|\vec{BC}|=|2\vec{XY}|=2|\vec{XY}|$ so XY = $\frac{1}{2}$ BC.

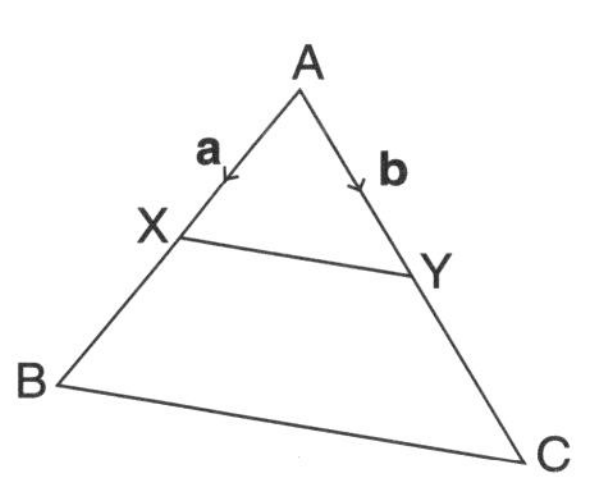

Let $\vec{AX}=\mathbf{a}$ and $\vec{AY}=\mathbf{b}$

$\vec{XY}={}^-\mathbf{a}+\mathbf{b}=\mathbf{b}-\mathbf{a}$

$\vec{AX}=\frac{1}{2}\vec{AB}$ so $\vec{AB}=2\mathbf{a}$

$\vec{AY}=\frac{1}{2}\vec{AC}$ so $\vec{AC}=2\mathbf{b}$

$\vec{BC}=\vec{BA}+\vec{AC}$
$={}^-2\mathbf{a}+2\mathbf{b}$
$=2\mathbf{b}-2\mathbf{a}$
$=2(\mathbf{b}-\mathbf{a})$

$\vec{BC}=2\vec{XY}$

E.g. PQRS is a trapezium with $\vec{QP}=2\mathbf{a}$, $\vec{RS}=\mathbf{a}$ and $\vec{QR}=\mathbf{b}$. If $\vec{XS}=\frac{1}{2}\mathbf{b}$ show that X is the mid-point of PR.

Express $\vec{PX}$ and $\vec{XR}$ in terms of $\mathbf{a}$ and $\mathbf{b}$.

By the triangle law,

$\vec{PX}=\vec{PS}+\vec{SX}$

$=\vec{PQ}+\vec{QR}+\vec{RS}+\vec{SX}$
$={}^-2\mathbf{a}+\mathbf{b}+\mathbf{a}-\frac{1}{2}\mathbf{b}$
$-\frac{1}{2}\mathbf{b}-\mathbf{a}$

$\vec{XR}=\vec{XS}+\vec{SR}$
$=\frac{1}{2}\mathbf{b}-\mathbf{a}$

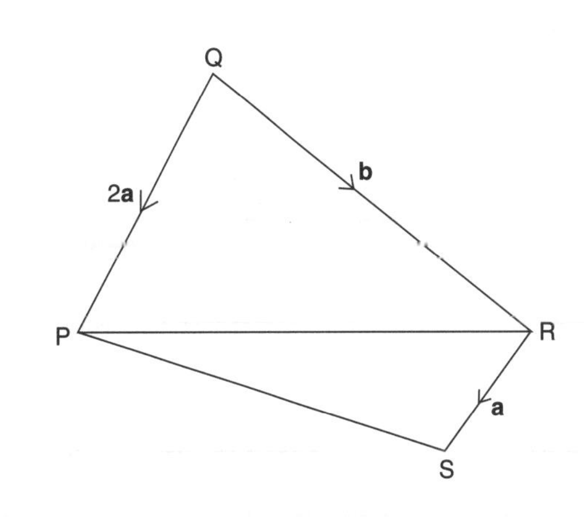

Therefore $\vec{PX}=\vec{XR}$

$\vec{PR}=\vec{PX}+\vec{XR}$
$=2\vec{PX}$

$\overrightarrow{PX}$ is in the same direction as $\overrightarrow{PR}$ so X must be on the line PR.

$|2\overrightarrow{PX}| = |\overrightarrow{PR}|$

$|\overrightarrow{PX}| = \frac{1}{2}|\overrightarrow{PR}|$

Therefore X is the mid-point of PR.

7 ABCD is a quadrilateral. The mid-points of AB, BC, CD and AD are W, X, Y and Z respectively. Show that the quadrilateral WXYZ is a parallelogram.

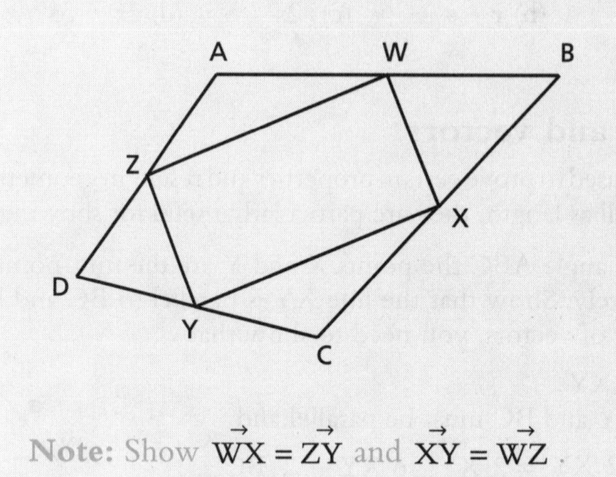

Note: Show $\overrightarrow{WX} = \overrightarrow{ZY}$ and $\overrightarrow{XY} = \overrightarrow{WZ}$.

Solving problems with vectors

You can use vector addition and subtraction to solve problems involving vector quantities such as force and velocity. In doing this type of problem it is very important to draw a good diagram, taking special care over the direction of the vectors and labelling the resultant clearly.

One way to solve this type of problem is **by drawing** an accurate scale drawing and measuring the length and angle of the resultant.

E.g. The velocity of a plane in still air is 800 km/h (called the airspeed) on a bearing of 060°.

If the wind is blowing at 100 km/h on a bearing of 300° find the actual speed (called the ground-speed) and direction of the plane.

The actual velocity of the plane is the sum of its velocity in still air and the wind velocity.

The resultant of the two vectors gives a bearing of 053° and a speed of 750 km/h.

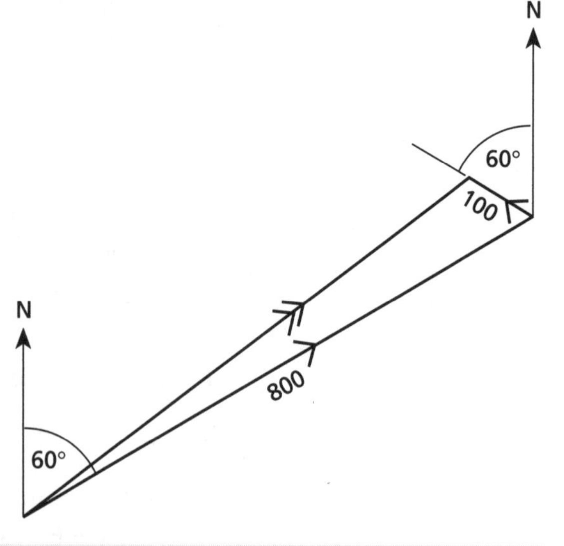

8 In still air a plane has air speed 300 km/h and flies on a bearing of 110°. If the wind is blowing at a speed of 100 km/h from a bearing of 060°, find the actual velocity of the plane.

Another way to solve problems involving vectors is **using trigonometry**, including the trigonometrical ratios and Pythagoras' theorem. This is easiest when the vectors are at right angles to each other.

E.g. A man rows from his house on the edge of a lake to an island 1 km due North in the middle of the lake. It takes him 30 minutes. When he reaches the island the man learns that the current is flowing due East with a speed of 1 km/h. What direction did the man have to row in to reach the island? How fast did he row?

To find the velocity of the man's course you have to subtract the velocity of the current from his actual velocity. The man took 30 minutes to travel 1 km so his actual speed was 2 km/h and his actual direction was North. The velocity of the current was 1 km/h East.

Let θ be the angle the man's course makes with North. His bearing will be $360° - \theta$.

$\tan \theta = \frac{\text{opposite}}{\text{adjacent}} = \frac{1}{2}$

$\theta = 26{\cdot}565051°$

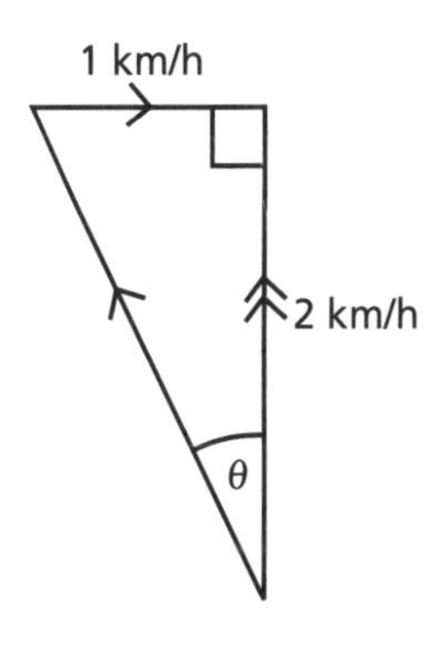

So the man's bearing was 333° (to the nearest degree).

To find his speed use Pythagoras:
$x^2 = 1^2 + 2^2 = 5$
$x = 2{\cdot}236068$

The man rowed at a speed of 2·24 km/h (to 2 d.p.).

9 A boat whose speed is 8 knots sets course on a bearing of 060°. If the tide is running at a speed of 3 knots from a bearing of 330°
(a) find the boat's actual speed to 1 d.p.
(b) find the direction of travel to the nearest degree.
Note: The tide is perpendicular to the boat's direction.

If the two vectors and their resultant do not form a right-angled triangle you can use **components** to solve the problem. (At **level 10** you can use the sine and cosine rules.)

E.g. Paul and Susan are fighting over a ball. Paul is taller than Susan. He exerts a force of 70 N in a direction 30° above the horizontal. Susan exerts a force of 100 N in a direction 10° below the horizontal. Find the resultant force on the ball. Give your answer to the nearest whole units.

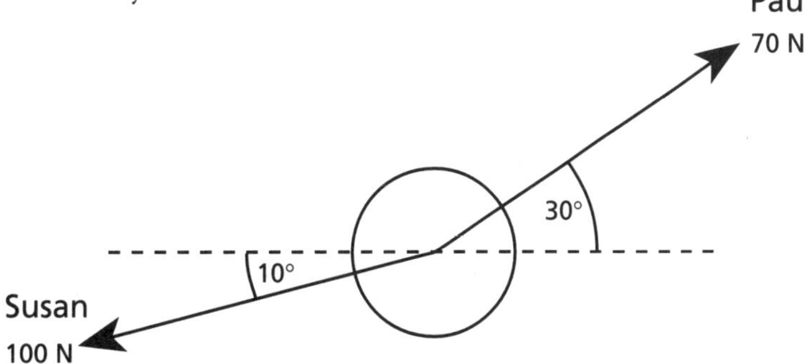

Let the force applied by Paul = **P** and the force applied by Susan = **S**.

Each force has a horizontal component and a vertical component. For example, for Paul :

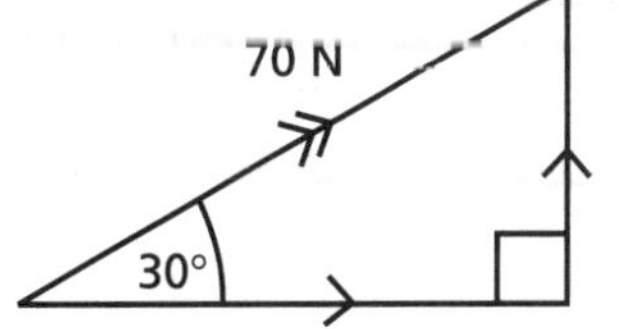

Imagine that 'up' is positive and 'towards Paul' is positive.

Horizontal component of **P** = 70 cos 30°
Vertical component of **P** = 70 sin 30°
Horizontal component of **S** = ⁻100 cos 10°
Vertical component of **S** = ⁻100 sin 10°

As you did with column vectors earlier in this unit, you can add the components of **P** and **S** to get the components of the resultant, **P** + **S**.

Horizontal component of **P** + **S** = 70 cos 30° + ⁻100 cos 10°
= ⁻37·86 (to 2 d.p.)
Vertical component of **P** + **S** = 70 sin 30° + ⁻100 sin 10°
= 17·64 (to 2 d.p.)

Use Pythagoras' theorem to find the magnitude of **P** + **S**:
$|\mathbf{P}+\mathbf{S}|^2 = (^-37{\cdot}86)^2 + (17{\cdot}64)^2$
$|\mathbf{P}+\mathbf{S}| = 41{\cdot}77$ (to 2 d.p.)

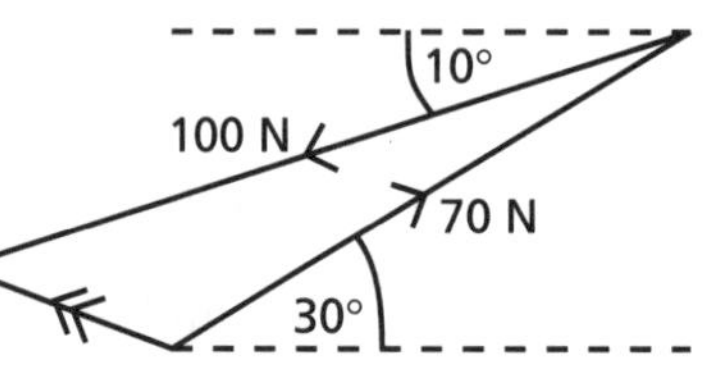

Use tan to find its direction:
$\tan\theta = \dfrac{17\cdot 64}{37\cdot 86}$

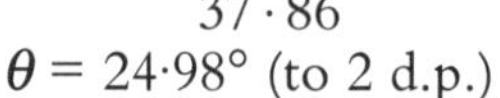

$\theta = 24{\cdot}98°$ (to 2 d.p.)

So the resultant is a force of 42 N in a direction 25° above the vertical towards Susan.

10 Jack and Jim are trying to move a piano. Jack can only push the piano forwards and Jim can only push it sideways. Jack pushes three times as hard as Jim.
(a) Find the angle the direction of the piano makes with the forward direction. (Give your answer to 2 d.p.)
(b) If Jim exerts a force of 40 N find the magnitude of the resultant force on the piano. (Give your answer to 2 d.p.)

11 A train travels at 125 mph on a bearing of 030°. A child on the train runs across a carriage at 5 mph. Her direction makes an angle of 45° clockwise with the forward direction of the train.
(a) Find the component of the child's velocity in the direction of the train.
(b) What is her total speed in this direction relative to the ground?
(c) Find the component of the child's velocity in the direction of North.
(d) Find the component of her velocity in the direction of East.
(e) By adding the components of the train's velocity, find the child's speed relative to the ground.
(f) Find her direction relative to the ground.

11.9 Sin, cos and tan of any angle

You know that in a right-angled triangle sin, cos and tan are defined like this:

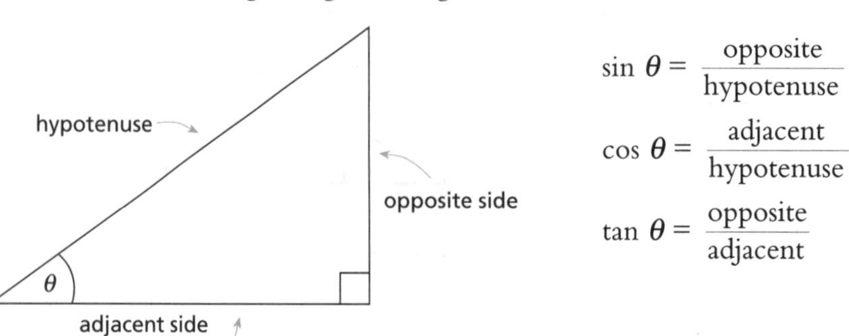

$\sin\theta = \dfrac{\text{opposite}}{\text{hypotenuse}}$

$\cos\theta = \dfrac{\text{adjacent}}{\text{hypotenuse}}$

$\tan\theta = \dfrac{\text{opposite}}{\text{adjacent}}$

But as you can see if you try to use your calculator, sin, cos and tan exist for all angles.

1 Write down the sin, cos and tan of the following angles to 3 d.p.

(a) 30° (b) 144° (c) 210° (d) 300°
(e) ⁻40° (f) 405° (g) ⁻110° (h) 520°

Note: Be careful not to omit negative signs.

To define sin, cos and tan for angles of any size you can use coordinates.

The point P with coordinates (x, y) moves on a circle with centre O and radius 1 unit.

OP makes an angle θ with the positive x-axis. The angle *increases* as P rotates *anticlockwise*.

For any angle θ, positive or negative, the sine and cosine of θ are given by the coordinates of P (because the 'hypotenuse' = 1).

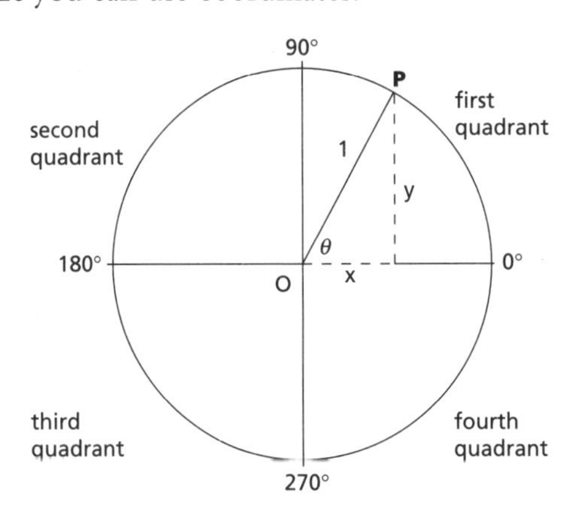

$\sin \theta = y$

$\cos \theta = x$

$\tan \theta = \dfrac{\sin\theta}{\cos\theta} = \dfrac{y}{x}$

As OP rotates, the coordinates of P change sign.

In the first quadrant (from 0° to 90°) x and y are both positive.
In the second quadrant (90° to 180°) x becomes negative.
In the third quadrant (180° to 270°) y also becomes negative.
In the fourth quadrant (270° to 360°) x becomes positive again.

This means sin, cos and tan also change sign depending on which quadrant the angle is in. The following diagram shows which of the trig ratios are positive in each quadrant.

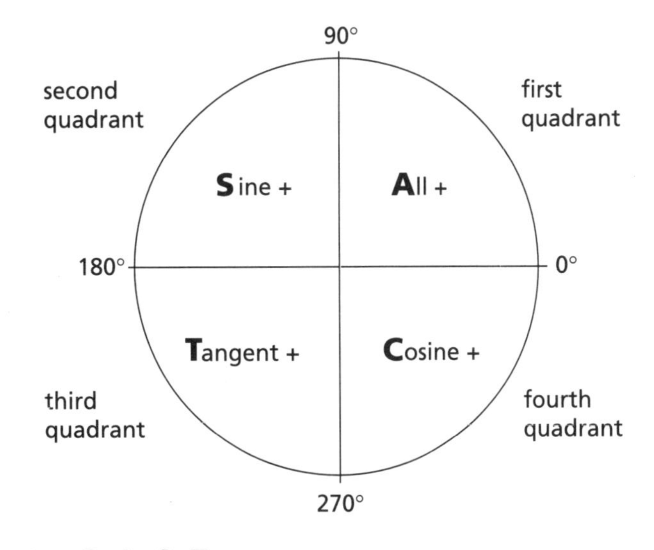

Note: Remember **C A S T**

After 360° angles continue to follow this same pattern with the point P continuing to rotate around the circle. Negative angles follow the same pattern with P rotating *clockwise* around the circle.

Repeating ratios

Look back at question 1. You may have noticed that apart from the + and – signs the answers to part (a) are the same as the answers to part (c). This is because as P rotates about O the coordinates keep on repeating the same values, with the sign being + or – depending on the quadrant. If you take an angle in the first quadrant you can find an angle in the second quadrant with the same sin, the same cos (but negative) and the same tan (but negative).

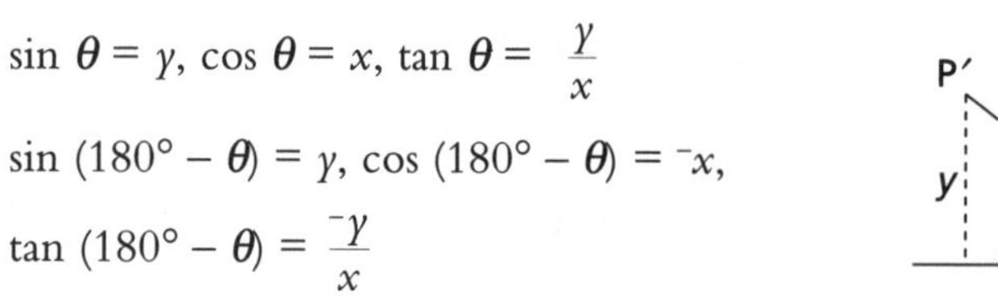

$\sin\theta = y$, $\cos\theta = x$, $\tan\theta = \dfrac{y}{x}$

$\sin(180° - \theta) = y$, $\cos(180° - \theta) = {}^{-}x$,

$\tan(180° - \theta) = \dfrac{{}^{-}y}{x}$

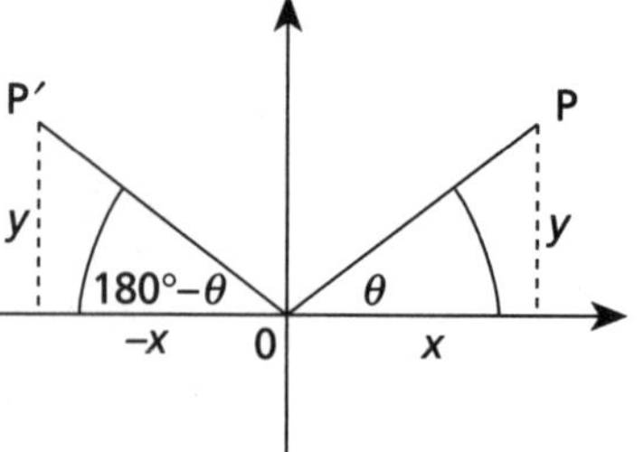

You can repeat this for any quadrant.

$\sin\theta = \sin(180° - \theta) = {}^{-}\sin(180° + \theta) = {}^{-}\sin(360° - \theta) = \sin(360° + \theta)$
$\cos\theta = {}^{-}\cos(180° - \theta) = {}^{-}\cos(180° + \theta) = \cos(360° - \theta) = \cos(360° + \theta)$
$\tan\theta = {}^{-}\tan(180° - \theta) = \tan(180° + \theta) = {}^{-}\tan(360° - \theta) = \tan(360° + \theta)$

2 (a) Write down an angle between 0° and 360° with the same sin as 52°.
(b) Write down all the angles between 0° and 720° with the same cos as 75°.
(c) Write down all the angles between ${}^{-}360°$ and 360° with the same tan as 80°.

3 Write each of the following as the sin, cos or tan of an acute angle:
(a) sin 528° (b) cos 1079° (c) tan ${}^{-}413°$

4 Find all the angles between 0° and 720° which satisfy the following equation:
$\sin\theta = 0{\cdot}5$

5 Find all the solutions between ${}^{-}360°$ and 360° of the following equation:
$2\cos\theta = \sqrt{3}$

6 Solve the following, giving your answers to 2 d.p.
$8\tan\theta - 3 = 0$ $(0° \leq \theta \leq 360°)$

Note: Remember sin, cos and tan of θ repeat for $180° \pm \theta$ and $360° \pm \theta$, with the + and – signs given by '**C A S T**'.

11.10 Sin, cos and tan graphs

You can plot trig functions using a computer or a graphical calculator. You can also draw the graphs yourself using your calculator to help you make a table of values.

1 (a) Use your calculator to make a table of the values of sin x correct to 2 d.p. for values of x from 0° to 180° in steps of 10°.
(b) Copy these axes and use the results in your table to plot the graph of $y = \sin x$ for $0° \leq x \leq 360°$. (The first four points have been plotted for you.)

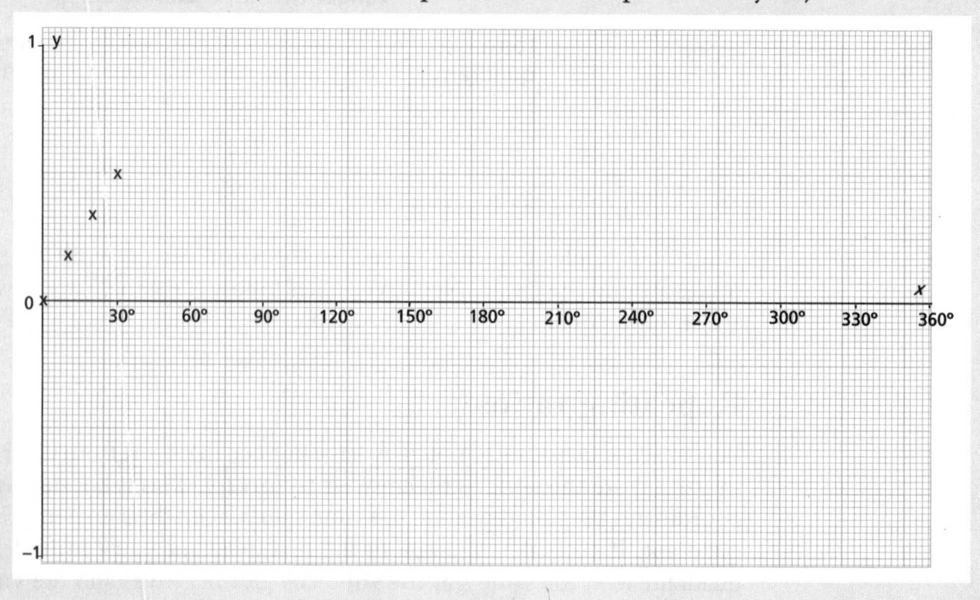

This very important graph is called a **sine curve** or sine wave. It is used to model many natural phenomena, including sound and light waves, heart beats and other types of regular motion. Because the sine function repeats every 360° the graph of $y = \sin x$ keeps on repeating the same pattern. The graph is described as **periodic** with period (wave length) 360°.

2 Repeat the method used in question 1 to draw the graph of $y = \cos x$ for $0° \leq x \leq 360°$. Use the same scale on the axes.

You should find that the graph of **cosine** is the same shape as the sine curve except that it has been translated (moved) 90° to the left. It is sometimes described as 90° *behind* the sine curve. The graph of cosine also repeats every 360°.

Note: Sine and cosine are always between 1 and $^{-}1$.

The graph of the **tangent** is a completely different shape to the graphs of the other two trig functions. The values of tan are not limited to lying between 1 and $^{-}1$.

3 Using your calculator and intervals of 10° try making a table of values of $\tan x$ for $0° \leq x \leq 180°$. Be careful not to omit the – signs.

Your calculator cannot give you a value for tan 90°. Explore what happens to $\tan x$ for values of x very close to 90°.

4 Using your table of values and the relationship $\tan \theta = \tan (180° + \theta)$ plot the graph of $y = \tan x$ for $0° \leq x \leq 360°$. Use the same horizontal axis as for the graphs of sine and cosine but you will need to alter the vertical axis.

You can see from the graph that although the curve of $\tan x$ gets very close to the lines $x = 90°$ and $x = 270°$ it never touches them. It gets very close from one side and then it jumps to negative values very close to the line but on the other side. These are described as *points of discontinuity*. The tangent of the angle cannot be calculated at these points. We say it tends to infinity.

Amplitude of sin and cos functions

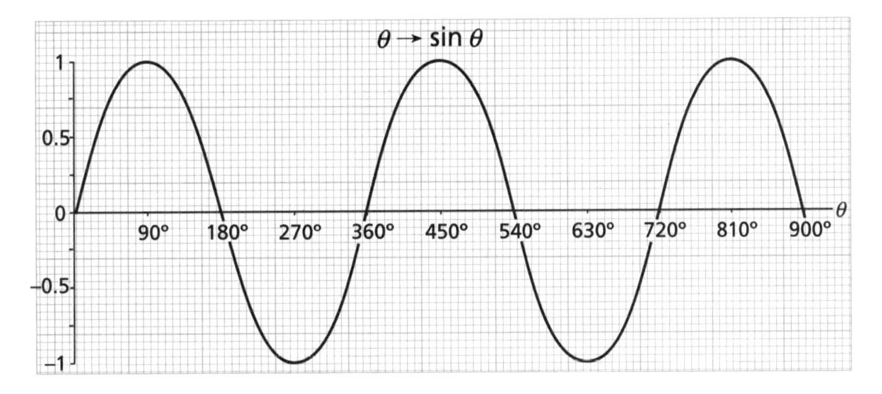

You have seen that the graph of $\sin \theta$ oscillates between 1 and $^{-}1$. So the **amplitude** of the sine curve is 1.

The amplitude can be altered by multiplying $\sin \theta$ by a number bigger than 1. This is the graph of $4 \sin \theta$.

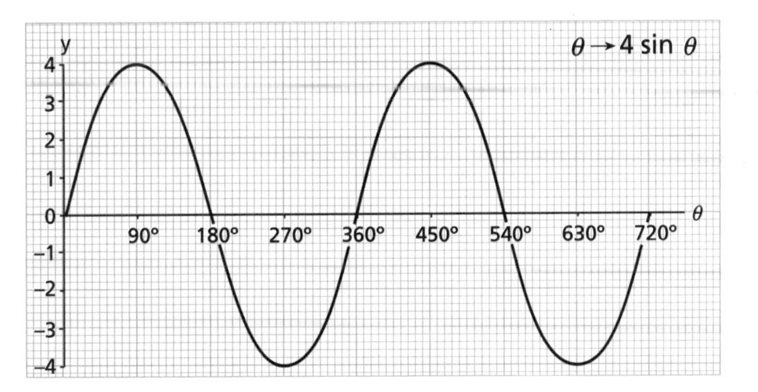

The amplitude of the wave has changed from 1 to 4 but the wave length is still 360°. It looks like the wave has been stretched vertically.

5 (a) What is the amplitude of this sine wave?
(b) Write down the function in the form $\theta \rightarrow$

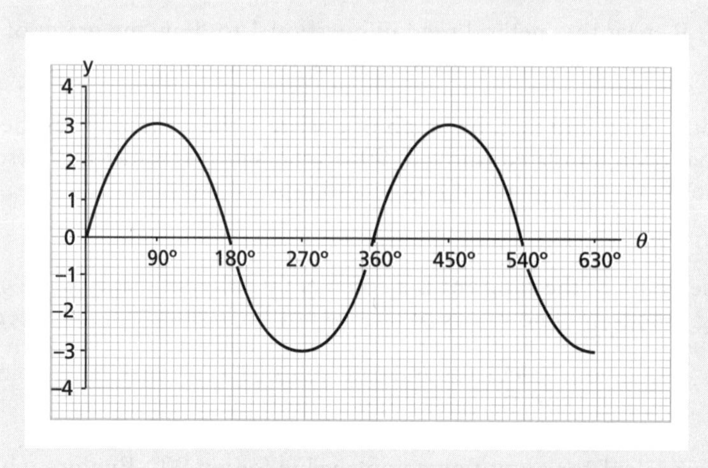

Note: The amplitude tells you the maximum and minimum values. The amplitude is given by the multiplier of sin or cos.

Period of sin, cos and tan functions

The functions sin θ and cos θ have **period** (wave length) 360°. The period can be altered by replacing θ with a multiple of θ to give functions such as sin 2θ or cos 7θ. This is the graph of sin 2θ.

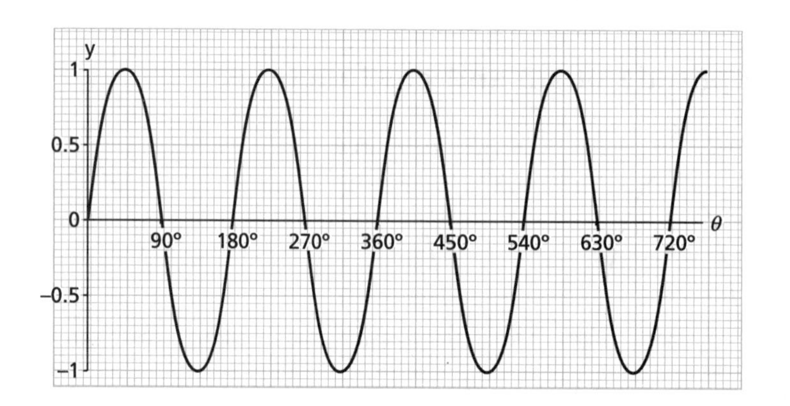

The period of the curve (the wave length) has changed from 360° to 180° because sin 2θ repeats twice in 360°. It looks like the wave has been telescoped along the horizontal axis.

6 Sketch the graph of the function $\theta \rightarrow \cos 3\theta$.

7 Write down the amplitude and period of the following functions:
(a) $\theta \rightarrow 4 \sin 2\theta$ (b) $\theta \rightarrow 5 \cos 3\theta$

8 Write down the period of the following functions:
(a) $\theta \rightarrow \tan \theta$ (b) $\theta \rightarrow \tan 2\theta$

Note: The period is the length the function takes to repeat itself. For sine and cosine functions the period is given by 360° divided by the multiplier of θ.

Solving equations

You can use graphs to solve equations involving trigonometrical functions.

E.g. Draw the graphs of $y = 6 \cos x$ and $y = 4$. Use these graphs to solve the equation $3 \cos x = 2$ for $0° \leq x \leq 360°$.

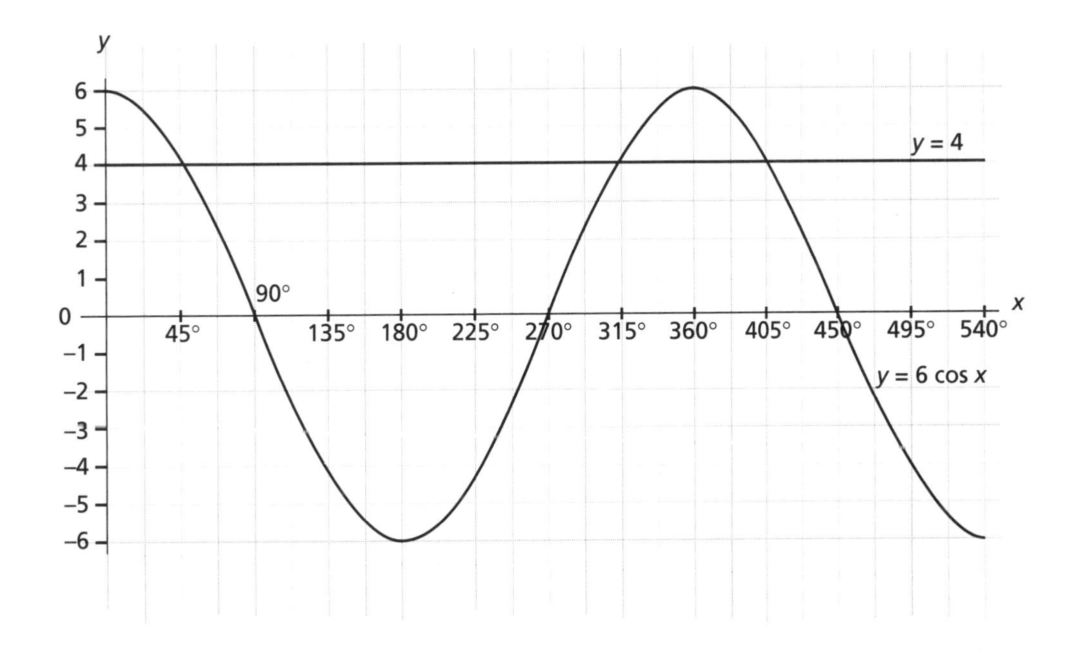

Where the graphs intersect, $6 \cos x = 4$. Dividing by 2 gives the equation you have been asked to solve. Therefore the points of intersection of the graphs will give you the solutions to the equation.
From the graph, the solutions are approximately 48° and 312°. (You can check these on your calculator.)

9 Draw the graphs of $y = 8 \sin x$ and $y = 2$. Use these graphs to solve the equation $\sin x = 0{\cdot}25$ for $0° \leq x \leq 360°$.

11.11 Sine and cosine rules

The sine and cosine rules apply to all triangles.

Sine rule

The sine rule can be used to find missing sides and angles given a side and two angles or two sides and the angle opposite one of the sides.

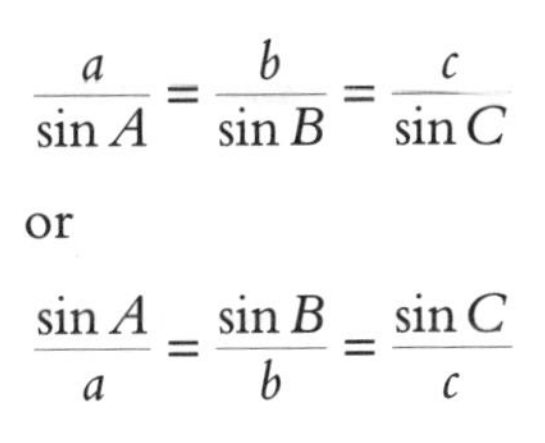

$$\frac{a}{\sin A} = \frac{b}{\sin B} = \frac{c}{\sin C}$$

or

$$\frac{\sin A}{a} = \frac{\sin B}{b} = \frac{\sin C}{c}$$

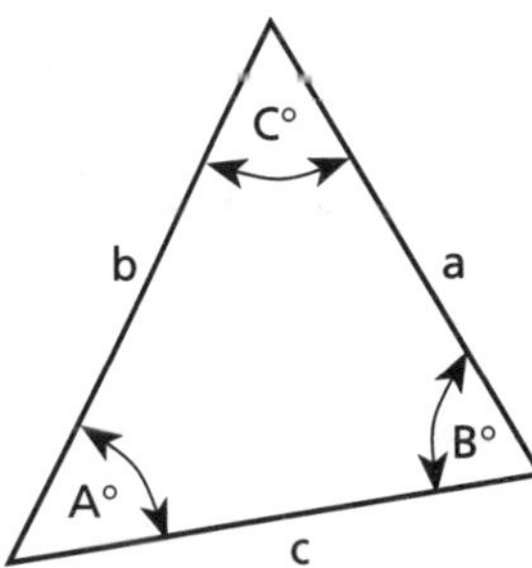

Finding missing sides

Given a side and two angles you can use the sine rule to find the other sides. You may first have to find the third angle using angle sum of a triangle = 180°.

E.g. During a survey of a triangular piece of land the following measurements were taken:

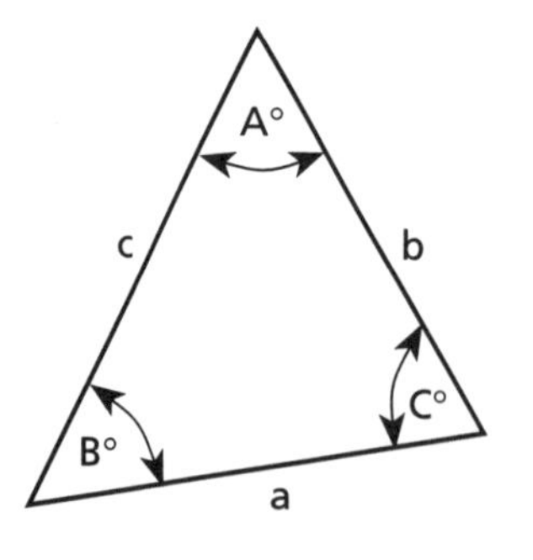

$a = 1000$ m
$B = 85°$
$C = 25°$

Calculate the length of side c.
First you need to find angle A.
$A + B + C = 180°$
therefore $A = 70°$

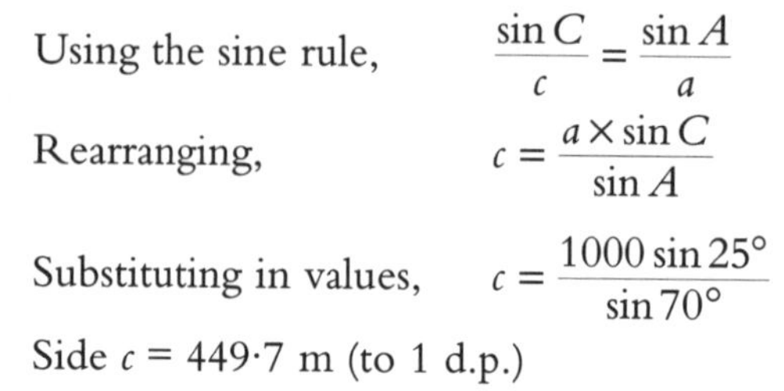

Using the sine rule, $\frac{\sin C}{c} = \frac{\sin A}{a}$

Rearranging, $c = \frac{a \times \sin C}{\sin A}$

Substituting in values, $c = \frac{1000 \sin 25°}{\sin 70°}$

Side $c = 449{\cdot}7$ m (to 1 d.p.)

Examiner's tip

Always use the given data rather than your calculated answers in case you have made a mistake!

Note: Remember to check whether an answer of this size make sense.

1 Calculate the size of the missing side b.

Finding missing angles

Given two sides and the angle opposite one of these sides you can use the sine rule to find the angle opposite the second side. You can then find the third angle using angle sum of a triangle = 180°.

E.g. In this triangle, calculate the angle C given that $A = 72°$, $a = 6{\cdot}3$ m and $c = 5{\cdot}6$ m.

Using the sine rule, $\frac{\sin C}{c} = \frac{\sin A}{a}$

Rearranging, $\sin C = \frac{c \times \sin A}{a}$

Substituting in values, $\sin C = \frac{5 \cdot 6 \sin 72°}{6 \cdot 3}$

Angle $C = 57{\cdot}7°$ (to 1 d.p.)

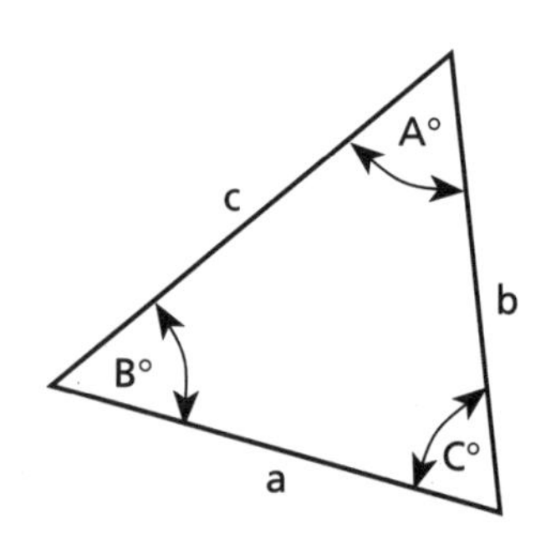

2 Find the third angle of this triangle.

3 Calculate the missing sides and angles in the following triangle.

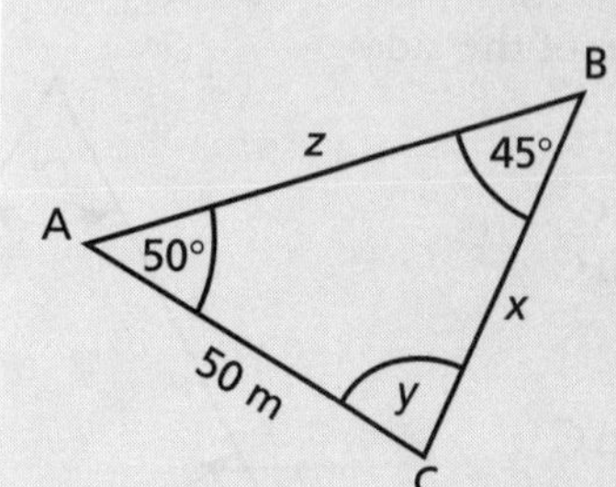

4 Two radar stations A and B pick up the same approaching aircraft at X. The distance between the stations is 143 km.
From A: The bearing of station B is 045°.
The bearing of the aircraft X is 322°.
From B: The bearing of the aircraft X is 312°.

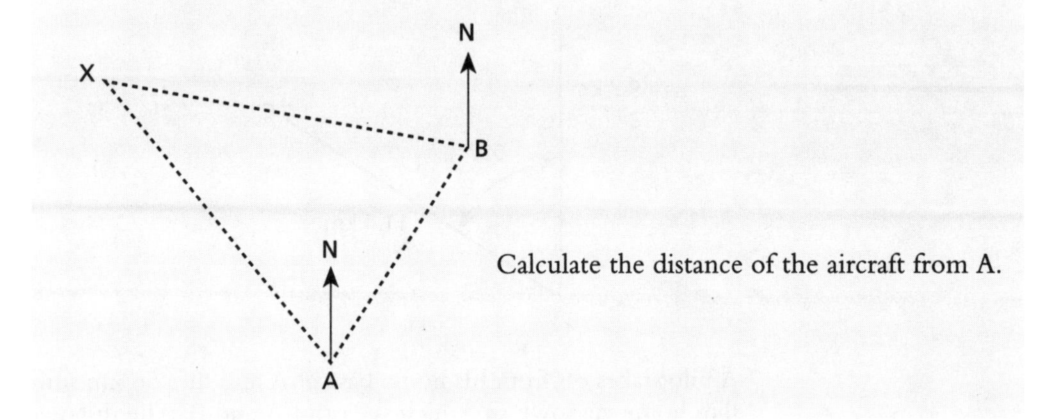

Calculate the distance of the aircraft from A.

Cosine rule

There are two ways to write the cosine rule, depending on whether you're finding a side or an angle.

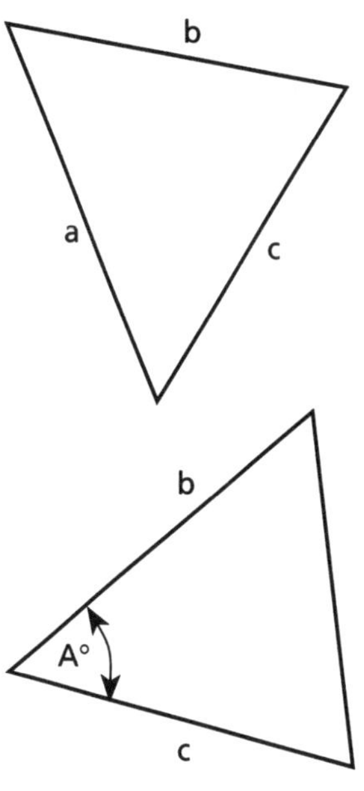

(i) $\cos A = \dfrac{b^2 + c^2 - a^2}{2bc}$

This is used to find an angle when you know all the sides.

(ii) $a^2 = b^2 + c^2 - 2bc \cos A$

This is used to find a side when you have two sides and the angle between them.

E.g. Find the missing angle A in this triangle.

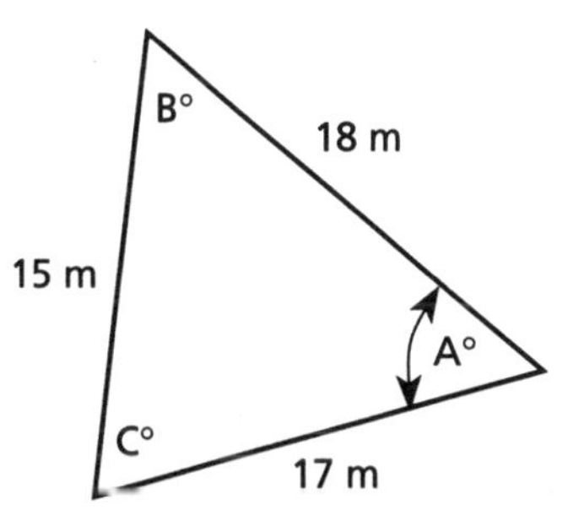

$\cos A = \dfrac{b^2 + c^2 - a^2}{2bc}$

Substituting in values,

$\cos A = \dfrac{17^2 + 18^2 - 15^2}{2 \times 18 \times 17}$

$= \dfrac{289 + 324 - 225}{612}$

$= \dfrac{388}{612}$

Angle $A = 50{\cdot}7°$ (to 1 d.p.)

Once you know two angles you can find the third in the easiest way possible.

5 Calculate angle B and hence find angle C.

6 Ayemouth is due North of Beecastle and the bearing from Beecastle to Ceewick is 057°. If Beecastle is 9·7 km from Ayemouth and 11·4 km from Ceewick, how far is Ayemouth from Ceewick?

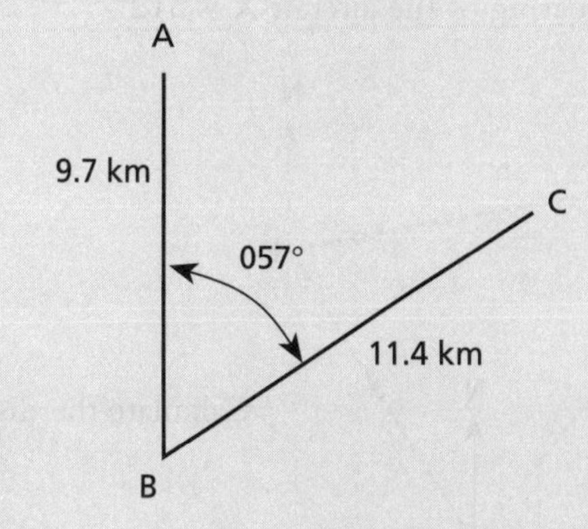

7 A pilot takes off from his home base at A and flies 56 km south to town B. He flies home via town C, which is east of A and B. The distance from town B to town C is 70 km and the distance from town C to home is 63 km.
(a) Calculate his bearing on the flight from B to C.
(b) Calculate the angle of the turn to be made at C.

Note: A good diagram helps.

The sine and cosine rules can also be used to solve problems in three dimensions by reducing the problem to a triangle in two dimensions.

11.12 Circle theorems

Cyclic quadrilateral theorems

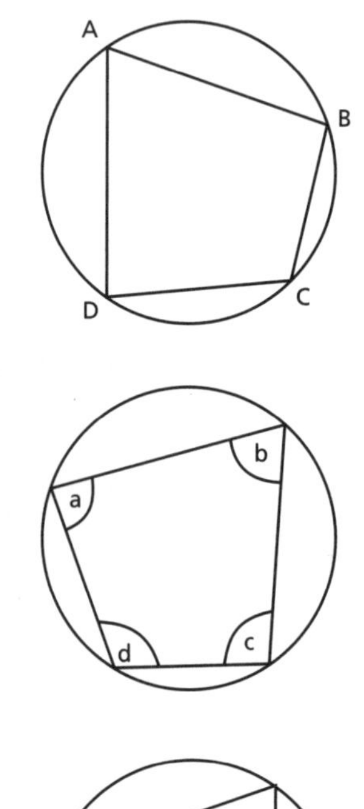

A **cyclic quadrilateral** is a quadrilateral drawn inside a circle so that all its 4 vertices (corners) lie on the circumference of the circle.
We say that the points A, B, C and D are *concyclic*.

(i) The opposite angles of a cyclic quadrilateral add up to 180° (they are supplementary angles).

ABCD is a cyclic quadrilateral.
$a + c = 180°$
$b + d = 180°$
Converse: If any two opposite angles in a quadrilateral add up to 180° then it is a cyclic quadrilateral.

(ii) The exterior angle of a cyclic quadrilateral is equal to the interior angle opposite.

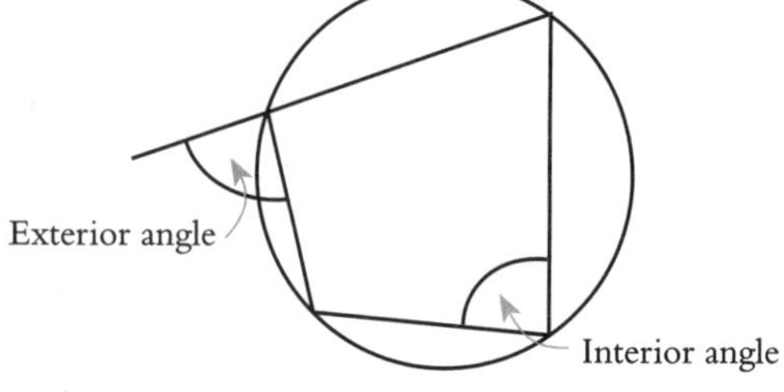

Angle theorems

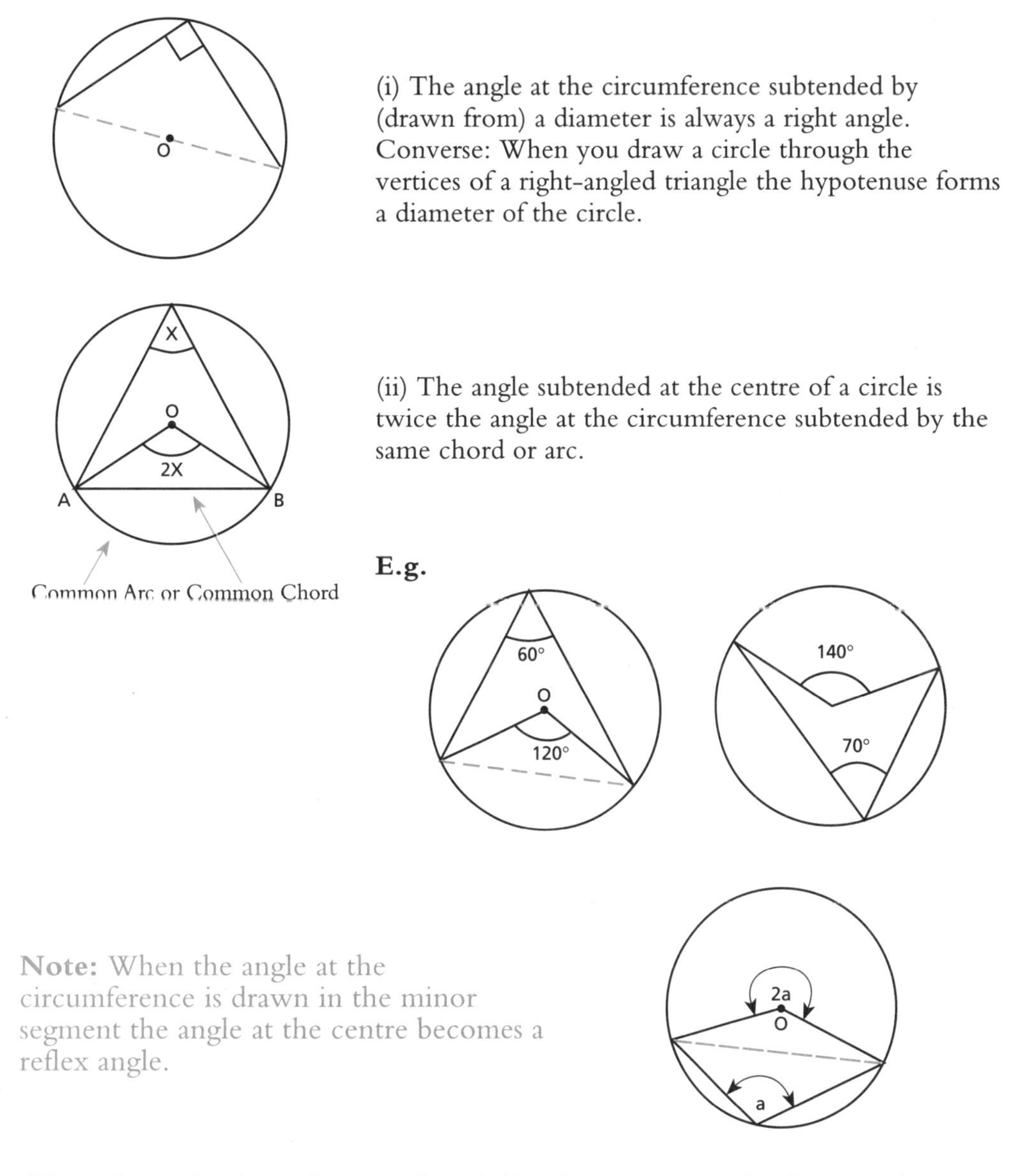

(i) The angle at the circumference subtended by (drawn from) a diameter is always a right angle. Converse: When you draw a circle through the vertices of a right-angled triangle the hypotenuse forms a diameter of the circle.

(ii) The angle subtended at the centre of a circle is twice the angle at the circumference subtended by the same chord or arc.

E.g.

Note: When the angle at the circumference is drawn in the minor segment the angle at the centre becomes a reflex angle.

(iii) Angles at the circumference subtended by the same arc or chord are equal.

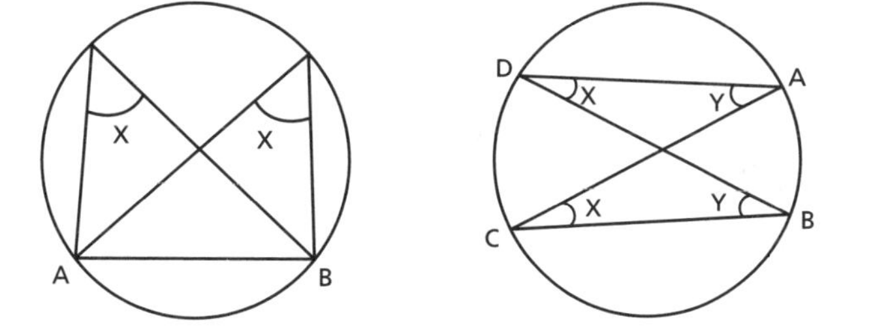

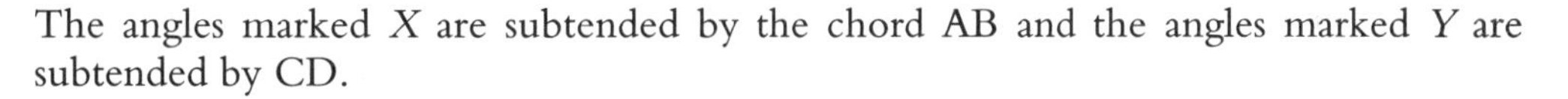

The angles marked X are subtended by the chord AB and the angles marked Y are subtended by CD.

Converse: If two triangles are drawn with a common side and the same angle opposite this side then the vertices of the triangles are concyclic.

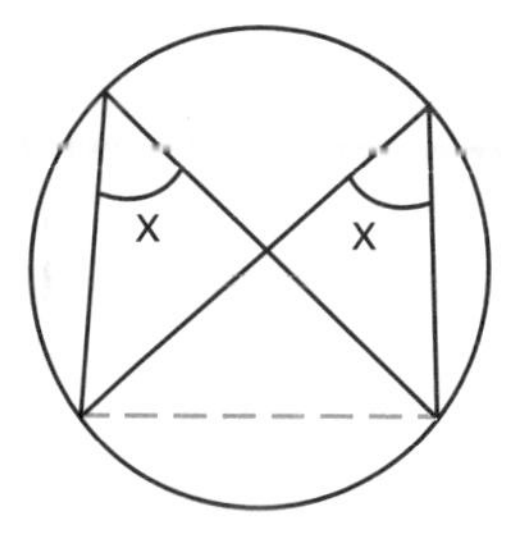

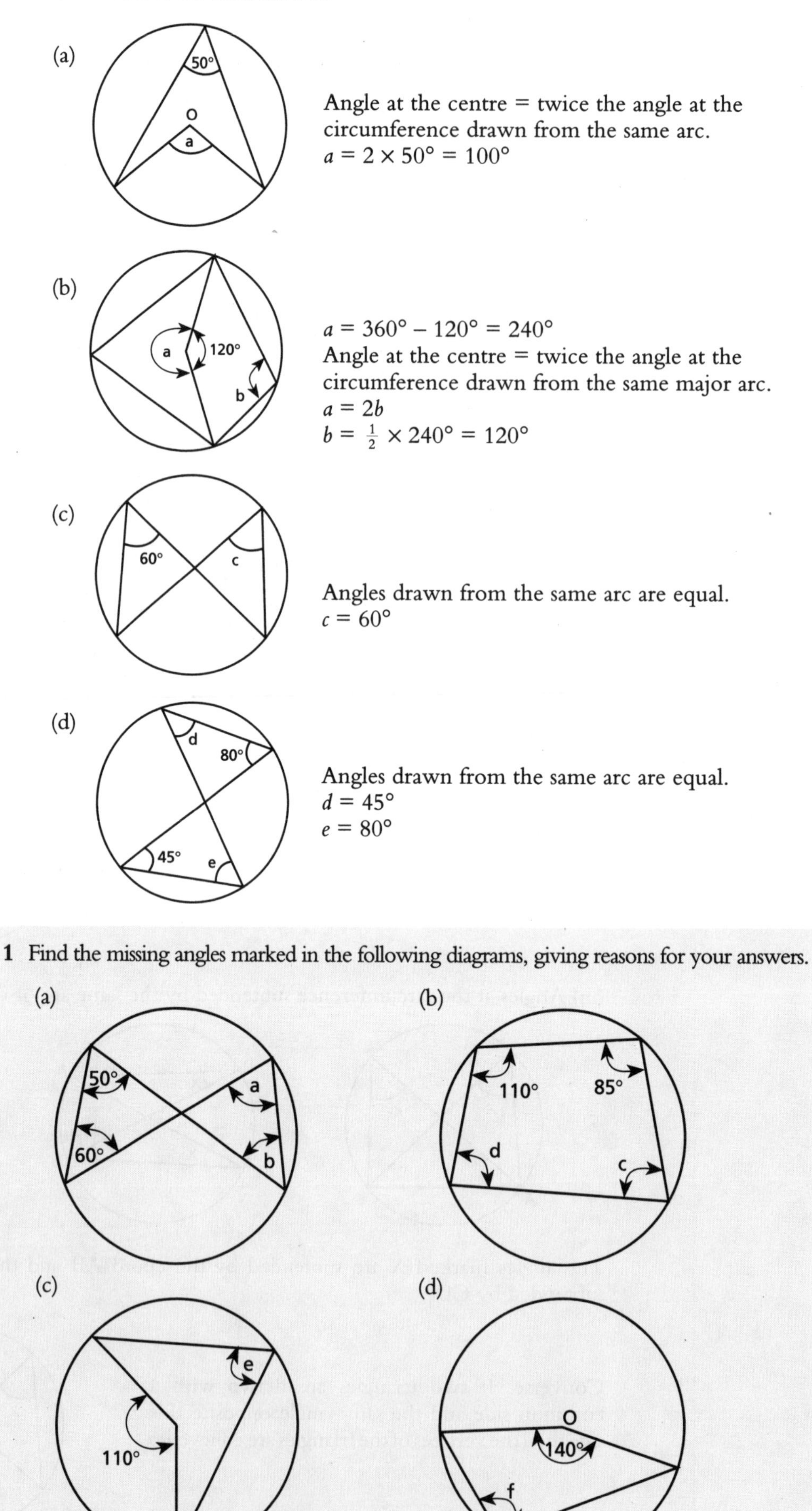

E.g. Find the missing angles in each of the following diagrams.
Give reasons for each answer.

(a) Angle at the centre = twice the angle at the circumference drawn from the same arc.
$a = 2 \times 50° = 100°$

(b) $a = 360° - 120° = 240°$
Angle at the centre = twice the angle at the circumference drawn from the same major arc.
$a = 2b$
$b = \frac{1}{2} \times 240° = 120°$

(c) Angles drawn from the same arc are equal.
$c = 60°$

(d) Angles drawn from the same arc are equal.
$d = 45°$
$e = 80°$

Examiner's tip

It often helps to put in all the angles you know.

Examiner's tip

You can also add chords if they help you solve the problem.

1 Find the missing angles marked in the following diagrams, giving reasons for your answers.

(a) (b) (c) (d)

Chord theorems

(i) The line joining the mid-point of a chord to the centre of a circle is perpendicular to the chord.
Converse: A perpendicular line from the centre of a circle to a chord bisects the chord.
This theorem is often used with Pythagoras' theorem to calculate the distance of a chord from the centre of the circle.

E.g. A chord 20 cm long is drawn in a circle of diameter 30 cm. Calculate the distance of the chord from the centre of the circle.
The shortest distance from the chord to the centre of the circle is along a line perpendicular to the chord. The theorem tells us that this perpendicular line bisects the chord.

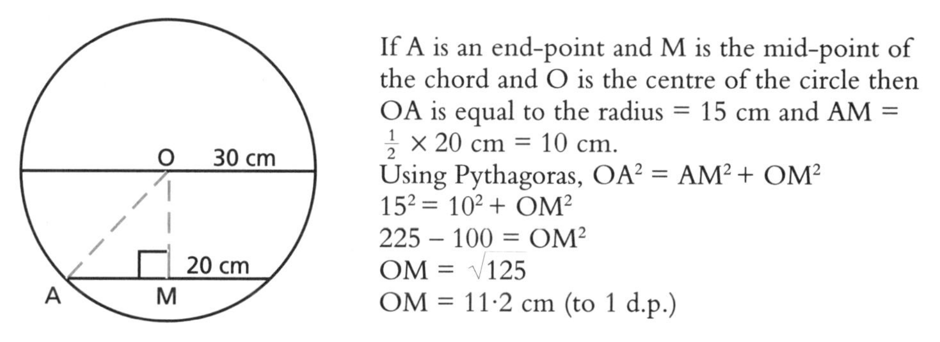

If A is an end-point and M is the mid-point of the chord and O is the centre of the circle then OA is equal to the radius = 15 cm and AM = $\frac{1}{2} \times 20$ cm = 10 cm.
Using Pythagoras, $OA^2 = AM^2 + OM^2$
$15^2 = 10^2 + OM^2$
$225 - 100 = OM^2$
$OM = \sqrt{125}$
OM = 11·2 cm (to 1 d.p.)

(ii) If two chords are the same length then they are the same distance from the centre of the circle.

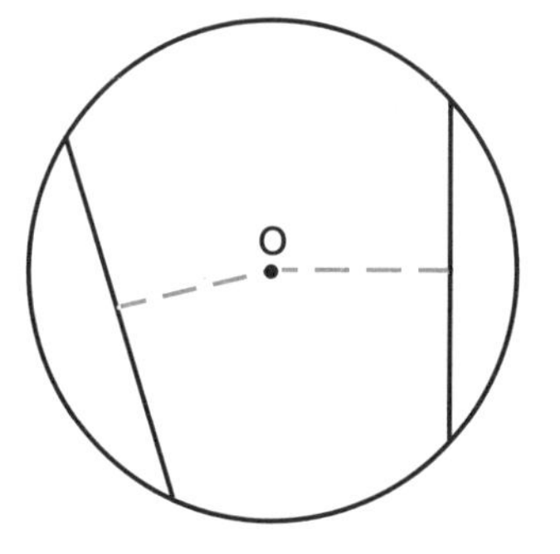

Converse: If two chords are the same distance from the centre of the circle then they are the same length.

Tangent theorems

A **tangent** to a circle is a line which touches the circle at only one point. A tangent is perpendicular to the radius at the point of contact.
(i) The two tangents to a circle from a given point are equal in length.

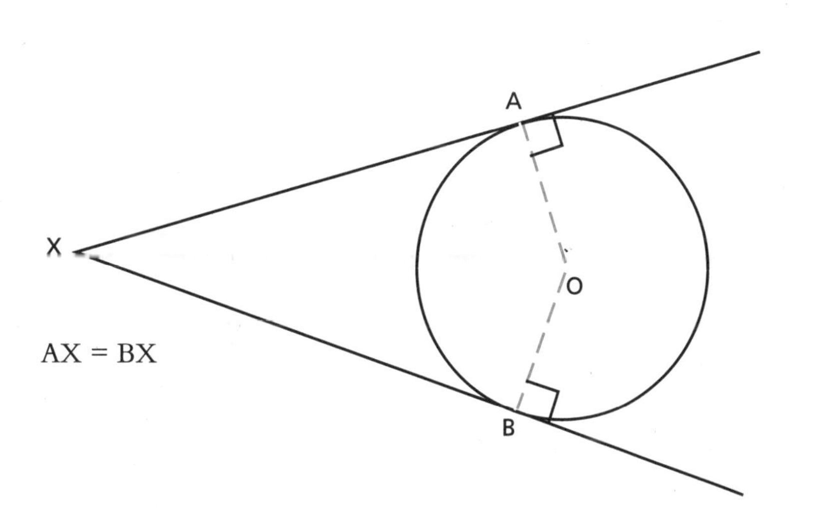

(ii) A line joining the centre of a circle to a point outside the circle:
(a) bisects the angle between the two tangents to the circle from that point.
(b) bisects the angle between the radii drawn perpendicular to the tangents.

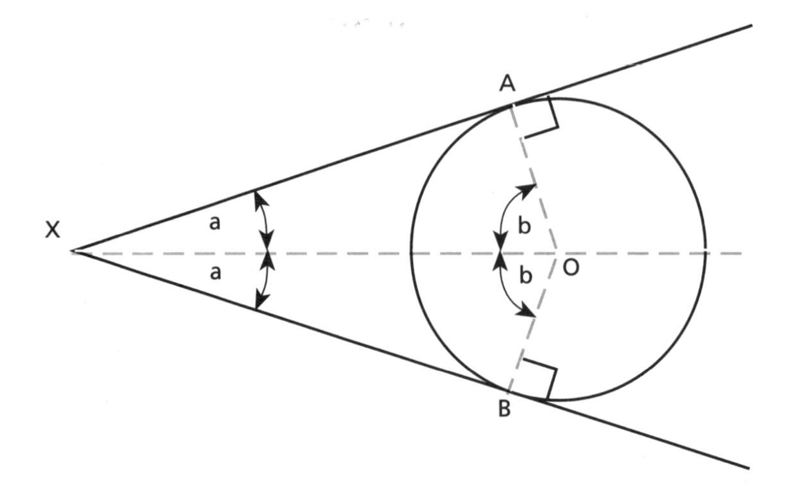

Problems on the circle often involve more than one of the theorems given in this section together with other simple angle theorems. Look for clues in the question to help you decide which theorems to use.

2 The radius of this circle is 5 cm. Chord AB is 8 cm long and chord CD is 3 cm from the centre of the circle. Show that the chords AB and CD are the same length.

3 AB and BC are tangents to this circle. The angle between them is 50°. Calculate the size of angles x and y.

4 AX and CX are tangents to the circle ABCDE. O is the centre of the circle and the angle OCA = 30°. Calculate each of the following angles, saying how you found each one.

(a) OAC (b) AOC
(c) ADC (d) AEC
(e) ABC (f) AXC

Chapter 12
Processing and interpreting

12.1 Gathered data

As part of your coursework you may have completed a survey. In an examination you will not have time to complete a survey but you may be asked to examine and criticise the results of one.

Data gathered by questionnaire

- A questionnaire should give sufficient choices to cover all possible answers.
- The information it provides must be clear and only have one possible meaning.
- Answers should be short.
- Be aware of things which might effect or change the results.

Data gathered by observation

When data is gathered by observation there are a number of factors which you will need to take into account.

- Was the survey requirement exact.
- Will the survey have been affected by the time or place at which it was carried out.
- Was the data gathered for sufficient time.
- Is the presentation of the data affecting the results.

Data gathered by experiment

- Does the experiment test the concept you wish to sample.
- Have sufficient experiments been carried out to produce results which reflect what is happening.

1 Explain what is wrong with each of the following questions:

(a) What time do you go to bed?
(b) Are you tall, average height or small?
(c) Do you prefer CDs, tapes or records?
(d) Where do you like to go on your holidays?
(e) Which colour cars do you prefer?

2 Give two possible criticisms of the following survey and results.

The results of a survey carried out in a town centre found that:
'Most people prefer shopping in large shops.'

12.2 Cumulative frequency

In data handling the frequency tells you how often a particular result was obtained. **Cumulative frequency** indicates how often a result was obtained which was less than (<) or less than or equal to (≤) a stated value in a collection of data.

The cumulative frequency is found by adding together the frequencies to give a running total.

E.g. This table of results shows the frequency distribution of a set of test marks for 120 children.

Marks	Number of candidates (Frequency)	Candidates up to this point (Cumulative frequency)
1 - 10	1	1
11 - 20	3	4
21 - 30	7	11
31 - 40	11	22
41 - 50	21	43
51 - 60	34	77
61 - 70	25	...
71 - 80	13	...
81 - 90	4	...
91 - 100	1	...

Note: The numbers in this column are obtained by adding those in the frequency column together.

The cumulative frequency of a class of marks tells you how many candidates obtained marks in that class or lower.

1 (a) Complete the table.
(b) Use the table to find the number of pupils who scored 30 marks or less.
(c) Use the table to find the number of pupils who scored more than 70 marks.

Note: The last entry in the cumulative frequency column = total frequency.

2 These are the heights of a class of 32 pupils measured to the nearest cm.

155 134 162 174 126
158 148 163 142 154
159 176 145 136 184
166 151 131 173 168
157 143 165 152 140
149 154 167 172 157
160 158

(a) Construct a cumulative frequency table for this data, grouping the heights in intervals of 10 cm starting at 120 cm.
(b) To get into a theme park half price children have to be under 150 cm tall. How many of these pupils can get in for half price?
(c) To ride the 'Looper' at the same park people have to be a minimum height of 160 cm. How many of this group can ride the 'Looper'?

3 Below are the approximate birth weights of 20 babies.

Birth weights (g)				
3270	3550	4225	2680	3140
3380	2150	3750	3227	4050
3760	4210	3900	3670	3420
2850	3270	3600	4515	3880

(a) Choosing suitable intervals construct a cumulative frequency table of this information.

(b) Use your table to find out how many of these babies weighed between 2·5 kg and 3·5 kg at birth.

12.3 Cumulative frequency diagrams

Examiner's tip

Cumulative frequency is plotted at the end of the interval.

To draw a **cumulative frequency diagram** for a set of grouped data you plot the upper boundary of each class of data against the cumulative frequency for that class. The cumulative frequency always goes on the vertical axis.

E.g. Draw a cumulative frequency curve for the test marks given on **page 174**. Plot the upper boundary of each class against the cumulative frequency.

You get a curve which has a very distinctive S shape.

Note: Plot the data at the end of the interval, e.g. 10–20 is plotted at 20.

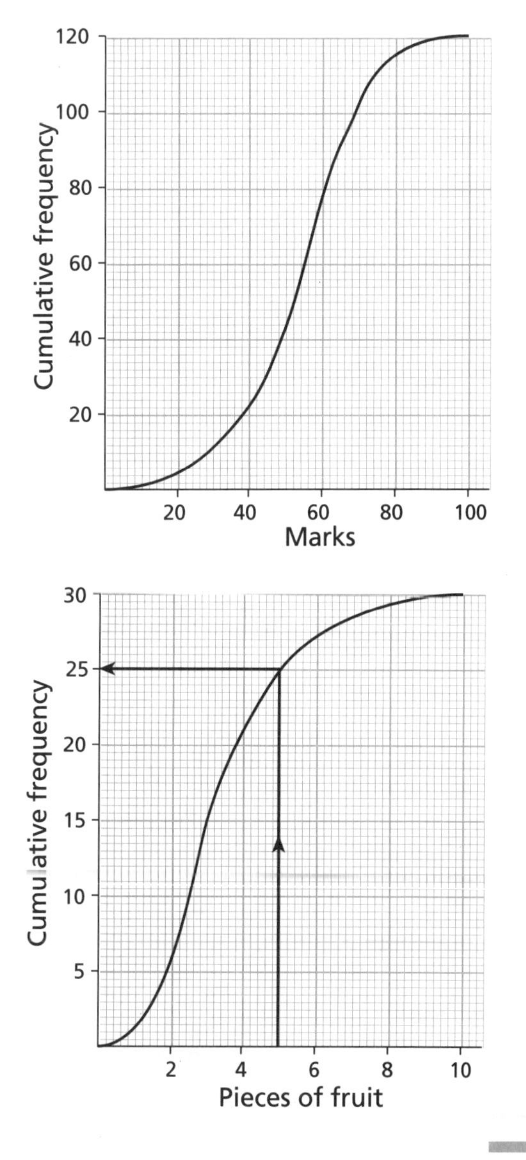

A cumulative frequency curve gives a continuous line so you can use it to estimate the number of results above or below any given value.

E.g. A group of children were asked how many pieces of fruit they eat each week. The results are shown on this cumulative frequency graph. To calculate the number of children who eat up to 5 pieces of fruit, find 5 on the horizontal axis. Draw a line vertically from there to the curve and then horizontally to the cumulative frequency axis. Read off the answer. From the previous diagram you can see that 25 children eat up to 5 pieces of fruit per week.

You can also use a cumulative frequency curve in the reverse way to find the value in a given position, e.g. the tenth highest value or the middle value (median).

Median

To find the median from a cumulative frequency curve you find $\frac{1}{2}(n + 1)$ on the vertical axis (where n is the total frequency), draw a horizontal line to the curve and read off the corresponding value from the horizontal axis.

When the total frequency is large you draw a line from the halfway mark on the vertical axis to the curve and then down to the horizontal axis, and read off the value.

E.g. From the cumulative frequency curve in the example above find out how many pieces of fruit the average (median) child eats per week.
Draw a line horizontally from the middle child on the cumulative frequency axis to the curve and then vertically down to the horizontal axis.
The average child eats 3 pieces of fruit per week.

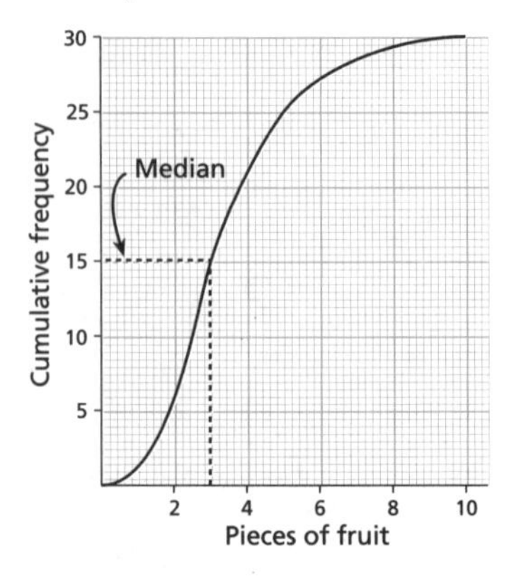

Note: Even if your graph is incorrect you will get marks for drawing in the lines to show you used the right method.

1 The table below shows the number of hours of television watched by a group of people per week.

Hours watched	Number of people	Cumulative frequency
< 15	1	1
< 20	2	3
< 25	7	10
< 30	11	21
< 35	25	46
< 40	23	...
< 45	17	...
< 50	10	...
< 55	3	...
< 60	1	...

(a) Complete the table.
(b) Draw a cumulative frequency graph using the information from the table.

Note: Check your final cumulative frequency equals the total number of people surveyed.

(c) How many people watch under 30 hours of television?
(d) What is the median amount of time spent watching television?
(e) What is the tenth highest amount of television watched?

Interquartile range

Knowing the range of a frequency distribution only tells you the extreme values. To see how the data are distributed around the median the range is divided into four quarters.

The value one quarter of the way from the lower end of the range is called the **lower quartile** (or first quartile). The middle value or **second quartile** is the median itself. The value three quarters of the way from the lower end of the range is called the **upper quartile** (or third quartile).

If the total frequency, n, is large then the 1st quartile has cumulative frequency $\frac{1}{4}n$ and the 3rd quartile is at $\frac{3}{4}n$. If n is small then the 1st quartile is at $\frac{1}{4}(n + 1)$ and the 3rd quartile is at $\frac{3}{4}(n + 1)$.

The difference between the lower and upper quartiles is called the **interquartile range**. In any frequency distribution half of the data lies in the interquartile range. This is a very useful way to measure the spread of a set of data, since it only includes the half of the data which is closest to the median, and avoids distortions caused by unusually large or small values.

E.g. Describe the distribution of the time spent by people watching television in question 1.

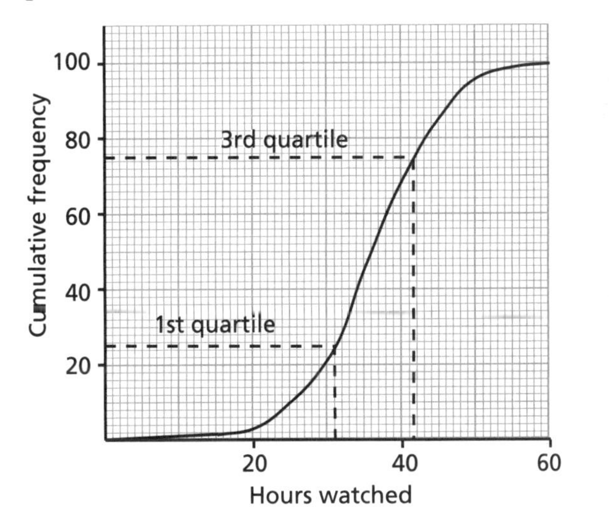

Note: The interquartile range is the third quartile taken away the first quartile.

From the curve, 1st (lower) quartile = 31 hours
3rd (upper) quartile = 41 hours
The interquartile range is 31–41 = 10 hours.
From this you can say that half the people surveyed watch between 31 and 41 hours of television a week.

2 The table below gives the mass to the nearest kg of 180 pupils.

(a) Draw a cumulative frequency curve for this information. Use a scale of 1 cm = 20 pupils on the vertical axis and 1 cm = 5 kg on the horizontal axis.
(b) Use your curve to work out the following:
(i) the number of pupils under 40 kg
(ii) the number of pupils over 59 kg
(iii) the median mass of the pupils
(iv) the lower quartile
(v) the upper quartile
(vi) the interquartile range
(c) What does the interquartile range tell you in this case?

Mass (kg)	Frequency
< 30	0
< 35	1
< 40	6
< 45	11
< 50	25
< 55	43
< 60	42
< 65	26
< 70	16
< 75	8
< 80	2

12.4 Choosing and calculating an average value

Mode

The **mode** or modal value of a set of data is the most common value or if the data is grouped, the largest group. Take into account only the most numerous type of data and ignore extreme values. It will not have a value if more than one set of data has the same number of entries.

Median

The median is the middle value (when the data is in order) or the mid point of two middle values in a set of data or the mid point value in the middle group in grouped data. It takes all values in a set of data into account but if the majority of the data is above or below the middle it may not be representative of the data.

Mean

The mean is given when all the data values are added and then divided by the number of values.

If the data is grouped, the mean is given by:

$$\text{Mean} = \frac{\text{The sum of the mid group values} \times \text{their frequencies}}{\text{The frequency of that data}}$$

The mean takes into account all the data but can be affected by unusually large values which may distort the average.

There will be occasions when each of these types of average best describe a set of data.

Calculating the mean of grouped data

E.g. The examination marks of 250 pupils are recorded below. What was the mean mark?

Class interval	0 - 9	10 - 19	20 - 29	30 - 39	40 - 49	50 - 59	60 - 69	70 - 79	80 - 89	90 - 99
Frequency	0	2	6	24	36	47	55	40	27	13

To calculate the mean you would normally add up all the values and then divide by the total number of values (in this case 250). You cannot do that with this information because you only know that a value is between say 20 and 29 and not exactly what the value is. With grouped data you use the middle value of each class interval and multiply by the frequency for the class.

Then divide by the total frequency.

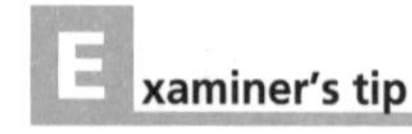

A statistical calculator will help here.

$$\text{Mean} = \frac{\text{Total (mid-value} \times \text{frequency)}}{\text{Total frequency}}$$

Class interval	Mid-value	Frequency	Mid-value × frequency
0 - 9	4·5	0	0
10 - 19	14·5	2	29
20 - 29	24·5	6	147
30 - 39	34·5	24	828
40 - 49	44·5	36	1602
50 - 59	54·5	47	2561·5
60 - 69	64·5	55	3547·5
70 - 79	74·5	40	2980
80 - 89	84·5	27	2281·5
90 - 99	94·5	13	1228·5
		Total 250	Total 15 205

If you draw a frequency polygon of this data you plot the mid-point of each interval.

$$\text{Mean} = \frac{\text{Total (mid-value} \times \text{frequency)}}{\text{Total frequency}} = \frac{15\,205}{250} = 60{\cdot}82$$

1 The weights of 24 pupils in 8M are given in the example at the start of this unit.
(a) Using the class intervals given in the example, write down the mid-class values.
(b) Calculate the mean weight of the pupils.

Range

The range is the spread of the data (largest value – smallest value = range).

E.g. Calculate the mean, mode, median and range of the following year 8 pupils.

Heights of 80 year 8 pupils.

Height (h)	Girls
$120 \leq h < 125$	1
$125 \leq h < 130$	3
$130 \leq h < 135$	6
$135 \leq h < 140$	12
$140 \leq h < 145$	17
$145 \leq h < 150$	18
$150 \leq h < 155$	15
$155 \leq h < 160$	5
$160 \leq h < 165$	2
$165 \leq h < 170$	1

To calculate the mean you first multiply the class mid-values by the frequencies.

$122{\cdot}5 \times 1 + 127{\cdot}5 \times 3 + 132{\cdot}5 \times 6 + 137{\cdot}5 \times 12 + 142{\cdot}5 \times 17 + 147{\cdot}5 \times 18 +$
$152{\cdot}5 \times 15 + 157{\cdot}5 \times 5 + 162{\cdot}5 \times 2 + 167{\cdot}5 \times 1 = 11\,595$

Then divide by the total frequency.

$$\text{Mean} = \frac{11\,595}{80} = 144{\cdot}9 \text{ (to 1 d.p.)}$$

The 40th and 41st girls are both in the class $145 \leq h < 150$ so this is the median class.
$145 \leq h < 150$ is also the modal class because it has the highest frequency (18).
The range is $170 - 120 = 50$

2 Kevin and Scott carried out a survey to find out whether buses were later on a Monday than a Saturday. They observed 19 buses each day and recorded how many minutes late each bus was. They included buses that were on time but ignored buses that were early.

Monday						
Minutes late	0-2	3-5	6-8	9-11	12-14	15-17
No. of buses	2	5	7	4	1	0
Saturday						
Minutes late	0-2	3-5	6-8	9-11	12-14	15-17
No. of buses	1	9	4	2	1	2

(a) Calculate the mean, median, mode and range of the data collected on Monday.
(b) Calculate the mean, median, mode and range of the data collected on Saturday.
(c) Use your answers to (a) and (b) to compare the two sets of data.

3 The ages of 5 members of two families are:

Family A 15, 17, 13, 16, 14 Family B 40, 16, 15, 3, 1

(a) Why is the mode not suitable to describe the average age for each of these families?
(b) What is the median age for each family?
(c) Explain why the median does not help you to compare the data.
(d) Calculate the mean age for each group.
(e) Calculate the age range of each family.
(f) How does this help you to make the data clearer to understand?

4 The following data gives the detentions received by a class last term

0, 0, 0, 0, 0, 0, 0, 0, 0, 0, 0, 0, 0, 1,
1, 2, 3, 3, 4, 5, 8, 9, 10, 12, 13, 34, 49

(a) Calculate the mean, median, mode and range.
(b) Give one reason for and one reason against using each of these to describe the average number of merits achieved by this class.

5 There are 6 forms in year 11 with the following numbers of pupils:

Set	Number of pupils
1	32
2	35
3	24
4	22
5	26
6	17

(a) There is no modal group size here. Explain why.
(b) Calculate the mean class size
(c) Calculate the median class size.
(d) If the average class size is over 25 pupils, a new group will be created.
Use your answers to (b) or (c) to support the need for an extra group.

12.5 Scatter graphs and correlation

Analysing data often involves investigating the relationship between two variables.

You might want to answer questions like "If you're good at Maths are you likely to be good at Science too?" or "Are people with longer names generally taller than people with shorter names?"

One method of finding out if there is a relationship between two groups of data is to draw a **scatter graph**.

E.g. The height and assessment test results in Maths and Science of a class of 25 pupils are given below. Draw a scatter graph of their Maths and Science results.

Name	Scott	Tim	Keith	Ian	Tony	Carl	Paul	Melvin	Kieran	Mark
Height (cm)	143	172	162	135	156	127	173	155	147	163
Maths	60	27	42	56	26	36	20	52	22	43
Science	48	30	45	52	22	40	25	58	26	48

Name	Lynne	Rosie	Jo	Vicky	Sarah	Tanya	Dawn	Jean	Omar	Sally
Height (cm)	153	165	170	139	167	157	149	152	161	163
Maths	32	54	17	57	47	45	38	28	40	30
Science	38	46	24	63	39	45	35	26	42	36

Name	Lisa	Peter	Robert	Abigail	Keely
Height (cm)	153	147	139	145	142
Maths	48	40	17	42	53
Science	23	46	30	43	47

Draw a pair of axes with Maths results on one axis and Science results on the other. Plot the scores of each pupil like a pair of coordinates. For example, Scott's results go on the graph at (60, 48).

The results of the first ten pupils on the list have been marked on this scatter graph.

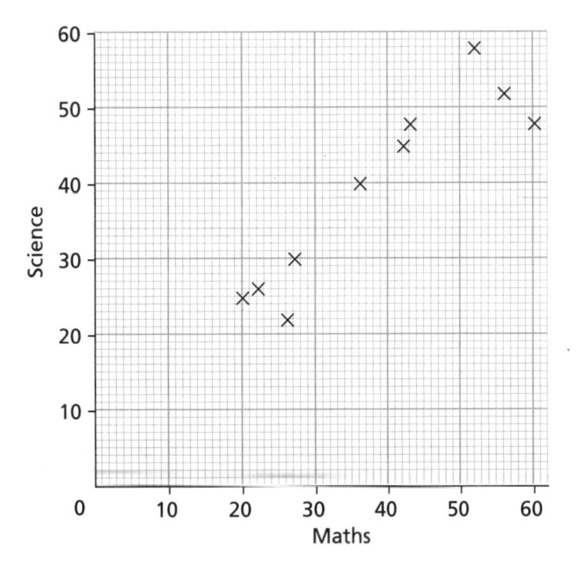

1 Complete the scatter graph by marking on the results of the remaining 15 pupils (from Lynne to Keely).

Correlation

There is a **correlation** between two variables when changes in one variable are linked to changes in the other.

Look at your scatter graph. Although the points are scattered they are mainly in a band going from the origin (0, 0) diagonally across the graph. This indicates that the better a pupil is at Maths the better they are likely to be at Science. So there is a **positive correlation** between Maths results and Science results.

If one variable increases as the other increases then their correlation is described as **positive**. The closer to a straight line the values lie the stronger the correlation.

The graph will look something like this.

An example of this might be the amount of pocket money you receive and the amount you spend.

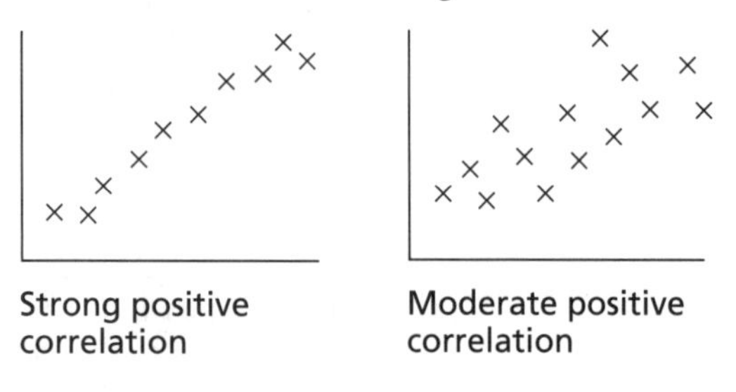

Strong positive correlation

Moderate positive correlation

If one variable increases as the second decreases the correlation is described as **negative**.

The graph will look something like this.

An example of this might be the more study you do now the less you will have to do in the future.

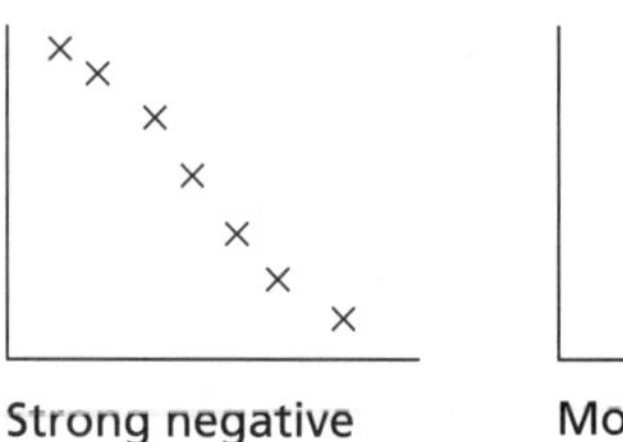

Strong negative correlation

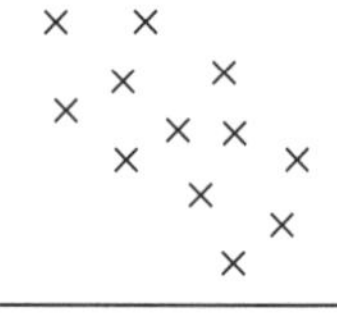

Moderate negative correlation

There is not necessarily any relationship between two quantities.

If the points are spread all over the graph so that there appears to be no pattern then we say that there is **no correlation**.

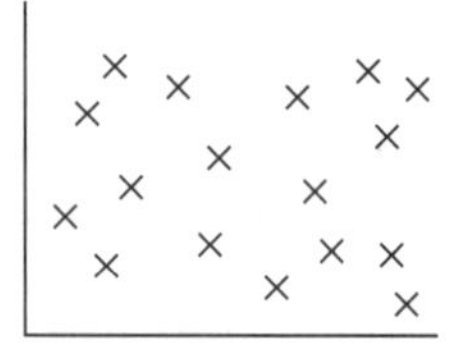

2 (a) Draw a scatter graph of the heights of the pupils and their Maths results.
(b) What can you say about the possible correlation?

Drawing a line of best fit

The points that are plotted on a scatter graph do not usually lie in a straight line but you have seen that when there is a positive or negative correlation the points tend to lie within a band across the graph.

The points look as though they are clustered around a single line. This line is called the **line of best fit**. This line is extremely useful because you can find the equation of the line and then use it to generate a formula linking the two variables. This allows you to predict the approximate value of one variable given the value of the other.

You can draw in the line of best fit 'by inspection' ('by eye') if you can see the line suggested by the points. You should try to get as many points on the line as possible and an equal number of points on either side. (You can ignore very way out points.)

E.g. This is the scatter graph of the Maths and Science marks for the first 10 pupils. Draw a line of best fit on this graph.

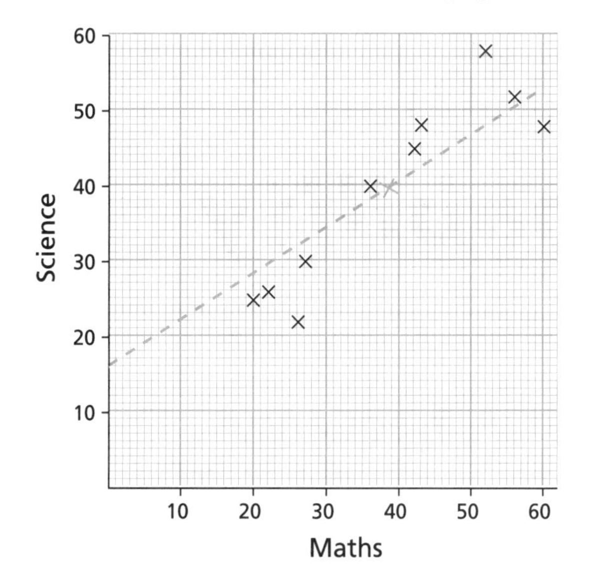

Note: The line of best fit divides the data into two roughly equal parts along the line of correlation.

Note: A typical question may ask you to find the equation of this line and ask what this means.

To find the equation representing the graph ($y = mx \pm c$) you use techniques common to all straight line graphs and developed earlier in this book.

(a) Find the gradient.

Note: Gradient (m) $= \dfrac{\text{rise}}{\text{tread}}$

(b) Find the y intercept (c).

The equation of the graph in this case is given by values taken from the diagram.

Maths score = 0.5
Science score +17.

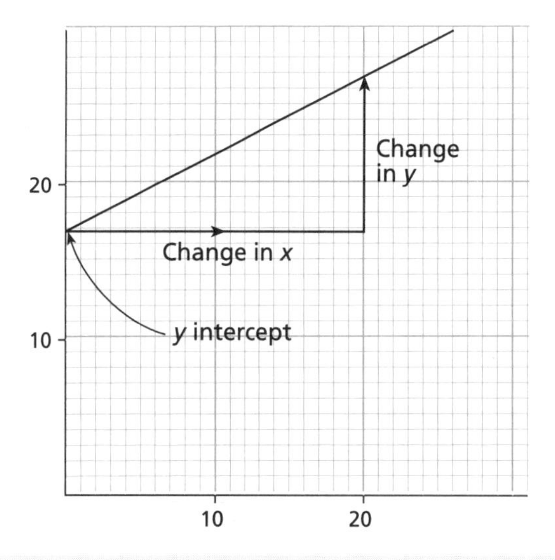

3 The following data gives the electricity bills from 12 homes.

Units used	560	1000	760	830	780	720	850	630	920	550	890	950
Cost (£)	43	78	55	71	61	60	63	45	74	46	71	69

(a) Plot the data on a scatter graph.
(b) Draw a line of best fit on your scatter graph.
(c) Find the equation of this line.
(d) Explain what the equation means.

Examiner's tip

The first variable is usually placed on the horizontal axis.

Chapter 13
Probability

13.1 Relative frequency

In some situations you can use symmetry to work out the probability of an event happening. For example, on a fair die the chance of getting any given number is 1 in 6 because there are six possible equally likely outcomes.

You can also estimate probability by repeating an experiment a large number of times and finding what proportion of the time you get the result you want. This is called **relative frequency**.

It is given by: $\dfrac{\text{number of results which give the event you want}}{\text{number of trials}}$

Using symmetry is more accurate because in reality you have to do a very large number of trials before the relative frequency of the event gets close to the true probability.

1 Toss a coin ten times and record the number of Heads you get. Use your result to estimate the probability of getting Heads.

Repeat this experiment several times.

You may have got 5 Heads, you may not. You can see that you don't always get 5 Heads. The more times you toss the coin the closer the experimental results will come to the number you would expect.

If you only tossed the coin once and it came up Heads then after the first trial you would estimate p(Heads) = 1 and p(Tails) = 0!

2 Use relative frequency to estimate the following:
(a) How many Tails would you expect to get in 20 tosses of a coin?
(b) How many times would you expect to get a 6 if you rolled a fair die 18 times?
(c) How many Hearts would you expect if you were dealt 12 cards at random?

3 At a summer fair 100 winning tickets are sold from a total of 800 tickets. If Gillian bought 1 ticket what is her chance of winning a prize?

13.2 Combining independent events

Two events are described as **independent** if they have no effect on each other. Rolling dice, tossing coins and any other actions you can repeat in exactly the same way over and over again will give independent events.

If you choose two items **with replacement** then events will be independent because the second choice will not be affected by the first choice.

When you combine two trials and events are independent then all the different combinations of outcomes of the two events are possible. (This is not true when events are not independent. Think of being dealt two cards: they can't both be the Ace of Hearts.)

xaminer's tip

In examination papers requiring a list of possible solutions, you will be given approximately the right number of lines to answer the problem (e.g. if there are 6 solutions the answer paper will probably have 6 or 7 lines).

E.g. A drinks machine contains Coke, Pepsi, Tango, 7UP, Vimto and Citrus Spring. List all the possible combinations of drinks that Amit and Tim might choose, assuming that they choose independently of each other. (This is like choosing with replacement.)

You could list all the possible combinations in any order as you thought of them.

Coke and Coke
7UP and Vimto
Pepsi and Tango ...

But then it's very hard to see if you've missed a possible combination. It is better to list the combinations in a systematic way, following a pattern.
List all the combinations which have Coke first:

Coke and Coke
Coke and Pepsi
Coke and Tango
Coke and 7UP
Coke and Vimto
Coke and Citrus Spring

Then look at the next drink on the list and write down all the combinations which have this first.

Pepsi and Coke
Pepsi and Pepsi
Pepsi and Tango
Pepsi and 7UP
Pepsi and Vimto
Pepsi and Citrus Spring

Always use the same order for the second choice.

To calculate the number of possible combinations, you multiply the number of possible outcomes for the individual trials.

There are 6 ways for Amit to choose and 6 ways that Tim could choose. Tim's choice and Amit's choice are independent so whatever Amit chooses there are still 6 possible choices for Tim. The total number of ways Amit and Tim can choose their drinks is $6 \times 6 = 36$.

It is useful to work this out to check that you have found all the possible combinations. Another way to display all the possible outcomes is to use a table called a **sample space**.

		Amit					
		C	P	T	7	V	S
Tim	C	CC	CP	CT	C7	CV	CS
	P	PC	PP	PT	P7	PV	PS
	T	TC	TP	TT	T7	TV	TS
	7	7C	7P	7T	77	7V	7S
	V	VC	VP	VT	V7	VV	VS
	S	SC	SP	ST	S7	SV	SS

The more possible outcomes each trial has the easier it is to find all the combinations using a sample space. You can clearly see all 36 combinations.

1 (a) How many different possible outcomes are there when you roll two dice?

(b) Draw a sample space to show all the possible outcomes.

You can also display the possible outcomes of two events using a **tree diagram**.

E.g. This is a tree diagram showing the results of tossing a coin twice.

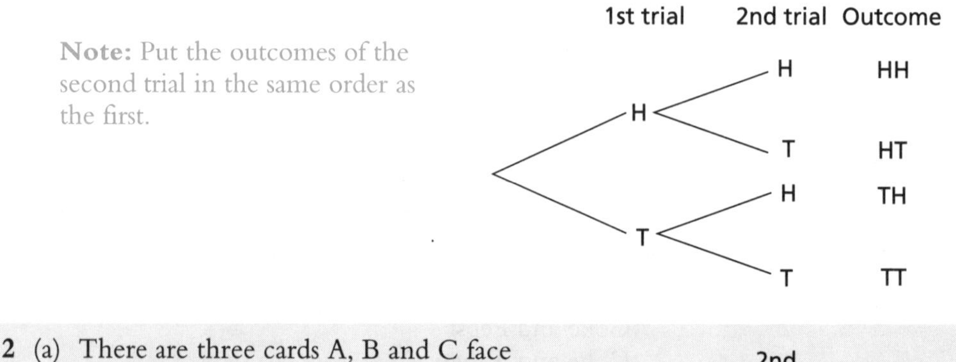

2 (a) There are three cards A, B and C face down on a table. One card is picked up and then replaced and then a second card is picked up. List the possible ways in which they could be chosen.

(b) Complete this sample space to show the possible ways of picking up the cards.

(c) Draw a tree diagram to show the possible ways of picking up the cards.

2nd

1st	A	B	C
A			
B			
C			

3 There are 3 children in the Webb family. Assuming there is an even chance of having boys and girls, complete a tree diagram to show the possible combinations of sexes for the children.

13.3 Mutually exclusive and complementary events

Two events are **mutually exclusive** if when one of them happens it stops the other happening. For example, we cannot both eat the last piece of cheesecake in the fridge. Either I eat it or you eat it (unless we are prepared to share). The events 'I eat it' and 'you eat it' are mutually exclusive.

When events are mutually exclusive then there is no overlap.

'Choosing a Heart' and 'choosing a Spade' are mutually exclusive events because no card can be a Heart and also a Spade. 'Choosing a Heart' and 'choosing a King' are **not** mutually exclusive events because you could choose the King of Hearts.

Examiner's tip

The words 'either... or...' often give a clue to events being mutually exclusive.

The total sum of the probabilities of mutually exclusive events in any trial is always 1. This is because the mutually exclusive events together cover all the possible outcomes and there is no overlap.

Examiner's tip

Probability should be expressed as a fraction ($\frac{1}{2}$), a decimal (0·5) or a percentage (50%) – not as a ratio (1:2).

E.g. (a) When you toss a coin it can't come down on both sides at once so 'getting a Tail' and 'getting a Head' are mutually exclusive events.

p(getting a Tail) = $\frac{1}{2}$

p(getting a Head) = $\frac{1}{2}$

So p(getting a Tail) + p(getting a Head) = $\frac{1}{2} + \frac{1}{2} = 1$

(b) In a game it is known that the probability of Rachel winning is 0·3 and the probability of Lubna winning is 0·4. What is the probability that neither Rachel nor Lubna will win?

We have three events: 'Rachel wins', 'Lubna wins' and 'neither Rachel nor Lubna wins'. Rachel and Lubna cannot both win so 'Rachel wins' and 'Lubna wins' are mutually exclusive events. Clearly if Rachel wins then it cannot also be true that 'neither Rachel nor Lubna wins' so these are mutually exclusive events. (Similarly if Lubna wins.)

So these three events are mutually exclusive and between them they cover all the possibilities.

Therefore p(Rachel wins or Lubna wins or neither) = 1
p(neither Rachel nor Lubna wins) = 1 – (0·3 + 0·4)
= 0·3

If mutually exclusive events are equally likely then the probability of each event is 1 divided by the number of events.

E.g. A bag contains five different coloured balls: a green one, a red one, a blue one, an orange one and a white one. What is the probability of choosing a ball of a particular colour?

A ball cannot be two colours at once so the events are mutually exclusive. The sum of all the probabilities must be 1.

p(green) + p(red) + p(blue) + p(orange) + p(white) = 1

But you are just as likely to choose a ball of one colour as a ball of another colour so all these probabilities are equal.

Therefore 5 × p(green) = 1

p(green) = $\frac{1}{5}$

This is the same for any colour.

Complementary events

The two events given by something 'happening' and 'not happening' are called **complementary** events. For example, the event 'throwing a 6' has the complementary event 'not throwing a 6' and 'getting a Tail' has the complementary event 'getting a Head'. If something is happening then it can't also not happen so complementary events are clearly mutually exclusive. Any two complementary events cover the whole range of possibilities because something must either happen or not happen. Using the fact that the total sum of mutually exclusive events is always 1,

p(event) + p(not event) = 1

This is very useful because it means that if you know the probability of something happening you can work out the probability of it not happening. Sometimes when you want to find the probability of an event it's far easier to calculate the probability of it not happening then take that away from 1.

E.g. If a fair die is rolled what is the probability of getting 1, 2, 3, 4 or 5?
This is the same as not getting a 6.
The probability of getting a 6 is $\frac{1}{6}$ so
p(not getting a 6) = 1 – p(getting a 6) = 1 – $\frac{1}{6}$ = $\frac{5}{6}$
Hence p(getting 1, 2, 3, 4 or 5) = $\frac{5}{6}$

1 (a) What is the probability of getting a 1 on a fair icosahedral die with 20 faces?
(b) Use this to calculate the probability of not getting a 1.

2 The probability of drawing a picture card (K, Q, J, A) from a pack is $\frac{4}{13}$. What is the probability of not choosing a picture card?

3 In a game of chance the probability of winning is $\frac{1}{5}$. What is the probability of losing?

4 There are red and blue counters in a bag. If the probability of choosing a red counter is $\frac{5}{8}$ what is the probability of choosing a blue counter?

13.4 Adding probabilities of mutually exclusive events

You already know that events are mutually exclusive if they can't both happen at the same time.

E.g. If Andy, Bev, Carl and Diane have a race and Bev wins, then Andy, Carl and Diane must lose. The events 'Andy wins', 'Bev wins', 'Carl wins' and 'Diane wins' are mutually exclusive.

Combining events

There are two ways to combine events.

1. Using AND. This gives events of the form 'Andy wins **and** Bev comes second'. You are interested in both events happening.

With mutually exclusive events you know that the probability of two events both happening is always zero.

2. Using OR. This gives events of the form 'Andy **or** Bev wins'. You are interested in at least one event happening.

With mutually exclusive events there is no overlap so **either** Andy wins **or** Bev wins **but not both**.

If you wish to work out the probability of **either** A **or** B you simply add the probabilities.

p(either A or B) = p(A) + p(B)

So p(Andy or Bev wins) = p(Andy wins) + p(Bev wins)

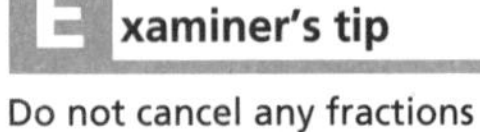

xaminer's tip

Do not cancel any fractions until the final stage.

E.g. A family bag of crisps contains 6 packets of crisps: 3 plain, 2 cheese and onion and 1 smoky bacon. What is the probability of picking plain or smoky bacon if you choose a packet without looking?
The events are mutually exclusive because a packet of crisps cannot be plain and smoky bacon flavour at the same time.
p(choosing plain) = $\frac{3}{6}$
p(choosing smoky bacon) = $\frac{1}{6}$
p(choosing plain or smoky bacon) = $\frac{3}{6} + \frac{1}{6} = \frac{4}{6} = \frac{2}{3}$

1 What is the probability you will get a 1 or a 2 when you roll a die?

2 A biscuit jar contains 3 chocolate, 4 cream, 2 wafer and 1 plain biscuits.
(a) Why are choosing a cream biscuit and choosing a wafer biscuit mutually exclusive?
(b) What is the probability of choosing a cream or a wafer biscuit if you choose without looking?
(c) What is the probability of choosing a chocolate or a cream biscuit if you choose without looking?

3 Jess always goes to school in one of the following ways:

	probability
by bicycle	0·4
by car	0·1
by bus	0·3
on foot	0·2

xaminer's tip

When events are mutually exclusive then you add probabilities.

(a) Calculate the probability that she will either walk or go by bus.
(b) Calculate the probability that she will go to school in a vehicle.

13.5 Calculating probabilities when independent events are combined

The probability of two independent events both happening is less than the probability for each of the individual events (unless one of the probabilities is 0 or 1).

E.g. You roll two fair dice, one green and one black. How does the probability of getting a 6 on both dice compare with the individual probabilities of getting a 6? You have already seen that when you combine two trials which involve independent events all the combinations of outcomes are possible. So there are $6 \times 6 = 36$ possible combinations for the scores on the dice.

The probability of getting a 6 on the black die is $\frac{1}{6}$ so the number of outcomes which give 6 on the black die is $\frac{1}{6} \times$ number of outcomes $= \frac{1}{6} \times 36 = 6$.

The probability of getting a 6 on the green die is also $\frac{1}{6}$ so of these 6 outcomes the number which also gives 6 on the green die is $\frac{1}{6} \times 6 = 1$.

So p(getting 6 on both dice) = 1 out of 36 = $\frac{1}{36}$

We can illustrate this by completing a possibility space.

		black die					
		1	2	3	4	5	6
green die	1	1,1	2,1	3,1	4,1	5,1	6,1
	2	1,2	2,2	3,2	4,2	5,2	6,2
	3	1,3	2,3	3,3	4,3	5,3	6,3
	4	1,4	2,4	3,4	4,4	5,4	6,4
	5	1,5	2,5	3,5	4,5	5,5	6,5
	6	1,6	2,6	3,6	4,6	5,6	6,6

You can see that there are 36 different possible results and that only one of these gives you two 6's.

If the probability of one event is 0 that means it can't happen so the probability of it and another event both happening must also be 0.

If the probability of one event is 1 that means it must happen so the probability of both events happening will be the same as the probability for the other event.

1 If you have a 50p coin, a 10p coin, a 5p and a 2p in your purse what is the probability that if you take out two coins they will be a 50p coin and a 1p coin?

2 (a) Each day 1 pupil from a mixed class is chosen at random to take the register to the school office. The probability that a girl will be chosen to take the register is p. Is the probability that a girl will be chosen 2 days running
(i) the same as p? (ii) less than p? (iii) greater than p?

(b) Which of the following is the lowest?
(i) the probability that a boy will be chosen on the first day of term
(ii) the probability that a girl will be chosen on the second day of term
(iii) the probability that a boy will be chosen on the first day and a girl will be chosen on the second day

You saw above that the probability of getting a 6 on two dice at the same time is $\frac{1}{36}$. This is the same as what you get if you multiply the individual probabilities together.

p(6 on both dice) = $\frac{1}{6} \times \frac{1}{6} = \frac{1}{36}$

When two events are independent then

p(event 1 **and** event 2) = p(event 1) × p(event 2)

E.g. A bag contains 3 red counters, 4 blue counters and 5 white counters. A counter is chosen at random from the bag and then replaced and a second counter is chosen. What is the probability of choosing two red counters?

You know that when items are chosen **with replacement** then events are independent.

The first counter has been replaced so the probabilities in the second trial are the same as those in the first trial.

The probability of choosing a red counter,

$$p(\text{red}) = \frac{3}{(3+4+5)} = \frac{3}{12} = \frac{1}{4}$$

$$p(\text{red then red}) = p(\text{red}) \times p(\text{red}) = \tfrac{1}{4} \times \tfrac{1}{4} = \tfrac{1}{16}$$

So the probability of choosing two red counters is $\frac{1}{16}$.

3 If you roll a die and toss a coin what is the probability of getting a 5 and Heads?

Diagrams

One way to illustrate the probabilities for combined events is using a **possibility space**.

E.g. What is the probability of taking a picture card from a pack, returning it and then taking a second picture card? Illustrate this using a probability space.

The probability of taking a picture card (A, K, Q, J) is $\frac{16}{52}$ which simplifies to $\frac{4}{13}$.

$p(\text{picture}) = \frac{4}{13}$ $\quad p(\text{not picture}) = 1 - \frac{4}{13} = \frac{9}{13}$

There are 13 different types of card, of which 4 are picture cards.

Choosing with replacement gives independent events so all combinations of outcomes are possible. Therefore choosing 2 cards gives $13 \times 13 = 169$ possibilities.

Of these, $4 \times 4 = 16$ give 2 picture cards.

So the probability of choosing 2 picture cards is $\frac{16}{169}$.

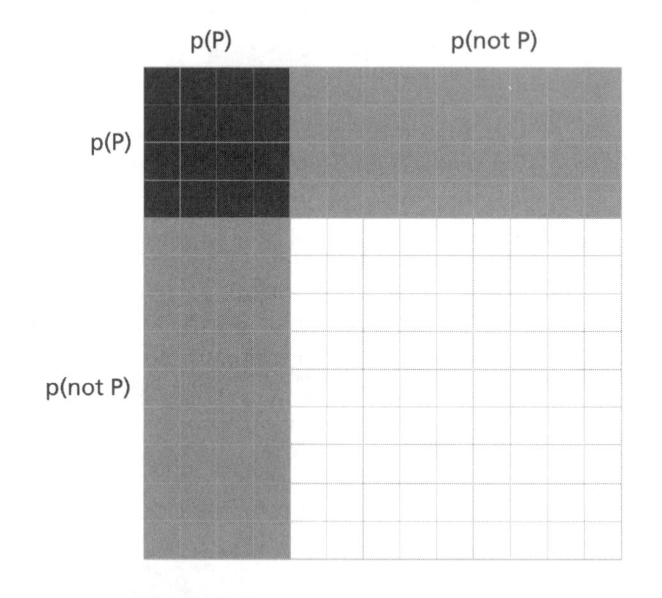

The probability space shows that out of 169 possibilities there are 16 outcomes which give 2 picture cards.

Another way to illustrate the probabilities for combined events is using a **tree diagram**.

Keep the outcomes in the same order for each trial. Remember the probabilities should add up to 1 for each group of branches.

Leave any simplification of fractions to the final calculation rather than simplifying fractions on the diagram.

E.g. Draw a tree diagram to illustrate the probability of taking a picture card from a pack, returning it and then taking a second picture card.

Let P be the event 'taking a picture card' and N be the complementary event 'not taking a picture card'.

Examiner's tip

The probabilities on each part of the tree diagram add up to 1. The final probabilities should also add up to 1.

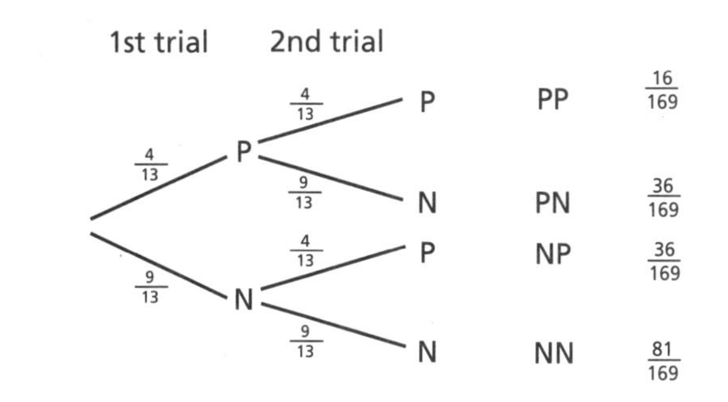

To calculate probabilities from a tree diagram you multiply along the branches.

p(2 picture cards) = p(P) × p(P)

$= \frac{4}{13} \times \frac{4}{13}$

$= \frac{16}{169}$

If you go on to three trials the probability space diagram becomes impractical. But you can draw a tree diagram for any number of trials.

E.g. Draw a tree diagram to illustrate the probabilities when tossing a coin three times.

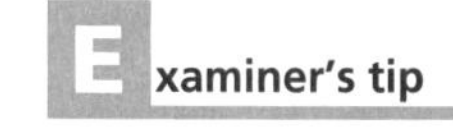

Examiner's tip

The greatest problem most people find in drawing this type of diagram is in the layout. Before you start drawing work out how many branches there are going to be!

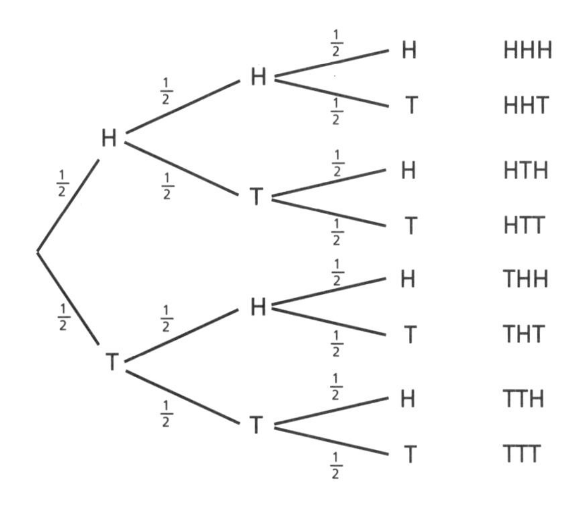

In each case the probability is $\frac{1}{2}$ so each of the possible outcomes of tossing the coin three times has probability $\frac{1}{2} \times \frac{1}{2} \times \frac{1}{2} = \frac{1}{8}$ or 0·125.

4 (a) What is the probability of getting more than 4 on two successive rolls of a fair die?

(b) Draw a probability space to illustrate your answer.

5 Lisa uses her mountain bike to ride to her friend's house. She has to go through two sets of traffic lights on the way.

At the first set of lights the probability that they will be on green is 0·6.

At the second set of traffic lights the probability that they will be on green is 0·5.

(a) Calculate the probability that the first set of traffic lights will not be green.

(b) Calculate the probability that the second set of traffic lights will not be green.

(c) Draw a tree diagram to illustrate the probabilities of the two sets of lights being green or not green.

(d) Calculate the probability that Lisa will be able to ride to her friend's house without having to stop at any traffic lights.

Chapter 14
Further data handling

14.1 Histograms

Properties of histograms

1. The width of each column is in proportion to the size of the class or group of data it represents (with no spaces between the columns). The columns may have different widths.
2. The quantity on the vertical axis is **frequency density** (or frequency per class of a given size).
3. The frequency for a particular class of data is given by the **area** of the column representing that class.
4. The horizontal axis must have a scale. This acts like a normal scale on a graph, with the same distance always representing the same number of units.

Note: Histograms are usually used with grouped data.

E.g. A school runs a cafeteria system at lunch times. The table below shows how much 600 pupils spent on lunch in a particular week. Draw a histogram of this information.

Amount spent (£)	Frequency
0 - 0·99	4
1·00 - 1·99	7
2·00 - 2·99	14
3·00 - 3·99	35
4·00 - 4·99	98
5·00 - 5·99	125
6.00 - 6.99	194
7·00 - 7·99	107
8·00 - 8·99	13
9·00 - 9·99	3

The classes given in this table are all the same size so if you drew a histogram using these class intervals then the columns would all have the same width. Therefore the areas of the columns would only depend on their heights.

The frequencies here range from 4 to 194 and on a histogram the frequency is equal to the area of the column so the tallest column would be about 65 times as tall as the shortest column. You can regroup the data using different class intervals to produce a more balanced histogram.

Amount spent (£)	Frequency
0 - 3·99	60
4·00 - 4·99	98
5·00 - 5·99	125
6·00 - 6·99	194
7·00 - 9·99	123

The range of frequencies is now 60 to 194. Now you need to work out the height and width of each column. The width is given by the class interval. To calculate the height (or frequency density) of a column you divide the frequency by the width.

frequency (area) = height × width

$$\text{height (frequency density)} = \frac{\text{frequency}}{\text{class interval}}$$

Frequency	Amount spent (p)	Frequency density
60	0 - 399	0·15
98	400 - 499	0·98
125	500 - 599	1·25
194	600 - 699	1·94
123	700 - 999	0·41

You can now draw a histogram of this data.

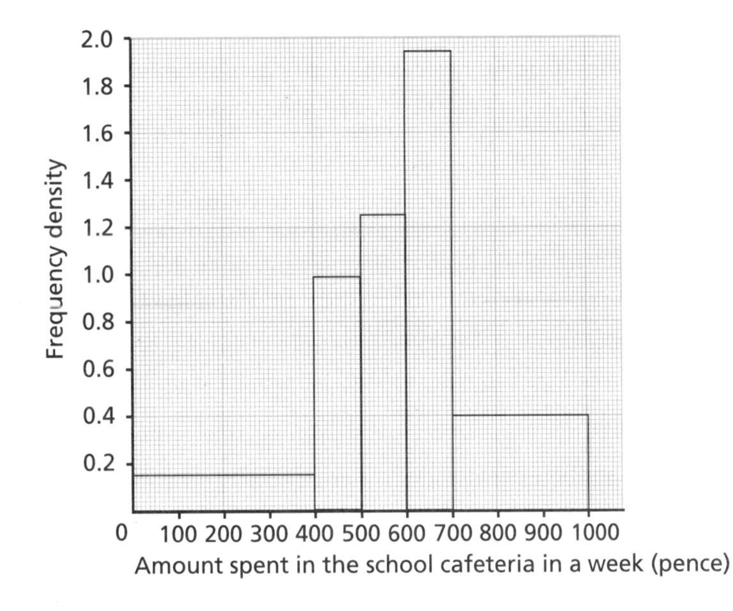

Interpreting histograms

If the columns in a histogram are all the same width then you can compare the frequencies of the classes by comparing the heights of the columns. The tallest column indicates the modal class.

If the columns are of different widths then you must compare the **areas** of the columns to compare frequencies. You don't always need to work out the actual areas. For example, if two columns are about the same height and one is twice the width then you can see that the wider column has about twice the area. In other words, if the columns are about the same height and the class interval is doubled then the frequency will be about doubled. The column with the largest area indicates the **modal class**.

The **height** of a column is like averaging out the frequency over all the values in the class.

$$\text{height} = \frac{\text{frequency}}{\text{class interval}}$$

So the taller the column the greater the average frequency for the values in that class. This means that the **mode** is probably in the class with the tallest column, even if this is not the modal class. You can find the total frequency by adding together the areas of all the columns.

E.g. What can you say about the distribution of spending in the school cafeteria by looking at the shape of the histogram in the example above?

First consider the areas of the columns. The tallest column must have a greater area than the other 2 columns with the same width. It also clearly has a greater area than the column on the far left, which is thinner and shorter.

The column on the far right is 3 times the width of the tallest column but less than $\frac{1}{4}$ of the height so its area must be less than $\frac{3}{4}$ of the area of the tallest column.

Therefore in this histogram the tallest column also has the greatest area. Therefore the class £6·00–6·99 is the modal class and also contains the mode.

This means there are more pupils spending £6·00–6·99 than the amount in any of the other classes. And the most frequently spent amount is somewhere between £6 and £6·99.

You could also say that the majority of children spend between £4 and £7 a week in the cafeteria because this range contains most of the area of the histogram.

1 The distances travelled to school by 330 pupils are shown in the grouped frequency table below.

(a) Regroup this data so that each new class interval has at least 40 pupils in it.
(b) Calculate the frequency density for each of these classes.
(c) Use your new classes to draw a histogram of distances travelled to school.
(d) Say as much as you can about the distribution of distances travelled by looking at the shape of the histogram.

Distance (km)	Frequency
$0 \le d < 0{\cdot}5$	4
$0{\cdot}5 \le d < 1{\cdot}0$	17
$1{\cdot}0 \le d < 1{\cdot}5$	30
$1{\cdot}5 \le d < 2{\cdot}0$	54
$2{\cdot}0 \le d < 2{\cdot}5$	62
$2{\cdot}5 \le d < 3{\cdot}0$	79
$3{\cdot}0 \le d < 3{\cdot}5$	52
$3{\cdot}5 \le d < 4{\cdot}0$	27
$4{\cdot}0 \le d < 4{\cdot}5$	11
$4{\cdot}5 \le d < 5{\cdot}0$	2
$5{\cdot}0 \le d < 5{\cdot}5$	1
$5{\cdot}5 \le d < 6{\cdot}0$	1

Note: In a histogram the frequency is given by the area of the column.

14.2 Sampling

In data handling the word **population** is used for a collection or group of objects which are being studied. A **sample** is a smaller group selected from a population.

When a large population is being studied it is not usually possible to collect data on every member of the population so a sample (or several samples) of the population is studied and conclusions are drawn about the population as a whole. This means that it is very important to choose a sample which is representative of the whole population. Otherwise the conclusions drawn may be very inaccurate.

Sampling is widely used in market research and polling where it is not possible to survey the entire population of a country every time you want to find out about product preference or voting habits.

Sampling is also very important in quality control in industry where it is used not only to check the quality of manufactured products but also to monitor efficiency and standards. Sampling is particularly important for things which can only be tested by wearing them out, such as the length of time a light bulb will last. With most products it would be too expensive to test every single item produced and it is not necessary to do so. No-one would be prepared to pay the extra cost involved in making sure that every single box of their favourite cereal contained exactly the stated weight: it's not that important.

However, there are some things which must work every time so every single item must be tested. A good example of this is the brakes on a car.

Choosing a sample

There are two factors that you need to consider when choosing a sample.

1. The size of the sample. The sample must be a large enough proportion of the population for the results to be significant. The larger your sample the more accurate your results.

However, there is usually a limit to the size of sample you can have because a larger sample requires more resources to test it. In cases where a product is tested to destruction, such as the life of a light bulb, choosing a very large sample would mean destroying most of your output!

2. The way the sample is chosen. The sample should be representative of the population. This means it should take account of variations in the characteristics of the population. These variations should be represented in the sample in the same ratios as in the total population.

For example, if the population to be surveyed contains twice as many women as men then the sample should also contain twice as many women as men.

This type of sampling is called **quota sampling** or **stratified sampling**.

Note: A stratified sample is one which reflects the way the original data is distributed.

E.g. (a) A researcher may be given a quota of people to interview:
10 housewives with children
2 housewives without children
6 women who work full-time and have children
12 women who work full-time and don't have children

(b) A sample may be stratified by age, so that the percentage of the sample in a particular age group is the same as the percentage of the total population in that age group. Then the results can be analysed by age.

(c) A sample of manufactured products from a factory must include the correct proportion of products from each shift and from each machine in order to be representative of the total output.

1 Say which of the following you would study by sampling. Give reasons for your answers. What are the factors you would take into account in the cases you would test by sampling?

(a) The average life of a battery.
(b) The type of cat food most cats prefer.
(c) The top ten singles sold last week.
(d) The cables on a lift.

Sometimes you have no information about the characteristics of a population. Then you should choose a sample in which all items are equally likely to be chosen. This is called a **random sample**.

Note: A random sample is used when you do not know how the original population is distributed.

To ensure the sample is random and as accurate as possible it should be repeated a number of times. The random samples can then be averaged.

2 To carry out the following experiment you will need 100 counters or other objects which are the same except for their colour. Put the counters in a bag. Choose a colour.

Experiment: Take 10 counters without looking and record the number of your chosen colour. Multiply the result by 10 to predict how many of your chosen colour are in the bag. Replace the counters.

Repeat the experiment 10 times, recording your results in a table.

Average out the results of the 10 experiments to find the mean number of counters you picked of your chosen colour.

Multiply the mean by 10 to get an estimate for the total number of counters of that colour.

Empty the bag and count how many counters of your chosen colour there are.

Compare this with your first prediction and the final mean estimate.

You should have found that the results obtained by repeating the trial were more accurate because they were based on more information.

The technique of random sampling can be used to estimate the size of a population.

E.g. The crested newt is an endangered species. Conservationists want to find out the number of crested newts in a pond. To do this they catch 10 newts and mark them in a harmless way.

The newts are released back into the pond and the next day 10 more newts are caught. Of the 10 newts 2 are found to have been marked the previous day. The result on the 2nd day is that 2 out of a sample of 10 newts are marked.

Applying the results of this sample to the whole population means that 20% of the population should be marked. But the conservationists know that 10 newts are marked. So 20% of the population is about 10 newts.

Let the size of the total population be P.

$$\frac{20}{100} \times P \approx 10$$

$$\frac{1}{5} \times P \approx 10$$

$$P \approx 50$$

So there are about 50 newts in the pond.

14.3 Conditional probabilities

If the probability of an event happening depends on whether another event took place or not, then we say the events are **dependent**. The probability is said to be **conditional**.

Whenever the outcome of one trial affects the possible outcomes of a second trial then events are dependent. If two items are chosen **without replacement** then the item chosen first cannot be chosen again so the probabilities for the second choice are conditional on what was chosen first.

E.g. In a biscuit barrel there are 5 chocolate biscuits, 4 plain and 6 wafers.
(a) A biscuit is taken at random and eaten. Write down the probability of choosing each type of biscuit.
(b) A second biscuit is taken. What is the probability that both biscuits were chocolate?
(a) The total number of biscuits is 5 + 4 + 6 = 15. The words 'at random' tell you that each biscuit is equally likely to be chosen so

p(choosing chocolate) = $\frac{5}{15}$
p(choosing plain) = $\frac{4}{15}$
p(choosing wafer) = $\frac{6}{15}$

(b) If the first biscuit is eaten then it cannot be replaced! So the probabilities for the second choice are conditional on which biscuit was chosen first.

The probability of choosing a chocolate biscuit in the first trial was $\frac{5}{15}$.

If that biscuit is eaten then there will only be 4 chocolate biscuits left and only 14 left in the barrel. This means that on the second occasion the probability of choosing a chocolate biscuit is $\frac{4}{14}$. This is conditional on having chosen chocolate in the first trial.

We write this as p(chocolate 2nd choice given chocolate 1st choice) or p(chocolate/chocolate).

The probability of choosing 2 chocolate biscuits is

p(chocolate 1st choice) × p(chocolate 2nd choice given chocolate 1st choice)

p(C) × p(C/C) = $\frac{5}{15} \times \frac{4}{14}$

= $\frac{2}{21}$

The tree diagram looks like this. To get the combined probabilities you multiply along the branches. Do your simplifying in the calculation and not on the diagram.

Note: In the 2nd trial the number you are choosing from is 1 less.

Examiner's tip

You should cancel your answers to express each fraction in its lowest form at the end of the calculating process.

xaminer's tip

The probabilities on each part of the tree diagram add up to 1.

1st trial	2nd trial	Outcome	Combined Probability
C ($\frac{5}{15}$)	C ($\frac{4}{14}$)	CC	$\frac{5}{15} \times \frac{4}{14} = \frac{2}{21}$
	P ($\frac{4}{14}$)	CP	$\frac{5}{15} \times \frac{4}{14} = \frac{2}{21}$
	W ($\frac{6}{14}$)	CW	$\frac{5}{15} \times \frac{6}{14} = \frac{1}{7}$
P ($\frac{4}{15}$)	C ($\frac{5}{14}$)	PC	$\frac{4}{15} \times \frac{5}{14} = \frac{2}{21}$
	P ($\frac{3}{14}$)	PP	$\frac{4}{15} \times \frac{3}{14} = \frac{2}{35}$
	W ($\frac{6}{14}$)	PW	$\frac{4}{15} \times \frac{6}{14} = \frac{4}{35}$
W ($\frac{6}{15}$)	C ($\frac{5}{14}$)	WC	$\frac{6}{15} \times \frac{5}{14} = \frac{1}{7}$
	P ($\frac{4}{14}$)	WP	$\frac{6}{15} \times \frac{4}{14} = \frac{4}{35}$
	W ($\frac{5}{14}$)	WW	$\frac{6}{15} \times \frac{5}{14} = \frac{1}{7}$

With conditional probability the probability of A followed by B is written

p(A and B) =p(A) × p(B given A) or p(A and B) = p(A) × p(B/A)

1 In a class there are 14 girls and 13 boys. Two pupils are to be chosen at random to give books out. Draw a tree diagram to illustrate the probabilities.

2 Mark has bought a packet of 9 hyacinth bulbs which all look the same. 4 of the bulbs will have red flowers, 3 blue and 2 white.
(a) If Mark chooses 2 bulbs from the packet calculate the probability that they will both have blue flowers.
(b) Calculate the probability that the first bulb chosen will have white flowers and the second will have red flowers.

An alternative to drawing a tree diagram to represent dependent probabilities is to use a sample space. This shows all the possible outcomes. If a combination is not possible then you blank out that square.

E.g. A teacher needs two pupils to help on parents' evening. Two pupils are to be chosen at random from Alice, Brian, Claire, Derek and Elaine.

Followed by

First choice	A	B	C	D	E
A		AB	AC	AD	AE
B	BA		BC	BD	BE
C	CA	CB		CD	CE
D	DA	DB	DC		DE
E	EA	EB	EC	ED	

Illustrate the possible combinations for choosing two pupils from these five.

Note: Since you need two pupils this is without replacement.

You cannot choose Alice and then Alice again so that choice can be blanked out.

The number of possibilities for the first choice is 5 but the number of possibilities for the second choice is 1 less. So the total number of possible combinations is 5 × 4 = 20.

3 In a packet of yoghurts there are 4 different varieties: strawberry, raspberry, lemon and blackcurrant. Mr Smith has one today and one tomorrow. Illustrate Mr Smith's choices using a sample space.

14.4 Standard deviation

If you have worked through this book you have already seen two methods of measuring the spread of a set of data.

The standard deviation is another more sophisticated method for measuring the spread of a set of data.

$$\sigma = \sqrt{\Sigma \frac{f(x-\bar{x})^2}{n}}$$

Note: For a normal distribution of data you would expect approximately 68% of the data to be within one standard deviation of the mean.

To apply this formula you:

1. Subtract the mean ($\bar{x}$) from each value in your set of data (x) and square the result $(x-\bar{x})^2$.
2. You then add all the results (Σ) and divide by the number of entries in your set of data (n).
3. Finally you take the square root ($\sqrt{\ }$). The result is called the **standard deviation**.

E.g. Sam records the number of birds visiting a bird table between 12 noon and 12:15 each day for 20 days. Her results are given below.

Calculate the mean and standard deviation of the number of visiting birds.

3 8 9 2 5 6 4 8 6 3
2 6 8 4 5 3 5 2 7 4

Birds (x)	Frequency(f)	xf
2	3	6
3	3	9
4	3	12
5	3	15
6	3	18
7	1	7
8	3	24
9	1	9
		Total = 100

$$\text{Mean} = \frac{\Sigma x}{n}$$

$$\text{Mean} = \frac{100}{20} = 5$$

There are on average 5 birds visiting the table each day between 12 and 12:15.

Birds (x)	$(x-\bar{x})$	$(x-\bar{x})^2$	Frequency(f)	$(x-\bar{x})^2 f$
2	$^-3$	9	3	27
3	$^-2$	4	3	12
4	$^-1$	1	3	3
5	0	0	3	0
6	1	1	3	3
7	2	4	1	4
8	3	9	3	27
9	4	16	1	16
				Total = 92

$$\text{Standard deviation} = \sqrt{\frac{\Sigma(x-\bar{x})^2 f}{n}}$$
$$= \sqrt{\frac{92}{20}}$$
$$= \sqrt{4 \cdot 6}$$
$$= 2{\cdot}14 \text{ (to 2 d.p.)}$$

This tells us that the number of birds visiting the table will normally be within about 2 of the mean. In other words the number of visiting birds will usually be between 3 and 7.

1 The efficiency of an office junior is being checked. He completes the following number of pieces of work per hour over 20 hours.

5	2	6	4	4	5	4	3	4	5
5	6	8	8	7	4	2	9	1	8

(a) Calculate the mean. (b) Calculate the standard deviation.

Note: In an examination you are expected to use the statistical functions of your calculator to do standard deviation questions.

A calculator should be used to complete mean and standard deviation questions at this level. There will be differences in the ways in which calculators work and you should make sure you understand how your calculator works. However the following features are common to most machines:

The keys you will need are $\bar{x}$ This gives you the mean.

n This tells you how many entries you have made.

Σx This adds up all your entries.

σn This gives you the standard deviation.

DATA This enables you to enter data.

SAC This will cancel data.

Examiner's tip

Warning: Pressing cancel will not remove values already entered from the memory of your calculator. You must use SAC. Always check how many entries your calculator is finding the standard deviation of.

To enter multiples of any data you simply use the multiplication key.

E.g. To enter an x value of 4 five times you would press:

4 x 5 DATA

Note: x value mutiplied by frequency. The order is important.

2 Repeat the example using your calculator to check that you understand how to use it correctly.

3 The following table gives the number of pupils and their marks in an exam.

Marks	Frequency
0–9	2
10–19	4
20–29	7
30–39	13
40–49	26
50–59	47
60–69	52
70–79	30
80–89	19
90–99	6

Note: If you are using grouped data the mid class value is used to represent x.

(a) Calculate the mean mark.
(b) Calculate the standard deviation

Using mean and standard deviation to compare data

A population described as normal will have approximately 68% of its members within one standard deviation of its mean.

Using this knowledge or by comparing the mean and standard deviation of two sets of data can help decide whether the data is sufficiently accurate.

E.g. Use the mean and standard deviation to compare the light bulbs produced by manufacturers A and B.

Manufacturer A

Life expectancy in hours	0–100	100–200	200–300	300–400	400–500	500–600	600–700	700–800	800–900	900–1000
Frequency	0	0	1	3	20	36	48	54	37	1

A calculator will give the following results:

Mean ($\bar{x}$) = 671 hours Standard deviation (σ) = 134·4 hours

Manufacturer B

Life expectancy in hours	0–100	100–200	200–300	300–400	400–500	500–600	600–700	700–800	800–900	900–1000
Frequency	0	1	4	7	12	29	48	60	37	2

A calculator will give the following results:

Mean ($\bar{x}$) = 672·5 hours Standard deviation (σ) = 149·1 hours

Although the modal life expectancy of both sets of bulbs has approximately the same value the smaller standard deviation of manufacturer A's bulbs show that they are more consistent.

4 Use the mean and standard deviation to compare the following set of data with that provided in the example above.

Manufacturer C

Life expectancy in hours	0–100	100–200	200–300	300–400	400–500	500–600	600–700	700–800	800–900	900–1000
Frequency	2	5	6	8	10	23	45	61	32	8

Using the standard deviation

Approximately 68% of any population is within one standard deviation of the mean: 34% on either side. Within two standard deviations you would expect approximately 96% of any population.

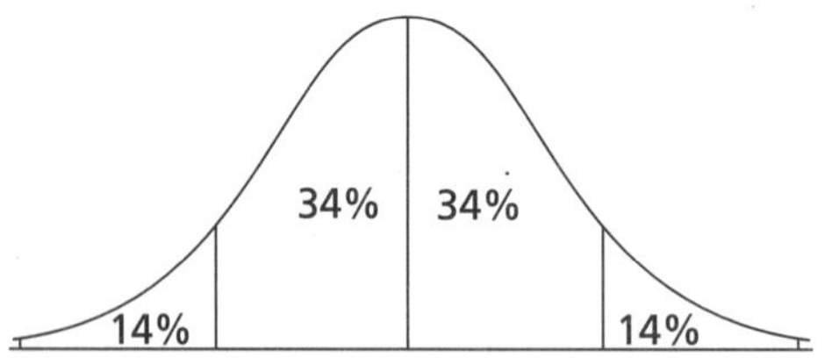

E.g. A drinks machine contains a selection of milk shakes which it dispenses in 500 ml cups. The mean quantity of milk shake dispensed is 500 ml, with a standard deviation of 7·5 ml. Estimate the probability that a drink from the machine will contain less than 480 ml.

480 ml is 20 ml below the mean. The standard deviation is 7·5 ml so two standard deviations would be 15 ml. 480 ml is therefore more than two standard deviations below the mean.

Only 4% of the population is more than two standard deviations from the mean. Therefore 2% of the population is more than two standard deviations **below** the mean (and 2% is more than two standard deviations above). This means that under 2% of drinks dispensed will contain less than 480 ml so the probability of a drink containing less than 480 ml is under 0·02.

5 What is the maximum amount of drink that could be dispensed by the machine in the example above if the drink was within one standard deviation of the mean?

6 What percentage of drinks dispensed are between one and two standard deviations above the mean?

Chapter summaries

Chapter 1

1 You may be asked to round an answer by expressing the answer to a number of significant figures (s.f.). Significant figures includes all the digits of a number. In some questions you will be asked to give your answer to a number of decimal places (d.p.). Decimal places includes only digits after the decimal point.

2 Ratio is a comparison between similar quantities. It can be expressed as a ratio m to n or $m : n$ or as a fraction m/n. m and n can be multiplied or divided by the same number without changing their ratio.

3 $+^{+}$ works like $+$
$-^{-}$ works like $+$
$+^{-}$ works like $-$
$-^{+}$ works like $-$

4 To change a number to standard form, put a decimal point after the first digit and then count how many places the decimal point has moved. This gives you the power of 10.

Chapter 2

1 $\sqrt{}$ means taking the positive square root.

2 To add and subtract fractions they should first be changed to give a common denominator (bottom value).

3 To multiply fractions first express them as top heavy or improper fractions.

4 It is very important that when you are writing two numbers as a ratio they must first be expressed in the same units.

5 % change is given by change ÷ original value.

Chapter 3

1 Speed is an example of a compound measure. It is a combination of two other measures: distance and time.

$$\text{average speed} = \frac{\text{distance travelled}}{\text{time taken}}$$

2 It is usual practice to give answers to one more decimal place in the answer than was used in the question.

3 Marks may be deducted if you do not give the units with your answer.

Chapter 4

1 If A and B are in **direct proportion**, then as one grows bigger the other also grows bigger by the same proportion e.g. if B doubles then A also doubles. If A is **inversely proportional** to B, then if B gets bigger A gets smaller by the same factor e.g. if B increases by a factor of 2 (B doubles) then A decreases by a factor of 2 (A is halved).

2 Inverse square law: $A \propto \dfrac{1}{B^2}$ or $A = \dfrac{k}{B^2}$

3 A **rational** number is any number that can be expressed as a vulgar fraction, i.e. written in the form $\frac{a}{b}$, where a and b are whole numbers. An **irrational** number is one which is **not** rational.

4 Any number to the power 0 is 1.

5 $a^{\frac{1}{2}} = \sqrt{a}$

Chapter 5

1 Sequences which are generated by adding or subtracting the same number each time are called **arithmetic** sequences. Sequences which are generated by multiplying or dividing by the same number each time are called **geometric** sequences.

2 These are the shapes of the most common types of curve:

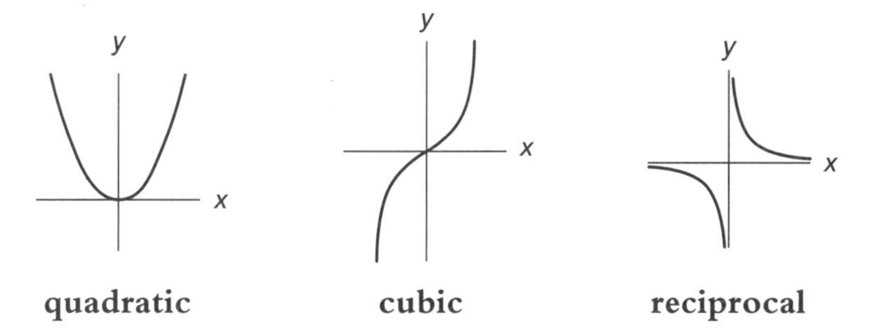
y
x
y
x
y
x

quadratic **cubic** **reciprocal**

Making any of these expressions negative will reflect the curve in the x-axis. Adding or subtracting a constant will move the curve up or down the y-axis.

3

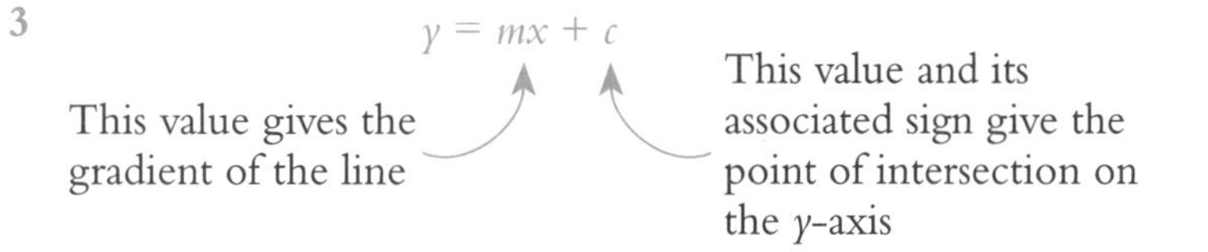
y = mx + c
This value gives the gradient of the line
This value and its associated sign give the point of intersection on the y-axis

Chapter 6

1 $(x + a)(x + b) = x^2 + (a + b)x + ab$

2 When you multiply expressions involving indices the indices appear to be added. When you divide expressions involving indices the indices appear to be subtracted.

3 When you raise a power to another power you multiply the indices (powers).

4 When multiplying or dividing both sides of an inequality by a negative value it is very important that you remember that the inequality sign reverses.

5 $a^2 - b^2 = (a + b)(a - b)$

Chapter 7

1 If you are asked to solve a quadratic equation to any number of decimal places you will have to use the formula:

$$\frac{-b \pm \sqrt{b^2 - 4ac}}{2a}$$

2 $x^{-n} = \frac{1}{x^n}$

3 $x^{\frac{1}{n}} = \sqrt[n]{x}$

4 An approximate value for the gradient of a curve at a particular point is given by the gradient of the **tangent** to the curve at that point. A **tangent** to a curve at a particular point is a straight line through the point following the direction of the curve at that point.

Chapter 8

1 For a regular polygon:
The **angle at the centre** is found by dividing 360° by the number of sides.
The **interior** or **internal angle** is 180° minus the angle at the centre.

The **exterior** or **external angle** is supplementary to the interior angle (they add to 180°) and equal to the angle at the centre.

2 If you call the hypotenuse c and the other sides a and b Pythagoras' theorem can be expressed as $c^2 = a^2 + b^2$.

3

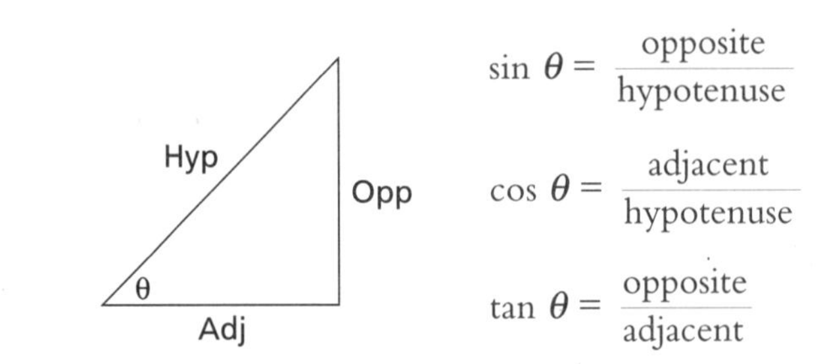

Chapter 9

1 A **vector** is a quantity which has both *magnitude* (size) and *direction*. Vectors can be used to represent displacement, velocity, force, momentum, acceleration. A **scalar** is a quantity which has magnitude (size) but not direction. You can multiply a vector by a scalar to get another vector.

2 To define a rotation you must give the centre of rotation, the direction of rotation and the distance you have rotated through.

3 To define a reflection you need to give the line of reflection.

4 To define an enlargement you need to give the centre of enlargement and the scale factor.

5 Two figures are **mathematically similar** if corresponding (matching) angles are all equal and corresponding sides are in the same ratio.

Chapter 10

1 1 km = $\frac{5}{8}$ miles

1 kg = 2.2 lb

1 litre = $1\frac{3}{4}$ pints

2 4 5 6

Anything within the shaded area is 5 to the **nearest unit**.

3 Area is measured in squared units. Volume is measured in cubed units.

Chapter 11

1 For any two shapes to be **congruent** to each other they must be *the same shape* and *the same size*.

2 There are two laws governing the addition of vectors. One law says that going from A to B and then from B to C is the same as going directly from A to C. This is called the **triangle law**. The second law says that going from A to C via D is the same as going from A to C via B. This is called the **parallelogram law**.

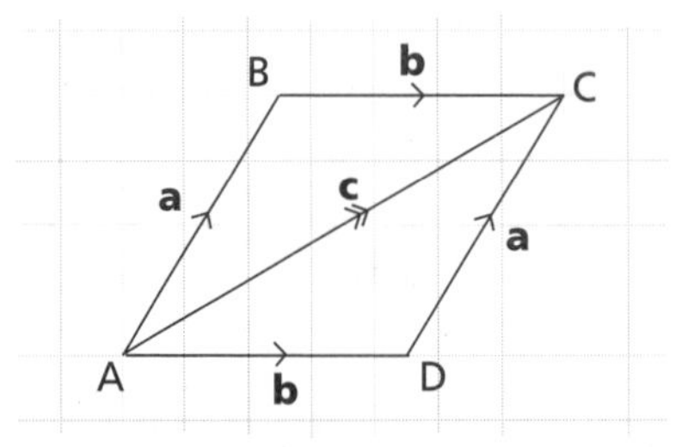

3 Sine rule: $\frac{a}{\sin A} = \frac{b}{\sin B} = \frac{c}{\sin C}$

4 Cosine rule: $\cos A = \frac{b^2 + c^2 - a^2}{2bc}$

Chapter 12

1 **Cumulative frequency** indicates how often a result was obtained which was less than (<) or less than or equal to (≤) a stated value in a collection of data.

2 The **mode** or modal value of a set of data is the most common value or if the data is grouped, the largest group.

3 The median is the middle value (when the data is in order) or the mid point of two middle values in a set of data or the mid point value in the middle group in grouped data.

4 The mean is given when all the data values are added and then divided by the number of values.

5 The range is the spread of the data (largest value – smallest value = range).

6

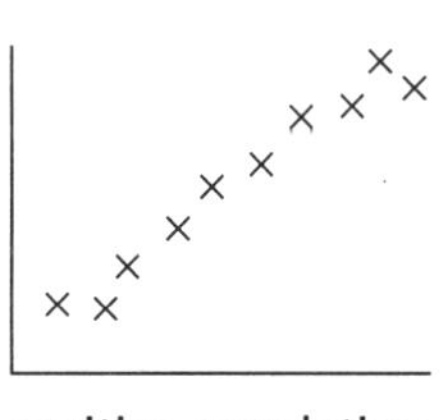

positive correlation

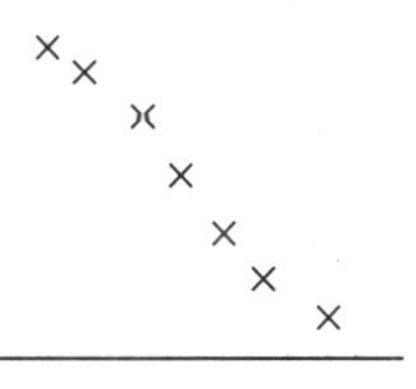

negative correlation

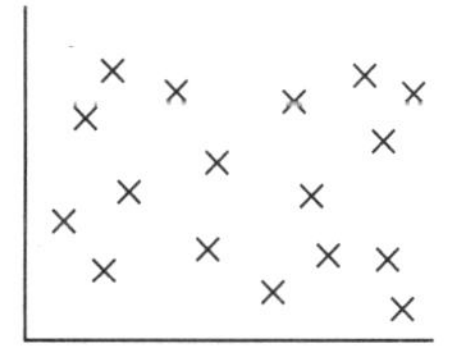

no correlation

Chapter 13

1 **Relative frequency** is given by:

$$\frac{\text{number of results which give the event you want}}{\text{number of trials}}$$

2 Two events are **mutually exclusive** if when one of them happens it stops the other happening.

3 The two events given by something 'happening' and 'not happening' are called **complementary** events. p(event) + p(not event) = 1

4 When two events are independent then
p(event 1 **and** event 2) = p(event 1) × p(event 2)

Chapter 14

1 For a histogram, the frequency for a particular class of data is given by the **area** of the column representing that class.

2 In data handling the word **population** is used for a collection or group of objects which are being studied. A **sample** is a smaller group selected from a population.

3 If the probability of an event happening depends on whether another event took place or not, then we say the events are **dependent**. The probability is said to be **conditional**.

4 Standard deviation:

$$\sigma = \sqrt{\Sigma \frac{f(x - \bar{x})^2}{n}}$$

Answers to in-text questions

Section 1 answers

1.1 Understanding place value – page 21

1 0·016 0·1 0·1006 0·1060 0·1600

2 (a) $\frac{4}{5}$ $\frac{5}{7}$ $\frac{7}{10}$ $\frac{2}{3}$ $\frac{5}{8}$ (b) $\frac{3}{7}$ $\frac{2}{5}$ $\frac{3}{8}$ $\frac{4}{11}$ $\frac{1}{4}$

1.2 Ratios – pages 21–2

1 (a) 3:2 (b) 3:4 (c) 3:2 (d) 3:2

2 (a) 2·4 m (b) 4·8 m

1.3 Negative numbers – pages 22–3

1 (a) 3 (b) 8 (c) 1 (d) $^{-}16$
(e) $^{-}20$ (f) $^{-}24$ (g) 11 (h) $^{-}13$

2 (a) 40 (b) $^{-}30$ (c) $^{-}42$ (d) 27
(e) 72 (f) $^{-}48$ (g) 28 (h) 60
(i) 8 (j) $^{-}8$ (k) $^{-}7$ (l) 9

1.4 Standard index form – pages 24–5

1 (a) $2{\cdot}42 \times 10^6$ m (b) $6{\cdot}085 \times 10^6$ m (c) $7{\cdot}14 \times 10^7$ m

2 (a) 3 000 000 m (b) 149 600 000 000 m

3 (a) 3×10^{-3} (b) $5{\cdot}2 \times 10^{-2}$ (c) $8{\cdot}61 \times 10^{-6}$ (d) $7{\cdot}03 \times 10^{-3}$

4 (a) 0·00005 (b) 0·8 (c) 0·00093 (d) 0·0632

5 (a) $3{\cdot}5 \times 10^{12}$ (b) 4×10^4 (c) $3{\cdot}354 \times 10^{15}$
(d) $2{\cdot}84 \times 10^5$ (to 3 s.f.)

6 $5{\cdot}1084 \times 10^{18}$ m

7 $1{\cdot}429 \times 10^3$ kg/m^3 (to 4 s.f.)

8 3×10^5

9 (a) 6×10^{-3} m (b) 2000 or 2×10^3 (1 mm = 1×10^{-3} m)

2.1 Working with powers and roots – page 27

1 (a) xy (b) a (c) $3y$ (d) $2a$ (e) b^2 (f) a^2b

2 (a) $x = \sqrt[6]{y}$ (b) $x = y^5$ (c) $x = \sqrt{y^3}$

3 (a) $\frac{1}{3}$ (b) $\frac{1}{4^2} = \frac{1}{16}$ (c) $\frac{1}{2^5} = \frac{1}{32}$

2.2 Fractions – pages 27–8

1 (a) $1\frac{1}{12}$ (b) $\frac{3}{20}$ (c) $\frac{7}{8}$ (d) $\frac{1}{4}$

2 (a) $8\frac{3}{4}$ (b) $2\frac{3}{8}$ (c) $3\frac{9}{10}$

3 (a) $\frac{3}{8}$ (b) $7\frac{7}{10}$ (c) $1\frac{1}{2}$ (d) $2\frac{1}{22}$

4 (a) $\frac{3}{5}$ (b) $\frac{2}{3}$ (c) $\frac{2}{3}$

2.3 Calculating with ratios – pages 28–30

1 (a) 1 : 3 (b) 9 : 1

2 (a) 6 cubic metres (b) 5 cubic metres (c) 6 cubic metres

3 2000 g stewing steak, 75 g plain flour, about $2\frac{1}{2}$ medium onions, about $7\frac{1}{2}$ medium leeks, 250 g button mushrooms, 125 g lard, 1000 g tinned tomatoes. (You can divide by 2 and multiply by 5 or use the multiplier 2·5.)

4 375 g apples, 150 g flour (You can divide by 4 and multiply by 3 or use the multiplier 0·75.)

2.4 Percentage change – pages 30–31

1 (a) £280 (b) 92·8 m (c) 8125 (d) £2616 (e) £1762·50

2 (a) £138 (b) £220 (c) £9775 (d) 799

3 (a) 8% (b) 4% (c) 7%

4 (a) $0{\cdot}65 \times B = 52$ (b) $S \times 0{\cdot}67 = 1139$

$B = \frac{52}{0{\cdot}65}$ $S = \frac{1139}{0{\cdot}67}$

$B = 80$ $S = £1700$

3.1 Compound interest – pages 32–3

1 (a) £3934·30 (b) £29 604 885·70 (c) £386 268·36

2 (a) 6·65 kg (2 d.p.) (b) 221 571 sq. miles

3 (a) £11 694 (b) £16 080 (c) £10 590

3.2 Compound measures – pages 33–4

1 (a) $\frac{120 \text{ miles}}{3 \text{ hours}} = 40$ mph (b) 6 mph × 0·5 hours= 3 miles (c) $\frac{40 \text{ km}}{8 \text{ km/h}} = 5$ hours

2 (a) 19·3 × 20 = 386 g (b) $\frac{810}{2{\cdot}7} = 300 \text{ cm}^3$ (c) $\frac{26{\cdot}7}{3} = 8{\cdot}9 \text{ g/cm}^3$

3 (a) To 2 decimal places, $\frac{500}{99} = 5{\cdot}05$ g/p and $\frac{200}{63} = 3{\cdot}17$ g/p so the 500 g bag is better value.

(b) To 2 decimal places, $\frac{2000}{875} = 2{\cdot}29$ g/p and $\frac{454}{175} = 2{\cdot}59$ g/p so the 454 g box of chocolates is better value.

3.3 Choosing an appropriate degree of accuracy – page 35

1 (a) Protractor (nearest degree)

(b) Stop watch ($\frac{1}{100}$ of a second)

(c) Ruler (cm)

(d) Speedometer (pedometer) (miles)

(e) Speedometer (miles per hour)

(f) Thermometer ($\frac{1}{10}$ of a degree)

(g) Bathroom scales (kilograms, stones or pounds)

(h) Kitchen scales (grams or ounces)

2 (a) 2 mm (b) 72·88 kg

3 6.6% or 7%

4 £182·04

5 (a) £770 (b) $(8000 \div 30) \times 5 \times 0{\cdot}5 \simeq 660$ (or similar)

4.1 Proportion – pages 37–8

1 (a) (multiplier rule) $\frac{m}{27{\cdot}5} = \frac{9}{5{\cdot}5}$ so $m = \frac{9 \times 27{\cdot}5}{5{\cdot}5} = 45$

(b) (constant ratio rule) $\frac{t}{43} = \frac{5{\cdot}5}{27{\cdot}5}$ so $t = \frac{5{\cdot}5 \times 43}{27{\cdot}5} = 8{\cdot}6$

2 £150 = 26 100 Pesetas so £1 = $\frac{26100}{150}$ = 174 Pesetas (The ratio of Pesetas to £ is 174)

(a) £250 = 250 × 174 = 43 500 Pesetas

(b) £60 = 60 × 174 = 10 440 Pesetas

(c) 10 092 Pesetas = $\frac{10092}{174}$ = £58

3 (a) The multiplier from 147 Hz to 110 Hz is 110 ÷ 147 = 0·7482993. You divide 65 cm by this number to give the answer.

65 ÷ 0·7482993 = 86·863636

The string with a frequency of 110 Hz is 86·9 cm long (to 1 d.p.).

(Using brackets on calculator: 65 ÷ (110 ÷ 147) = 86·863636.)

(b) The multiplier from 147 Hz to 196 Hz is 1·3333333.

65 ÷ 1·3333333 = 48·75

The string with a frequency of 196 Hz is 48·8 cm (to 1 d.p.).

4 (a) 10 N (b) 1000 N

4.2 Rational and irrational numbers – pages 39–40

1 Your investigation. You may have found that all fractions with a denominator (bottom number) of 3 or 9 repeat after 1 decimal place, and those with a denominator of 11 repeat after 2 places. It looks like all fractions with a denominator of 7 repeat after 6 decimal places, but on your calculator you can't be sure.

2 (a) $0\cdot\dot{1}4285\dot{7}$ (b) $0\cdot\dot{1}5384\dot{6}$ (c) $0\cdot\dot{1}9047\dot{6}$

3 (a) $\frac{2}{7} = 0\cdot\dot{2}8571\dot{4}$

$\frac{1}{19}$ which repeats after 18 terms

$\frac{5}{43}$ which repeats after 42 terms

(b) $4^{\frac{1}{2}}$ is rational (2)

2^{-2} is rational $= \frac{1}{2^2} = \frac{1}{4}$

(c) $\sqrt{2} \times \sqrt{8}$

(d) $3 + \sqrt{5}$ is irrational (rational + irrational = irrational)

$3\sqrt{5}$ is irrational (rational × irrational = irrational in this case)

4.3 Upper and lower bounds – pages 40–3

	Lower bound	Upper bound
1	(a) £11·50	£12·49
	(b) £55·00	£64·99
	(c) £725·00	£774·99
	(d) £8·85	£8·94
2	(a) 637·5 kg	638·5 kg
	(b) 1650 g	1750 g
	(c) 9·5 m	10·5 m
	(d) 492·5 cm	497·5 cm
3	(a) 3·65 m	3·75 m
	(b) 10 500	11 499
	(c) (i) 2·605 kg	2·615 kg
	(ii) 2·6095 kg	2·6105 kg

4 lower bound perimeter = 2(39·5 + 17·5) = 114 m

5 (a) upper bound perimeter = 2(4·25 + 1·85) = 12·2 m
lower bound perimeter = 2(4·15 + 1·75) = 11·8 m

(b) upper bound perimeter = 2(110·5 + 65·5) = 352 m
lower bound perimeter = 2(109·5 + 64·5) = 348 m

6 new upper bound = max fencing – min size of gate = 302·5 m – 2·25 m
= 300·25 m
new lower bound = min fencing – upper bound size of gate = 297·5 m – 2·35 m
= 295·15 m

7 upper bound a = 4·85 – 1·65 × 2 = 1·55
lower bound a = 4·75 – 1·75 × 2 = 1·25

8 (a) 477 (b) 153

9 (a) upper bound area = 15·5 × 8·5 = 131·75 m²
(b) lower bound area = 14·5 × 7·5 = 108·75 m²
(c) upper bound = 30·5 g/m² × 131·75 m² = 4018·4 g

10 (a) To calculate the minimum amount of paint needed you divide the minimum ceiling area by the maximum paint coverage.

(b) lower bound of wall area = 2(2·05 × 5·15) + 2(2·05 × 6·55) = 47·97 m²
47·97 ÷ 13·5 = 3·553 which rounds to 4 litre tins

(c) upper bound of wall area = 2(2·15 × 5·25) + 2(2·15 × 6·65) = 51·17 m²
51·17 ÷ 12·5 = 4·0936 which gives a maximum of 5 litre tins

4.4 Using index notation for powers and roots – pages 43–5

1 (a) 5^4 (b) 3^7 (c) $\left(\frac{1}{2}\right)^3$ or $\frac{1}{2^3}$ (d) 6^1 (e) $\left(\frac{1}{7}\right)^4$ or $\frac{1}{7^4}$ (f) $0\cdot21^2$

2 (a) 525·22 (to 2 d.p.) (b) 296·61 (to 2 d.p.) (c) 0·015625

3 16 777 216

4 (a) $\frac{1}{9}$ (b) $\frac{1}{16}$ (c) $\frac{1}{32}$ (d) $\frac{1}{25}$

5 (a) 27, 9, 3, 1, $0\cdot\dot{3}$ or $\frac{1}{3}$, $0\cdot\dot{1}$ or $\frac{1}{9}$, $0\cdot\dot{0}3\dot{7}$ or $\frac{1}{27}$
(b) 125, 25, 5, 1, 0·2 or $\frac{1}{5}$, 0·04 or $\frac{1}{25}$, 0·008 or $\frac{1}{125}$
(c) 64, 16, 4, 1, 0·25 or $\frac{1}{4}$, 0·0625 or $\frac{1}{16}$, 0·015625 or $\frac{1}{64}$

6 (a) 1 (b) 1 (c) 1 (d) 1 (e) 1

7 (a) 23 (b) 24 (c) 16 (d) 4 (e) 0·024

8 (a) $9^{\frac{1}{2}}$ (b) $64^{\frac{1}{3}}$ (c) $10^{\frac{1}{5}}$ (d) $487\cdot49^{\frac{1}{16}}$

9 (a) 17 (b) 2·5 (c) 36 (d) 2

10 (a) $3\sqrt{5}$ (b) $2\sqrt{3}$ (c) $6\sqrt{3}$ (d) $\frac{\sqrt{7}}{\sqrt{3}}$

Section 2 answers

5.1 Rules for generating sequences – see pages 46–7

1 (a) 1, 4, 7, 10, 13 (b) 20, 18, 16, 14, 12, (c) 1, 5, 25, 125, 625
(d) 1, $^{-}1$, $^{-}3$, $^{-}5$, $^{-}7$

2 (a) 1, 5, 17, 53, 161, (b) 1, 0, $^{-}2$, $^{-}6$, $^{-}14$ (c) 10, 24, 66, 192, 570

3 (a) Starting with 1 add 2 then 3, then 4 and so on (consecutive numbers) – these are called triangular numbers.

(b) Starting with 1 and 1, each term is produced by adding together the last two numbers.

4 (a) + 1 starting at 3 ($n \rightarrow n + 2$)

(b) + 3 starting at 3 ($n \rightarrow 3n$)

(c) $\times$ 2 + 1 starting at 1 ($n \rightarrow 2n - 1$)

(d) $\times$ 4 – 1 starting at 1

5.2 Sequence notation – pages 48–50

1 (a) 3, 12, 27, 48, 75 (b) 3, 7, 11, 15, 19
(c) $\frac{1}{2}$ or 0·5, 2, $\frac{9}{2}$ or 4·5, 8, $\frac{25}{2}$ or 12·5 (d) $\frac{2}{3}$, $\frac{4}{3}$, $\frac{6}{3}$ or 2, $\frac{8}{3}$, $\frac{10}{3}$

2 (a) 20 (b) 160 (c) 2560

3 (a) $3n - 2$ (b) $2n + 1$ (c) $5n - 1$

4 If the bricks are laid out in a single row you get:

bricks	*hidden faces*
1	1
2	4
3	7

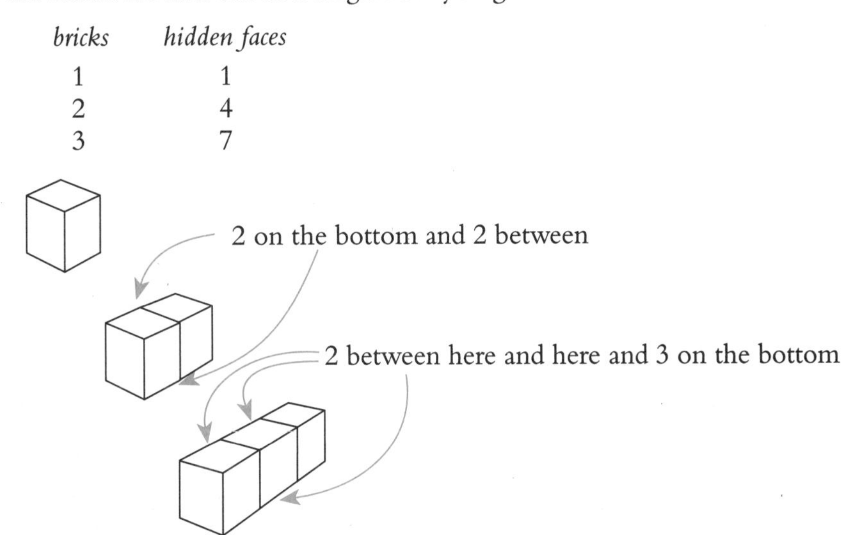
2 on the bottom and 2 between
2 between here and here and 3 on the bottom

The rule is $N = 3n - 2$ where N is the number of hidden faces and n the number of bricks. (Every brick has 3 hidden faces except the two at the ends.)

5 (a) £12 100 (b) £14 800 (c) £18 400 (d) £34 600

6 (a) 3^{n-1} (b) 5^n (c) $4 \times 5^{n-1}$ (d) $7 \times 3^{n-1}$
(e) $(\frac{1}{3})^{n-1}$ or $\frac{1}{3^{n-1}}$

7 (a) 2^n (b) 3×2^n

8 (a) $n^2 - 1$ (b) $(n + 1)^2$ (c) $2n^2$

9 (a) $\frac{n}{3n-1}$ (b) $\frac{2^n}{2n+1}$

5.3 Graphs of real-life situations – pages 52–4

1 (a) goes with (i) (b) goes with (iii) (c) goes with (ii)

2 (a) B (b) C (c) D

3 (a) (b) (c)

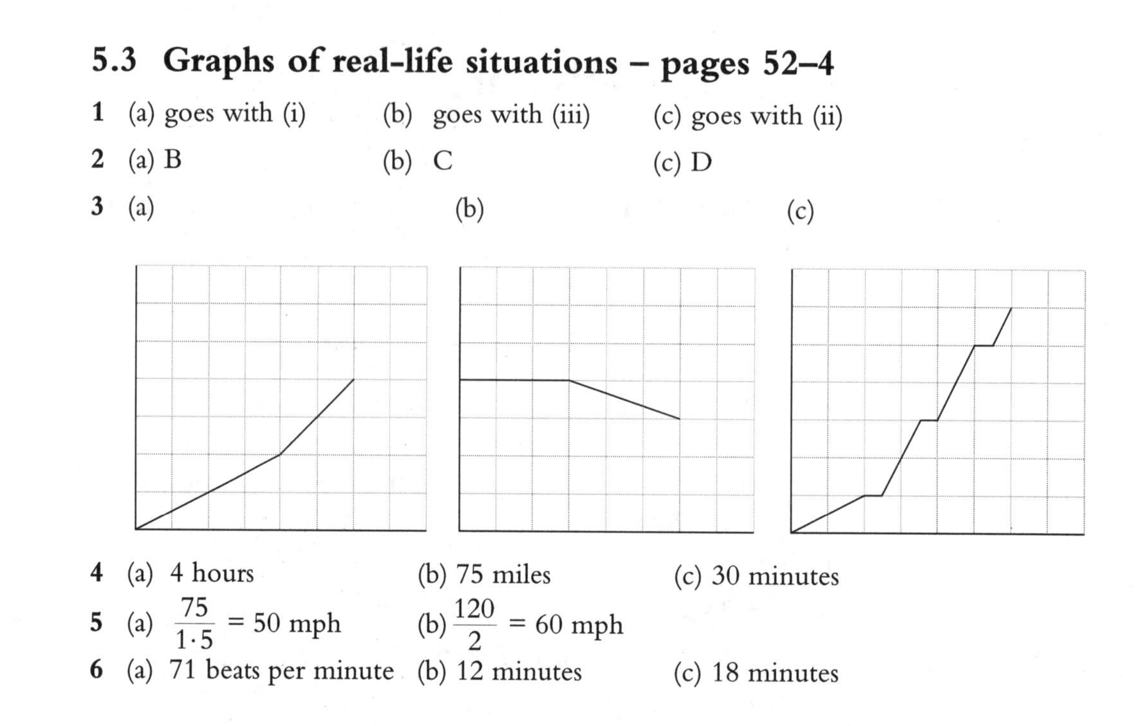

4 (a) 4 hours (b) 75 miles (c) 30 minutes

5 (a) $\frac{75}{1\cdot5} = 50$ mph (b) $\frac{120}{2} = 60$ mph

6 (a) 71 beats per minute (b) 12 minutes (c) 18 minutes

5.4 Graphs of simple functions – pages 55–8

1

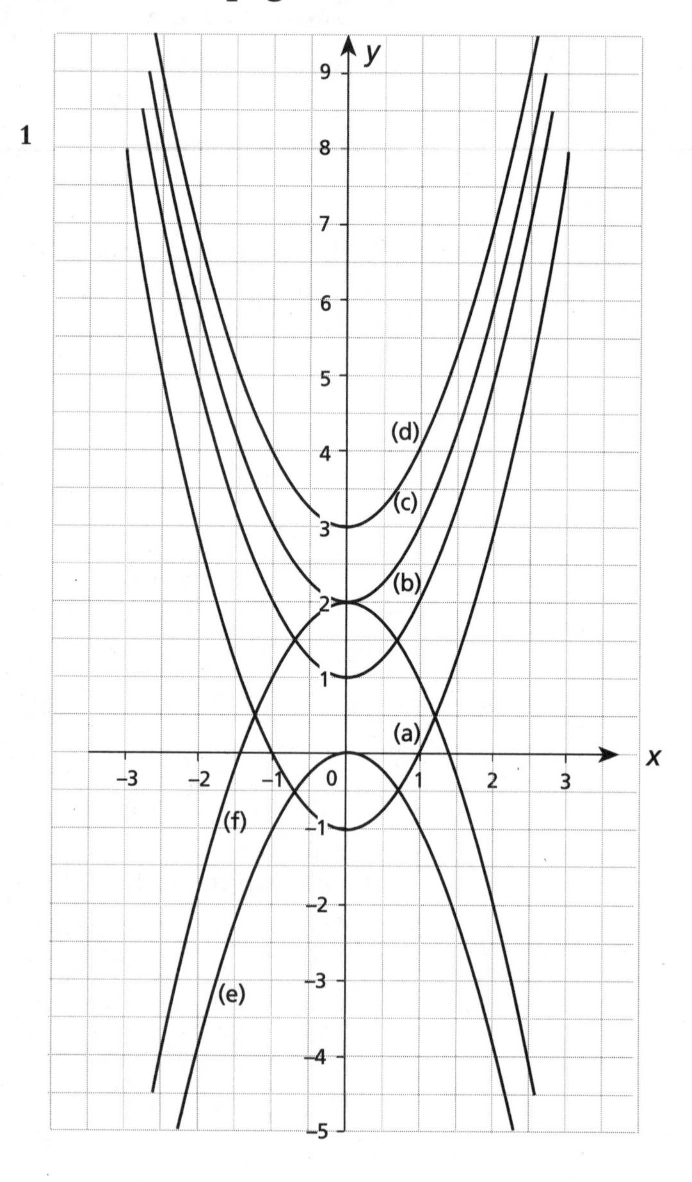

2 (a) Adding n to the x^2 term moves the graph n places up the y–axis. Subtracting n moves the graph n places down. (This type of move is called a translation.)

(b) Making x^2 into $^-x^2$ has the effect of turning the graph upside down.

3 (a) $y = 5 - x^2$

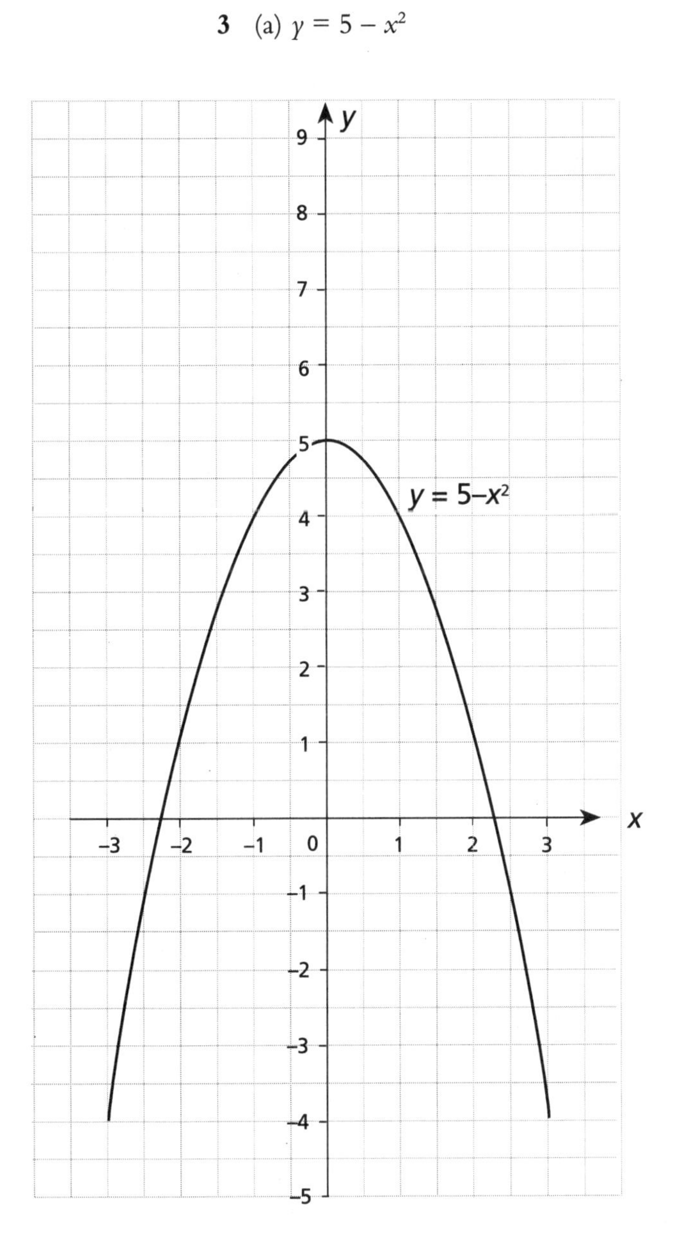

(b) $y = 2x^2 - 3x - 2$

x	3	2	1	$\frac{1}{2}$	0	$-\frac{1}{2}$	$^-1$	$^-2$
$2x^2$	18	8	2	$\frac{1}{2}$	0	$\frac{1}{2}$	2	8
$-3x$	$^-9$	$^-6$	$^-3$	$-\frac{3}{2}$	0	$\frac{3}{2}$	3	6
-2	$^-2$	$^-2$	$^-2$	$^-2$	$^-2$	$^-2$	$^-2$	$^-2$
y	7	0	$^-3$	$^-3$	$^-2$	0	3	12

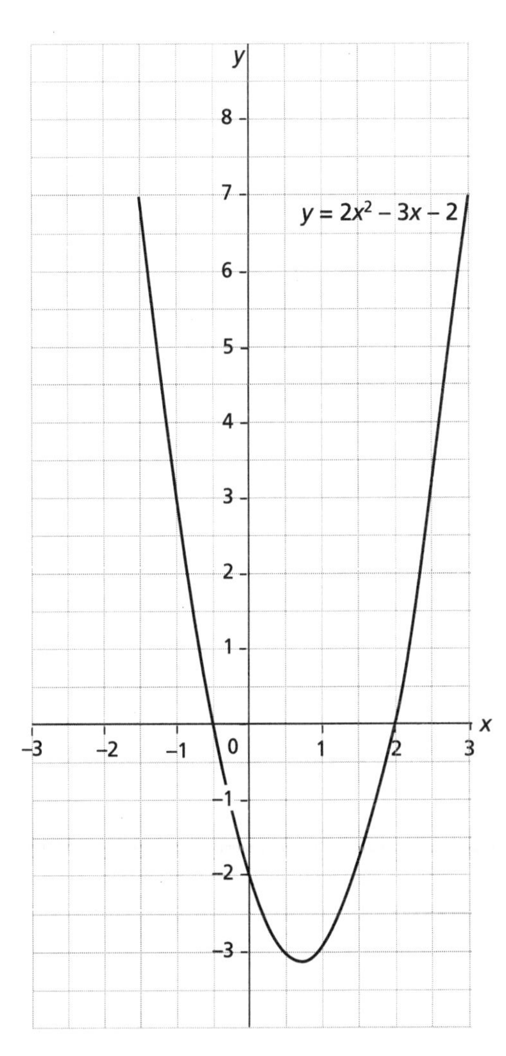

(c) $y = x^2 + 5x + 6$

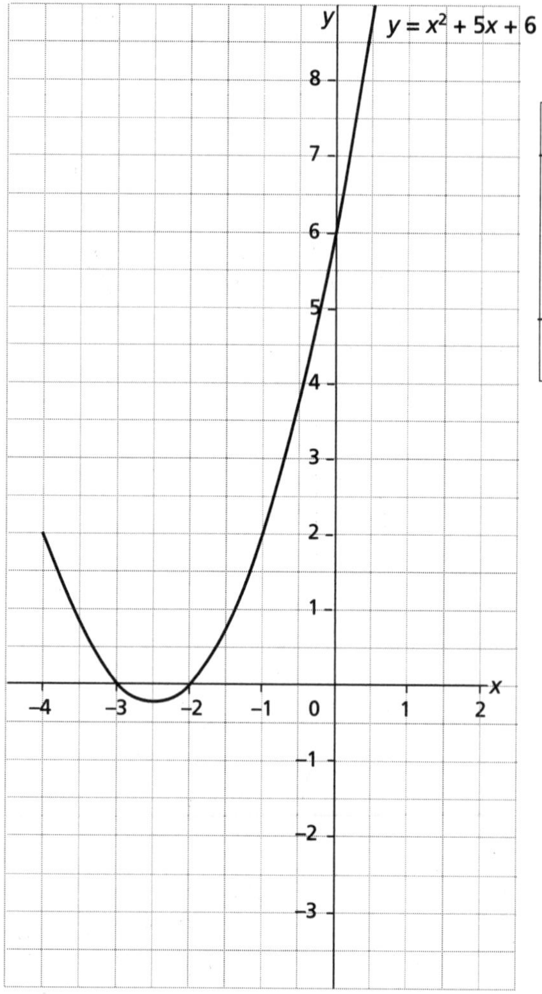

x	1	0	$^-1$	$^-2$	$^-2\frac{1}{2}$	$^-3$	$^-4$	$^-5$
x^2	1	0	1	4	$6\frac{1}{4}$	9	16	25
$+5x$	5	0	$^-5$	$^-10$	$^-12\frac{1}{2}$	$^-15$	$^-20$	$^-25$
$+6$	6	6	6	6	6	6	6	6
y	12	6	2	0	$-\frac{1}{4}$	0	2	6

4 (a) $y = \frac{1}{2}x^3$

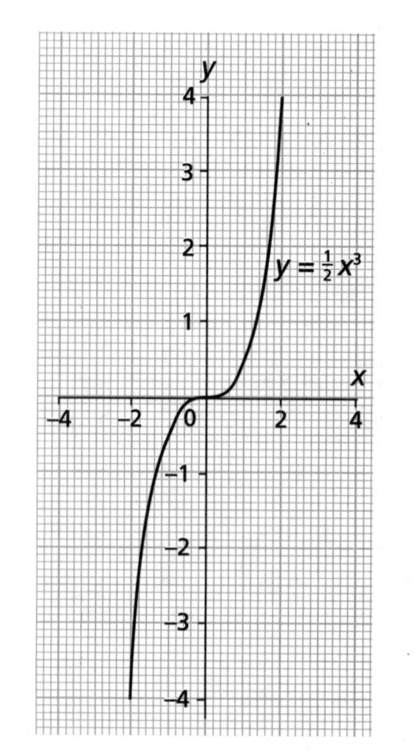

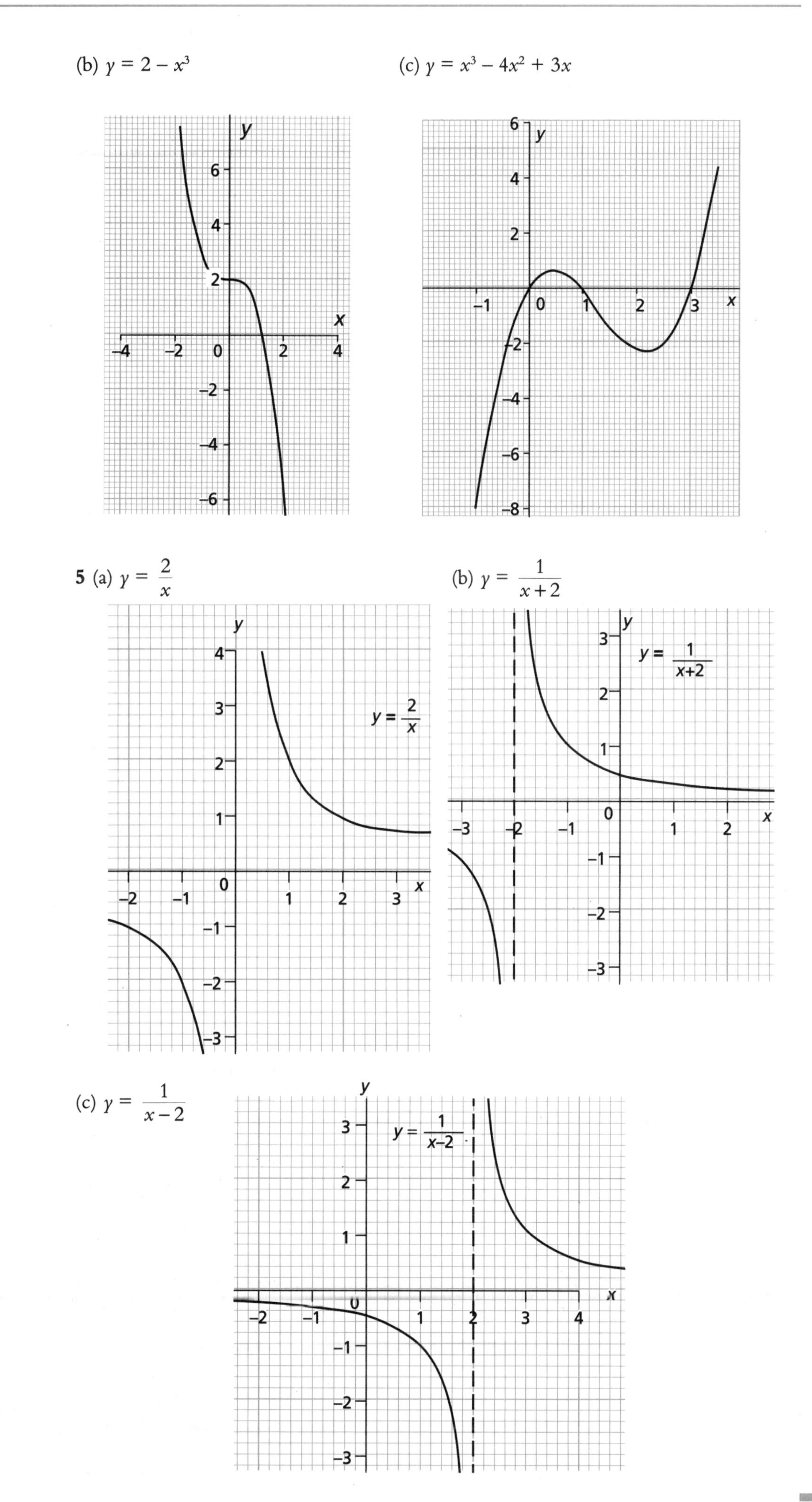
(b) $y = 2 - x^3$
(c) $y = x^3 - 4x^2 + 3x$
5 (a) $y = \frac{2}{x}$
$y = \frac{2}{x}$
(b) $y = \frac{1}{x+2}$
$y = \frac{1}{x+2}$
(c) $y = \frac{1}{x-2}$
$y = \frac{1}{x-2}$
x
y

(d) $y = \frac{-4}{x}$

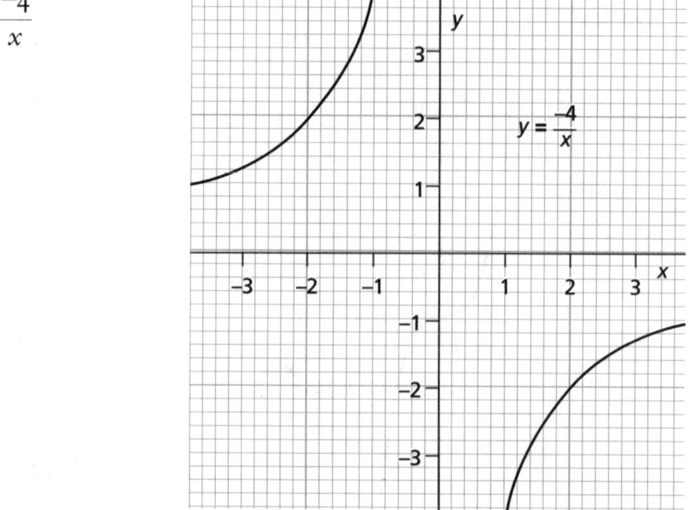

5.5 Gradient and y intercepts ($y = mx + c$) – pages 59–60

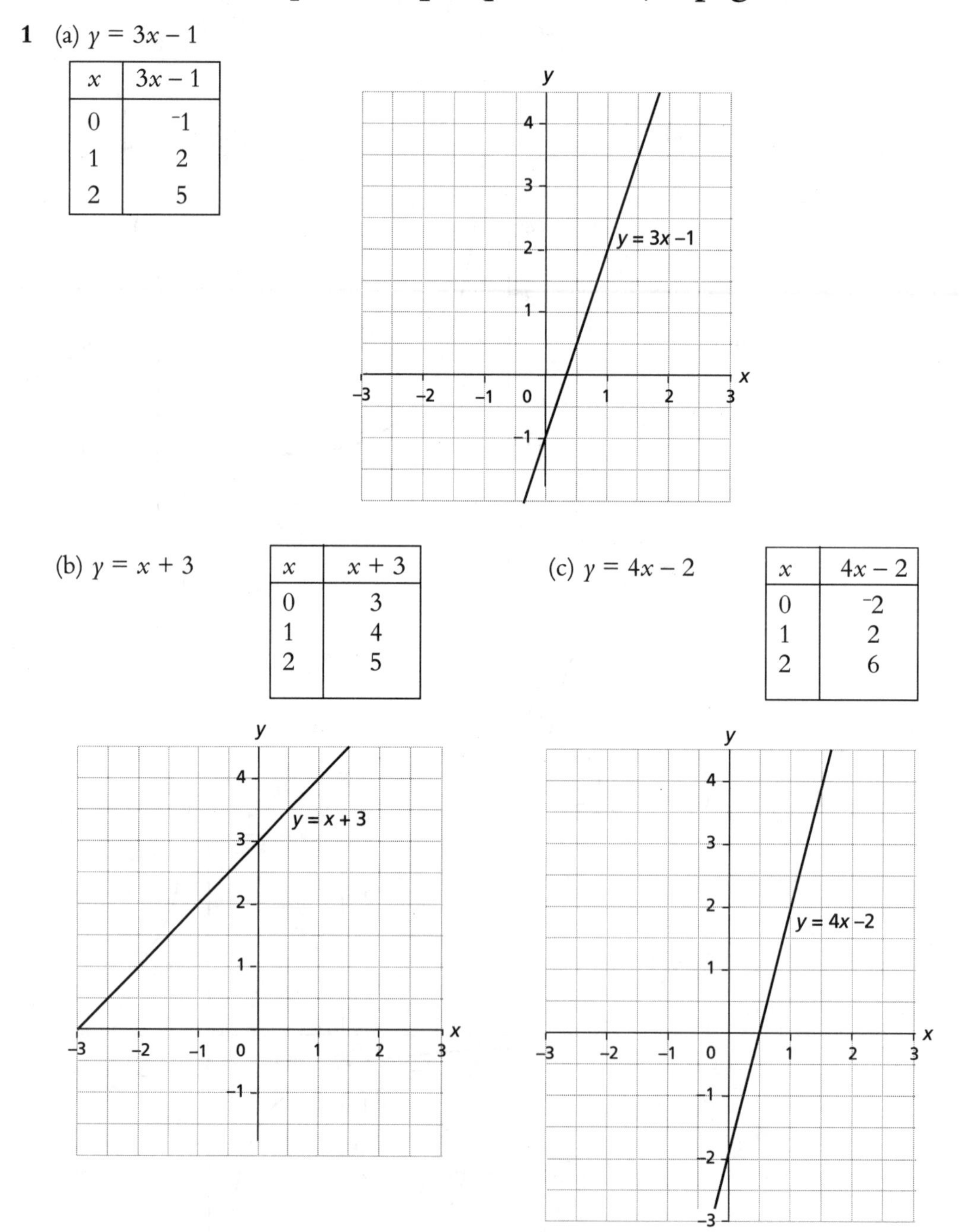

1 (a) $y = 3x - 1$

x	$3x - 1$
0	$^-1$
1	2
2	5

(b) $y = x + 3$

x	$x + 3$
0	3
1	4
2	5

(c) $y = 4x - 2$

x	$4x - 2$
0	$^-2$
1	2
2	6

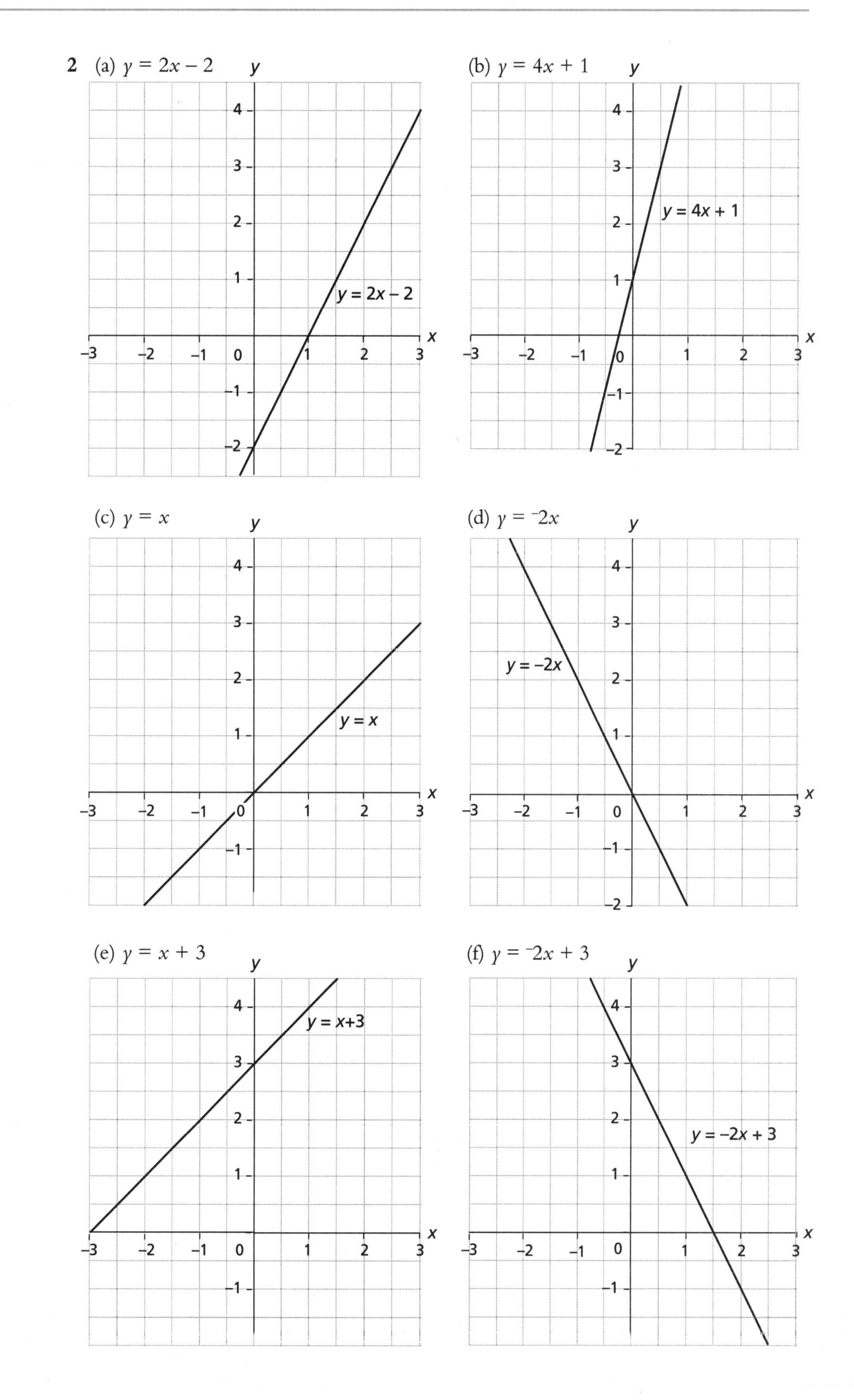
2 (a) y = 2x − 2
y = 2x − 2
(b) y = 4x + 1
y = 4x + 1
(c) y = x
y = x
(d) y = ⁻2x
y = −2x
(e) y = x + 3
y = x+3
(f) y = ⁻2x + 3
y = −2x + 3
x
y

3 (a) $2x + 3y = 12$
$3y = {}^-2x + 12$
$y = -\frac{2}{3}x + 4$

(b) $5x + y = 5$
$y = {}^-5x + 5$

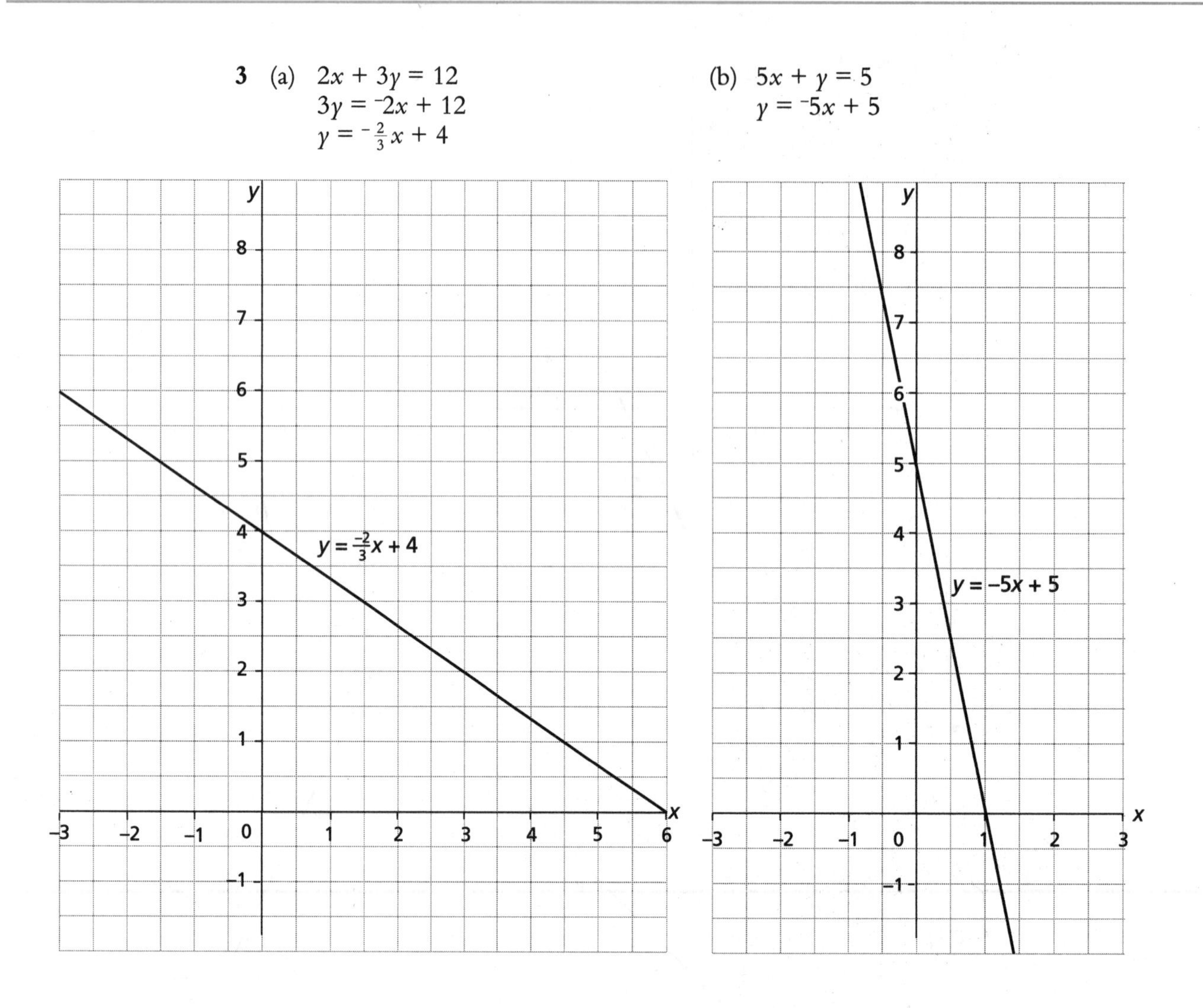

(c) $4x + 3y = 15$

$y = -\frac{4}{3}x + 5$

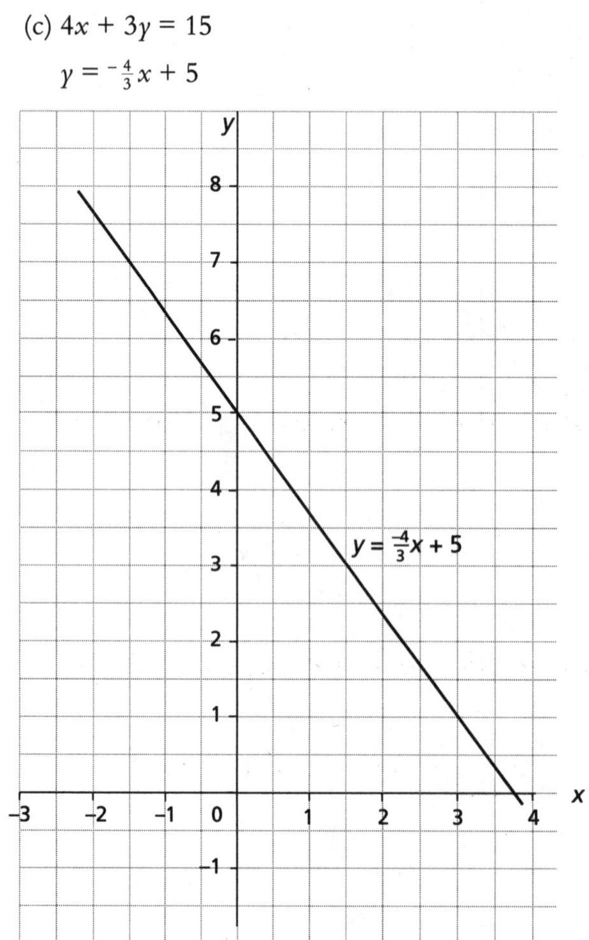

(d) $3x - 5y = 15$

$y = \frac{3}{5}x - 3$

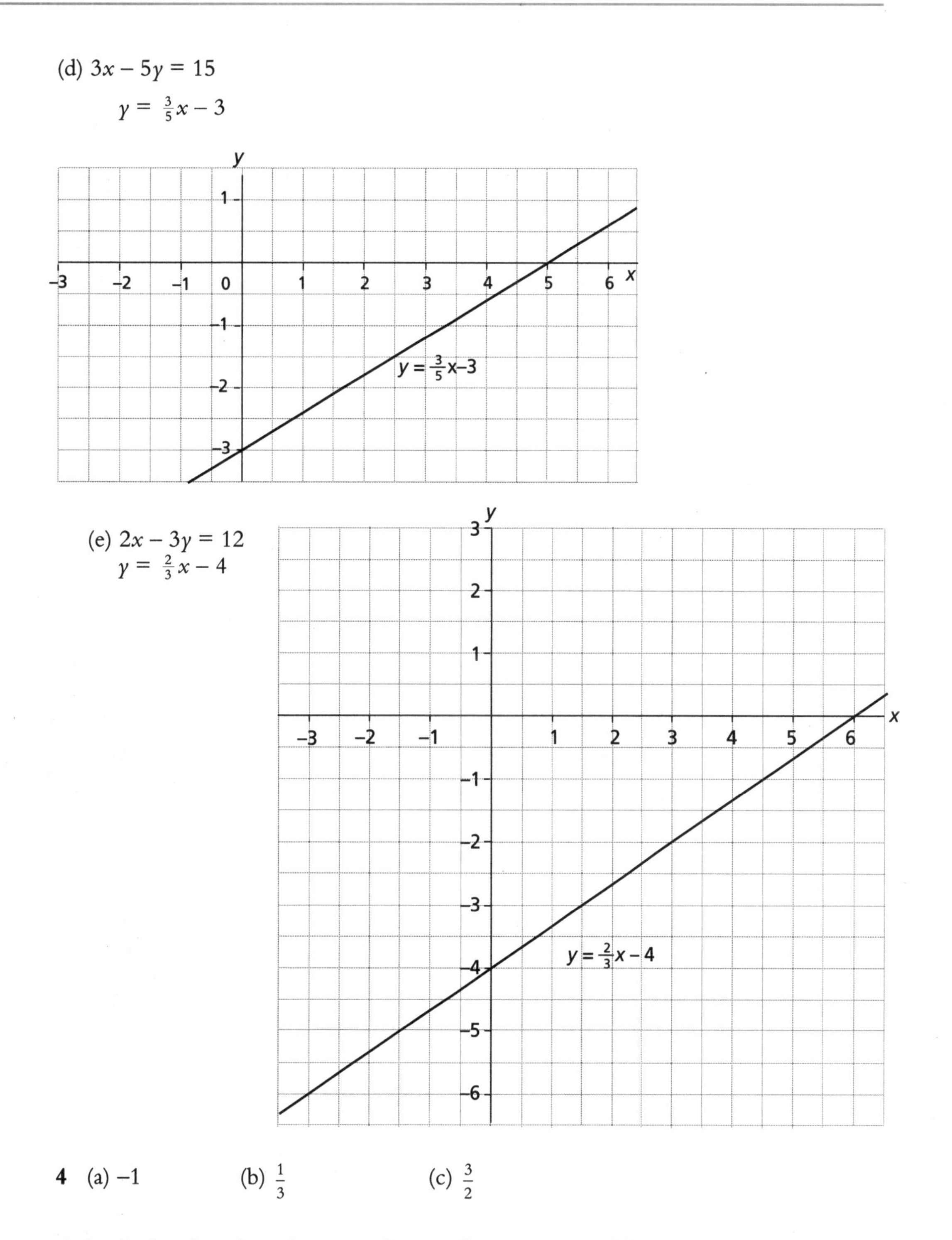

(e) $2x - 3y = 12$

$y = \frac{2}{3}x - 4$

4 (a) -1 (b) $\frac{1}{3}$ (c) $\frac{3}{2}$

6.1 Substituting into a formulae – page 61

1 (a) $s = 42$ (b) $s = 4$ (c) $s = 2{\cdot}25$

2 (a) $v = 4$ (b) $v = 7$ (c) $2{\cdot}21$ (to 2 d.p.)

3 (a) $f = 0{\cdot}3$ (b) $f = 4{\cdot}1\dot{6}$ (c) $f = -0{\cdot}29$

6.2 Collecting like terms – pages 61–2

1 (a) $9x + 7y$ (b) $7a + b - 2c$ (c) $2r - 3p$

2 (a) $ab + 3ac$ (b) $3ab + 8ac$ (c) $21x + 14y$

6.3 Manipulating brackets – page 62–3

1 (a) $3x + 15$ (b) $^{-}2x - 10$ (c) $^{-}3x^2 + 12x$ or $12x - 3x^2$
(d) $x(12x + 8 - 6x + 12) = x(6x + 20) = 6x^2 + 20x$
(e) $6n - 3y - y = 6n - 4y$ (f) $8x + 4y - 3x + 6y = 5x + 10y$

2 (a) $x^2 + 2x + 3x + 6 = x^2 + 5x + 6$ (b) $x^2 - 2x + 3x - 6 = x^2 + x - 6$
(c) $x^2 - 4x - 2x + 8 = x^2 - 6x + 8$

3 (a) $a^2 - ab + ab - b^2 = a^2 - b^2$ (b) $a^2 + ab + ab + b^2 = a^2 + 2ab + b^2$
(c) $a^2 - ab - ab + b^2 = a^2 - 2ab + b^2$

4 (a) $x^2 + 5x + 5x + 25 = x^2 + 10x + 25$ (b) $x^2 - 2x - 2x + 4 = x^2 - 4x + 4$
(c) $x^2 - y^2$ (d) $2x^2 + 7x + 6$ (e) $15x^2 + 47x + 28$
(f) $acx^2 + (ad + bc)x + bd$

6.4 Factorising – pages 63–5

1 (a) $2(a + 2b)$ (b) $2a(a - 2)$ (c) $^{-}2(2a + 3b)$
(d) $5y(y^2 + 2y - 5)$ (e) $a(x + 2) + 2b(x + 2) = (a + 2b)(x + 2)$

2 (a) $(x + 2)(x + 3)$ (b) $(x - 4)(x + 3)$ (c) $(x - 4)(x - 2)$
(d) $(x + 1)(x - 6)$ (e) $(x + 3)(x - 3)$

3 (a) $a(\sqrt{a} + 1)$ (b) $a^3\sqrt{a}\,(a + 1)$ (c) $a^2(\sqrt{a} + 1)$ (d) $\sqrt{2a}\,(2a + 1)$

6.5 Indices – pages 65–6

1 (a) $8a^2$ (b) $4(x^3 + x^2)$ or $4x^2(x + 1)$ (c) $3x^3 + 7y^2$ (d) $4b^5$
2 (a) $8x^7$ (b) $18a^9$ (c) $40y^{11}$ (d) $3x^3y^5$
3 (a) 10^{31} (b) 7^{14} (c) 6×5^{15}
4 (a) a^4 (b) $1{\cdot}5x^3$ (c) $4x^3$ (d) $2ab$
5 (a) 7^2 (b) 9^3 (c) $5^2 \times 2^2$ (d) 10^{13}
6 (a) a^8 (b) $9x^6$ (c) $256n^{12}$ (d) $a^8b^{12}c^4$
7 (a) $a^{10}b^2$ (b) x^5y^4 (c) $64a^{15}b^3$

6.6 Rearranging formulae – page 68

1 (a) $a - y = bx$

$$\frac{a-y}{b} = x$$

(b) $wx = u - v$

$$wx + v = u$$

(c) $s = ut + \frac{1}{2}at^2$

$$s - ut = \frac{1}{2}at^2$$

$$2(s - ut) = at^2$$

$$\frac{2(s - ut)}{t^2} = a$$

(d) $byz = ax$

$$\frac{byz}{a} = x$$

(e) $m + p = 4n^2$

$$\frac{1}{2}\sqrt{m+p} = n$$

(f) $\frac{3}{x+2} = y^2$

$$\frac{x+2}{3} = \frac{1}{y^2}$$

$$x + 2 = \frac{3}{y^2}$$

$$x = \frac{3}{y^2} - 2$$

2 (a) 26·7 °C (to 1 d.p.) (b) 43·3 °C (to 1 d.p.) (c) $^{-}$6·7 °C (to 1 d.p.)

6.7 Solving inequalities – pages 68–70

1 (a) 1, 2, 3, 4 (b) −5, −4, −3, −2, −1

2 (a) $6x < 30$
$x < 5$

(b) $12x + 20 < 32$
$12x < 12$
$x < 1$

(c) $2x < -4$
$x < -2$

(d) $x + 9 > 6$
$x > -3$

3 (a) $12 - x > 8$
$12 > 8 + x$
$4 > x$

(b) $15 - 3x < 2(x - 5)$
$15 - 3x < 2x - 10$
$25 < 5x$
$5 < x$

4 (a) $2x^2 - 1 > 1$
$2x^2 > 2$
$x^2 > 1$
$x > 1$ and $x < -1$

(b) $x(x - 2) < 2(2 - x)$
$x^2 - 2x < 4 - 2x$
$x^2 < 4$
$-2 < x < 2$

6.8 Graphs of linear inequalities – pages 70–1

1 & **2** (a)

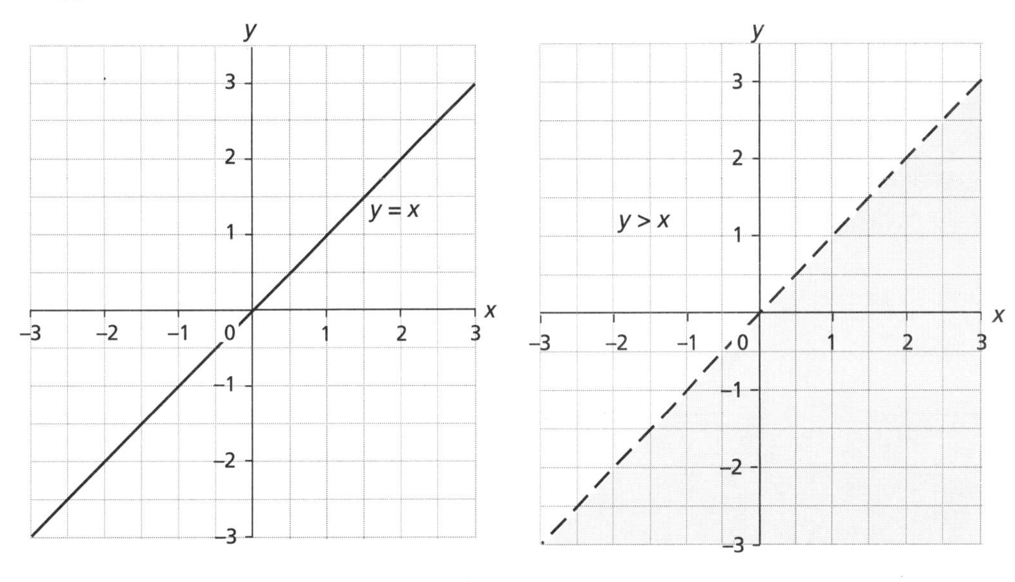

(b)

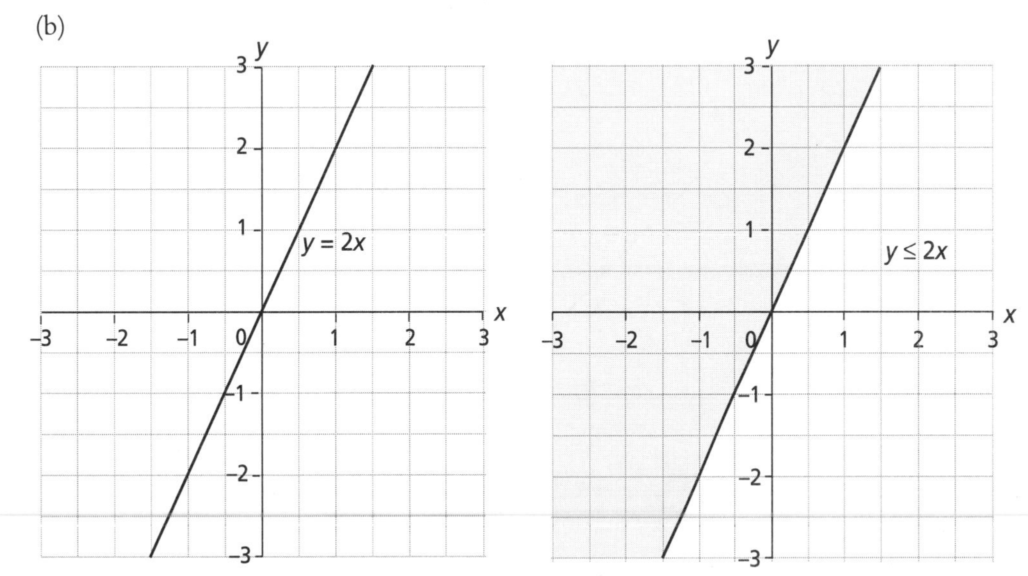

(c)

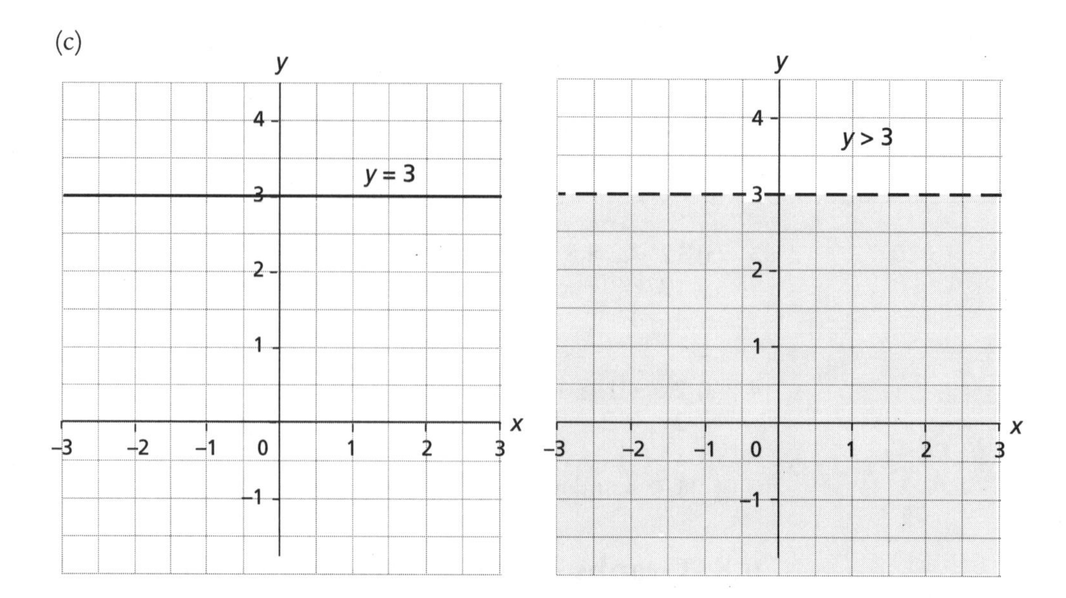
y
x
y = 3
y > 3
4
3
2
1
0
–1
–3
–2
–1
1
2
3

(d)

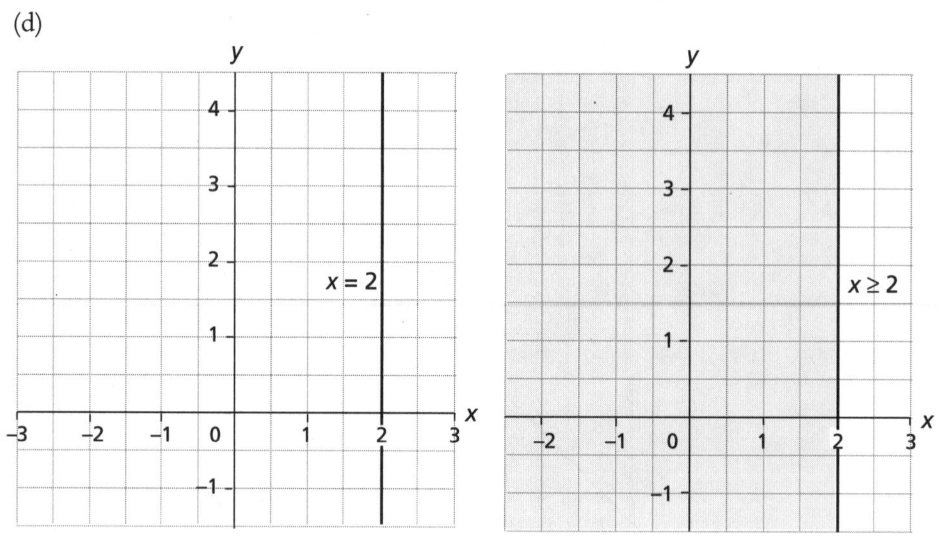
y
x
x = 2
x ≥ 2
4
3
2
1
0
–1
–3
–2
–1
1
2
3

(e)

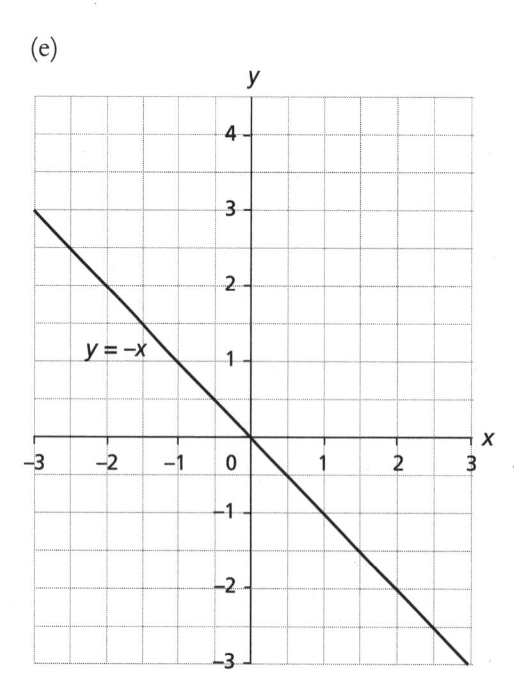
y
x
y = –x
4
3
2
1
0
–1
–2
–3
–3
–2
–1
1
2
3

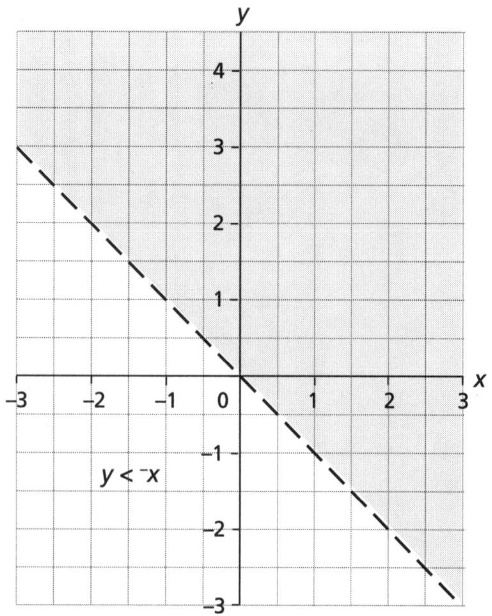
y
x
y < ⁻x
4
3
2
1
0
–1
–2
–3
–3
–2
–1
1
2
3

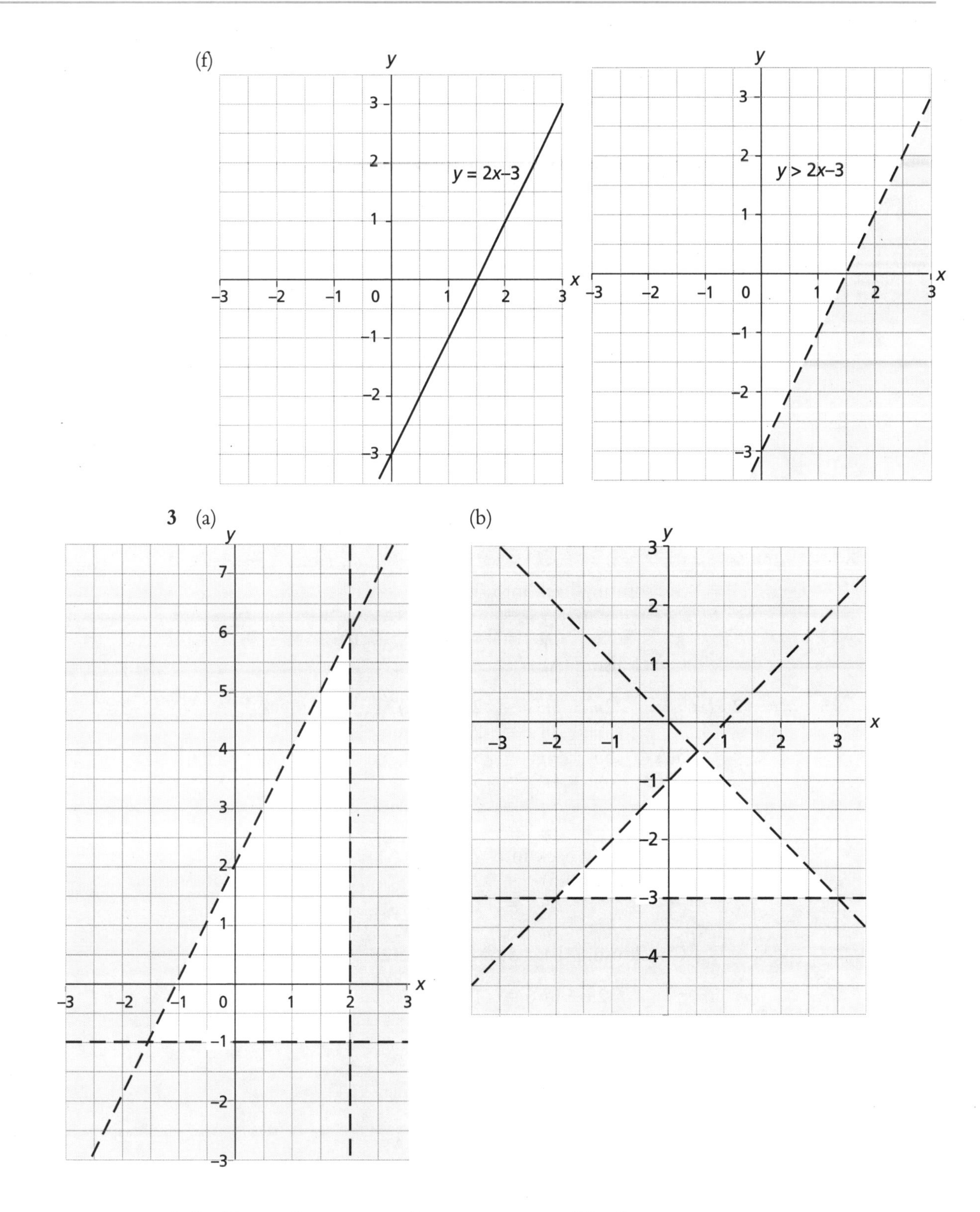

6.9 Forming equations – pages 71–3

1 $5(n-6) = 3(n-4)$
$5n - 30 = 3n - 12$
$2n = 18$
$n = 9$

2 Put Sandra's age $= x$ then Martin's age is $x + 3$ and Abdul's age is $x - 2$.
$(x + 3) + x + (x - 2) = 43$ so $x = 14$.
Sandra is 14, Martin is 17 and Abdul is 12.

3 (a) $(w + 14) + w + (w - 6) = 44$ or $3w + 8 = 44$ (b) 12

4 (a) $4x + 40° = 180°$
$x = 35°$
(b) $(x + 20°) + (x - 20°) + (2x - 10°) + (80°) = 4x + 70° = 360°$
$4x = 290°$
$x = 72{\cdot}5°$

5 $4(\frac{1}{2}(5 \times (4x - 3))) + 25 = 155$

$x = 3$

6.10 Simultaneous equations – pages 73–7

1 (a)

$$\begin{aligned} a + 2b &= 9 \ldots \text{(A)} \\ 3a + b &= 7 \ldots \text{(B)} \\ 3\text{(A)} \quad 3a + 6b &= 27 \\ -\text{(B)} \quad 3a + b &= 7 \\ 5b &= 20 \\ b &= 4 \end{aligned}$$

Substitute $b = 4$ back into (A):

$$\begin{aligned} a + 2(4) &= 9 \\ a &= 1 \end{aligned}$$

Check using (B): $3(1) + 4 = 7$

(b)

$$\begin{aligned} 7x + 3y &= 27 \ldots \text{(A)} \\ 2x + y &= 8 \ldots \text{(B)} \\ \text{(A)} \quad 7x + 3y &= 27 \\ -3\text{(B)} \quad 6x + 3y &= 24 \\ x &= 3 \end{aligned}$$

Substituting back into (B):

$$\begin{aligned} 6 + y &= 8 \\ y &= 2 \end{aligned}$$

Check using (A): $7(3) + 3(2) = 27$

2 (a)

$$\begin{aligned} 2m + 3n &= 27 \ldots \text{(A)} \\ 3m + 2n &= 28 \ldots \text{(B)} \\ 3\text{(A)} \quad 6m + 9n &= 81 \\ -2\text{(B)} \quad 6m + 4n &= 56 \\ 5n &= 25 \\ n &= 5 \end{aligned}$$

Substituting back into (A):

$$\begin{aligned} 2m + 3(5) &= 27 \\ 2m &= 12 \\ m &= 6 \end{aligned}$$

Check using (B): $3(6) + 2(5) = 28$

(b)

$$\begin{aligned} 2a + 5b &= 13 \ldots \text{(A)} \\ 5a + 3b &= 23 \ldots \text{(B)} \\ 5\text{(A)} \quad 10a + 25b &= 65 \\ -2\text{(B)} \quad 10a + 6b &= 46 \\ 19b &= 19 \\ b &= 1 \end{aligned}$$

Substituting back into (A):

$$\begin{aligned} 2a + 5(1) &= 13 \\ 2a &= 8 \\ a &= 4 \end{aligned}$$

Check using (B): $5(4) + 3(1) = 23$

3 (a)

$$\begin{aligned} 2a + 3b &= 16 \ldots \text{(A)} \\ 3a - b &= 13 \ldots \text{(B)} \\ \text{(A)} \quad 2a + 3b &= 16 \\ -3\text{(B)} \quad 9a - 3b &= 39 \end{aligned}$$

Adding equations gives

$$\begin{aligned} 11a &= 55 \\ a &= 5 \end{aligned}$$

Substituting back

$$\begin{aligned} 3(5) - b &= 13 \\ {}^{-}b &= {}^{-}2 \\ b &= 2 \end{aligned}$$

Check: $2(5) + 3(2) = 16$

(b)

$$\begin{aligned} 7p + 3q &= 6 \ldots (A) \\ 4p - 2q &= 20 \ldots (B) \\ 2(A) \qquad 14p + 6q &= 122 \\ +3(B) \qquad 12p - 6q &= 60 \end{aligned}$$

Adding equations gives

$$\begin{aligned} 26p &= 182 \\ p &= 7 \end{aligned}$$

Substituting back

$$\begin{aligned} 49 + 3q &= 61 \\ 3q &= 12 \\ q &= 4 \end{aligned}$$

Check: $4(7) - 2(4) = 20$

(c)

$$\begin{aligned} 4m + 3n &= 93 \ldots (A) \\ 3m - 4n &= 1 \ldots (B) \\ 4(A) \qquad 16m + 12n &= 372 \\ +3(B) \qquad 9m - 12n &= 3 \\ 25m &= 375 \\ m &= 15 \end{aligned}$$

Substituting back

$$\begin{aligned} 60 + 3n &= 93 \\ n &= 11 \end{aligned}$$

Check: $3(15) - 4(11) = 1$

4

$$\begin{aligned} 2r - 3s &= 19 \ldots (A) \\ 3r - s &= 11 \ldots (B) \end{aligned}$$

From (B) you can get $s = 3r - 11$

Substituting back into (A) gives

$$\begin{aligned} 2r - 3(3r - 11) &= 19 \\ 2r - 9r + 33 &= 19 \\ 33 - 19 &= 9r - 2r \\ 14 &= 7r \\ 2 &= r \end{aligned}$$

Substituting $r = 2$ back into (A)

$$\begin{aligned} 2(2) - 3s &= 19 \\ 4 - 3s &= 19 \\ 4 - 19 &= 3s \\ {}^{-}15 &= 3s \\ {}^{-}5 &= s \end{aligned}$$

Check: $3(2) - {}^{-}5 = 11$

5 (a) $4h + c = 7{\cdot}35$, $3h + 2c = 7{\cdot}20$

(b) ham rolls cost £1·50 and cheese rolls cost £1·35.

6 (a) $2a + 3c = 1880$, $3a + 2c = 2110$

(b) £514 per adult, £284 per child

7 (a) $x = 3$, $y = 4$ or $(3, 4)$ (b) $x = 2$, $y = 5$ or $(2, 5)$

8 (a)

x	$x - 1$	x	$7 - x$
0	$^{-}1$	0	7
1	0	1	6
2	1	2	5

$x = 4$, $y = 3$

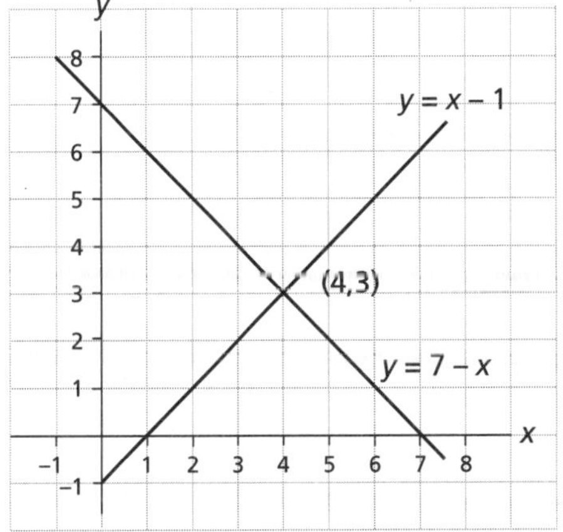

(b) Rearranging equations gives

$y = 3x - 2$

$y = \frac{1}{2}x + 3$

x	$3x - 2$	x	$\frac{1}{2}x + 3$
0	⁻2	0	3
1	1	1	3·5
2	4	2	4

$x = 2,\ y = 4$

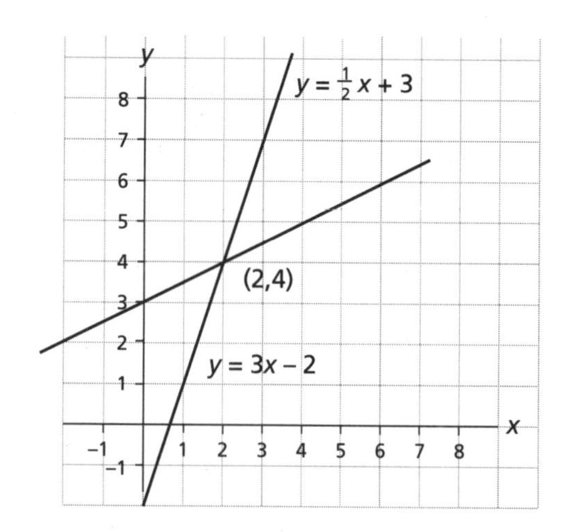

9 (a) $18S + 2G = 610,\ 25S + 5G = 925$
(b) $G = {}^{-}9S + 305,\ G = {}^{-}5S + 185$
(c) See graph opposite
(d) $G = 35,\ S = 30$

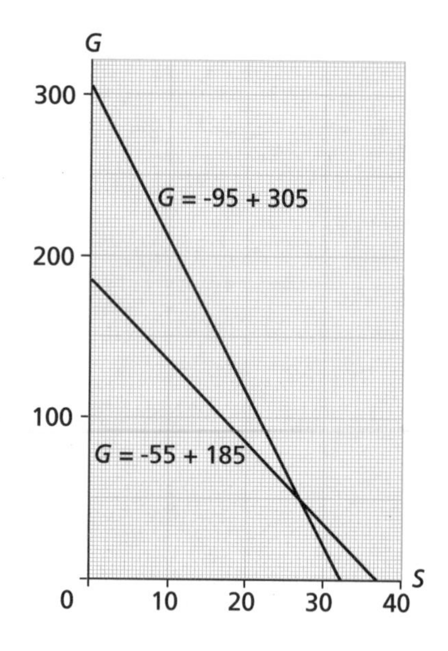

6.11 Factorising quadratics – page 78

1 (a) $(x + 4)(x + 2)$ (b) $(x + 7)(x - 1)$
(c) $(x + 5)(x + 3)$ (d) $(x - 4)(x - 5)$
(e) $(x - 3)(x + 1)$ (f) $(x - 15)(x + 2)$

2 (a) $(x + 2)(x - 2)$ (b) $(3x + 1)(3x - 1)$

6.12 Solving simple quadratics and cubics using graphs – pages 80–3

1 (a) $x = 1$ or 4 (b) $x = 1$ or 2 (c) $x = {}^{-}1$ or 2 (d) $x = 2$ (e) no solution

2 (a) The line $y = 4$ crosses the parabola $y = x^2$ at $({}^{-}2, 4)$ and $(2, 4)$ so $x^2 = 4$ has the solutions $x = {}^{-}2$ and $x = 2$.

(b) The line $y = 2x + 3$ crosses the parabola at $({}^{-}1, 1)$ and $(3, 9)$ so the solutions of $x^2 = 2x + 3$ are $x = {}^{-}1$ and $x = 3$.

(c) The line $y = {}^{-}x$ crosses the parabola at $({}^{-}1, 1)$ and $(0, 0)$ so the solutions are $x = {}^{-}1$ and $x = 0$.

3 The curve and the line cross at the points $({}^{-}3, {}^{-}1)$ and $(2, 4)$ so the solutions of $x^2 + 2x - 4 = x + 2$ are $x = {}^{-}3$ and $x = 2$.

4 (a) $x = {}^{-}1$ (b) $x = 0$ and $x = 3$

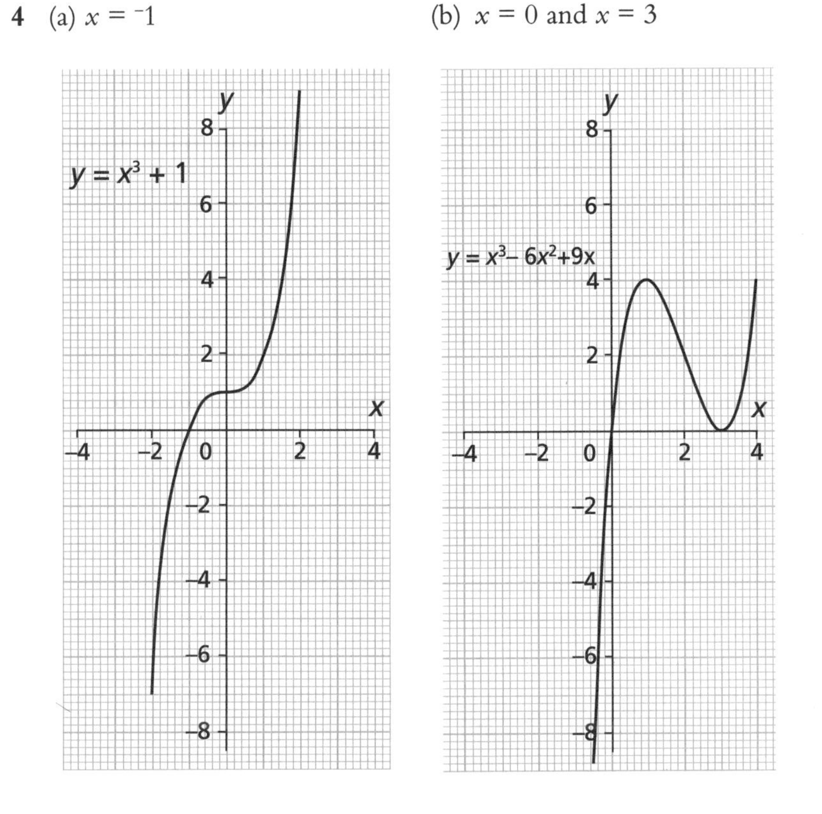

5 (a) The solution of $x^3 = 0$ is given by the point of intersection of $y = x^3$ with the x-axis. The solution is $x = 0$.
(b) The solution of $x^3 = x^2 - x + 1$ is given by the point of intersection of $y = x^3$ with $y = x^2 - x + 1$. The solution is $x = 1$.
(c) The solution of $x^3 = 2x - 4$ is given by the point of intersection of $y = x^3$ and $y = 2x - 4$. The solution is $x = {}^{-}2$.
(d) The solution of $x^3 + x = 0$ is given by the point of intersection of $y = x^3$ and $y = {}^{-}x$. The solution is $x = 0$.
(e) The solutions of $x^3 - x^2 - 2x = 0$ are given by the points of intersection of $y = x^3$ and $y = x^2 + 2x$. The solutions are $x = {}^{-}1$, 0 and 2.

6.13 Solving polynomials by trial and improvement – page 83

1 (a) $x^3 + x = 12$ substituting 2 gives $2^3 + 2 = 10$ and substituting 3 gives $3^3 + 3 = 30$

If you start with $x = 2{\cdot}1$ you get 11·361
2·2 gives 12·848
2·14 gives 11·940344
2·145 gives 12·014199
so $x = 2{\cdot}14$ (to 2 d.p.)

(b) $x^3 + 2x = 20$ substituting 2 gives $2^3 + 4 = 12$ and substituting 3 gives $3^3 + 9 = 36$

If you start with $x = 2{\cdot}5$ you get 21·87
2·4 gives 19·584
2·41 gives 19·806
2·42 gives 20·029
so $x = 2{\cdot}41$ (to 2 d.p.)

7.1 Expressing general laws in symbolic form – pages 85–7

1 Cost = $\frac{1}{20} \times$ number of copies + 80

2 (a) & (c) See diagram right

(b) 8·25

(d) $h = 8{\cdot}25 - (t - 2{\cdot}5)^2$

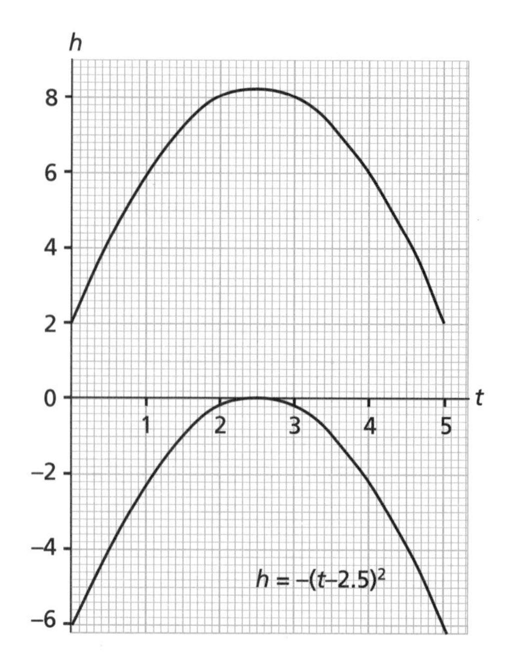

7.2 Quadratic equations – pages 88–9

1 (a) $x = -\frac{1}{2}$ or $-\frac{3}{2}$ (b) $x = {}^{-}\frac{4}{3}$ or ${}^{-}\frac{5}{3}$ (c) $x = {}^{-}\frac{1}{3}$ or 7

2 (a) $x = 2{\cdot}77$ or $^{-}1{\cdot}27$ (to 2 d.p.) (b) $x = 1{\cdot}85$ or $^{-}0{\cdot}18$ (to 2 d.p.)

3 (a) $x = 1{\cdot}19$ or $^{-}4{\cdot}19$ (to 2 d.p.) (b) $x = 6{\cdot}92$ or $^{-}4{\cdot}92$ (to 2 d.p.)

7.3 Using graphs to solve equations – page 90

1 (a)

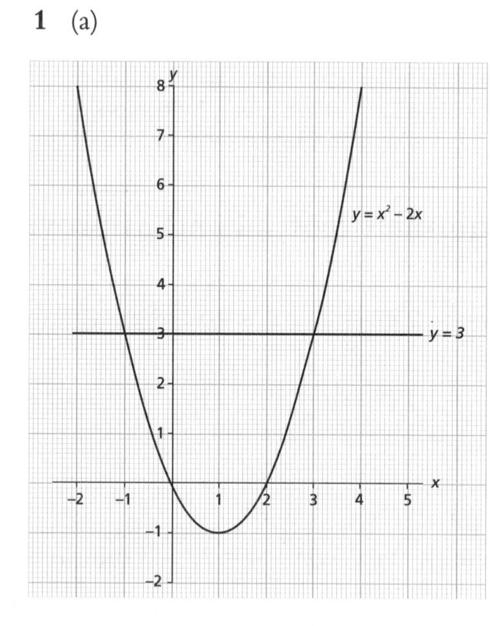

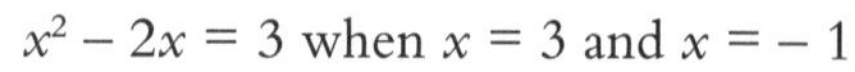

$x^2 - 2x = 3$ when $x = 3$ and $x = -1$

(b)

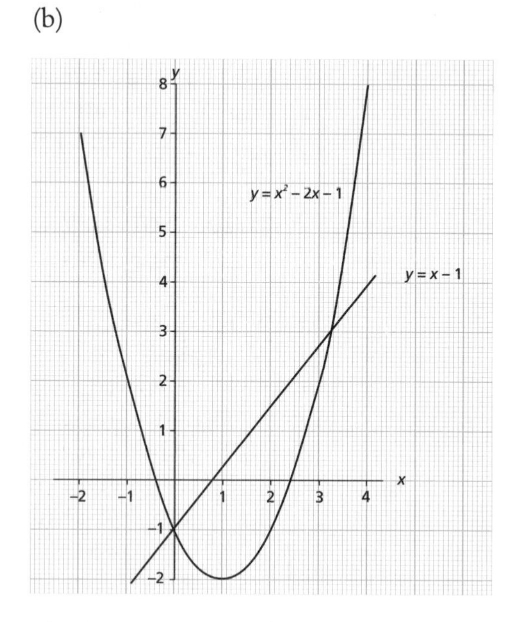

$x^2 - 2x - 1 = x - 1$ when $x = 0$ and $x \simeq 3{\cdot}3$

2 (a)

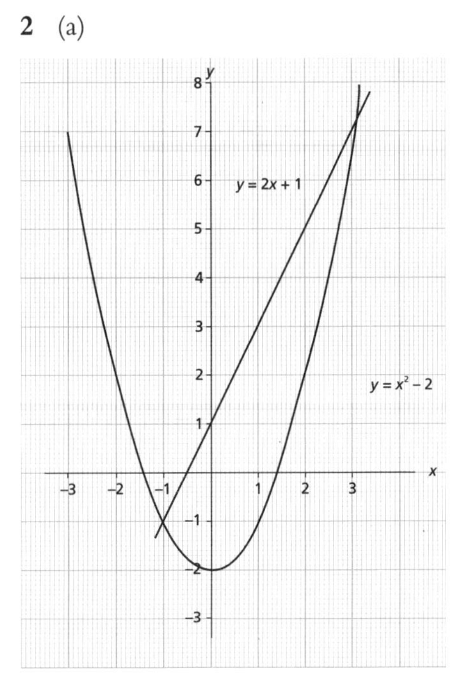

$x^2 - 2 = 2x + 1$ when $x = 3$ and $x = -1$

(b)

$y = x^2 - x - 2$

$y = x + 1$

$x^2 - x - 2 = x + 1$ when $x = 3$ and $x = -1$

(c)

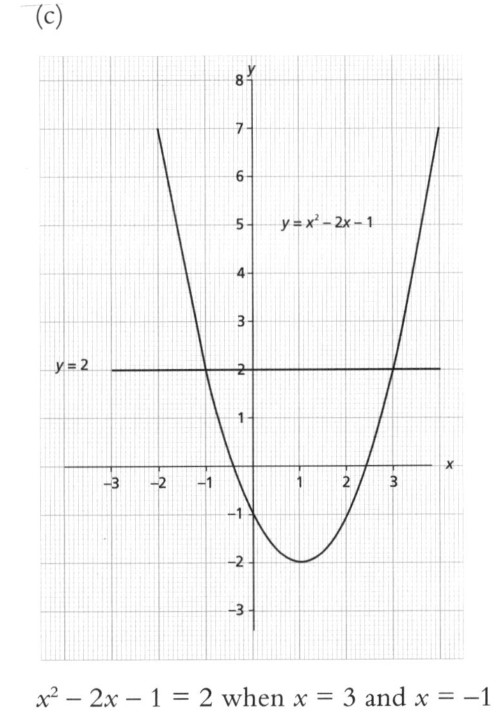

$x^2 - 2x - 1 = 2$ when $x = 3$ and $x = -1$

(d) Each of the 3 pairs of equations can be rewritten as the other pairs.

Note: There are a number of ways to solve difficult equations graphically which give the same results.

7.4 Algebraic fractions – page 91

1 $\dfrac{(x-4)(x+2)(x+4)(x+1)}{(x+4)(x-4)(x+2)} = (x + 1)$

2 (a) $\dfrac{(x-1)-(x+1)}{(x-1)(x+1)} = \dfrac{-2}{x^2-1}$ (b) $\dfrac{3-2x}{3x^2}$ (c) $\dfrac{3-2x}{x^3-x}$

3 (a) $x = 2$ (b) $x = 12$ (c) $x = 3$

7.5 Rearranging more difficult formulae – page 92

1 (a) $m = \dfrac{Pt}{(v+u)}$ (b) $v = \dfrac{u}{uf+1}$

(c) $y = \sqrt{\dfrac{w}{x+t}}$ (d) $A = \dfrac{Pxt}{(y - Px)}$

7.6 The rules of indices for negative and fractional indices – pages 93–4

1 (a) $x^{-4} \times x^{-3} = x^{-7}$ (b) $6x^{-6}$ (c) $4x^{-3}$ (d) $6a^{-10}$

(e) $60b^3$ (f) $7x^{-5}y^{-2}$

2 (a) $x^{-6} \div x^{-2} = x^{-4}$ (b) $4x^{-4}$ (c) $7x^{-6}$ (d) $5x^7$

(e) $7a^{-5}b^3c^9$

3 (a) a^{-21} (b) $\dfrac{b^{-4}}{2}$ or $\dfrac{1}{2b^4}$ (c) $\dfrac{n^{12}}{256}$ or $\dfrac{1}{4n^{-3}}$ (d) $x^{-10}y^{15}z^5$

4 (a) $\sqrt[5]{x^2}$ (b) $\sqrt[7]{x^3}$ (c) $\sqrt[3]{x^2}$ (d) $\sqrt{x^3}$

5 (a) $x^{\frac{5}{6}}$ (b) $x^{\frac{5}{3}}$ (c) $x^{\frac{29}{28}}$

6 (a) $x^{\frac{2}{5}}$ (b) $a^{\frac{7}{6}}$

7 (a) a^2 (b) $x^{\frac{7}{2}}$ or $\sqrt{x^7}$ (c) $x^{\frac{2}{5}}y^{\frac{1}{5}}$ or $\sqrt[5]{x^2y}$

7.7 Finding the area under a curve – pages 95–8

1 (a) Upper bound $(22 \times 10) + (15 \times 10) + (11 \times 10) + (9 \times 10) = 570$
Lower bound $(15 \times 10) + (11 \times 10) + (9 \times 10) + (8 \times 10) = 430$

(b) The lower bound is a slightly better approximation.

(c) $\dfrac{570 + 430}{2} = 500$

2 $y = x^2(4 - x)$

x	y
0	0
0·5	0·875
1	3
1·5	5·625
2	8
2·5	9·375
3	9
3·5	6·125
4	0

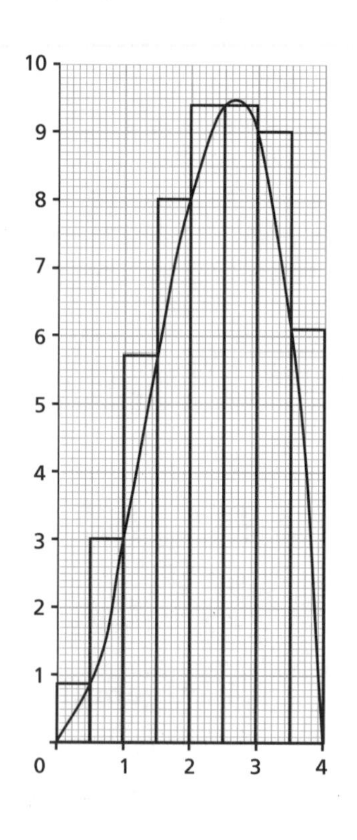

Area under step-graph = $0{\cdot}5 \times (0{\cdot}875 + 3 + 5{\cdot}625 + 8 + 9{\cdot}375 + 9{\cdot}375 + 9 + 6{\cdot}125) = 30{\cdot}375$
Approximate area under curve is 30 square units.

3 $y = 10 - x^2$

x	−3	−2	−1	0	1	2	3
y	1	6	9	10	9	6	1

$1 \times (\frac{1}{2}(1 + 1) + 6 + 9 + 10 + 9 + 6) = 41$ square units

4 13·5 m

5 $2(\dfrac{25+0}{2} + 24 + 21 + 16 + 9) = 165$ m

7.8 Finding gradients using tangents – pages 99–100

1 (a) 1 (b) 2

2 (a) approx. 4·5 m/s² (b) approx. 10·2 m/s² (c) approx. 20·1 m/s²

7.9 Sketching the graphs of functions derived from other functions – pages 100–1

1

x	⁻3	⁻2	⁻1	0	1	2	3
$f(x)$	10	4	0	⁻2	⁻2	0	4

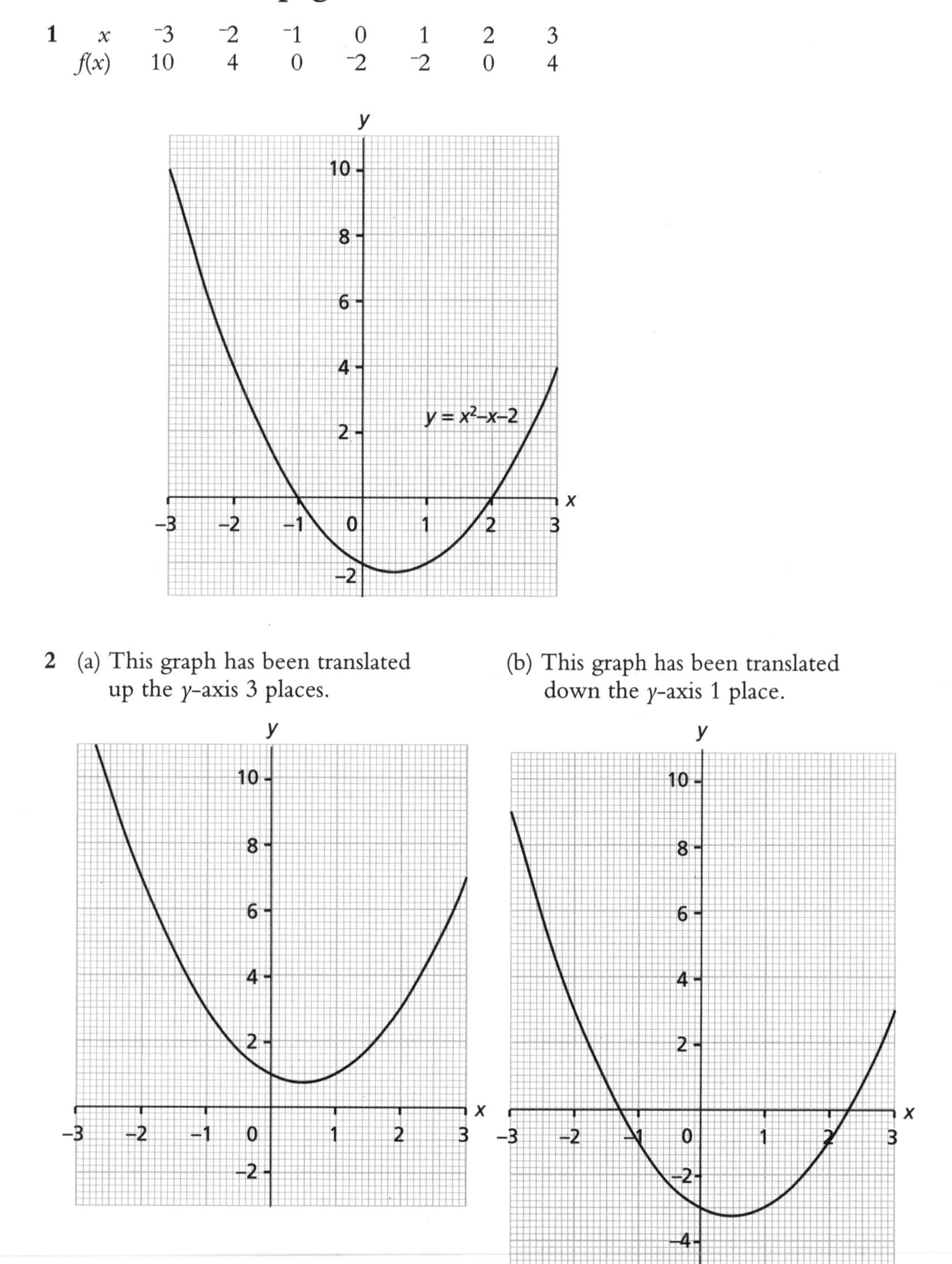

2 (a) This graph has been translated up the y-axis 3 places.

(b) This graph has been translated down the y-axis 1 place.

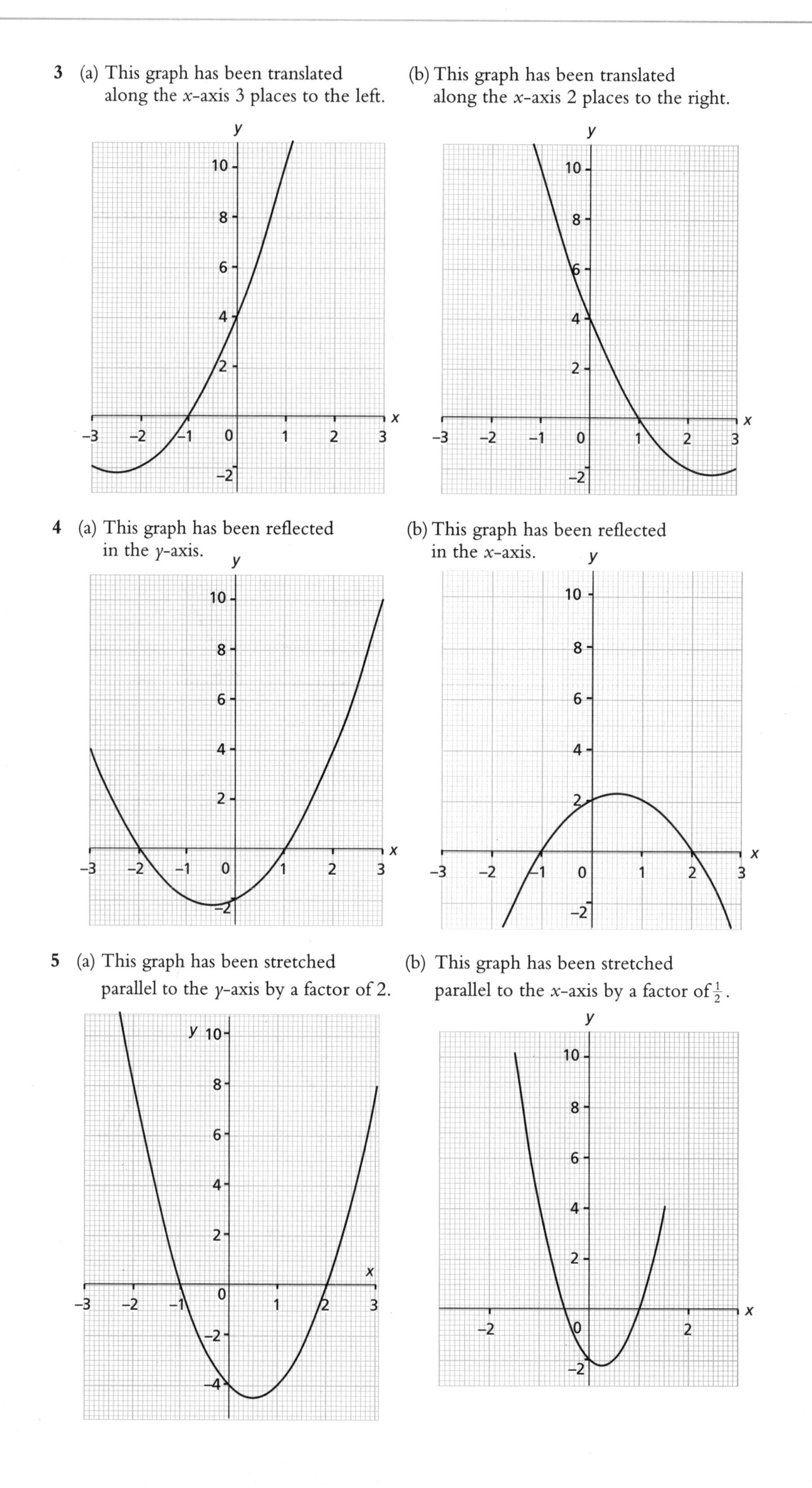
3 (a) This graph has been translated along the x-axis 3 places to the left.
(b) This graph has been translated along the x-axis 2 places to the right.
4 (a) This graph has been reflected in the y-axis.
(b) This graph has been reflected in the x-axis.
5 (a) This graph has been stretched parallel to the y-axis by a factor of 2.
(b) This graph has been stretched parallel to the x-axis by a factor of 1/2.
y
x
10
8
6
4
2
0
−2
−4
−3
−1
1
3

6 This graph has been translated 2 places up and 1 place to the left.

7 (a) (b)

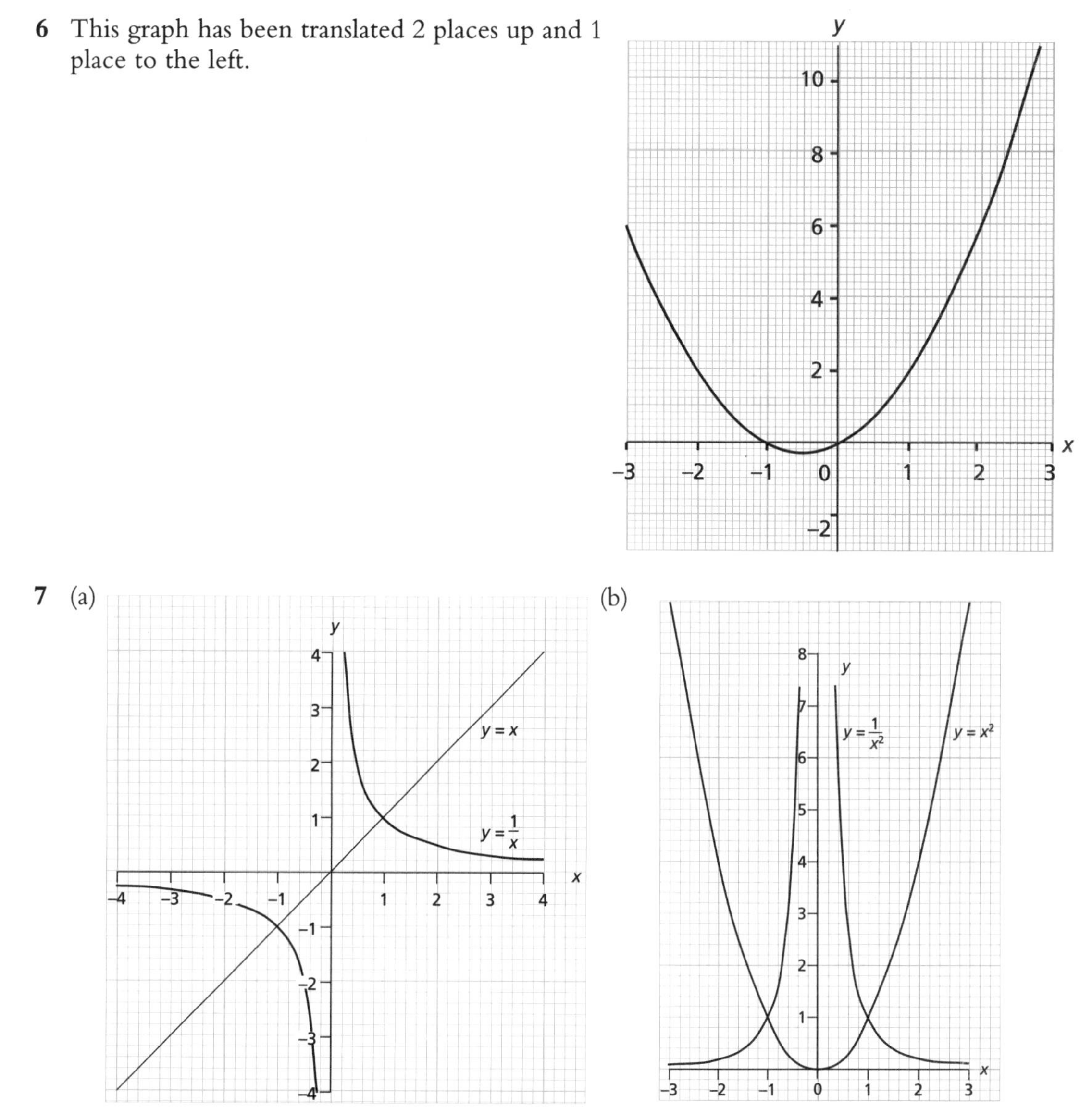

8 (a) When a is even the graph is in the 1st and 2nd quadrants. When a is odd the graph is in the 1st and 3rd quadrants.

(b) Points where $f(x) = 1$ remain fixed.

(c) $\dfrac{1}{f(x)}$ has lines of discontinuity at points where $f(x) = 0$.

7.10 Growth and decay rates

1

Minutes	Micro-organisms
0	1
1	2
2	4
3	8
4	16
5	32
6	64
7	128
8	256
9	512
10	1024
11	2048
12	4096
13	8192
14	16 384
15	32 768

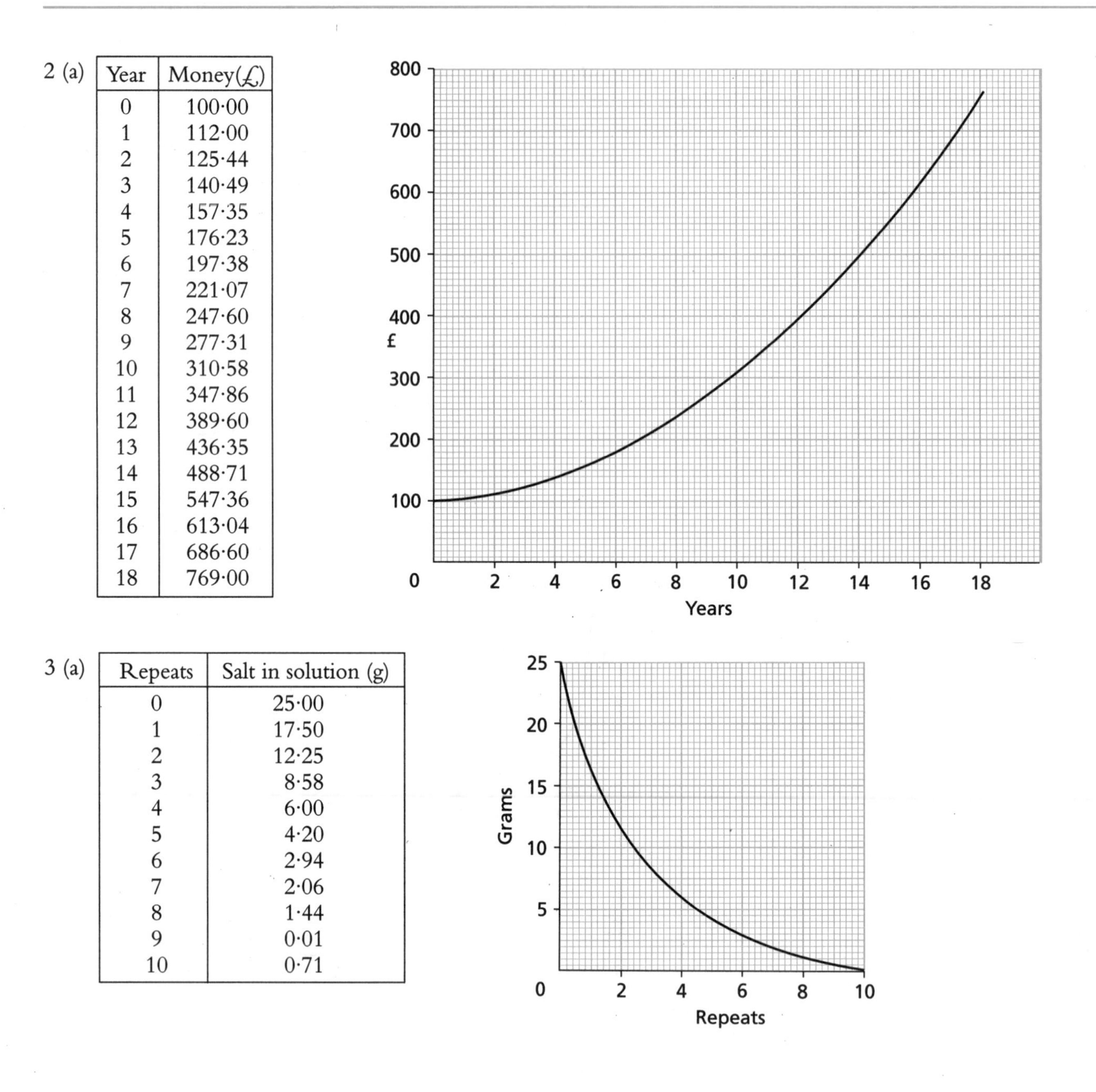

2 (a)

Year	Money(£)
0	100·00
1	112·00
2	125·44
3	140·49
4	157·35
5	176·23
6	197·38
7	221·07
8	247·60
9	277·31
10	310·58
11	347·86
12	389·60
13	436·35
14	488·71
15	547·36
16	613·04
17	686·60
18	769·00

3 (a)

Repeats	Salt in solution (g)
0	25·00
1	17·50
2	12·25
3	8·58
4	6·00
5	4·20
6	2·94
7	2·06
8	1·44
9	0·01
10	0·71

Section 3 answers

8.1 Triangles – page 105

1 Your 10, 7, 9, triangle. Check sides by measuring.

2 Your triangle with sides 7 and 8 and an included angle of 60°.

3 Your triangles fitted together correctly.

4 $x = 135°$ $y = 120°$ $z = 125°$

8.2 Regular polygons – pages 106–7

1 (a)

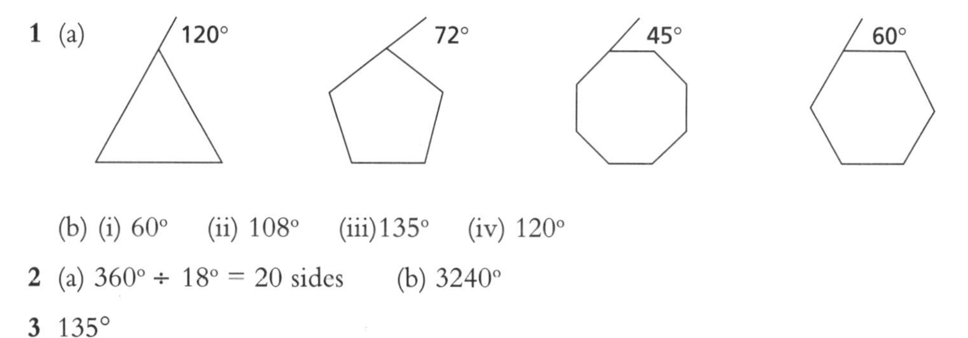

(b) (i) 60° (ii) 108° (iii) 135° (iv) 120°

2 (a) 360° ÷ 18° = 20 sides (b) 3240°

3 135°

8.3 Pythagoras' theorem – pages 108–10

1 (a) 7·21 m (to 2 d.p.) (b) 5 m (c) 2·82 m (to 2 d.p.)

2 There are 3 triangles that belong to the 3, 4, 5 family: (9, 12, 15), (12, 16, 20) and (15, 20, 25).

3

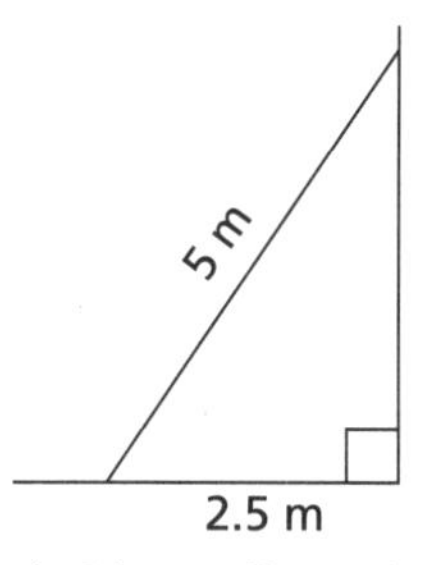

The ladder will reach 4·33 m up the wall (to 2 d.p.).

4 (a) $7^2 + 6^2 \neq 8^2$ so this triangle is not right-angled
(b) $6^2 + 8^2 = 10^2$ so this triangle is right-angled
(c) $24^2 + 7^2 = 25^2$ so this triangle is right-angled

5 The length of the vector is 10 units. (This is another 3, 4, 5 triangle!)

6 4061 m (to the nearest metre)

7 (a) 6·24 (to 2 d.p.) (b) 10·39 (to 2 d.p.)

8 2·06 (to 2 d.p.)

8.4 Sin, cos and tan – pages 111–14

1 (a) *a* is the hypotenuse
b is the side adjacent to the angle
c is the side opposite to the angle

(b) *d* is the side opposite to the angle
e is the hypotenuse
f is the side adjacent to the angle

(c) g is the side adjacent to the angle
h is the hypotenuse
i is the side opposite to the angle

(d) j is the side opposite to the angle
k is the side adjacent to the angle
l is the hypotenuse

2 (a) $x = 3 \times \tan 35° = 2{\cdot}10$ m (to 2 d.p.) (b) $x = 7 \times \sin 40° = 4{\cdot}50$ m (to 2 d.p.)
(c) $x = 100 \times \cos 18° = 95{\cdot}11$ m (to 2 d.p.)

3 (a) 6·71 m (to 2 d.p.) (b) 8·20 m (to 2 d.p.)
(c) 4·04 m (to 2 d.p.) (d) 14·65 m (to 2 d.p.)

4 (a) 6·93 m (b) 28·79 m

5 (a) $\tan \theta = \frac{7 \cdot 3}{6 \cdot 8}$ so $\theta = 47{\cdot}03°$ (b) $\cos \theta = \frac{7 \cdot 2}{16 \cdot 3}$ so $\theta = 63{\cdot}79°$

(c) $\sin \theta = \frac{4 \cdot 2}{5 \cdot 6}$ so $\theta = 48{\cdot}59°$ (d) $\sin \theta = \frac{3 \cdot 8}{8 \cdot 4}$ so $\theta = 26{\cdot}90°$

6 (a) $\cos \theta = \frac{6 \cdot 2}{8 \cdot 4}$ so $\theta = 42{\cdot}43°$ (to 2 d.p.)
(b) $x = 7{\cdot}2 \times \tan 48° = 8{\cdot}00$ m (to 2 d.p.)
(c) $x = 8{\cdot}2 \times \cos 70° = 2{\cdot}80$ m (to 2 d.p.)
(d) $\sin \theta = \frac{5 \cdot 5}{7 \cdot 5}$ so $\theta = 47{\cdot}17°$ (to 2 d.p.)
(e) $x = 18{\cdot}6 \times \tan 15° = 4{\cdot}98$ m (to 2 d.p.)
(f) $\cos \theta = \frac{4 \cdot 8}{6 \cdot 5}$ so $\theta = 42{\cdot}40°$ (to 2 d.p.)

7 (a) $16{\cdot}5 \cos 40° = 12{\cdot}64$ km (to 2 d.p.)
(b) $16{\cdot}5 \sin 40° = 10{\cdot}61$ km (to 2 d.p.)
(c) $9{\cdot}8 \cos 85° = 0{\cdot}85$ km (to 2 d.p.)
(d) $9{\cdot}8 \sin 85° = 9{\cdot}76$ km (to 2 d.p.)
(e) $\sqrt{(12 \cdot 64 + 0 \cdot 85)^2 + (10 \cdot 61 + 9 \cdot 76)^2} = 24{\cdot}43$ km (to 2 d.p.)
(f) $\tan^{-1}\left(\frac{10 \cdot 61 + 9 \cdot 76}{12 \cdot 64 + 0 \cdot 85}\right) = 056°$ (to nearest degree)

8 17·41 m² (to 2 d.p.)

9.1 Recognising simple reflections – page 115

1

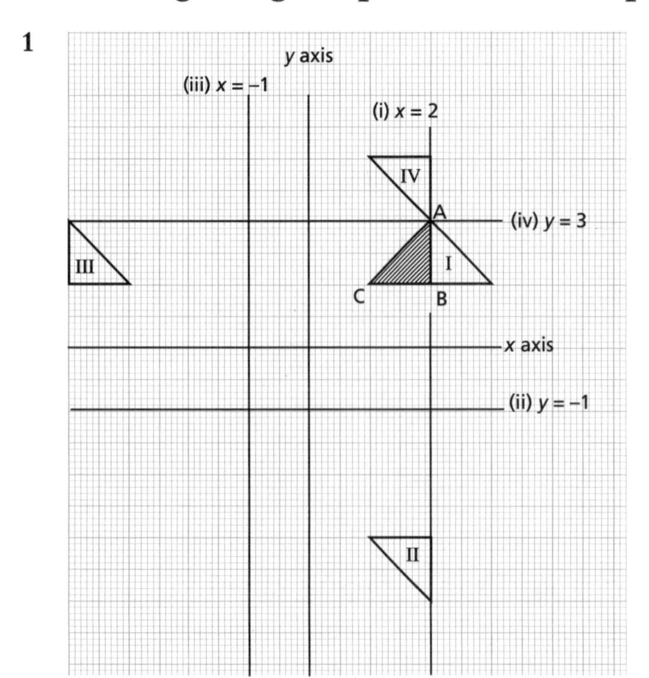

2

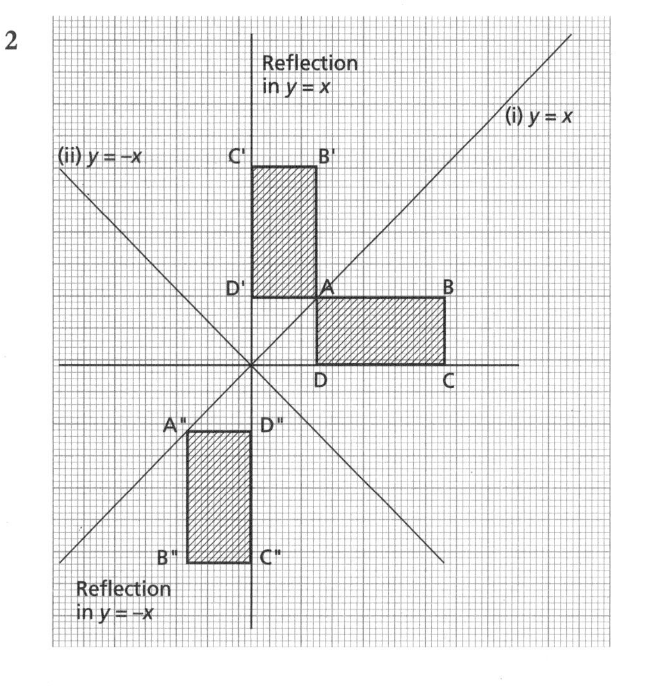

9.2 Vector notation and translations – pages 117–18

1 (a) $\begin{pmatrix}1\\2\end{pmatrix}$ (b) $\begin{pmatrix}2\\1\end{pmatrix}$ (c) $\begin{pmatrix}2\\-1\end{pmatrix}$ (d) $\begin{pmatrix}1\\-2\end{pmatrix}$ (e) $\begin{pmatrix}-1\\-2\end{pmatrix}$

2

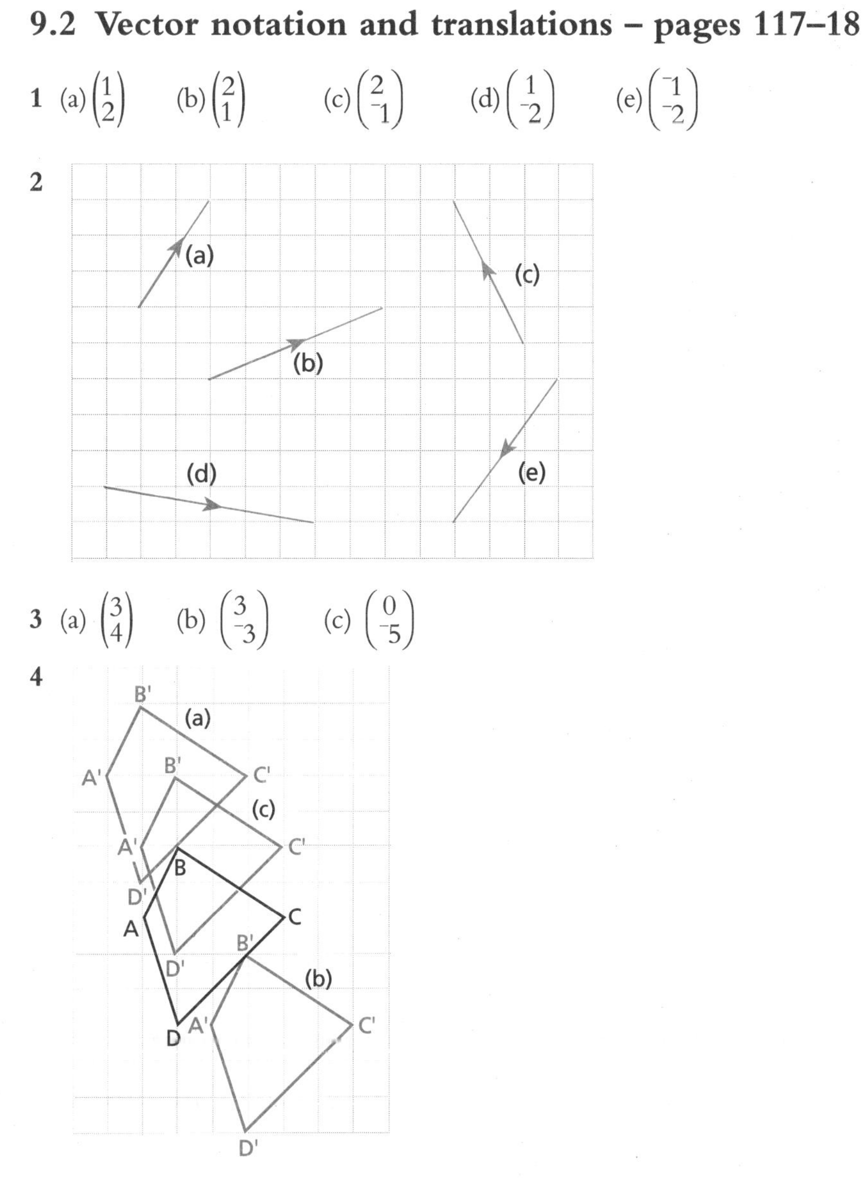

3 (a) $\begin{pmatrix}3\\4\end{pmatrix}$ (b) $\begin{pmatrix}3\\-3\end{pmatrix}$ (c) $\begin{pmatrix}0\\-5\end{pmatrix}$

4

5 (a) $\begin{pmatrix}-2\\-3\end{pmatrix}$ (b) $\begin{pmatrix}-5\\-2\end{pmatrix}$ (c) $\begin{pmatrix}2\\-4\end{pmatrix}$ (d) $\begin{pmatrix}-6\\1\end{pmatrix}$ (e) $\begin{pmatrix}3\\4\end{pmatrix}$

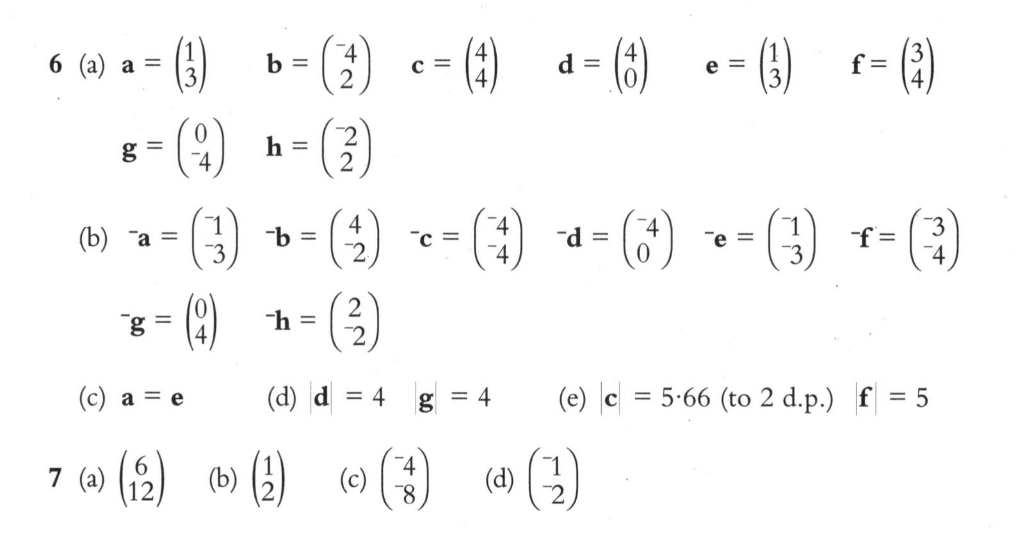

6 (a) $\mathbf{a} = \begin{pmatrix} 1 \\ 3 \end{pmatrix}$ $\mathbf{b} = \begin{pmatrix} -4 \\ 2 \end{pmatrix}$ $\mathbf{c} = \begin{pmatrix} 4 \\ 4 \end{pmatrix}$ $\mathbf{d} = \begin{pmatrix} 4 \\ 0 \end{pmatrix}$ $\mathbf{e} = \begin{pmatrix} 1 \\ 3 \end{pmatrix}$ $\mathbf{f} = \begin{pmatrix} 3 \\ 4 \end{pmatrix}$

$\mathbf{g} = \begin{pmatrix} 0 \\ -4 \end{pmatrix}$ $\mathbf{h} = \begin{pmatrix} -2 \\ 2 \end{pmatrix}$

(b) $-\mathbf{a} = \begin{pmatrix} -1 \\ -3 \end{pmatrix}$ $-\mathbf{b} = \begin{pmatrix} 4 \\ -2 \end{pmatrix}$ $-\mathbf{c} = \begin{pmatrix} -4 \\ -4 \end{pmatrix}$ $-\mathbf{d} = \begin{pmatrix} -4 \\ 0 \end{pmatrix}$ $-\mathbf{e} = \begin{pmatrix} -1 \\ -3 \end{pmatrix}$ $-\mathbf{f} = \begin{pmatrix} -3 \\ -4 \end{pmatrix}$

$-\mathbf{g} = \begin{pmatrix} 0 \\ 4 \end{pmatrix}$ $-\mathbf{h} = \begin{pmatrix} 2 \\ -2 \end{pmatrix}$

(c) $\mathbf{a} = \mathbf{e}$ (d) $|\mathbf{d}| = 4$ $|\mathbf{g}| = 4$ (e) $|\mathbf{c}| = 5{\cdot}66$ (to 2 d.p.) $|\mathbf{f}| = 5$

7 (a) $\begin{pmatrix} 6 \\ 12 \end{pmatrix}$ (b) $\begin{pmatrix} 1 \\ 2 \end{pmatrix}$ (c) $\begin{pmatrix} -4 \\ -8 \end{pmatrix}$ (d) $\begin{pmatrix} -1 \\ -2 \end{pmatrix}$

9.3 Combinations and inverses of transformations – pages 119–26

1 **2** (a) & (b)

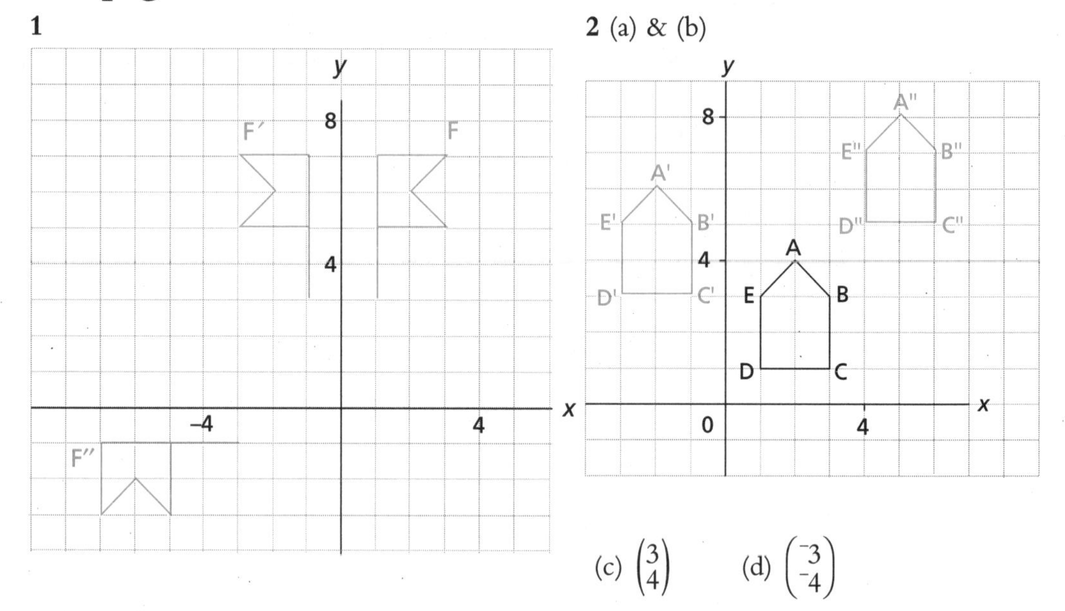

(c) $\begin{pmatrix} 3 \\ 4 \end{pmatrix}$ (d) $\begin{pmatrix} -3 \\ -4 \end{pmatrix}$

3 (a) & (b)

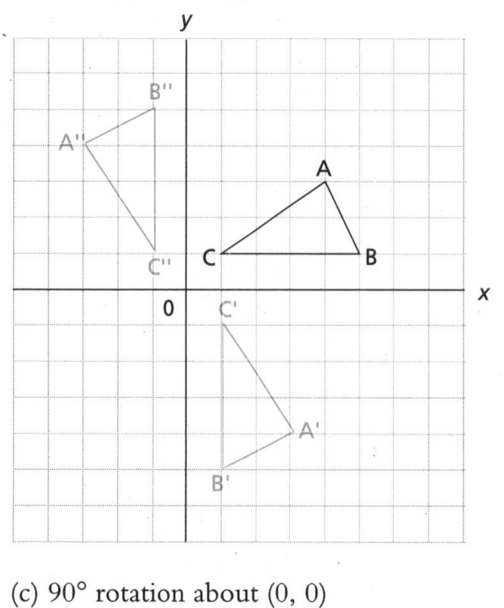

(c) 90° rotation about (0, 0)

(d) 270° or −90° rotation about (0, 0)

4 (a) & (b)

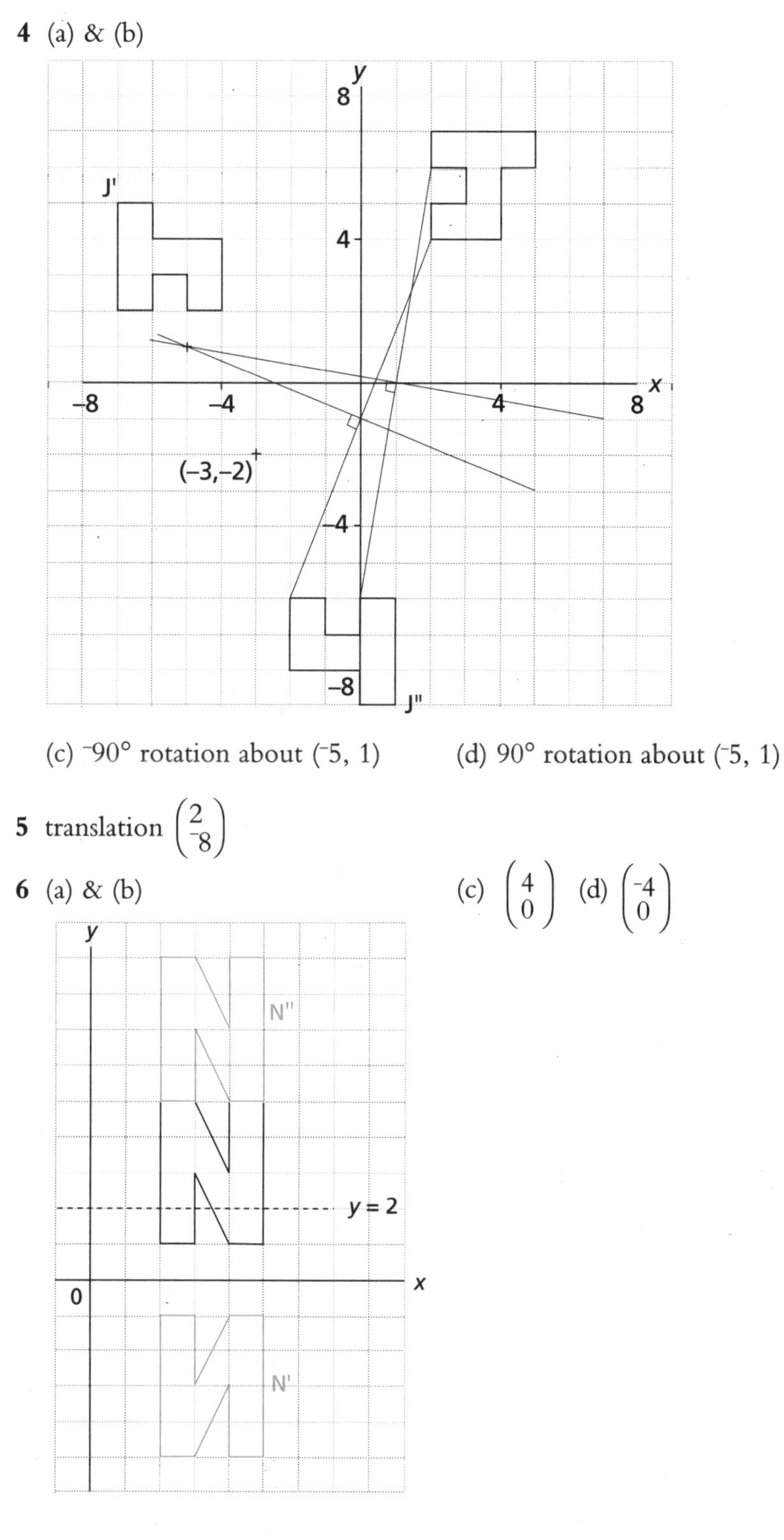

(c) $^{-}90°$ rotation about ($^{-}5$, 1)   (d) 90° rotation about ($^{-}5$, 1)

5 translation $\begin{pmatrix}2\\ ^{-}8\end{pmatrix}$

6 (a) & (b)   (c) $\begin{pmatrix}4\\ 0\end{pmatrix}$ (d) $\begin{pmatrix}^{-}4\\ 0\end{pmatrix}$

7 (a) & (b)

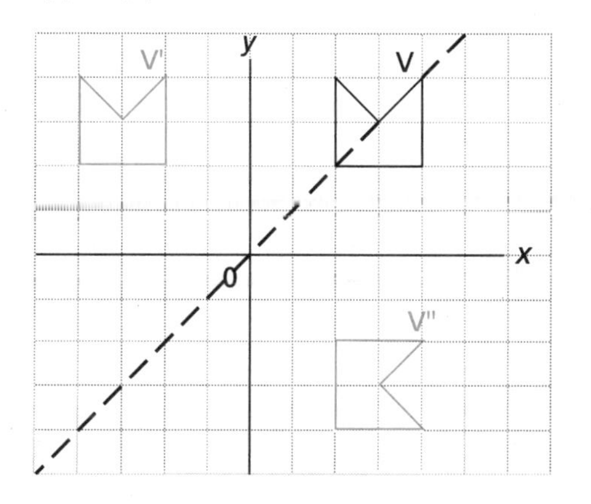

(c) rotation $^{-}90°$ about (0, 0)

(d) rotation 90° about (0, 0)

8

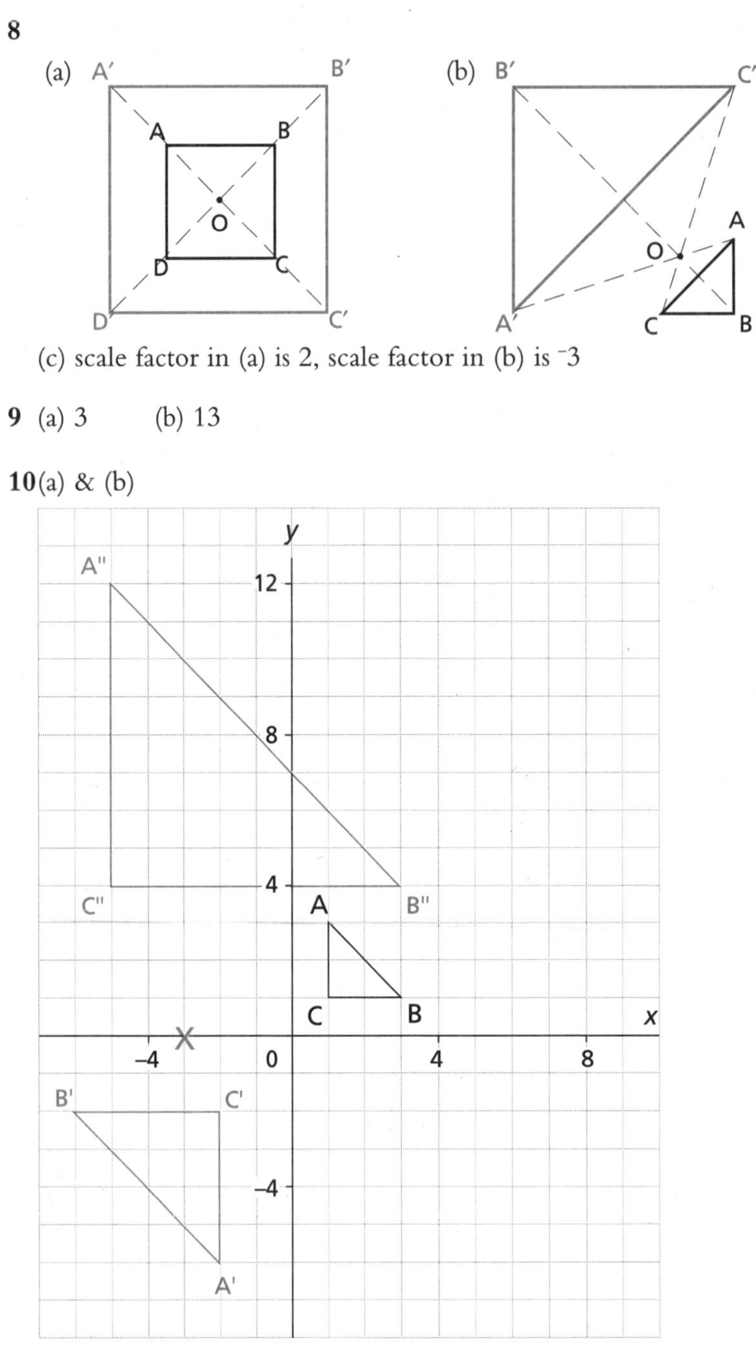

(c) scale factor in (a) is 2, scale factor in (b) is $^{-}3$

9 (a) 3 (b) 13

10(a) & (b)

(c) enlargement centre (3, 0) scale factor 4

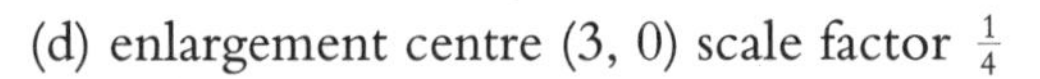

(d) enlargement centre (3, 0) scale factor $\frac{1}{4}$

11(a) & (b)

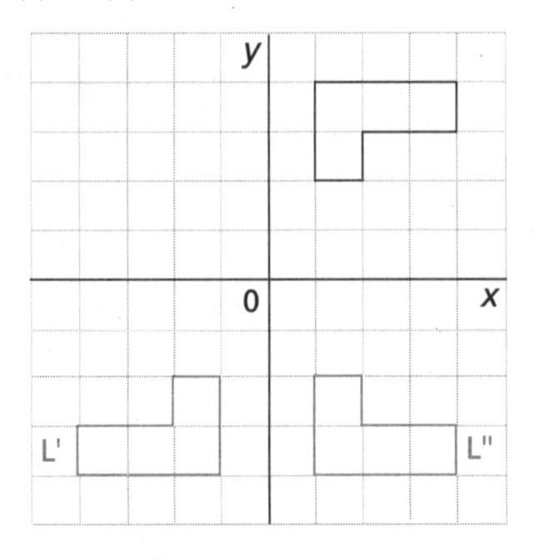

(c) reflection in the x-axis ($y = 0$)

12 (a) & (b)

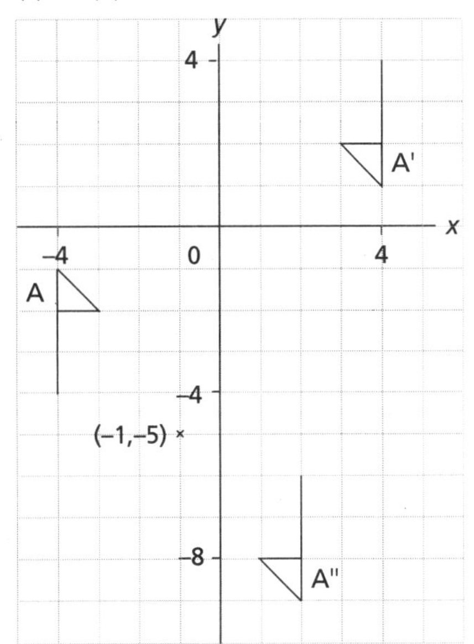

(c) rotation 180° about ($^-1$, $^-5$)

9.4 Similar figures – pages 127–9

1 The angles in each triangle should be the same: 90°, about 53° and about 37°.

2 These angles should also be the same.

3 (a) Two corresponding angles are equal. The angles of a triangle add to 180° so the third must also be equal. Hence ABC and CDE are similar.

(b) $\frac{DE}{AB} = \frac{CE}{AC}$ therefore DE $= 48 \times \frac{12}{24} = 24$ units

(c) $\frac{BC}{DC} = \frac{AC}{EC}$ therefore BC $= \frac{18 \times 24}{12} = 36$ units

4 (a) $\frac{\text{AB}}{\text{AC}} = \frac{2}{4} = \frac{1}{2}$ and $\frac{\text{AE}}{\text{AD}} = \frac{5}{10} = \frac{1}{2}$ so two corresponding sides are in the same ratio.

The angle between the two sides is angle A in each case. Hence the triangles are similar.

(b) Corresponding sides are in the same ratio so $\frac{\text{BC}}{\text{AB}} = \frac{\text{DE}}{\text{AE}}$

therefore BC $= \frac{8 \times 2}{5} = 3{\cdot}2$ cm

5 IJKL is not similar to the other three quadrilaterals.

9.5 Loci – pages 130–2

1 This is a circle with radius 2 cm.

2

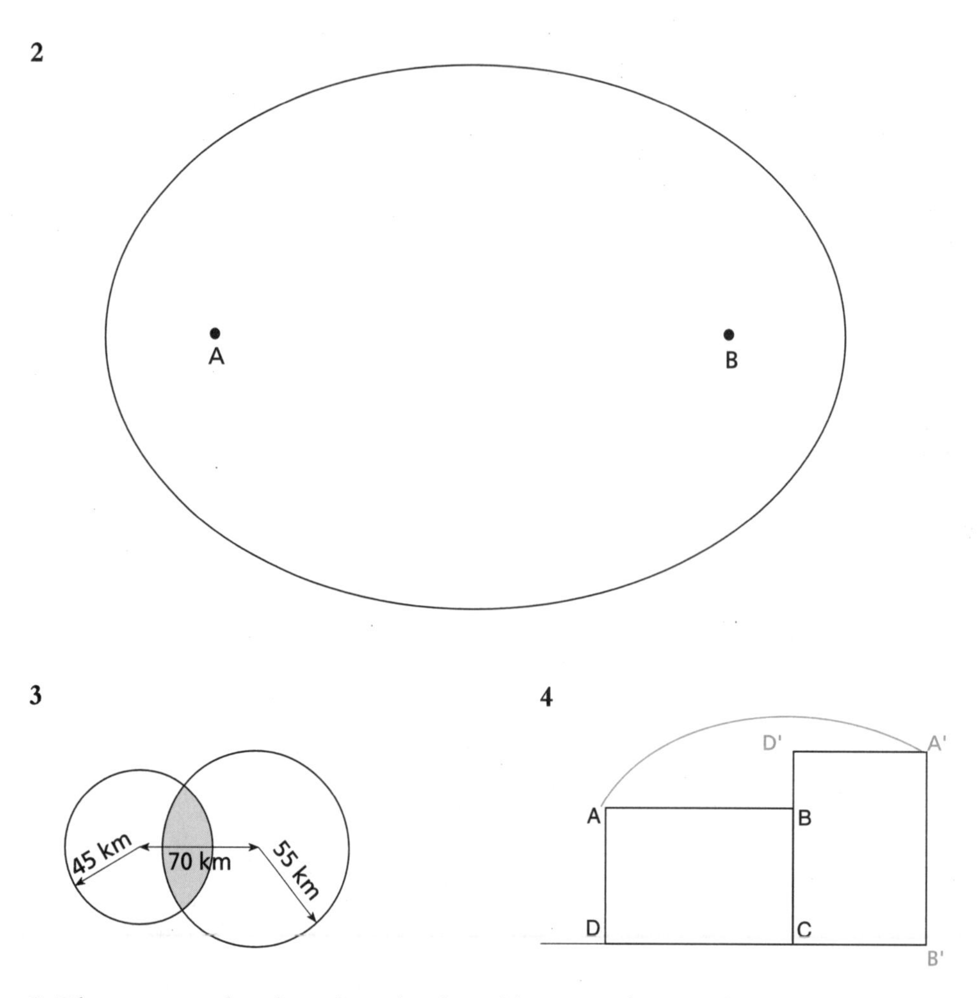

5 The tree must be planted on the dotted line anywhere in the area that is not shaded.

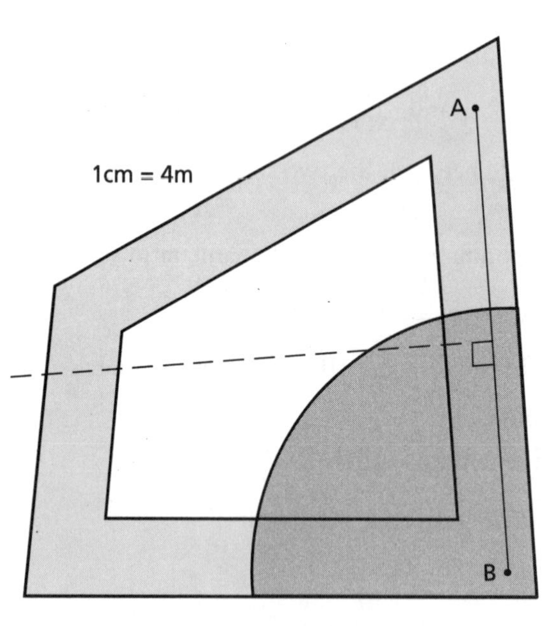

10.1 Estimating measurements – page 133

1 (a) 180 cm (b) 100 m (c) 3kg – 4kg (d) 25 feet
(e) 10 litres (f) Your own answer (g) 9 times the last answer

10.2 Discrete and continuous measures – page 133

1 (a) Continuous (b) Continuous (c) Discrete
(d) Discrete (e) Continuous (f) Discrete

10.3 Recognising possible error – page 134

1

	Measurement	Minimum	Maximum	Range
Height	158 cm	157·5 cm	158·5 cm	157·5 cm $\leq x <$ 158·5 cm
Weight	48 kg	47·5 kg	48·5 kg	47·5 kg $\leq x <$ 48·5 kg
Waist	67 cm	66·5 cm	67·5 cm	66·5 cm $\leq x <$ 67·5 cm
Neck	32 cm	31·5 cm	32·5 cm	31·5 cm $\leq x <$ 32·5 cm
Leg	70 cm	69·5 cm	70·5 cm	69·5 cm $\leq x <$ 70·5 cm

10.4 Areas of plane shapes – page 136–7

1 A 0·5 × 42 m × 26 m = 546 m^2 B 0·5 × 45 m × 26 m = 585 m^2
C 0·5 × 16 m × 22 m = 176 m^2 D 0·5 × 71 m × 22 m = 781 m^2

Total = 2088 m^2

2 (a) 5·25 m^2
(b) The banisters form a parallelogram with base 1 m and height 3·5 m giving 3·5 m^2.

3 (a) A 66 m^2 B 126 m^2 C 76 m^2 D 95 m^2
(b) window in B 20 m^2 window in D 17·5 m^2 doors 12 m^2 each
(c) 301·5 m^2

4 (a) 156 m^2 (b) 156 000 m^3

5 962·11 mm^3 (to 2 d.p.)

6 (a) 125 (b) 10 × 10 × 12 or 2 × 10 × 60 or 2 × 50 × 12

10.5 Distinguishing between formulae – page 138

1 (a) Area (b) Area (c) Area (d) Length (e) Area
(f) Volume (g) Length (h) Length (i) Volume (j) Area
(k) Area (l) Area

11.1 Enlargement by a negative scale factor – page 139

1

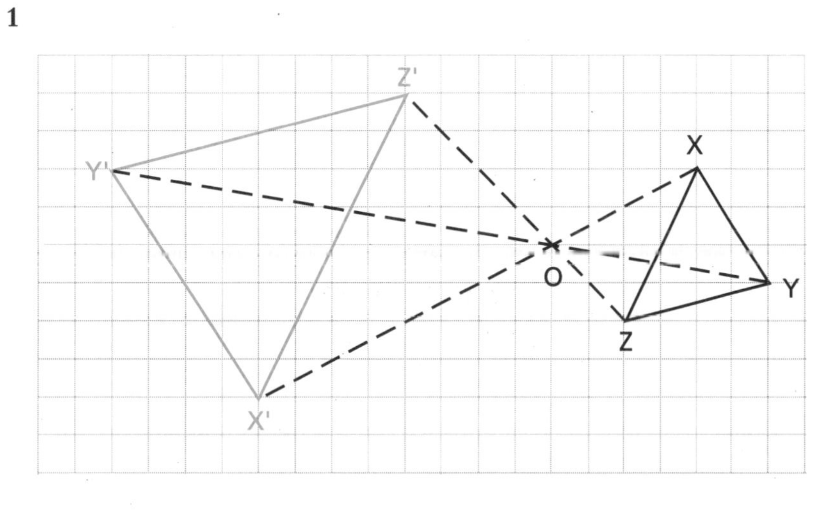

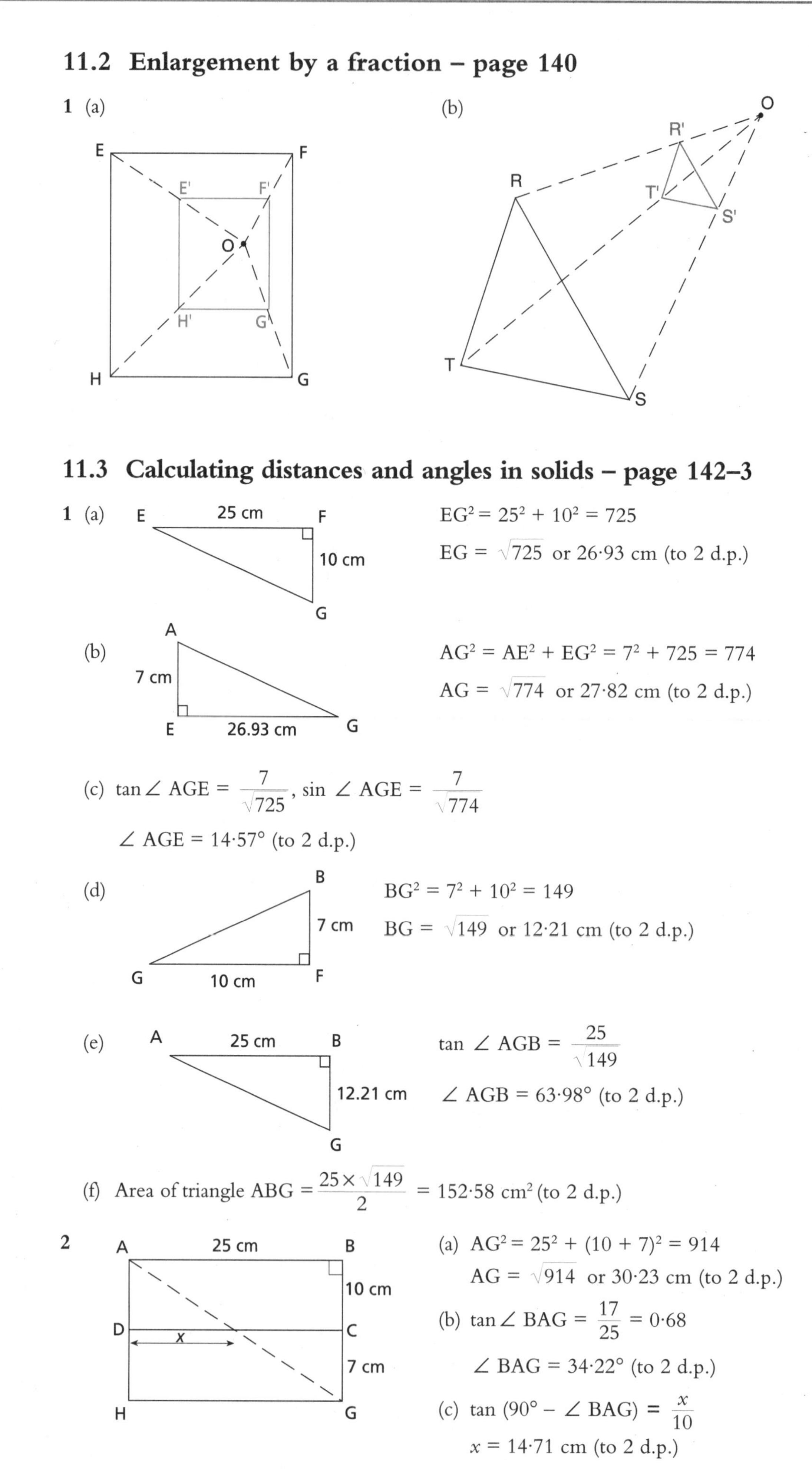

11.2 Enlargement by a fraction – page 140

1 (a) (b)

11.3 Calculating distances and angles in solids – page 142–3

1 (a)

$EG^2 = 25^2 + 10^2 = 725$

$EG = \sqrt{725}$ or 26·93 cm (to 2 d.p.)

(b)

$AG^2 = AE^2 + EG^2 = 7^2 + 725 = 774$

$AG = \sqrt{774}$ or 27·82 cm (to 2 d.p.)

(c) $\tan \angle AGE = \dfrac{7}{\sqrt{725}}$, $\sin \angle AGE = \dfrac{7}{\sqrt{774}}$

$\angle AGE = 14{\cdot}57°$ (to 2 d.p.)

(d)

$BG^2 = 7^2 + 10^2 = 149$

$BG = \sqrt{149}$ or 12·21 cm (to 2 d.p.)

(e)

$\tan \angle AGB = \dfrac{25}{\sqrt{149}}$

$\angle AGB = 63{\cdot}98°$ (to 2 d.p.)

(f) Area of triangle ABG $= \dfrac{25 \times \sqrt{149}}{2} = 152{\cdot}58$ cm² (to 2 d.p.)

2

(a) $AG^2 = 25^2 + (10 + 7)^2 = 914$

$AG = \sqrt{914}$ or 30·23 cm (to 2 d.p.)

(b) $\tan \angle BAG = \dfrac{17}{25} = 0{\cdot}68$

$\angle BAG = 34{\cdot}22°$ (to 2 d.p.)

(c) $\tan (90° - \angle BAG) = \dfrac{x}{10}$

$x = 14{\cdot}71$ cm (to 2 d.p.)

3 (a) 7·93 m (to 2 d.p.) (b) 7·81 m (to 2 d.p.) (c) 8·13 m (to 2 d.p.)

11.4 Polar coordinates – page 143

1

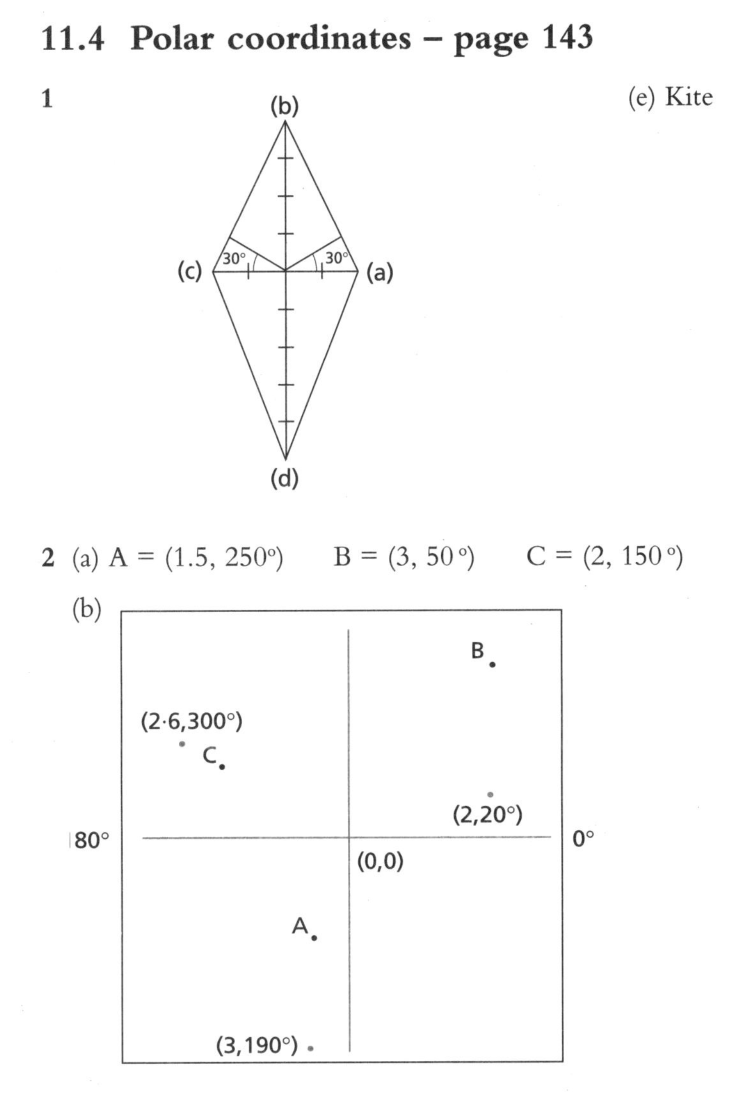

(e) Kite

2 (a) A = (1.5, 250°) B = (3, 50 °) C = (2, 150 °)

(b)

11.5 Congruent triangles – pages 144–5

1 ABC is congruent to KLJ because all corresponding angles and all corresponding sides are equal.
ABC and DEF cannot be congruent because they have different angles.
ABC and GHI cannot be congruent because the sides are not in the same ratio.
Since JKL is congruent to ABC and ABC is not congruent to DEF or GHI, the triangle JKL cannot be congruent to DEF or GHI.
DEF and GHI are not congruent because they have different angles.

2 (a) Side, angle, side (SAS) (b) Not congruent: sides of different length
(c) Angle, angle, side (AAS) (d) Right angle, hypotenuse, side (RHS)
(e) Side, side, side (SSS) (f) Not congruent: the sides of length 8 are opposite different angles.

3

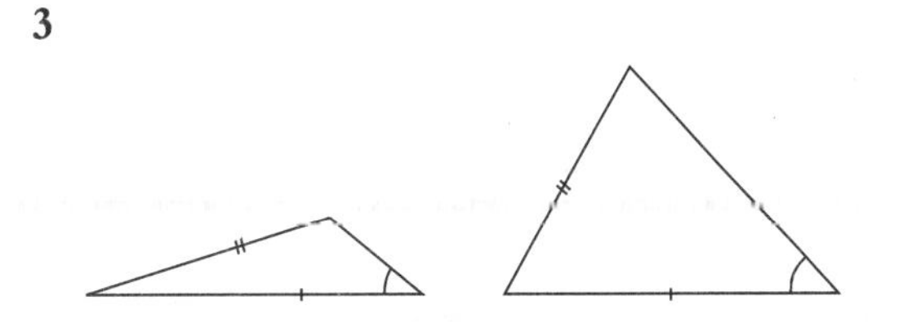

4 Jonathan is right. (AAS)

11.6 Lengths, areas and volumes – pages 146–53

1 (a) $\frac{72}{360} \times \pi \times 18 = 11{\cdot}31$ m (b) $\frac{90}{360} \times \pi \times 12 = 9{\cdot}42$ m

2 radius of outer track = 38 m so length of outside track is $\frac{180}{360} \times \pi \times (2 \times 38) = 119{\cdot}38$ m

3 103° plus overlap

4 (a) $\frac{60}{360} \times \pi \times 6 \times 6 = 18{\cdot}85\text{ cm}^2$ (b) $\frac{120}{360} \times \pi \times 5 \times 5 = 26{\cdot}18\text{ m}^2$

(c) $\frac{360-72}{360} \times \pi \times 20 \times 20 = 1005{\cdot}31\text{ m}^2$

5 $(\frac{110}{360} \times \pi \times 45 \times 45) - (\frac{110}{360} \times \pi \times 13 \times 13) = 1781{\cdot}63\text{ cm}^2$

6 (a) Sector is $\frac{100}{360} \times \pi \times 20 \times 20 = 349{\cdot}065$

Area of triangle = 196·961

Area of segment = 349·065 – 196·961 = 152·10 cm^2 (to 2 d.p.)

(b) Volume = 1500 cm × 152·10 cm^2 = 228 150 cm^3 or 228·15 litres

7 (a) $\sin(\frac{1}{2} \angle \text{AOB}) = \frac{20}{25}$

$\angle$ AOB = 106·26° (to 2 d.p.)

(b) Area of sector = $\frac{106{\cdot}26}{360} \times \pi \times 25^2 = 579{\cdot}56\text{ mm}^2$ (to 2 d.p.)

(c) Using Pythagoras gives OX = 15 mm (X is mid-point of AB).

Area of triangle = $\frac{1}{2} \times 40 \times 15 = 300\text{ mm}^2$

(d) Area of segment = 579·56 – 300 = 279·56 mm^2 (to 2 d.p.)

8 (a) $\pi \times 80 \times 100 = 25\ 133\text{ cm}^2$

(b) 30 159 cm^2

9 25·13 (to 2 d.p.)

10 624 000 m^3

11 13 333·33 m^3 (to 2 d.p.)

12 $V = \frac{1}{3}\pi r^2 h$ $\quad 150 = \frac{1}{3} \times \pi \times r \times r \times 6$ $\quad r^2 = \frac{150 \times 3}{\pi \times 6} = 23{\cdot}873241$

so radius = 4·89 cm (to 2 d.p.)

13 $l^2 = 3^2 + 12^2 = 153$

curved surface area = $\pi rl = \pi \times 3 \times \sqrt{153} = 116{\cdot}58\text{ cm}^2$ (to 2 d.p.)

14 (a) Volume of Phoebe = $\frac{4}{3}\pi r^3 = \frac{4}{3} \times \pi \times 110^3 = 5\ 575\ 280\text{ km}^3$

(b) Surface area = $4\pi r^2 = 4 \times \pi \times 110^2 = 152\ 053\text{ km}^2$

15 (a) 15 708 km^2 (b) 261 799 km^3

16 $v = \frac{1}{3}\pi r^2 h + \frac{2}{3}\pi r^2 = 113{\cdot}09 + 56{\cdot}58 = 169{\cdot}67\text{ cm}^3$ (to 2 d.p.)

11.7 Areas and volumes of similar figures – page 154

1 The length of D is twice the length of C therefore the ratio of areas is $1^2 : 2^2$ or 1 : 4.
Surface area of D = 4 × 600 = 2400 m^2

2 (a) 1 : 50 (b) $1^2 : 50^2$ = 1 : 2500 (c) $1^3 : 50^3$ = 1 : 125 000

3 (a) 1 : 10 (b) 200 litres (c) 15 litres

11.8 Vectors – pages 156–60

1

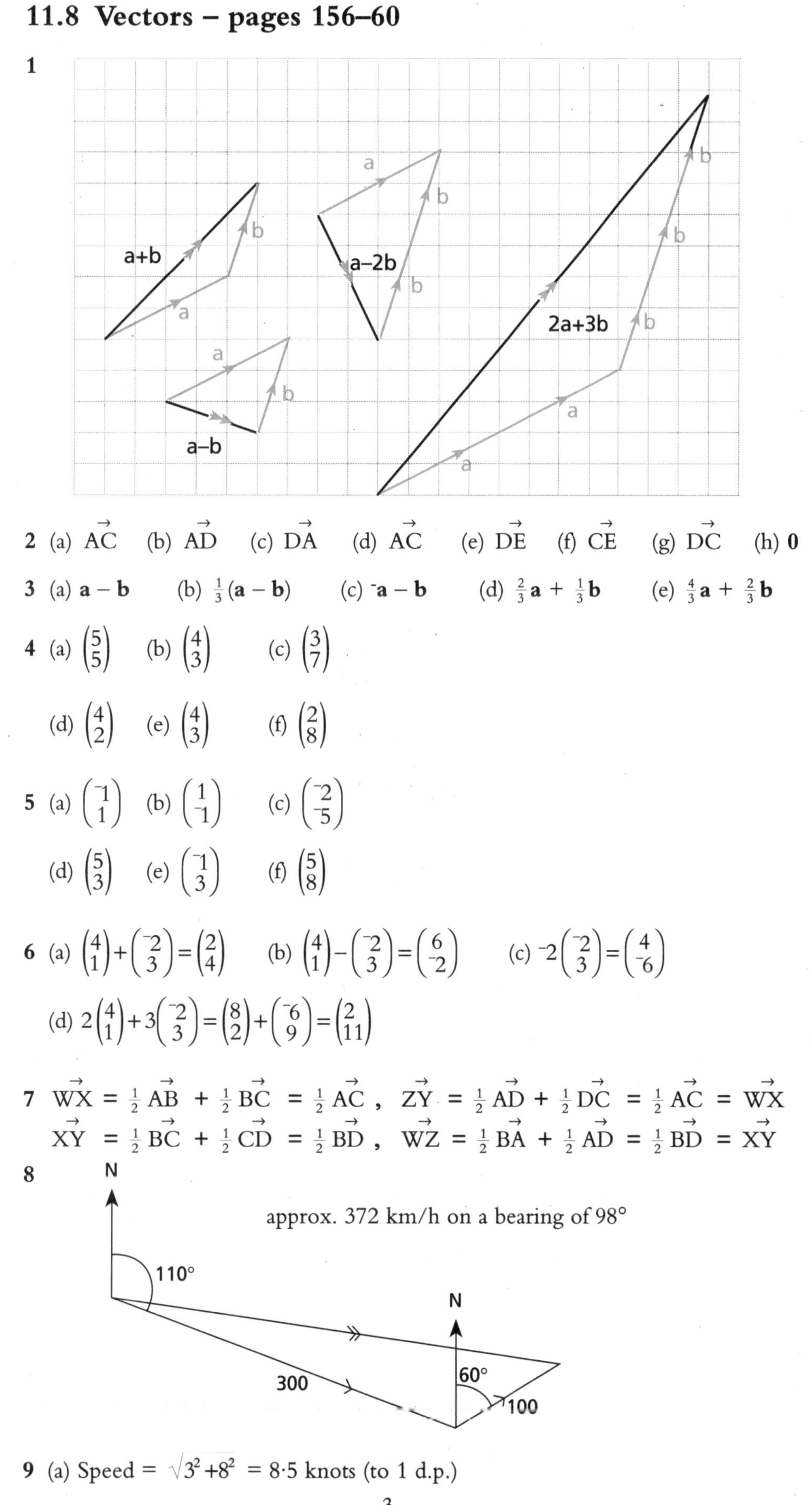

2 (a) $\overrightarrow{AC}$ (b) $\overrightarrow{AD}$ (c) $\overrightarrow{DA}$ (d) $\overrightarrow{AC}$ (e) $\overrightarrow{DE}$ (f) $\overrightarrow{CE}$ (g) $\overrightarrow{DC}$ (h) **0**

3 (a) $\mathbf{a} - \mathbf{b}$ (b) $\frac{1}{3}(\mathbf{a} - \mathbf{b})$ (c) $^-\mathbf{a} - \mathbf{b}$ (d) $\frac{2}{3}\mathbf{a} + \frac{1}{3}\mathbf{b}$ (e) $\frac{4}{3}\mathbf{a} + \frac{2}{3}\mathbf{b}$

4 (a) $\begin{pmatrix}5\\5\end{pmatrix}$ (b) $\begin{pmatrix}4\\3\end{pmatrix}$ (c) $\begin{pmatrix}3\\7\end{pmatrix}$

(d) $\begin{pmatrix}4\\2\end{pmatrix}$ (e) $\begin{pmatrix}4\\3\end{pmatrix}$ (f) $\begin{pmatrix}2\\8\end{pmatrix}$

5 (a) $\begin{pmatrix}^-1\\1\end{pmatrix}$ (b) $\begin{pmatrix}1\\^-1\end{pmatrix}$ (c) $\begin{pmatrix}^-2\\^-5\end{pmatrix}$

(d) $\begin{pmatrix}5\\3\end{pmatrix}$ (e) $\begin{pmatrix}^-1\\3\end{pmatrix}$ (f) $\begin{pmatrix}5\\8\end{pmatrix}$

6 (a) $\begin{pmatrix}4\\1\end{pmatrix}+\begin{pmatrix}^-2\\3\end{pmatrix}=\begin{pmatrix}2\\4\end{pmatrix}$ (b) $\begin{pmatrix}4\\1\end{pmatrix}-\begin{pmatrix}^-2\\3\end{pmatrix}=\begin{pmatrix}6\\^-2\end{pmatrix}$ (c) $^-2\begin{pmatrix}^-2\\3\end{pmatrix}=\begin{pmatrix}4\\^-6\end{pmatrix}$

(d) $2\begin{pmatrix}4\\1\end{pmatrix}+3\begin{pmatrix}^-2\\3\end{pmatrix}=\begin{pmatrix}8\\2\end{pmatrix}+\begin{pmatrix}^-6\\9\end{pmatrix}=\begin{pmatrix}2\\11\end{pmatrix}$

7 $\overrightarrow{WX} = \frac{1}{2}\overrightarrow{AB} + \frac{1}{2}\overrightarrow{BC} = \frac{1}{2}\overrightarrow{AC}$, $\overrightarrow{ZY} = \frac{1}{2}\overrightarrow{AD} + \frac{1}{2}\overrightarrow{DC} = \frac{1}{2}\overrightarrow{AC} = \overrightarrow{WX}$
$\overrightarrow{XY} = \frac{1}{2}\overrightarrow{BC} + \frac{1}{2}\overrightarrow{CD} = \frac{1}{2}\overrightarrow{BD}$, $\overrightarrow{WZ} = \frac{1}{2}\overrightarrow{BA} + \frac{1}{2}\overrightarrow{AD} = \frac{1}{2}\overrightarrow{BD} = \overrightarrow{XY}$

8 approx. 372 km/h on a bearing of 98°

N
110°
300
N
60°
100

9 (a) Speed = $\sqrt{3^2+8^2}$ = 8·5 knots (to 1 d.p.)

(b) Bearing = 60° + θ and tan $\theta = \frac{3}{8}$ so bearing = 081° (to nearest degree)

10 (a) 18·43° (b) 126·49 N

11 (a) 3·54 mph (b) 128·54 mph (c) 1·29 mph (d) 4·83 mph
(e) 128·58 mph (f) bearing 031·58°

11.9 Sin, cos and tan of any angle – pages 161–2

1 (a) sin 30° = 0·5 cos 30° = 0·866 tan 30° = 0·577
(b) sin 144° = 0·588 cos 144° = −0·809 tan 144° - −0·727
(c) sin 210° = −0·5 cos 210° = −0·866 tan 210° = 0·577
(d) sin 300° = −0·866 cos 300° = 0·5 tan 300° = −1·732
(e) sin −40° = −0·643 cos −40° = 0·766 tan −40° = −0·839
(f) sin 405° = 0·707 cos 405° = 0·707 tan 405° = 1
(g) sin −110° = −0·940 cos −110° = −0·342 tan −110° = 2·747
(h) sin 520° = 0·342 cos 520° = −0·940 tan 520° = −0·364

2 (a) 128° (b) 285°, 435°, 645° (c) 260°, −100°, −280°

3 (a) sin 12° (b) cos 1° (c) tan −53°

4 30°, 150°, 390°, 510°

5 30°, 330°, −30°, −330°

6 θ = 20·56° or 200·56°

11.10 Sin, cos and tan graphs – pages 162–5

1 (a) (b)

x°	sin x
0	0
10	0.17
20	0.34
30	0.50
40	0.64
50	0.77
60	0.87
70	0.94
80	0.98
90	1.00
100	0.98
110	0.94
120	0.87
130	0.77
140	0.64
150	0.50
160	0.34
170	0.17
180	0

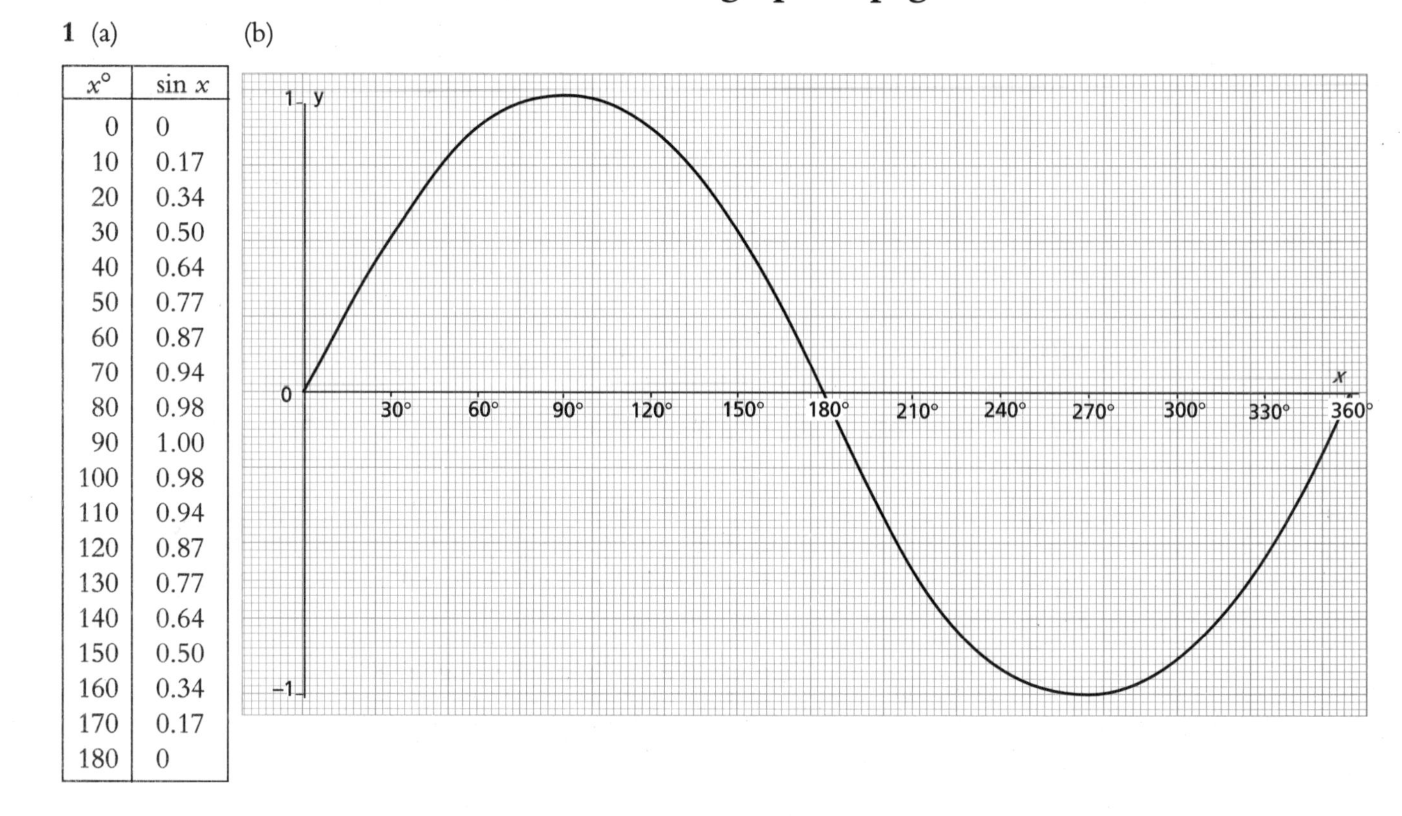

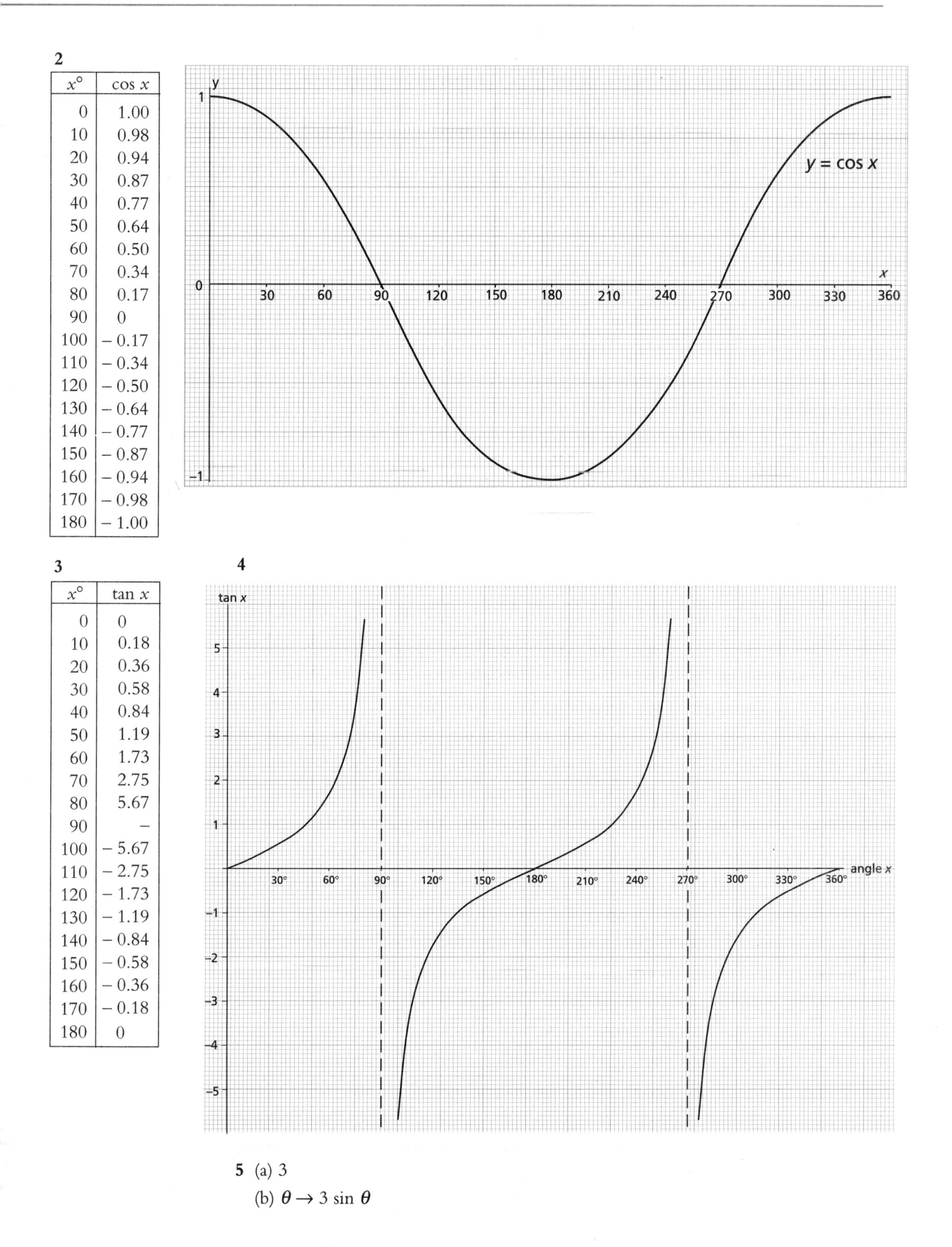

2

x°	$\cos x$
0	1.00
10	0.98
20	0.94
30	0.87
40	0.77
50	0.64
60	0.50
70	0.34
80	0.17
90	0
100	− 0.17
110	− 0.34
120	− 0.50
130	− 0.64
140	− 0.77
150	− 0.87
160	− 0.94
170	− 0.98
180	− 1.00

3

x°	$\tan x$
0	0
10	0.18
20	0.36
30	0.58
40	0.84
50	1.19
60	1.73
70	2.75
80	5.67
90	–
100	− 5.67
110	− 2.75
120	− 1.73
130	− 1.19
140	− 0.84
150	− 0.58
160	− 0.36
170	− 0.18
180	0

4

5 (a) 3

(b) $\theta \rightarrow 3 \sin \theta$

6

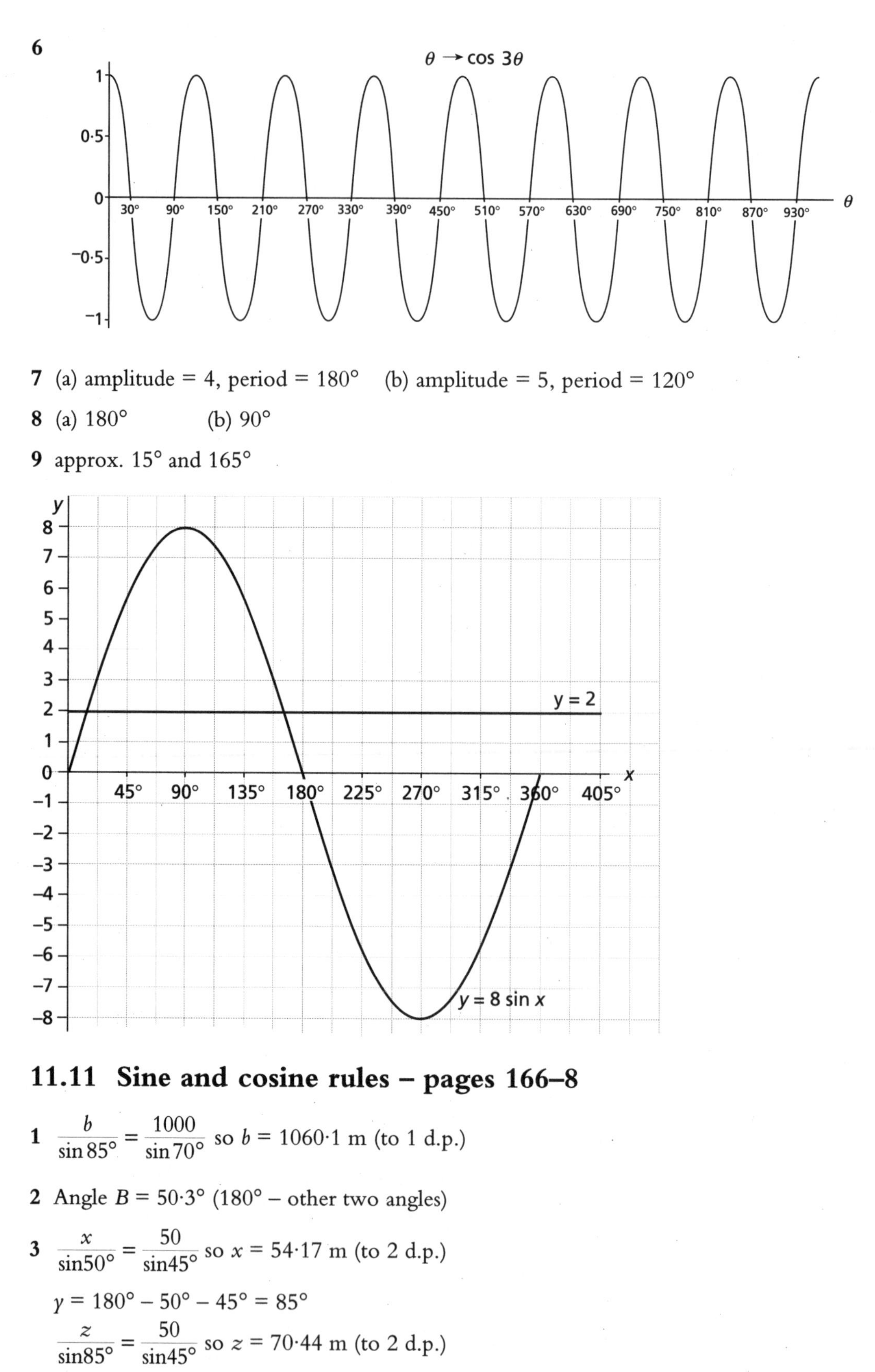

7 (a) amplitude = 4, period = 180° (b) amplitude = 5, period = 120°

8 (a) 180° (b) 90°

9 approx. 15° and 165°

11.11 Sine and cosine rules – pages 166–8

1 $\dfrac{b}{\sin 85°} = \dfrac{1000}{\sin 70°}$ so b = 1060·1 m (to 1 d.p.)

2 Angle B = 50·3° (180° – other two angles)

3 $\dfrac{x}{\sin 50°} = \dfrac{50}{\sin 45°}$ so x = 54·17 m (to 2 d.p.)

y = 180° – 50° – 45° = 85°

$\dfrac{z}{\sin 85°} = \dfrac{50}{\sin 45°}$ so z = 70·44 m (to 2 d.p.)

4 $\dfrac{143}{\sin 10°} = \dfrac{AX}{\sin 87°}$ so AX = 822·38 km (to 2 d.p.)

5 $\cos B = \dfrac{15^2+18^2-17^2}{2\times 15\times 18}$ so B = 61·2° (to 1 d.p.) and C = 68·1° (to 1 d.p.)

6 10·18 km (to 2 d.p.)

7 (a) 059° (b) 130·5°

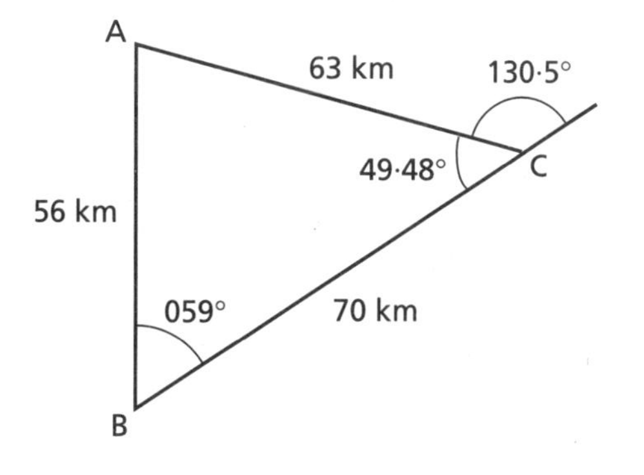

11.12 Circle theorems – pages 170–2

1 (a) $a = 50°$ because a and 50° are drawn from the same arc
$b = 60°$ because b and 60° are drawn from the same arc
(b) $c = 70°$ because opposite angles of a cyclic quadrilateral = 180°
$d = 95°$ because opposite angles of a cyclic quadrilateral = 180°
(c) $e = 55°$ because the angle at the circumference is half the angle at the centre
(d) $f = 110°$ The angle at the circumference is half the angle at the centre, which in this case is 360° – 140°

2 $(\frac{1}{2}\text{CD})^2 = 52 - 32 = 42$ so CD = 8 = AB

3 Tangents to a circle are always the same length so ABC is an isosceles triangle.
Therefore $x = \frac{1}{2}(180° - 50°) = 65°$

$\angle BCA = x = 65°$ and $\angle BCO = 90°$ so $y = 90° - 65° = 25°$

4 OCA = 30° hence
(a) OAC = 30° because triangle OAC is isosceles
(b) AOC = 120° because angles in triangle add up to 180°
(c) ADC = 60° because this angle is at the circumference and is therefore half of AOC (the angle at the centre)
(d) AEC = 60° because it is drawn from the same chord as ADC
(e) ABC = 120° because it is the opposite angle in the cyclic quadrilateral to the angle AEC
(f) AXC = 60° because XAO = 90°, XCO = 90°, and AOC = 120° and angles in a quadrilateral add up to 360°

Section 4 answers

12.1 Gathered data – page 173

1 (a) The variety of possible responses is too wide.
(b) Question requires an opinion.
(c) Question is open to a yes/no response which would not be appropriate.
(d) The variety of possible responses is too wide.
(e) The variety of possible responses is too wide.

2 Choice of location may affect the survey result.
Question fails to specify what a large shop is.

12.2 Cumulative frequency – pages 174–5

1 (a)

Marks	Number of candidates (Frequency)	Candidates up to this point (Cumulative frequency)
1 - 10	1	1
11 - 20	3	4
21 - 30	7	11
31 - 40	11	22
41 - 50	21	43
51 - 60	34	77
61 - 70	25	102
71 - 80	13	115
81 - 90	4	119
91 - 100	1	120

(b) 11 (c) $120 - 102 = 18$

2 (a)

Height (cm)	Tally	Frequency	Cumulative frequency
$120 \leq h < 130$	|	1	1
$130 \leq h < 140$	|||	3	4
$140 \leq h < 150$	~~||||~~ |	6	10
$150 \leq h < 160$	~~||||~~ ~~||||~~	10	20
$160 \leq h < 170$	~~||||~~ ||	7	27
$170 \leq h < 180$	||||	4	31
$180 \leq h < 190$	|	1	32

(b) 10 (c) $32 - 20 = 12$

3 (a) Range = $4515 - 2150 = 2365$
Class intervals of 500 g starting from 2 kg gives 6 classes.

Weight (kg)	Tally	Frequency	Cumulative frequency
$2 \leq w < 2.5$	|	1	1
$2.5 \leq w < 3$	||	2	3
$3 \leq w < 3.5$	~~||||~~ |	6	9
$3.5 \leq w < 4$	~~||||~~ ||	7	16
$4 \leq w < 4.5$	|||	3	19
$4.5 \leq w < 5$	|	1	20

(b) 8

12.3 Cumulative frequency diagrams – pages 176–7

1 (a)

Hours watched	Number of people	Cumulative frequency
< 15	1	1
< 20	2	3
< 25	7	10
< 30	11	21
< 35	25	46
< 40	23	69
< 45	17	86
< 50	10	96
< 55	3	99
< 60	1	100

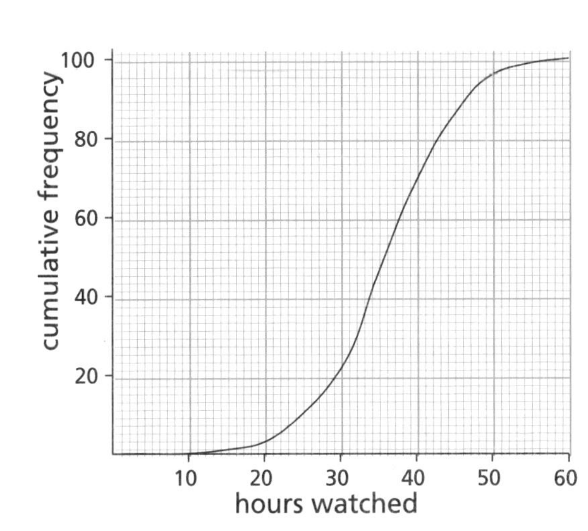

(c) 21 (d) 36 (e) 47

2 (a)

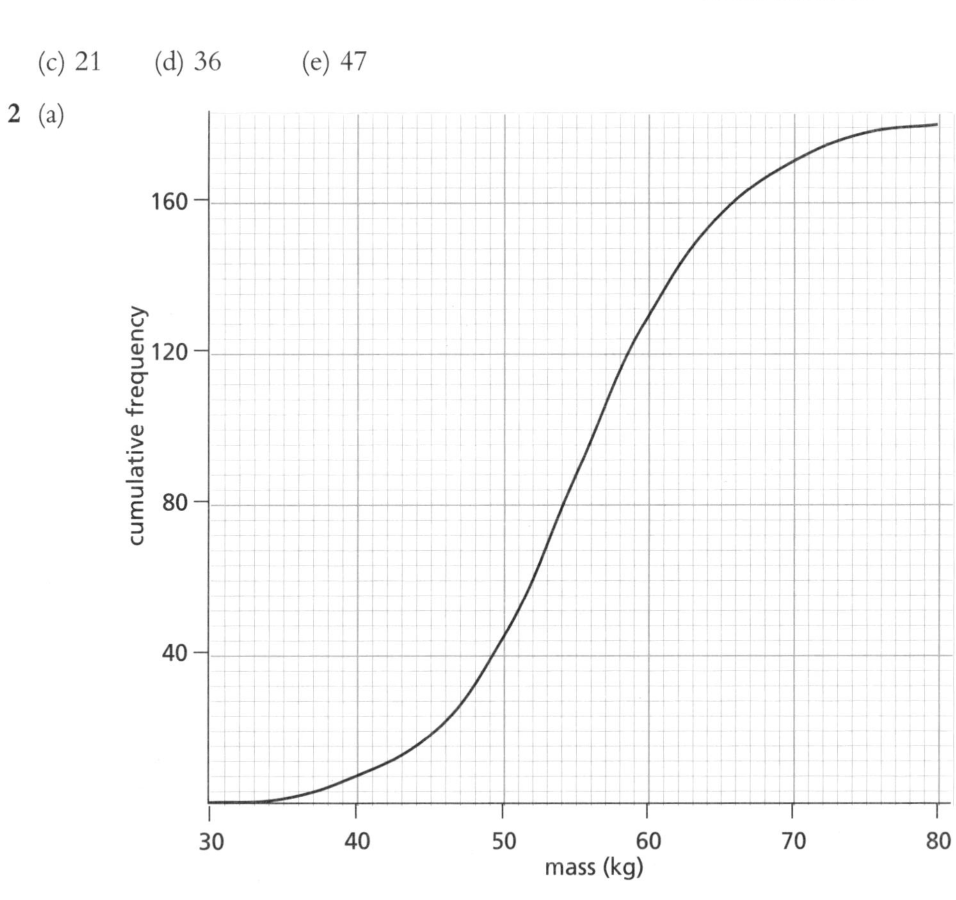

(b) (i) 7 (ii) 52 (iii) 56 kg (iv) 59 kg (v) 61 kg (vi) 11 kg

(c) Half the people weigh between 50 kg and 61 kg.

12.4 Choosing and calculating an average value – pages 179–80

1 (a)

Class interval	Class mid-value
26-30	28
31-35	33
36-40	38
41-45	43
46-50	48
51-55	53

(b) $28 \times 1 + 33 \times 5 + 38 \times 3 + 43 \times 6 + 48 \times 6 + 53 \times 3 = 1012$

Mean $= \frac{1012}{24} = 42{\cdot}17$ kg (to 2 d.p.)

2 (a) mean $= \frac{124}{19} = 6{\cdot}53$ mins late (to 2 d.p.) median = 6–8 mins late

mode = 6–8 mins late range = 14 mins late

(b) mean $= \frac{130}{19} = 6{\cdot}84$ mins late (to 2 d.p.) median = 3–5 mins late

mode = 3–5 mins late range = 17 mins late

(c) On Saturday two buses were very late, making the mean number of minutes late greater on Saturday than on Monday. However, most buses on Saturday were between 3 and 5 minutes late. On Monday more buses were between 6 and 8 minutes late: most buses were between 3 and 8 minutes late.

3 (a) There is no modal value in either group.
(b) A = 15 B = 15
(c) Median values are the same for both groups.
(d) A = 15 B = 15
(e) A = 4 B = 39

4 (a) Mean $\frac{154}{27} = 5.7$ Median = 1 Mode = 0 Range = 49
(b) The mean is affected by the extreme values.
The mean value takes all values into account.
The median fails to reflect the spread of the data.
The median gives the middle value.
The mode fails to take 154 detentions into account.
The mode reflects that most pupils got no detentions.

5 (a) Two groups are the same size.
(b) 26
(c) 25
(d) Mean class size is 26 therefore a new group could be formed if this measure of average is used.

12.5 Scatter graphs and correlation – pages 181–3

1

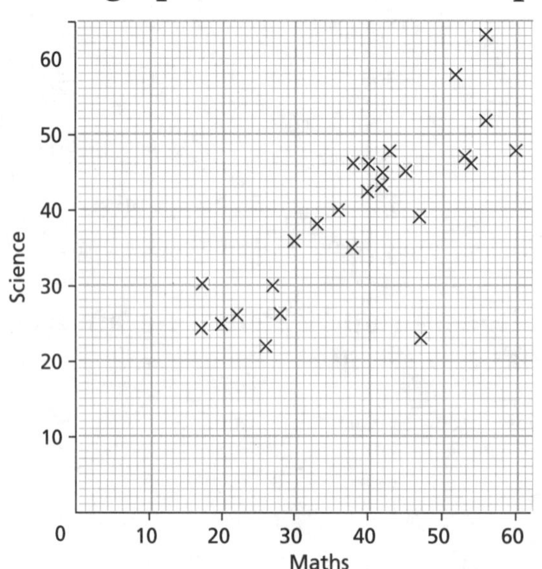

2 (a)

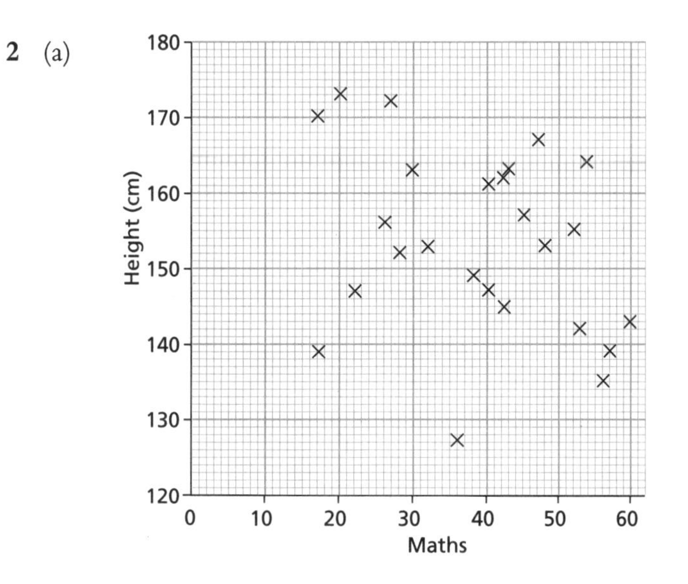

(b) The points are spread all over the graph. You can say that there appears to be no correlation.

3 (a)

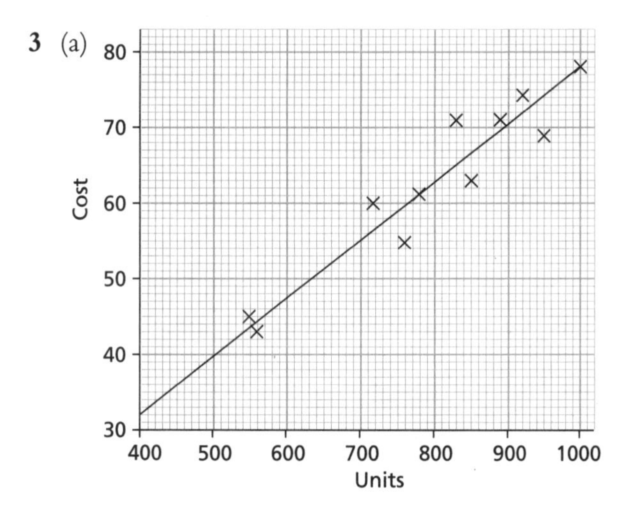

(b) Line of best fit

(c) c = 0·077 units + 32

(d) The gradient gives the cost per unit and the added value represents the standing charge.

13.1 Relative frequency – page 184

1 Pupil's experiments

2 (a) 10 (b) 3 (c) 3

3 $\frac{1}{8}$

13.2 Combining independent events – page 186

1 (a) $6 \times 6 = 36$ (b)

	first die					
second die	1	2	3	4	5	6
1	1,1	2,1	3,1	4,1	5,1	6,1
2	1,2	2,2	3,2	4,2	5,2	6,2
3	1,3	2,3	3,3	4,3	5,3	6,3
4	1,4	2,4	3,4	4,4	5,4	6,4
5	1,5	2,5	3,5	4,5	5,5	6,5
6	1,6	2,6	3,6	4,6	5,6	6,6

2 (a) AA, AB, AC, BA, BB, BC, CA, CB, CC

(b)

		2nd		
		A	B	C
1st	A	AA	AB	AC
	B	BA	BB	BC
	C	CA	CB	CC

(c)

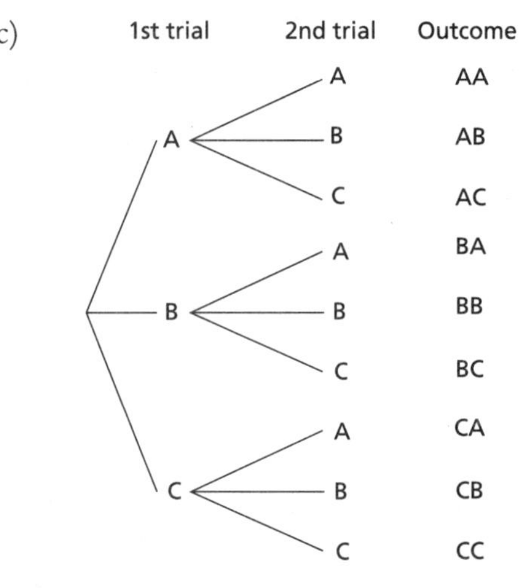

3

1st child 2nd child 3rd child Outcome

1st child	2nd child	3rd child	Outcome
B	B	B	BBB
		G	BBG
	G	B	BGB
		G	BGG
G	B	B	GBB
		G	GBG
	G	B	GGB
		G	GGG

13.3 Mutually exclusive events – page 187

1 (a) $\frac{1}{20}$ (b) $\frac{19}{20}$

2 $\frac{9}{13}$

3 $\frac{4}{5}$

4 $\frac{3}{8}$

13.4 Adding probabilities – page 188

1 $\frac{1}{6} + \frac{1}{6} = \frac{1}{3}$

2 (a) The biscuit chosen cannot be a cream biscuit and a wafer at the same time.

(b) $\frac{4}{10} + \frac{2}{10} = \frac{6}{10} = \frac{3}{5}$ (c) $\frac{3}{10} + \frac{4}{10} = \frac{7}{10}$

3 (a) $0{\cdot}2 + 0{\cdot}3 = 0{\cdot}5$ (b) $0{\cdot}1 + 0{\cdot}3 = 0{\cdot}4$

13.5 Calculating probabilities – pages 189–91

1 0

2 (a) (ii) (b) (iii)

3 $\frac{1}{6} \times \frac{1}{2} = \frac{1}{12}$

4 (a) $\frac{1}{3} \times \frac{1}{3} = \frac{1}{9}$

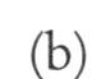
(b)

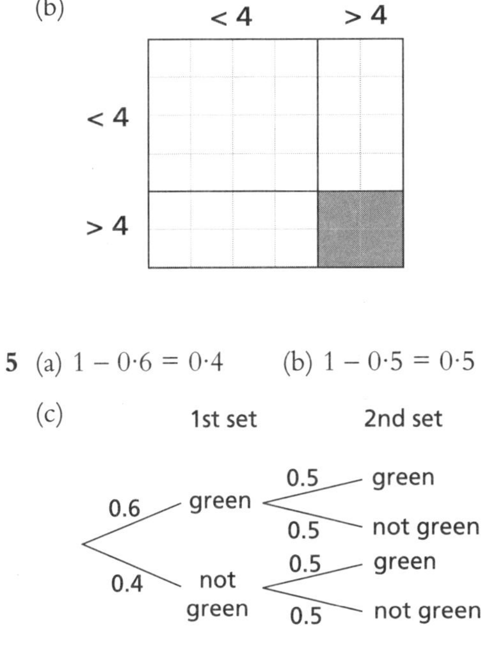

5 (a) $1 - 0{\cdot}6 = 0{\cdot}4$ (b) $1 - 0{\cdot}5 = 0{\cdot}5$

(c)

1st set 2nd set

0.6 green — 0.5 green; 0.5 not green

0.4 not green — 0.5 green; 0.5 not green

(d) $0{\cdot}6 \times 0{\cdot}5 = 0{\cdot}3$

14.1 Histograms – page 194

1 (a) & (b)

Distance (km)	Frequency	Frequency density
$0 \leq d < 1{\cdot}5$	51	34.0
$1{\cdot}5 \leq d < 2{\cdot}0$	54	108.0
$2{\cdot}0 \leq d < 2{\cdot}5$	62	124.0
$2{\cdot}5 \leq d < 3{\cdot}0$	79	158.0
$3{\cdot}0 \leq d < 3{\cdot}5$	52	104.0
$3{\cdot}5 \leq d < 6{\cdot}0$	42	16.8

(c)

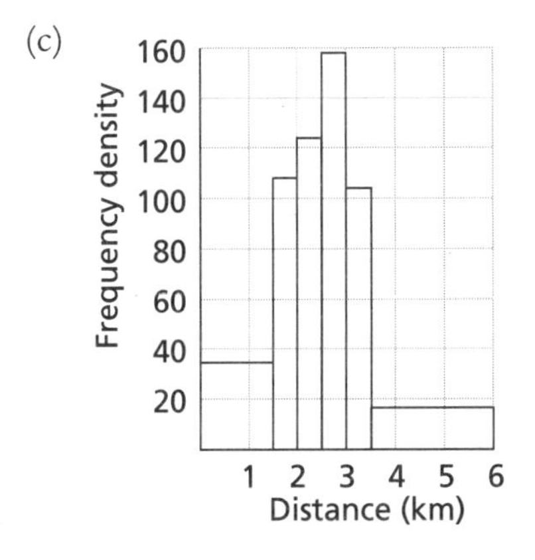

(d) The most commonly travelled distance is 2·5 to 3 km. Most people travel between 1·5 and 3·5 km. Very few people live more than 3·5 km from school.

14.2 Sampling – page 195

1 (a) Test by sampling. Take into account shift, production line, etc.

(b) Test by sampling. Age, breed of cat

(c) Test by sampling. Various shops in a variety of areas, taking into account the age of customers, how much money they have, whether the shop is a specialist shop, etc.

(d) This cannot be tested by sampling. All cables must be tested as all must be safe.

2 Your experiment

14.3 Conditional probabilities – pages 197–8

1

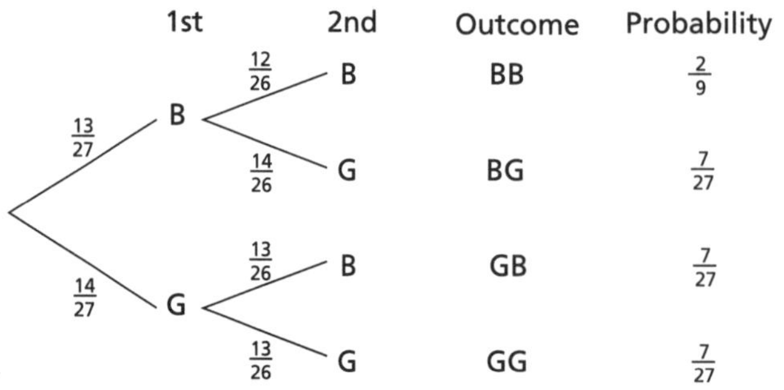

1st		2nd		Outcome	Probability
$\frac{13}{27}$	B	$\frac{12}{26}$	B	BB	$\frac{2}{9}$
		$\frac{14}{26}$	G	BG	$\frac{7}{27}$
$\frac{14}{27}$	G	$\frac{13}{26}$	B	GB	$\frac{7}{27}$
		$\frac{13}{26}$	G	GG	$\frac{7}{27}$

2 (a) p(B) = $\frac{3}{9}$ and p(B/B) = $\frac{2}{8}$

p(B and B) = $\frac{\not{3}^{1}}{\not{9}_{3}} \times \frac{\not{2}^{1}}{\not{8}_{4}} = \frac{1}{12}$

(b) p(W) = $\frac{2}{9}$ and p(R/W) = $\frac{4}{8}$

p(W then R) = $\frac{1}{9}$

3

Tomorrow

Today		S	R	L	B
	S		SR	SL	SB
	R	RS		RL	RB
	L	LS	LR		LB
	B	BS	BR	BL	

14.4 Standard deviation – pages 199–201

1 Mean = 5 Standard deviation = 2·14 (to 2 d.p.)

2 Answer as example

3 Mean = 59·06 (to 2 d.p.) Standard deviation = 17·78 (to 2 d.p.)

4 Mean = 660·5 Standard deviation = 185·31
Data has a lower mean but wider spread

5 507·5 ml

6 14%

Examination questions

The following questions range in difficulty. Questions 1–15 are aimed at intermediate level; questions 16–33 at higher level. Intermediate candidates may not be able to complete questions 16–33; higher level candidates should attempt all.

1 A **US** Centillion is the number 10^{303}
A **UK** Centillion is the number 10^{600}
(a) How many **US** Centillions are there in a **UK** Centillion? (2 marks)
Give your answer in standard form.
(b) Write the number 40 **US** Centillions in standard form. (2 marks)

(London)

2 It is estimated that the world population in the year 2100 will be 10 200 000 000.
(a) Write the estimated population in standard form. (2 marks)
The land area of the world, to three significant figures, is $1{\cdot}49 \times 10^8$ km^2.
(b) Calculate the estimated population density (the number of people per km^2) of the world in the year 2100. Give your answer to the nearest whole number. (2 marks)

(CCEA)

3 The surface area of a planet, A square kilometres, varies directly as the square of the diameter, D kilometres, of the planet.
The surface of the Moon is $3{\cdot}8 \times 10^7$ square kilometres.
Calculate the surface area of a planet with diameter double the diameter of the Moon. (3 marks)
Give your answer in scientific notation.

(SEB)

4 The graph of $y = x^3 - 2x$ is drawn on the grid.
(a) Show how to use the graph to find the solution of $x^3 = 2x + 3$.
Write down a solution to this equation. (2 marks)
(b) By drawing a suitable straight line on the grid, use the graph to find all the solutions of
$x^3 = 3x - 1$. (4 marks)

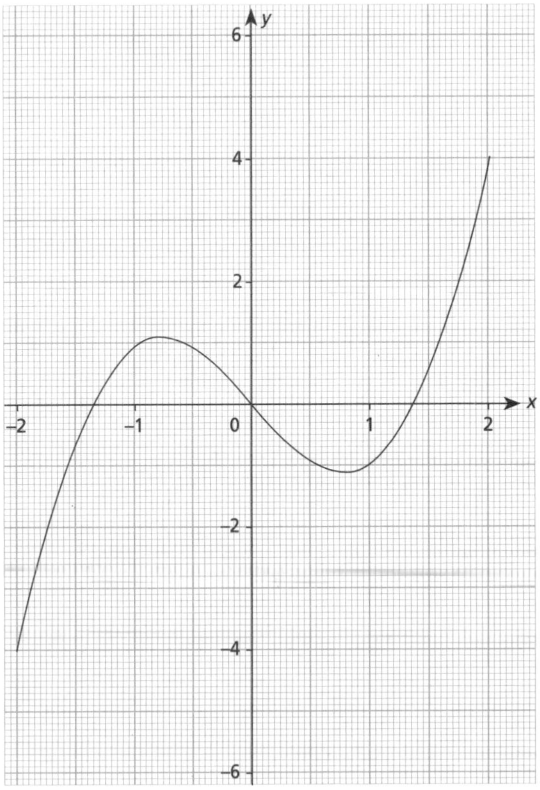

y
6
4
2
–2
–1
0
1
2
x
–2
–4
–6

5 A dairy produces a 500 gram pack of butter in the shape of a cylinder.

The radius of the circular end of the pack is 3·9 centimetres and the length of the pack is 10·5 centimetres.

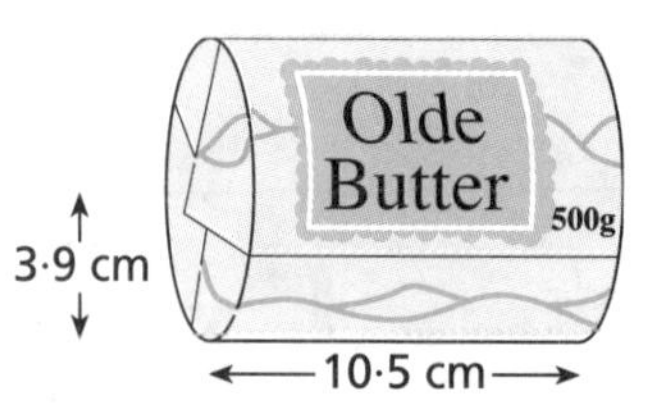

(a) Calculate the volume of the pack of butter. (3 marks)
Give your answer to the nearest whole number.

The 500 gram pack is redesigned.
It is now produced in the shape of a cuboid with a square end of side 6·5 centimetres.

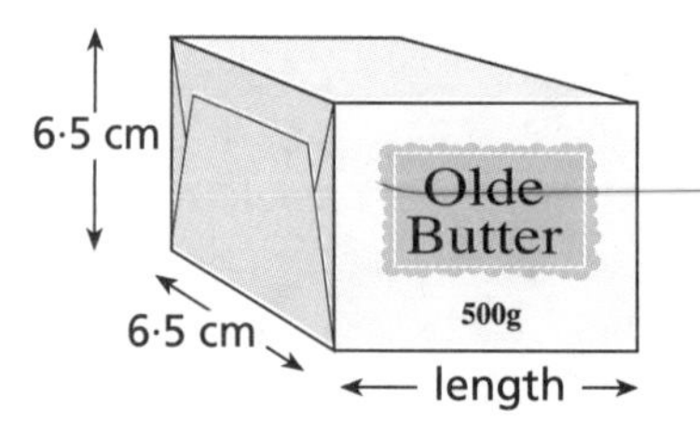

(b) Calculate the length of the redesigned pack of butter. (3 marks)
Give your answer correct to 1 decimal place.

(*SEB*)

6 The table gives information about the weights of 100 new born babies.

Weight (w) in kg	Frequency
$1{\cdot}0 \leq w < 1{\cdot}5$	4
$1{\cdot}5 \leq w < 2{\cdot}0$	9
$2{\cdot}0 \leq w < 2{\cdot}5$	11
$2{\cdot}5 \leq w < 3{\cdot}0$	21
$3{\cdot}0 \leq w < 3{\cdot}5$	26
$3{\cdot}5 \leq w < 4{\cdot}0$	18
$4{\cdot}0 \leq w < 4{\cdot}5$	9
$4{\cdot}5 \leq w < 5{\cdot}0$	2

(a) Complete the cumulative frequency table below. (2 marks)

Weight (w) in kg	Cumulative Frequency
$1{\cdot}0 \leq w < 1{\cdot}5$	
$1{\cdot}0 \leq w < 2{\cdot}0$	
$1{\cdot}0 \leq w < 2{\cdot}5$	
$1{\cdot}0 \leq w < 3{\cdot}0$	
$1{\cdot}0 \leq w < 3{\cdot}5$	
$1{\cdot}0 \leq w < 4{\cdot}0$	
$1{\cdot}0 \leq w < 4{\cdot}5$	
$1{\cdot}0 \leq w < 5{\cdot}0$	

(b) On a copy of the grid below, draw a cumulative frequency graph for your table. (2 marks)

(c) Use your cumulative frequency diagram to estimate the median weight, in kilograms, of the new born babies. (2 marks)
Show your method clearly.

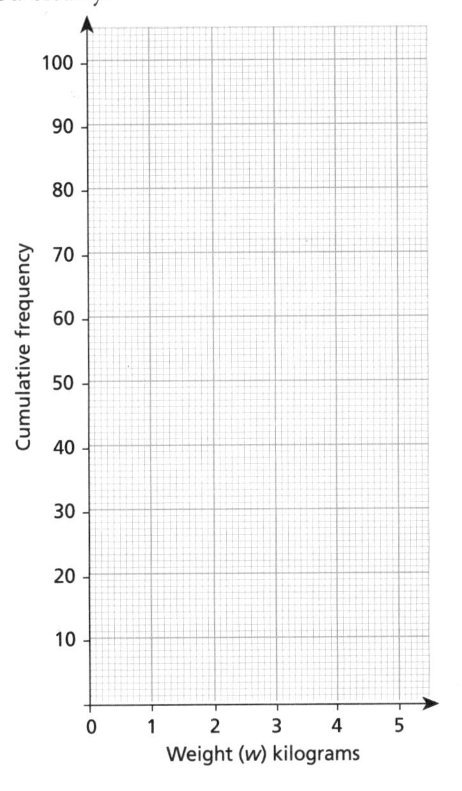

(London)

7 When I go to work I have to cycle through two sets of traffic lights, A and B. The probability that I have to stop at A is 0·4.

If I have to stop at A, the probability that I have to stop at B is 0·8.

If I do not have to stop at A the probability that I have to stop at B is 0·3.

(a) Fill in the probabilities on the tree diagram.

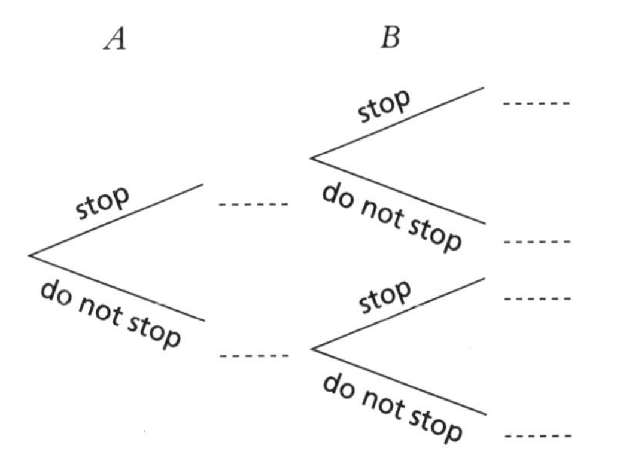

(b) What is the probability that I have to stop at both A and B? (2 marks)

(c) Calculate the probability that I have to stop at least once. (3 marks)

(NEAB)

8 When a drawing pin is dropped onto the floor it lands either point up or point down.

The probability of any one drawing pin landing point up is 0·46.

What is the probability that

(a) the first three drawing pins all land point down? (2 marks)

(b) two of the first three drawing pins dropped land point down? (2 marks)

(c) at least one of the first three drawing pins dropped will land point up? (2 marks)

(NEAB)

9 Rick makes a plank bridge.

The relationship between a plank's breaking strength, length and thickness is given by the formula:

$$b = \frac{32 \cdot 5t^2}{l}$$

where b kg is the breaking strength
t mm is the thickness
l m is the length.

Rick needs a plank which has a breaking strength of 150 kilograms and a length of 6 metres. Find the thickness of the plank correct to the nearest centimetre. (4 marks)

(*NEAB*)

10

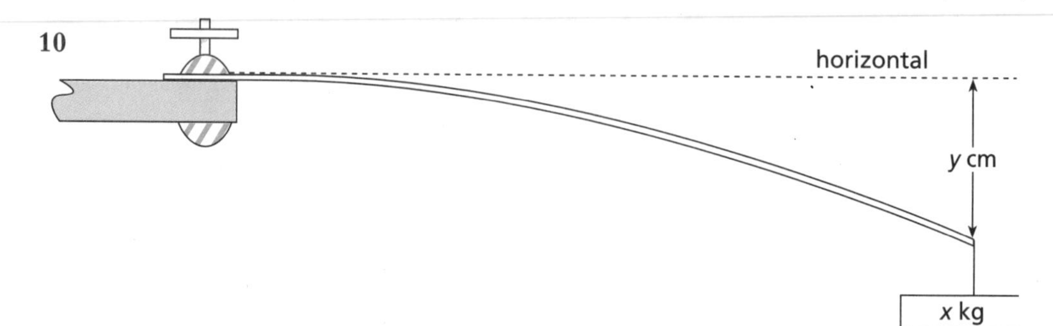

One end of a plastic rod is clamped to a horizontal bench.

The diagram shows the other end held y cm below the horizontal by a load of x kg hanging from that end.

Some corresponding values of x and y are given on the table:

x (kg)	0·4	0·8	1·1	1·4
y (cm	2·8	3·8	4·55	5·3

(a) (i) Plot these values and draw the graph on the graph paper below. (2 marks)
(ii) Explain why the values of x and y satisfy a law of the form $y = mx + c$. (1 mark)

(b) Using information from your graph, determine the values of m and c, correct to 2 significant figures. (5 marks)

(c) (i) Write down the equation of your graph. (1 mark)
Use this equation to find,
(ii) the distance of the unclamped end of the rod below the horizontal when the load is removed, (1 mark)
(iii) the maximum load that can be hung on the unclamped end if the rod snaps when that end moves down more than 11·3 cm. (2 marks)

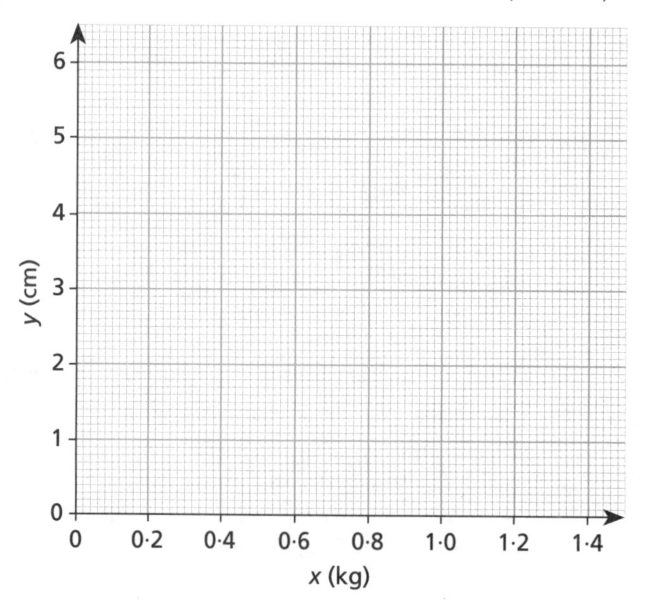

(*CCEA*)

11 The surface area of a sphere of radius r is $4\pi r^2$.

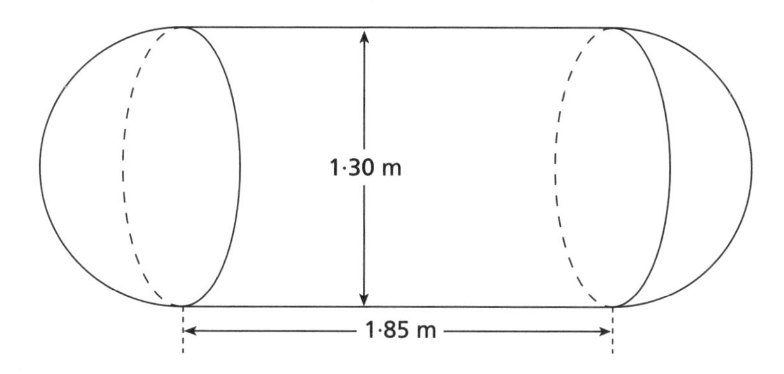

The gas container shown is cylindrical in shape with hemispherical ends.

The cylindrical portion is 1·85 m long and has a diameter of 1·30 m.

Calculate the surface area of this container, correct to 3 significant figures. You may take $\pi = 3{\cdot}14$. (6 marks)

(*CCEA*)

12

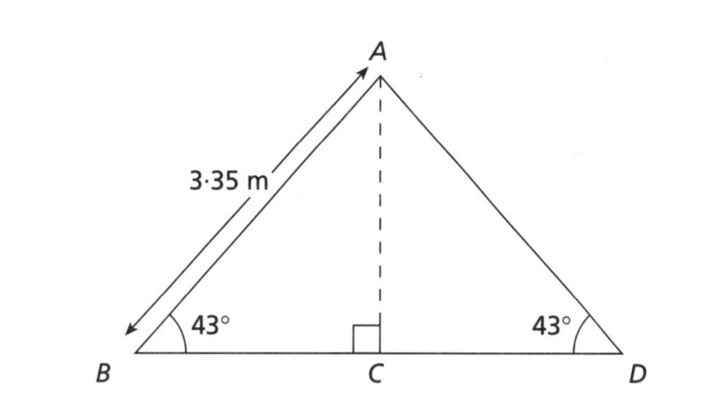

The diagram shows the cross-section of a loft. The length AB is 3·35 m.

The roof slopes at 43° to the horizontal.

(a) Calculate the height AC. (3 marks)

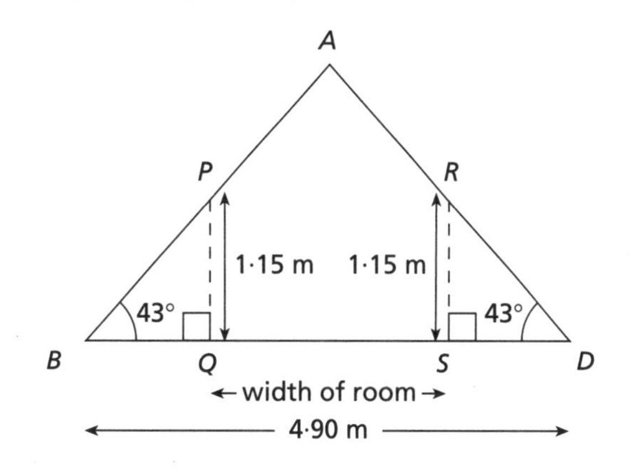

The loft is 4·90 m wide.

The lines PQ and RS show where walls, 1·15 m high, are to be built to make a room in the loft.

(b) (i) Calculate the length BQ. (3 marks)

(ii) Calculate the width of this room. (1 mark)

(*MEG*)

13

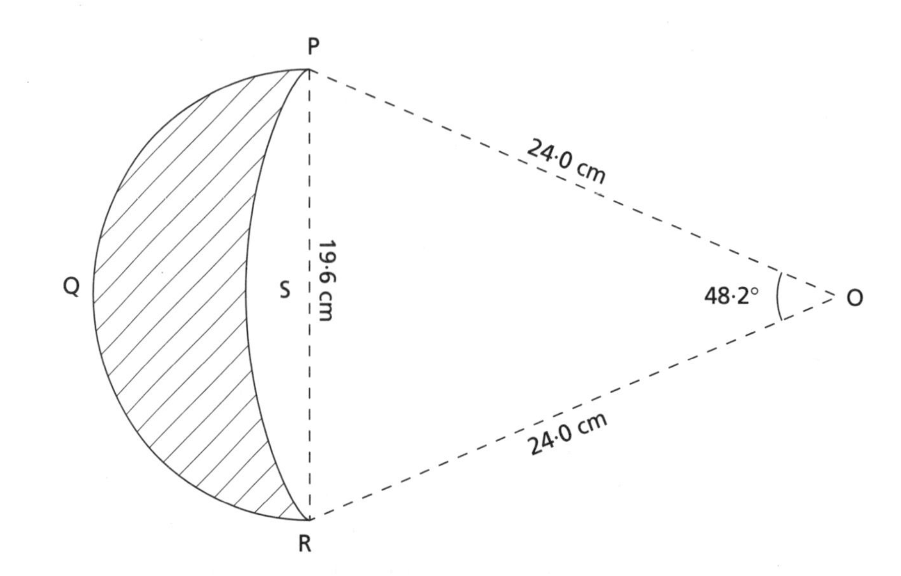

The crescent, shaded in the diagram, is like that found on many flags.
PSR is an arc of a circle, centre O and radius 24·0 cm.
Angle POR = 48·2°
PQR is a semicircle on PR as diameter, where PR = 19·6 cm.
You may take $\pi = 3{\cdot}14$.

Calculate, correct to 3 significant figures,
(a) the perimeter of the crescent, (6 marks)
(b) the area of the sector POR, (2 marks)
(c) the area of the crescent. (7 marks)

(CCEA)

14 The table below shows the distribution of the weights of 150 apples.

Weight (w grams)	Number of apples	Mid-interval value	
$50 < w \leq 60$	23		
$60 < w \leq 70$	42		
$70 < w \leq 80$	50		
$80 < w \leq 90$	20		
$90 < w \leq 100$	15		

Calculate an estimate of the mean weight of an apple. (5 marks)

(MEG)

15 (a) Use the formula $v = \sqrt{u^2 + 2as}$ to find the value of v when $u = 24$, $a = -9{\cdot}8$ and $s = 10\frac{1}{4}$. (2 marks)

(b) **Without using a calculator**, use approximation to check that your answer to (a) is of the correct order of magnitude. (2 marks)
You **must** show all your working.

(SEG)

16 A door of height 180 cm contains a circular window of radius r cm.

The window is 10 cm from the edges of the door, as shown in the diagram.

The area of the window is one-quarter of the area of the door (including the window).

(a) Show that $\pi r^2 = 90r + 900$. (1 mark)

(b) Solve this equation to find the radius of the window, correct to the nearest millimetre. (3 marks)

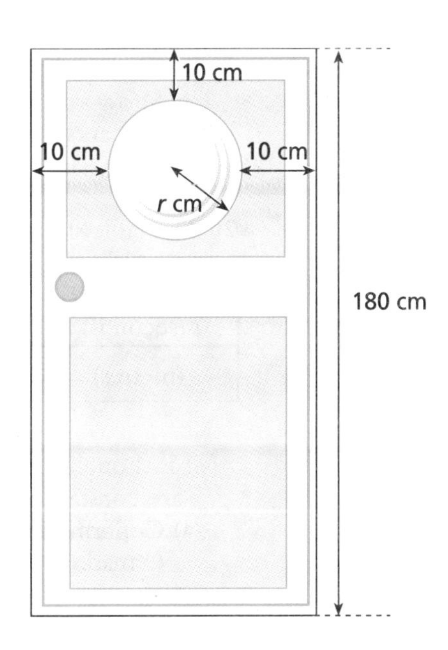

(*CCEA*)

Note: A solution by scale drawing will receive no credit.

17

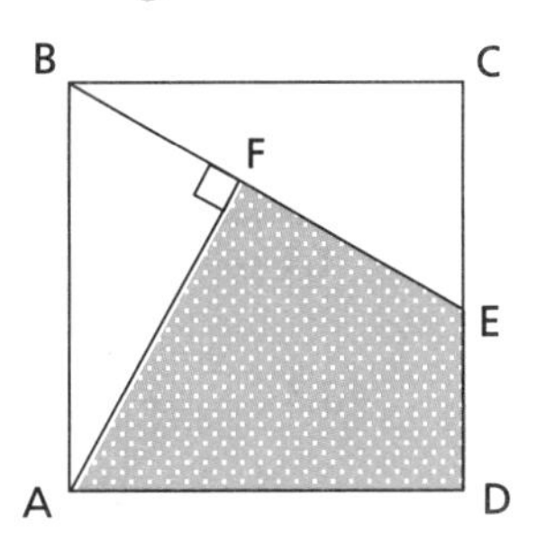

The diagram shows a square tile. E is a point on CD and AF is perpendicular to BE.

(a) Explain why the triangles ABF and BEC are similar. (2 marks)

Each side of the tile is 8 cm. BE is 10 cm and CE 6 cm.

(b) (i) Write down the ratio of the lengths of corresponding sides of the triangles ABF and BEC. (1 mark)

(ii) Calculate the lengths of AF and BF. (3 marks)

On the tile, the quadrilateral AFED is coloured black.

(c) (i) Calculate the area of AFED. (3 marks)

(ii) Calculate the area of the quadrilateral coloured black on a similar tile of side 12 cm. (3 marks)

(*CCEA*)

18 Here are some irrational numbers.

$$\sqrt{3},\ \sqrt{5},\ \sqrt{8},\ \pi,\ \sqrt{12},\ \sqrt{50}.$$

(a) Use two of these numbers to show that, if two irrational numbers are multiplied together, the result can be a rational number. (2 marks)

(b) Use two of these numbers to show that, if two irrational numbers are divided, the result can be a rational number. (2 marks)

(*MEG*)

19 A manufacturer needs to determine the volume of an irregularly shaped component.

The mass of the component is measured in grams as $17{\cdot}2 \pm 5\%$.

The component is made of material with density, in grams per cm^3, of $9{\cdot}6 \pm 3\%$.

The volume of the component is calculated as $\dfrac{\text{mass}}{\text{density}}$.

(a) Use the figures 17·2 g and 9·6 g/cm^3 to calculate the volume of the component. (1 mark)

(b) Find the maximum and minimum possible values of this volume. (5 marks)
(c) Show that it would be sensible to quote the volume with an error of ± 8%. (2 marks)

(MEG)

20 The table shows the distance, s metres, travelled by an object from the point P in t seconds.

t (seconds)	0·5	1·0	1·5	2·0	2·5
s (metres)	1·125	1·2	1·325	1·5	1·725

It is thought the relationship between s and t has the form $s = at^2 + b$, where a and b are constants.

(a) Confirm the relationship by plotting a suitable graph on a copy of the grid below. (3 marks)

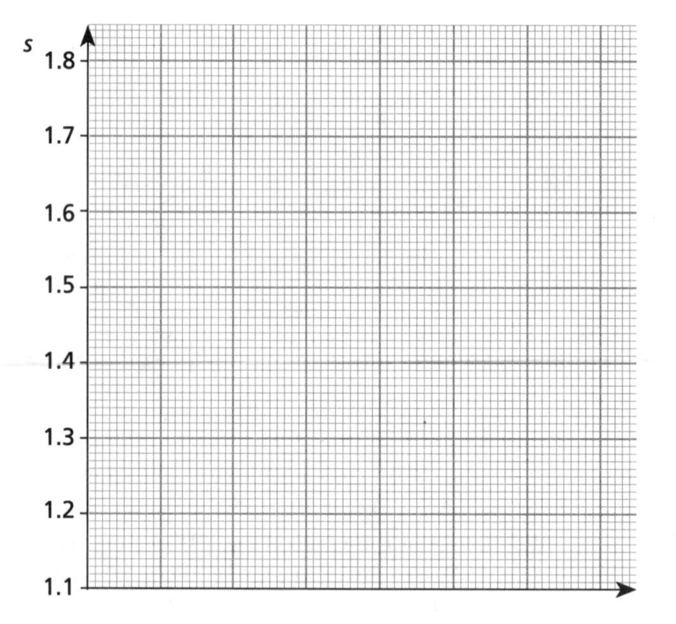

(b) Use the graph to estimate the values of a and b. (3 marks)

(London)

21 The graph on page 262 shows the curve

$$y = x^3 - 7x^2 + 10x$$

between $x = 0$ and $x = 5$.

(a) (i) Write down the value of x at a point where the gradient of the curve is zero. (1 mark)
(ii) Use the graph to calculate the gradient of the curve at $x = 4·5$. (3 marks)

(b) By drawing an appropriate line on your graph, find the value of x which satifies the equation

$$x^3 - 7x^2 + 18x - 8 = 0$$

and lies between $x = 0$ and $x = 5$. (4 marks)

(c) **Without making any calculations**, use the graph of $y = x^3 - 7x^2 + 10x$ to draw the graph of

$$y = x^3 - 7x^2 + 10x + 2. \text{ (1 mark)}$$

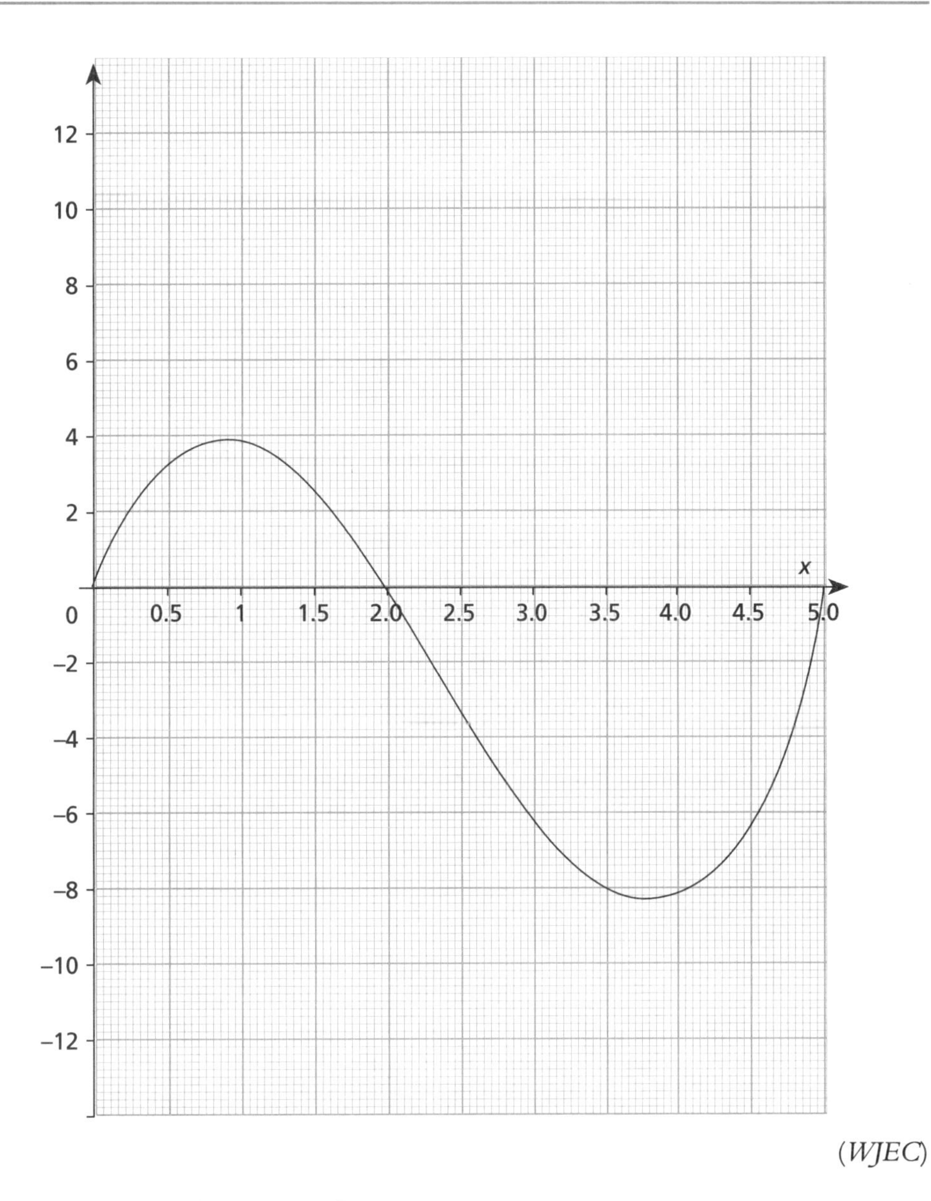

(*WJEC*)

22 Solve the quadratic equation $2x^2 - x - 5 = 0$. (4 marks)
Give your answers correct to 3 significant figures.

(*MEG*)

23 (a) (i) Show that the equation

$$\frac{1}{x} - \frac{1}{x+2} = \frac{2}{15}$$

can be written in the form

$$x^2 + 2x - 15 = 0. \quad \text{(3 marks)}$$

(ii) Hence solve the equation

$$\frac{1}{x} - \frac{1}{x+2} = \frac{2}{15}. \quad \text{(2 marks)}$$

(b) (i) Express $\dfrac{1}{x} - \dfrac{1}{x+1}$

as a single fraction, simplifying your answer as far as possible. (2 marks)

(ii) Using your answer to (b)(i), write down a positive solution to the equation

$$\frac{1}{x} - \frac{1}{x+1} = \frac{1}{72}. \quad \text{(1 mark)}$$

(*WJEC*)

24 The function $y = f(x)$ is illustrated below.

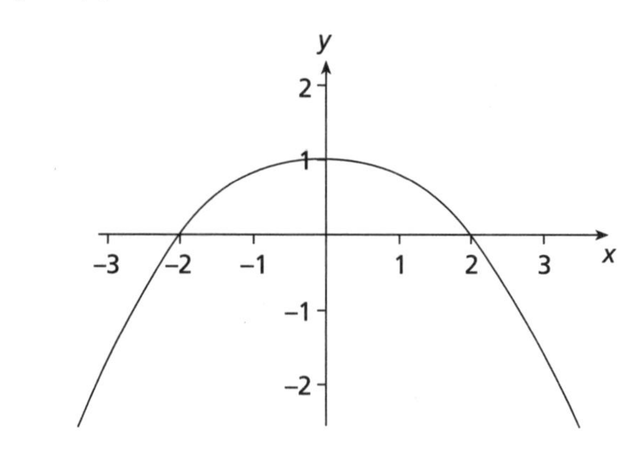

Sketch graphs of the functions

(a) $y = f\left(\frac{x}{2}\right)$ (1 mark)

(b) $y = f(x - 1)$ (1 mark)

Label each graph clearly.

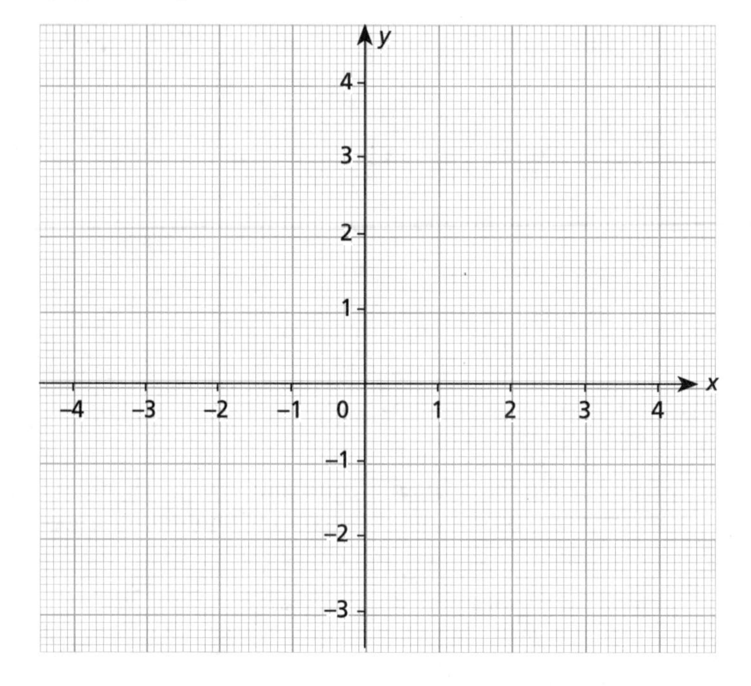

(SEG)

25 Two similar boxes have volumes of 2000 cm^3 and 16 000 cm^3.
The area of the base of the larger box is 60 cm^2.
Calculate the area of the base, in cm^2, of the smaller box. (4 marks)

(London)

26 A farmer's storage container is in the shape of a cylinder with a hemisphere on top.
The height of the cylinder is 9·5 m.
The radius of both the cylinder and the hemisphere is 2·4 m.

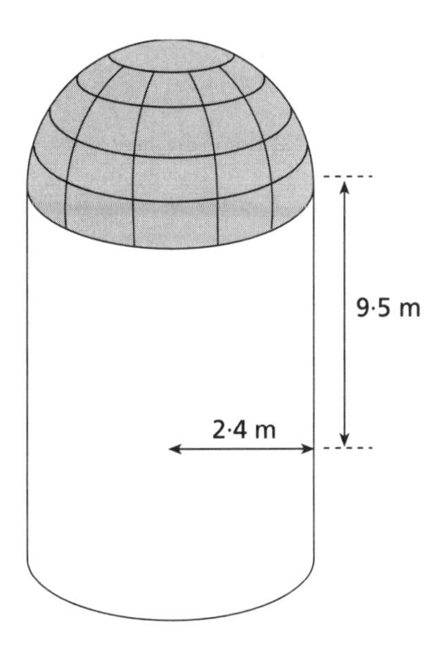

(a) Calculate the volume of the farmer's storage container. (3 marks)
(b) The volume of a similar storage container is half the volume of the farmer's container. Calculate the radius of this new container. (2 marks)

(SEG)

27 Find two different values of x between 0 and 180 for which

$$\sin(2x)^\circ = \sin 30^\circ \quad \text{(2 marks)}$$

(London)

28 The depth of water in a harbour varies according to the formula

$$y = 10 + 5\sin(30t)^\circ$$

{y is the depth of the water in feet; t is the time in hours}

Here is a sketch of the graph of this formula.

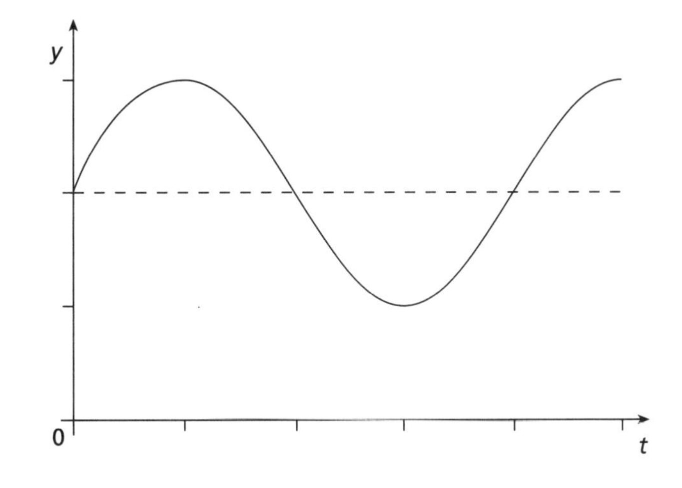

(a) Complete the labelling on the t and y axes for this graph. (3 marks)

A ship wishes to leave the harbour, but needs a depth of water of 13 feet to do so safely.

When the time is 1200 hours the value of t is zero.

(b) At what time can the ship first leave the harbour safely? (3 marks)

(London)

29

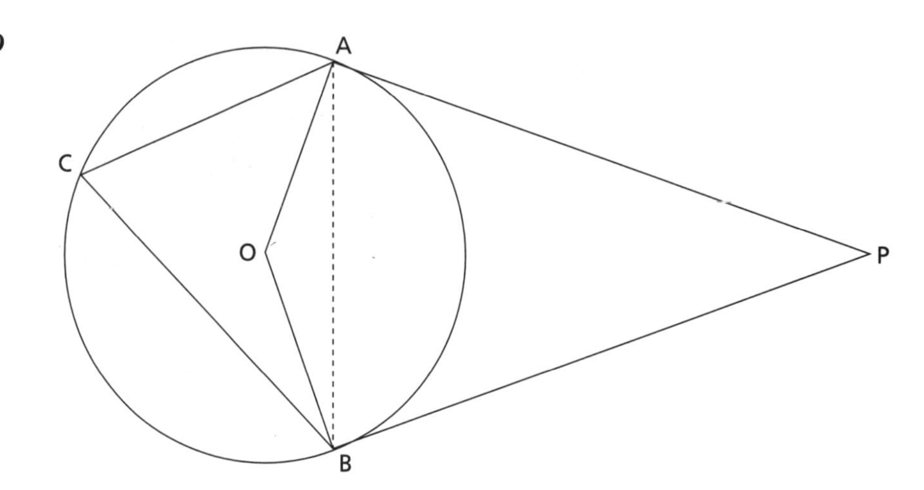

In the diagram, the lines PA and PB are tangents to the circle with centre O which passes through A, B and C.

(a) State the sizes of angles PAO and PBO. (1 mark)

Angle APB = 40°.

(b) Find angle AOB, explaining your reasoning. (2 marks)

(c) Explain how you can tell that angle ACB = 70°. (1 mark)

(d) Given the lengths CA = 11·2 cm and CB = 19·9 cm, calculate length AB. (4 marks)

(MEG)

30

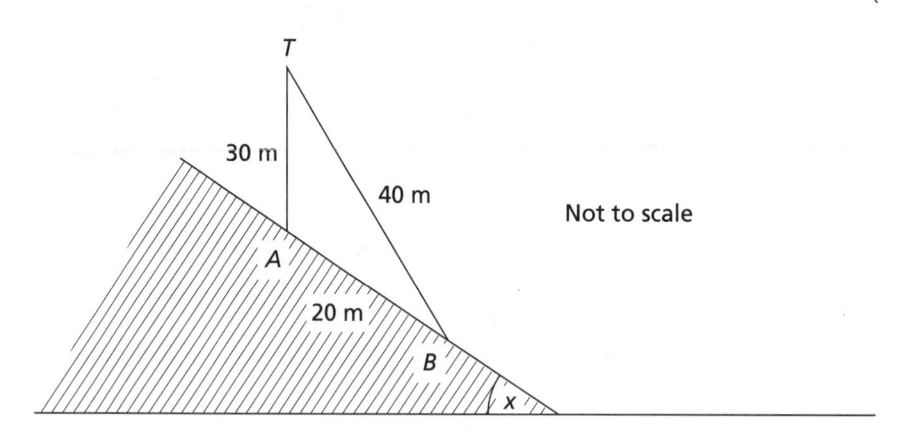

A vertical mast, AT, 30 m high is erected on a straight hillside AB. From the top, T, of the mast a rope, TB, 40 m long is secured at a point B, 20 m from the foot of the mast A. Points A, T and B lie in the same vertical plane.

Calculate the angle, x, that the hillside makes with the horizontal. (6 marks)

(MEG)

31 A tanker is on a bearing of 315° from a lighthouse.

A ferry is due East of the lighthouse.

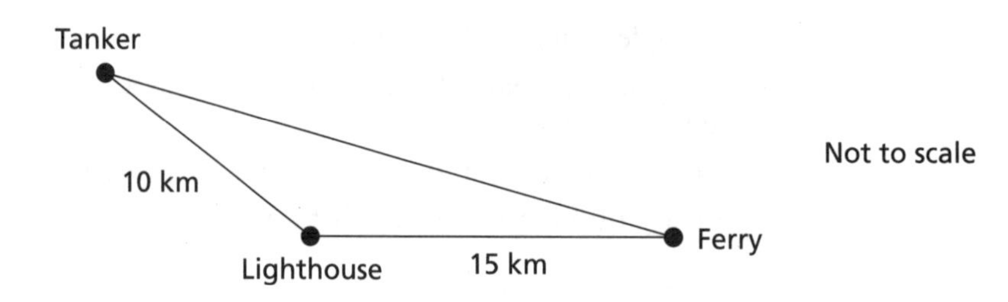

(a) Calculate the distance of the ferry from the tanker. (2 marks)

(b) Calculate the bearing of the tanker from the ferry. (3 marks)

(SEG)

32 A doctor's patients are divided by age into groups as shown in the table below.

Age (x) in years	$0 \leq x < 5$	$5 \leq x < 15$	$15 \leq x < 25$	$25 \leq x < 45$	$45 \leq x < 75$
Number of patients	14	41	59	70	16

(a) On the grid below complete the histogram to represent this distribution. (5 marks)

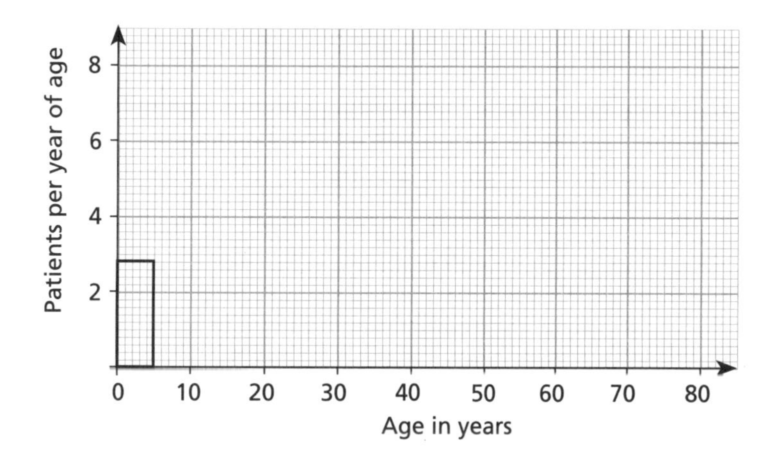

(b) The doctor wishes to choose a stratified random sample of 40 patients.
Explain with any appropriate calculations, how this can be done. (4 marks)

(*MEG*)

33 In an experiment, Nazia measured the time it took for a ball bearing to sink down to the bottom of a tube of oil. She made 5 measurements. Her results are given below.

2·4s, 2·5s, 2·4s, 2·6s, 2·7s

(a) Calculate the standard deviation of these times. (3 marks)
Give your answer correct to 3 decimal places.

Nazia found that her timing had been 0·2 seconds too short each time.

(b) For these corrected times, find
(i) the mean time,
(ii) the standard deviation (3 marks)

(*London*)

Answers to examination questions

1 (a) $\dfrac{10^{600}}{10^{303}} = 10^{600-303} = 10^{297}$

(b) $40 \times 10^{303} = 4 \times 10^{304}$

(Remember to subtract indices when dividing)

2 (a) $10\ 200\ 000\ 000 = 1{\cdot}02 \times 10^{10}$

(b) Population density $= \dfrac{1{\cdot}02 \times 10^{10}}{1{\cdot}49 \times 10^{8}} = 68{\cdot}456$

$= 68$ people per km^2

3 Either use the fact that area scale factor = (linear scale factor)^2 or work it out from first principles:

$A \,\alpha\, D^2$

A moon = constant × (Dia moon)^2

A planet = constant × (Dia planet)^2

= constant × (2 Dia moon)^2

$$\frac{\text{A planet}}{\text{A moon}} = \frac{\text{constant} \times (2 \text{ Dia moon})^2}{\text{constant} \times (\text{Dia moon})^2} = 4$$

A planet $= 4 \times 3{\cdot}8 \times 10^7$ square kilometres

$= 15{\cdot}2 \times 10^7$ square kilometres

$= 1{\cdot}52 \times 10^8$ square kilometres

4 (a) $y = x^3 - 2x$

if $y = 3$ then $3 = x^3 - 2x$

i.e. $x^3 = 2x + 3$

∴ Draw line parallel to x axis through

$y = 3$ cuts curve at $x = 1{\cdot}9$

solution $x = 1{\cdot}9$

(b) Plotted $y = x^3 - 2x$

i.e. $y + 2x = x^3$

require solution to $3x - 1 = x^3$

by inspection/comparison $y + 2x$

becomes $3x - 1$ if $y = x - 1$

∴ need to draw $y = x - 1$

solutions are $-1{\cdot}87$, $0{\cdot}35$, $1{\cdot}53$

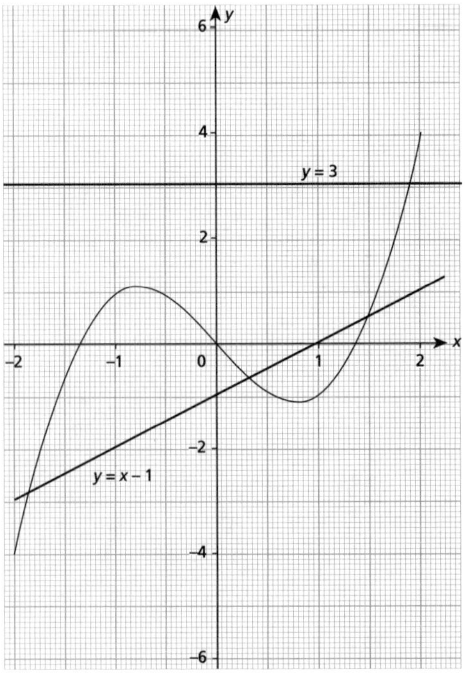

5 (a) Volume $= \pi r^2 l$

Taking $\pi = 3{\cdot}14$

$v = 3{\cdot}14 \times 3{\cdot}9^2 \times 10{\cdot}5$

$= 501{\cdot}728$

$= 502$ cm^3 (to nearest whole number)

(Remember to use 501·728 to continue the calculation in part (b).)

(b) Volume of cuboid $= 6{\cdot}5^2 \times l$

$\therefore\ 6.5^2 \times l = 501{\cdot}728$

$$l = \frac{501{\cdot}728}{6{\cdot}5^2}$$

$= 11{\cdot}875$

$= 11{\cdot}9$ cm (to 1 d.p.)

6 (a) Cumulative frequencies are

Weight (w) in kg	Cumulative Frequency
$1{\cdot}0 \le w < 1{\cdot}5$	4
$1{\cdot}0 \le w < 2{\cdot}0$	13
$1{\cdot}0 \le w < 2{\cdot}5$	24
$1{\cdot}0 \le w < 3{\cdot}0$	45
$1{\cdot}0 \le w < 3{\cdot}5$	71
$1{\cdot}0 \le w < 4{\cdot}0$	89
$1{\cdot}0 \le w < 4{\cdot}5$	98
$1{\cdot}0 \le w < 5{\cdot}0$	100

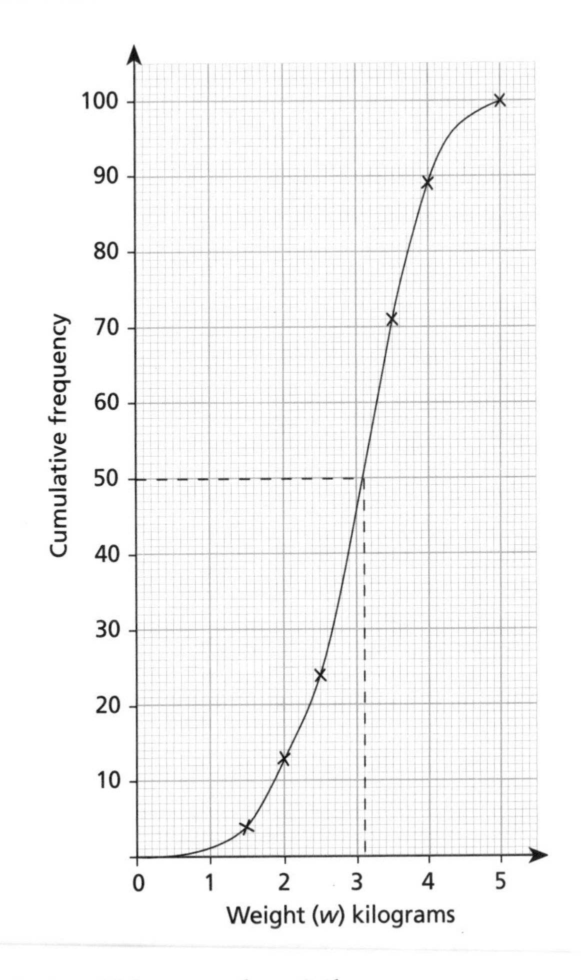

(c) Median weight is at 50th percentile $= 3{\cdot}1$kg

7 (a)

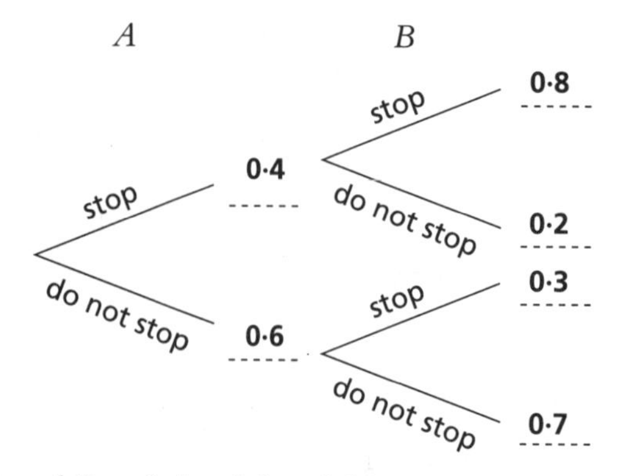

(b) Stop at both A and B = 0·4 × 0·8 = 0·32

(c) Stop at least once = (stop at A + stop at B) + (stop at A only)
+ (stop at B only)
= 0·32 + (0·4 × 0·2) + (0·6 × 0·3)
= 0·32 + 0·08 + 0·18
= 0·58

8 (a) probability of landing point up = 0·46
∴ probability of landing point down = 0·54
probability that all 3 drawing pins land point down = 0·54 × 0·54 × 0·54
= 0·157

(b) There are 3 possible solutions:
(i) down, down, up = 0·54 × 0·54 × 0·46 = 0·134
(ii) down, up, down = 0·54 × 0·46 × 0·54 = 0·134
(iii) up, down, down = 0·46 × 0·54 × 0·54 = 0·134
adding these gives 0·402

(c) probability that all 3 land point down = 0·157
∴ probability that at least 1 lands point up = 1 – 0·157
= 0·843

9 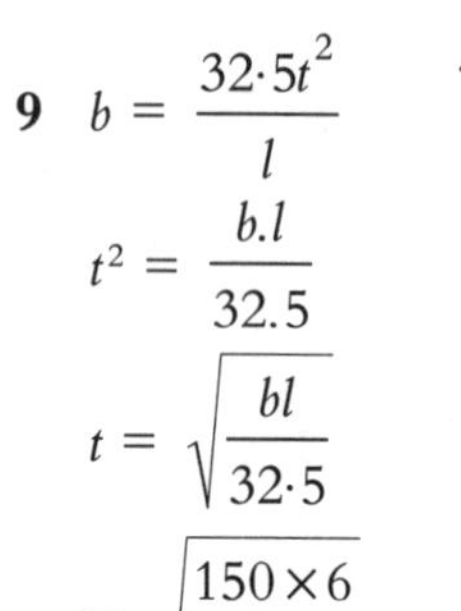

$b = \frac{32{\cdot}5t^2}{l}$

$t^2 = \frac{b.l}{32.5}$

$t = \sqrt{\frac{bl}{32{\cdot}5}}$

$= \sqrt{\frac{150 \times 6}{32{\cdot}5}}$

= 5·26 mm
= 1 cm (correct to nearest cm)

10 (a) (i) See graph

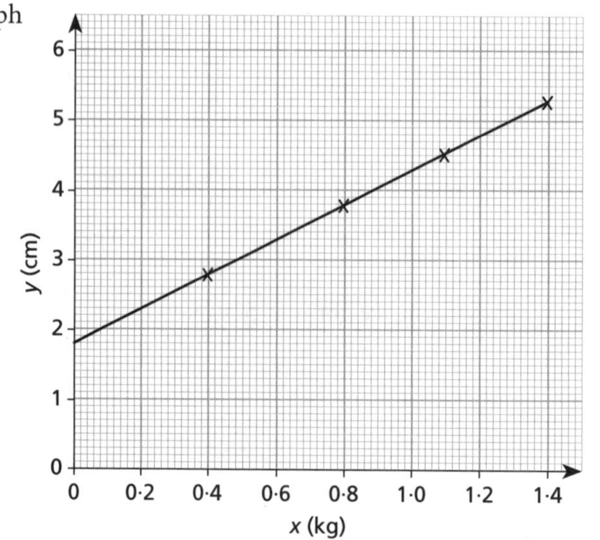

(i) Straight line obtained

(b) $m = \dfrac{1}{0{\cdot}4} = 2{\cdot}5$

$c = 1{\cdot}8$

(c) (i) $y = 2{\cdot}5x + 1{\cdot}8$

(ii) if $x = 0$, $y = 1{\cdot}8$ cm

(iii) $y = 2{\cdot}5x + 1{\cdot}8$

$11{\cdot}3 = 2{\cdot}5 \times x + 1{\cdot}8$

$x = 3{\cdot}8$ kg

11 Shape consists of a sphere + curved face of a cylinder

$\therefore$ Surface area $= 4\pi r^2 + 2\pi rl$

$= 4 \times 3{\cdot}14 \times 0{\cdot}65^2 + 2 \times 3{\cdot}14 \times 0{\cdot}65 \times 1{\cdot}85$

$= 5{\cdot}3066 + 7{\cdot}5517$

$= 12{\cdot}8583$

$= 12{\cdot}9$ m^2 (to 3 s.f.)

12 (a) AC = AB sin 43

$= 3{\cdot}35 \times \sin 43$

$= 2{\cdot}284$

$= 2{\cdot}28$ m (to 2 d.p.)

(b) (i) PQ = BQ tan 43

$1{\cdot}15 = \text{BQ} \times \tan 43$

$\therefore \text{BQ} = \dfrac{1{\cdot}15}{\tan 43}$

$= 1{\cdot}233$

$= 1{\cdot}23$ m (to 2 d.p.)

(ii) width $= 4{\cdot}90 - (2 \times 1{\cdot}233)$

$= 2{\cdot}434$ m

$= 2{\cdot}43$ m (to 2 d.p.)

13 (a) Length PQR $= \frac{1}{2} \times 2\pi r = \frac{1}{2} \times 2 \times 3{\cdot}14 \times 9{\cdot}8$

$= 30{\cdot}772$ cm

length PSR $= \dfrac{\theta}{360} \times 2\pi r = \dfrac{48{\cdot}2}{360} \times 2 \times 3{\cdot}14 \times 24$

$= 20{\cdot}1797$ cm

perimeter of crescent $= 30{\cdot}772 + 20{\cdot}1797$

$= 51{\cdot}0$ (to 3 s.f.)

(b) Area of sector POR $= \dfrac{\theta}{360} \times \pi \times r^2 = \dfrac{48{\cdot}2}{360} \times 3{\cdot}14 \times 24^2$

$= 242{\cdot}16$ cm^2 $= 242$ cm^2 (to 3 s.f.)

(could also be found by using $\frac{1}{2}ac \sin \text{B}$)

(c) in triangle POR

height, $h = 24{\cdot}0 \cos 24{\cdot}1 = 21{\cdot}91$ cm

Area $= \frac{1}{2}\,bh = \frac{1}{2} \times 19{\cdot}6 \times 21{\cdot}91$

$= 214{\cdot}70$ cm^2

$\therefore$ Area of shape PSR remaining $= 242{\cdot}16 - 214{\cdot}70 = 27{\cdot}46$ cm^2

14 Mean $= \dfrac{(23 \times 55) + (42 \times 65) + (50 \times 75) + (20 \times 85) + (15 \times 95)}{150}$

$= 72{\cdot}47$ gm (to 2 d.p.)

15 (a) $v = \sqrt{u^2 + 2as}$

$= \sqrt{24^2 + 2 \times {}^{-}9{\cdot}8 \times 10{\cdot}25}$

$= 19{\cdot}37$ (to 2 d.p.)

(b) $v = \sqrt{25^2 + 2 \times {}^{-}10 \times 10}$
$= \sqrt{625 - 200}$
$= \sqrt{425}$
$\simeq 20$

16 (a) Area of door = $180 \times (20 + 2r)$
$= 3600 + 360r)$
∴ Area of window = $\frac{1}{4}(3600 + 360r)$
$= 900 + 90r$
Area of window = πr^2
∴ $\pi r^2 = 90r + 900$

(b) $\pi r^2 - 90r - 900 = 0$

∴ $\left[\text{using formula } x = \frac{-b \pm \sqrt{b^2 - 4ac}}{2a}\right]$

$$r = \frac{90 \pm \sqrt{90^2 + 4 \times \pi \times 900}}{2 \times \pi}$$

$$= \frac{90 \pm \sqrt{1940{\cdot}97}}{2 \times \pi} = \frac{90 \pm\ 139{\cdot}32}{2\pi}$$

$r = 36{\cdot}49$ cm or $r = -7{\cdot}84$ cm
radius = 36·5 cm (correct to nearest millimetre)

17 (a) in triangle ABF, ∠ABF = 90° – ∠CBE
in triangle BEC, ∠CEB = 90° – ∠CBE
∴ ∠ABF = ∠CEB
and ∠BFA = ∠BCE = 90°
∴ By angle sum, ∠BAF = ∠CBE
∴ triangles ABF and BEC are similar

(b) (i) The full set of ratios is

$$\frac{BF}{CE} = \frac{FA}{CB} = \frac{AB}{BE}$$

AB = 8, BE = 10 ∴ Ratio of length = $\frac{8}{10} = 0{\cdot}8$

(ii) $\frac{AF}{CB} = 0{\cdot}8$ $\qquad \frac{BF}{CE} = 0{\cdot}8$

$\frac{AF}{8} = 0{\cdot}8$ $\qquad \frac{BF}{6} = 0{\cdot}8$

∴ AF = 6·4 cm $\qquad$ BF = 4·8 cm

(c) (i) Area of triangle BCE = $\frac{1}{2} \times 8 \times 6 = 24$ cm^2
Area of triangle BFA = $\frac{1}{2} \times 6{\cdot}4 \times 4{\cdot}8 = 15{\cdot}36$ cm^2
∴ Area of quadrilateral AFED $= 64 - 24 - 15{\cdot}36$
$= 24{\cdot}64$ cm^2

(ii) Ratio of areas of similar shapes = (ratio of corresponding lengths)2

$$\therefore \frac{\text{required area}}{24{\cdot}64} = \left(\frac{12}{8}\right)^2$$

∴ Area of quadrilateral = $(1{\cdot}5)^2 \times 24{\cdot}64$
$= 55{\cdot}44$ cm^2

18 (a) $\sqrt{3} \times \sqrt{12} = \sqrt{36} = 6$ Rational
(b) $\sqrt{12} \div \sqrt{3} = \sqrt{4} = 2$

19 (a) Volume = $\frac{\text{mass}}{\text{density}} = \frac{17{\cdot}2}{9{\cdot}6} = 1{\cdot}7917$
$= 1{\cdot}79$ cm^3 (to 2 d.p.)

(b) (i) Maximum value when $\dfrac{\text{maximum mass}}{\text{minimum density}} = \dfrac{18\cdot06}{9\cdot312} = 1\cdot9394$

$= 1\cdot94\ \text{cm}^3$ (to 2 d.p.)

(ii) Minimum value when $\dfrac{\text{minimum mass}}{\text{maximum density}} = \dfrac{16\cdot34}{9\cdot888} = 1\cdot6525$

$= 1\cdot65\ \text{cm}^3$ (to 2 d.p.)

(c) Error $= \dfrac{1\cdot9394 - 1\cdot6525}{1\cdot7917}$

$= 0\cdot16 = 16\% = \pm8\%$

20 (a) See graph (graph is of shape $y = x^2$).

(b) If $t = 0$, $s = b$, and extending graph to $t = 0$ gives $b = 1\cdot1$

When $t = 1$, $s = 1\cdot2$

$\therefore$ in equation $s = a\,(1)^2 + 1\cdot1$

$1\cdot2 = a + 1\cdot1$

$a = 0\cdot1$

$\therefore\ a = 0\cdot1$

$\therefore\ b = 1\cdot1$

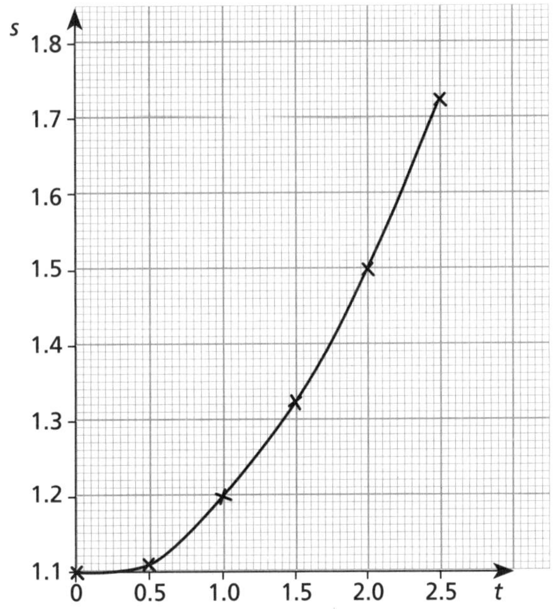

21 (a) (i) Gradient = 0 at the turning points

$x = 0\cdot9$ and $x = 3\cdot8$

(ii) By drawing tangent to the curve α $x = 4\cdot5$ When $x = 5$ $y = -1\cdot7$

When $x = 4$ $y = -8\cdot9$

gradient is $\dfrac{8-4}{5-4\cdot2}$

$= 5$

(b) Original equation is $y = x^3 - 7x^2 + 10x$

required equation is $y = x^3 - 7x^2 + 18x - 8$

change required into original by $-8x + 8$

$\therefore$ draw line $y = -8x + 8$

Where this line meets $y = x^3 - 7x^2 + 10x$

then $x^3 - 7x^2 + 10x = -8x + 8$

i.e. $x^3 - 7x^2 + 18x - 8 = 0$

This occurs as $x = 0\cdot55$ or $0\cdot56$

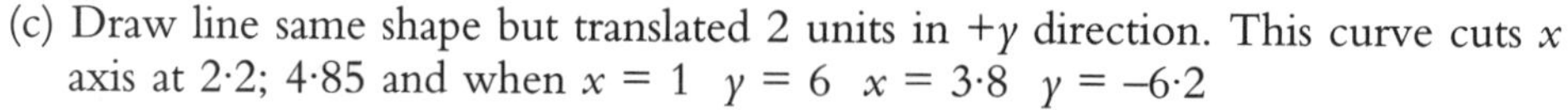

(c) Draw line same shape but translated 2 units in $+y$ direction. This curve cuts x axis at 2·2; 4·85 and when $x = 1$ $y = 6$ $x = 3{\cdot}8$ $y = -6{\cdot}2$

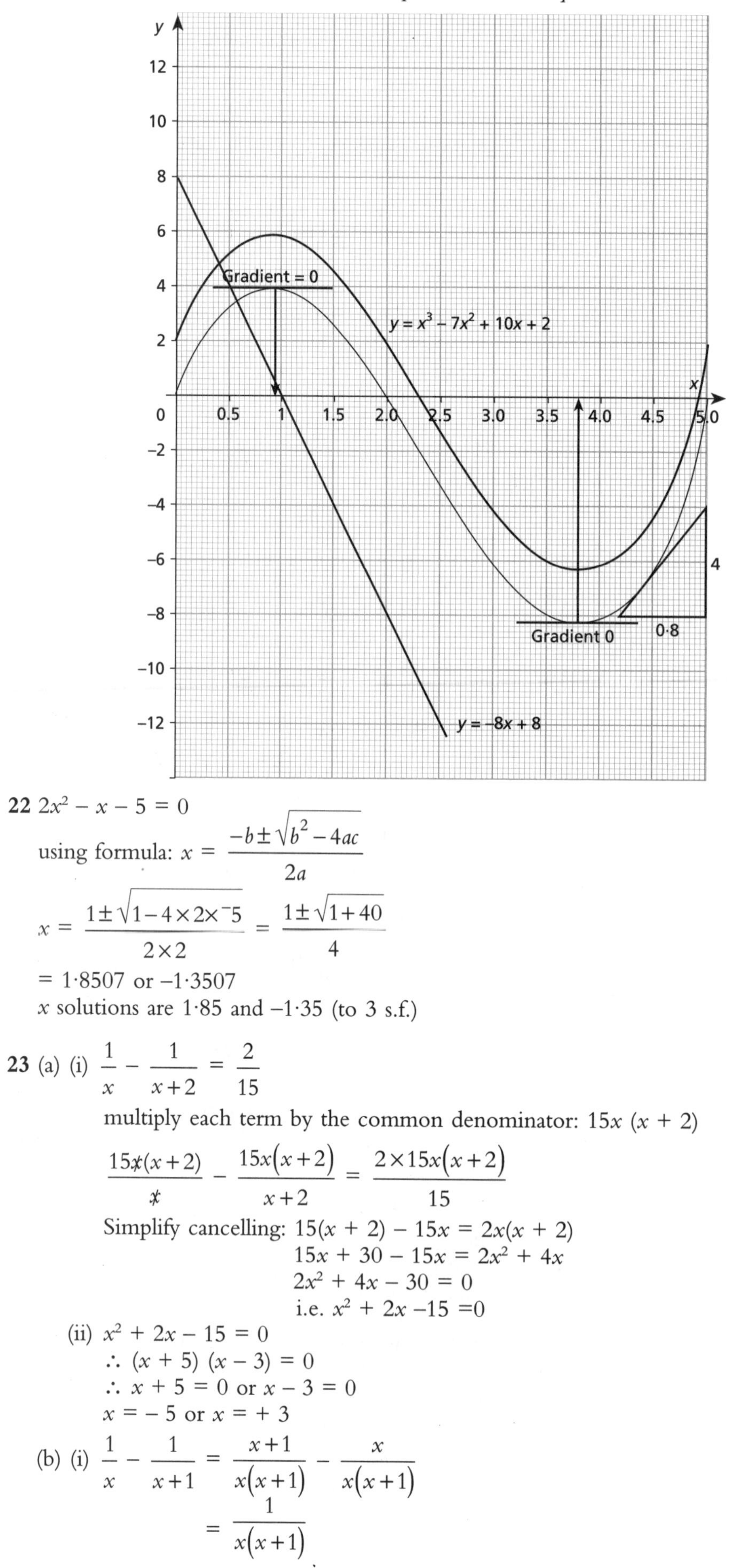

22 $2x^2 - x - 5 = 0$

using formula: $x = \dfrac{-b \pm \sqrt{b^2 - 4ac}}{2a}$

$x = \dfrac{1 \pm \sqrt{1 - 4 \times 2 \times {}^{-}5}}{2 \times 2} = \dfrac{1 \pm \sqrt{1 + 40}}{4}$

$= 1{\cdot}8507$ or $-1{\cdot}3507$

x solutions are 1·85 and −1·35 (to 3 s.f.)

23 (a) (i) $\dfrac{1}{x} - \dfrac{1}{x+2} = \dfrac{2}{15}$

multiply each term by the common denominator: $15x\,(x + 2)$

$$\frac{15\not{x}(x+2)}{\not{x}} - \frac{15x(x+2)}{x+2} = \frac{2 \times 15x(x+2)}{15}$$

Simplify cancelling: $15(x + 2) - 15x = 2x(x + 2)$

$15x + 30 - 15x = 2x^2 + 4x$

$2x^2 + 4x - 30 = 0$

i.e. $x^2 + 2x - 15 = 0$

(ii) $x^2 + 2x - 15 = 0$

$\therefore (x + 5)(x - 3) = 0$

$\therefore x + 5 = 0$ or $x - 3 = 0$

$x = -5$ or $x = +3$

(b) (i) $\dfrac{1}{x} - \dfrac{1}{x+1} = \dfrac{x+1}{x(x+1)} - \dfrac{x}{x(x+1)}$

$= \dfrac{1}{x(x+1)}$

(ii) $\frac{1}{x} - \frac{1}{x+1} = \frac{1}{72}$

$\therefore \frac{1}{x(x+1)} = \frac{1}{72}$

$\therefore 72 = x(x + 1)$
$\therefore x^2 + x - 72 = 0$
$\therefore (x + 9)(x - 8) = 0$
$\therefore x = -9$ or $x = +8$

24

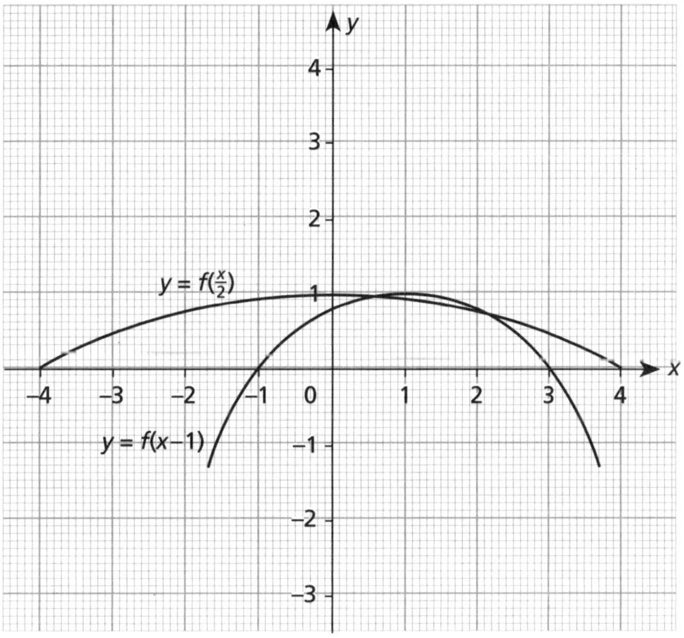

$y = f(\frac{x}{2})$

$y = f(x-1)$

25 (Remember (linear scale factor)^2 = area scale factor
(linear scale factor)^3 = volume scale factor)

Volume scale factor $= \frac{16000}{2000} = 8$

$\therefore$ Linear scale factor $= \sqrt[3]{8} = 2$

$\therefore$ Area scale factor $= 2^2 = 4$

$\therefore$ Area of smaller box $= \frac{60}{4} = 15\text{ cm}^2$

26 (a) Volume $= \pi r^2 h + \frac{1}{2} \times \frac{4}{3}\pi r^3$
$= \pi \times 2{\cdot}4^2 \times 9{\cdot}5 + \frac{4}{6} \times \pi \times 2{\cdot}4^3 = 200{\cdot}86$
$= 200\text{ cm}^3$ (to 3 s.f.)

(b) Ratio of volumes $= \frac{1}{2}$
ratio of volumes = (ratio of length)^3

i.e. $\left(\frac{\text{radius of similar container}}{\text{radius of farmer's container}}\right)^3 = \frac{1}{2}$

radius of similar container $= \left(\sqrt[3]{\frac{1}{2}}\right) \times 2{\cdot}4$

$= 1{\cdot}90$ m (to 3 s.f.)

27 Sin $(2x) = \sin 30$
$2x = 30°$ or $150°$
$x = 15°$ or $75°$

28 (a) On the t axis, scale points are at

$t = 0, 3, 6, 9, 12, 15$

on the y axis scale points are at $y = 5, 10, 15$

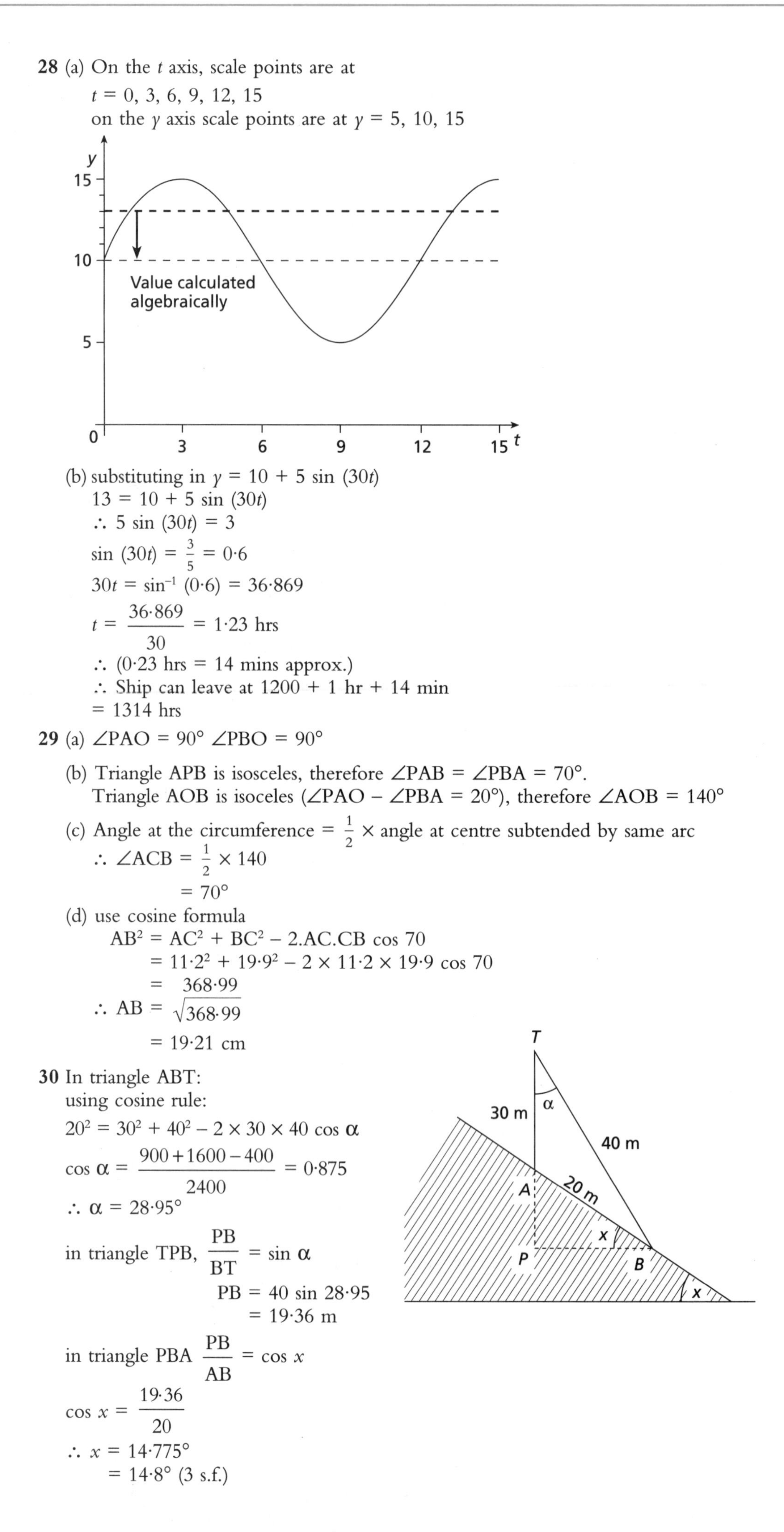

(b) substituting in $y = 10 + 5 \sin (30t)$

$13 = 10 + 5 \sin (30t)$

$\therefore\ 5 \sin (30t) = 3$

$\sin (30t) = \frac{3}{5} = 0{\cdot}6$

$30t = \sin^{-1} (0{\cdot}6) = 36{\cdot}869$

$t = \dfrac{36{\cdot}869}{30} = 1{\cdot}23$ hrs

$\therefore$ (0·23 hrs = 14 mins approx.)

$\therefore$ Ship can leave at 1200 + 1 hr + 14 min

= 1314 hrs

29 (a) $\angle PAO = 90°\ \ \angle PBO = 90°$

(b) Triangle APB is isosceles, therefore $\angle PAB = \angle PBA = 70°$.

Triangle AOB is isoceles ($\angle PAO - \angle PBA = 20°$), therefore $\angle AOB = 140°$

(c) Angle at the circumference $= \frac{1}{2} \times$ angle at centre subtended by same arc

$\therefore\ \angle ACB = \frac{1}{2} \times 140$

$= 70°$

(d) use cosine formula

$AB^2 = AC^2 + BC^2 - 2.AC.CB \cos 70$

$= 11{\cdot}2^2 + 19{\cdot}9^2 - 2 \times 11{\cdot}2 \times 19{\cdot}9 \cos 70$

$= \ \ 368{\cdot}99$

$\therefore\ AB = \sqrt{368{\cdot}99}$

$= 19{\cdot}21$ cm

30 In triangle ABT:

using cosine rule:

$20^2 = 30^2 + 40^2 - 2 \times 30 \times 40 \cos \alpha$

$\cos \alpha = \dfrac{900 + 1600 - 400}{2400} = 0{\cdot}875$

$\therefore\ \alpha = 28{\cdot}95°$

in triangle TPB, $\dfrac{PB}{BT} = \sin \alpha$

$PB = 40 \sin 28{\cdot}95$

$= 19{\cdot}36$ m

in triangle PBA $\dfrac{PB}{AB} = \cos x$

$\cos x = \dfrac{19{\cdot}36}{20}$

$\therefore\ x = 14{\cdot}775°$

$= 14{\cdot}8°$ (3 s.f.)

31

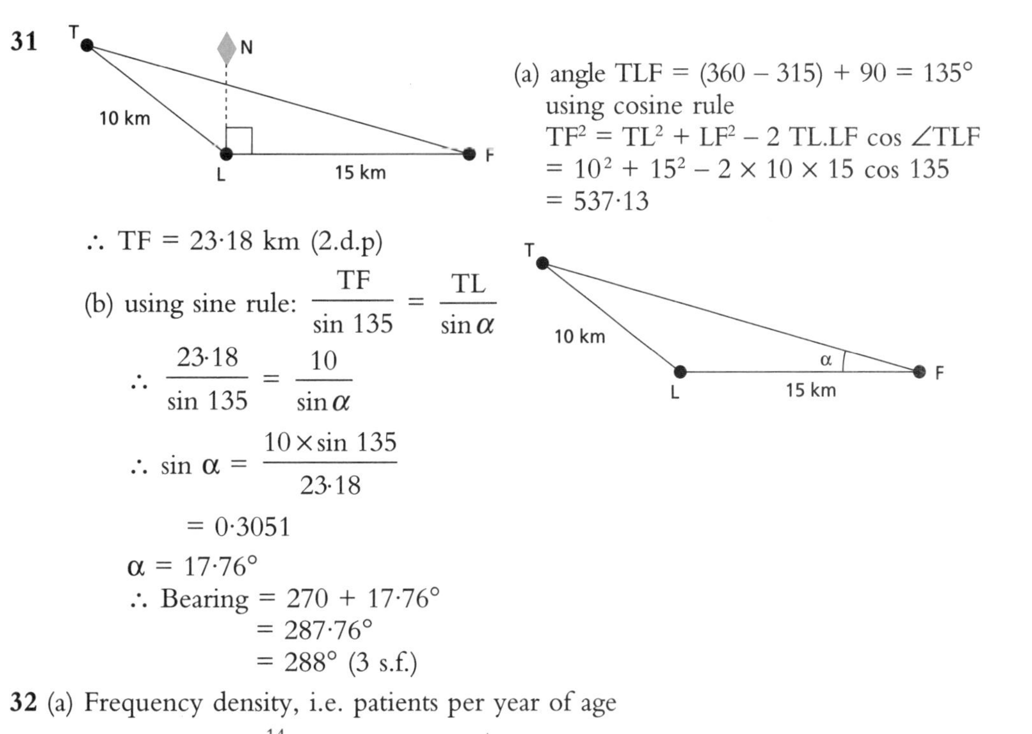

(a) angle TLF = (360 – 315) + 90 = 135°
using cosine rule
$TF^2 = TL^2 + LF^2 - 2\ TL.LF \cos \angle TLF$
$= 10^2 + 15^2 - 2 \times 10 \times 15 \cos 135$
$= 537{\cdot}13$

$\therefore$ TF = 23·18 km (2.d.p)

(b) using sine rule: $\dfrac{TF}{\sin 135} = \dfrac{TL}{\sin \alpha}$

$\therefore \dfrac{23{\cdot}18}{\sin 135} = \dfrac{10}{\sin \alpha}$

$\therefore \sin \alpha = \dfrac{10 \times \sin 135}{23{\cdot}18}$

$= 0{\cdot}3051$

$\alpha = 17{\cdot}76°$

$\therefore$ Bearing = 270 + 17·76°
= 287·76°
= 288° (3 s.f.)

32 (a) Frequency density, i.e. patients per year of age

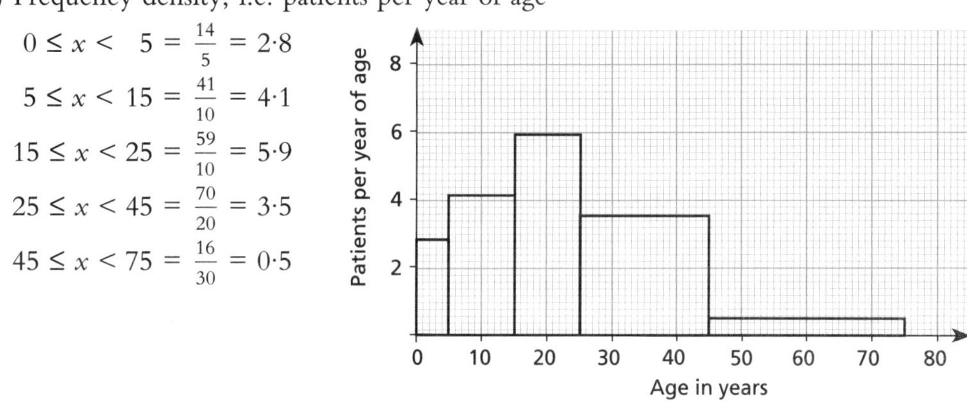

$0 \le x < 5 = \frac{14}{5} = 2{\cdot}8$

$5 \le x < 15 = \frac{41}{10} = 4{\cdot}1$

$15 \le x < 25 = \frac{59}{10} = 5{\cdot}9$

$25 \le x < 45 = \frac{70}{20} = 3{\cdot}5$

$45 \le x < 75 = \frac{16}{30} = 0{\cdot}5$

(b) In a stratified sample the percentage of the sample in an age range should be the same as for the total survey
Number of patients = 14 + 41 + 59 + 70 + 16 = 200
Number in stratified sample = 40 i.e. 20% of total
Therefore he should choose 20% of the original numbers i.e.

20% of 14 = 2·8 i.e. 3 patients
20% of 41 = 8·2 i.e. 8 patients
20% of 59 = 11.8 i.e. 12 patients
20% of 70 = 14 i.e. 14 patients
20% of 16 = 3·2 i.e. 3 patients
Total = 40 patients

33 (a) Mean $\bar{x} = \dfrac{2{\cdot}4 + 2{\cdot}5 + 2{\cdot}4 + 2{\cdot}6 + 2{\cdot}7}{5} = 2{\cdot}52$

x	$\bar{x}$	$\lvert(x - \bar{x})\rvert$	$\lvert(x - \bar{x})\rvert^2$
2·4	2·52	0·12	0·0144
2·5		0·02	0·0004
2·4		0·12	0·0144
2·6		0·08	0·0064
2·7		0·18	0·0324

$\sum \lvert(x - \bar{x})\rvert^2 = 0{\cdot}068$

$\therefore$ standard deviation $= \dfrac{0{\cdot}068}{5} = 0{\cdot}117$

(b) (i) mean time = 2·52 + 0·2 = 2·72 secs
(ii) SD does not change
i.e. SD = 0·117

Index